To Mt

for your 80th birthday —

with best wishes

The Chemistry Department at Imperial College London

A History, 1845 – 2000

The Chemistry Department at Imperial College London

A History, 1845 – 2000

Hannah Gay
Simon Fraser University, Canada & Imperial College London, UK

William P. Griffith
Imperial College London, UK

World Scientific

NEW JERSEY · LONDON · SINGAPORE · BEIJING · SHANGHAI · HONG KONG · TAIPEI · CHENNAI · TOKYO

Published by

World Scientific Publishing Europe Ltd.

57 Shelton Street, Covent Garden, London WC2H 9HE

Head office: 5 Toh Tuck Link, Singapore 596224

USA office: 27 Warren Street, Suite 401-402, Hackensack, NJ 07601

Library of Congress Cataloging-in-Publication Data
Names: Gay, Hannah. | Griffith, W. P. (William Pettitt), 1936–
Title: The Chemistry Department at Imperial College, London : a history, 1845–2000 /
    Hannah Gay (Simon Fraser University, Canada & Imperial College London, UK),
    William Griffith (Imperial College London, UK).
Description: New Jersey : World Scientific, 2016. | Includes bibliographical references and index.
Identifiers: LCCN 2016007124 | ISBN 9781783269730 (hc : alk. paper)
Subjects: LCSH: Imperial College, London. Chemistry Department. | Imperial College of
    Science, Technology and Medicine. Department of Chemistry. | Imperial College of Science
    and Technology. Department of Chemistry | Royal College of Chemistry (Great Britain) |
    Imperial College, London--History. | Chemistry--Study and teaching (Higher)--Great Britain.
Classification: LCC QD49.G7 G39 2016 | DDC 540.71/14212--dc23
LC record available at https://lccn.loc.gov/2016007124

British Library Cataloguing-in-Publication Data
A catalogue record for this book is available from the British Library.

Desk Editors: Kalpana Bharanikumar/Mary Simpson

Typeset by Stallion Press
Email: enquiries@stallionpress.com

Printed in Singapore

Contents

Acknowledgements   ix

Authors' Biographies   xi

Chapter One   **Introduction**   **1**
                     1.1. Historical Background   1
                     1.2. Some Organisational Points   4

Chapter Two   **The Founding of the Royal College
                     of Chemistry**   **9**
                     2.1. Justus Liebig's Following in Britain
                           Before 1845   9
                     2.2. The Founding of the Royal College
                           of Chemistry   11
                     2.3. The Working Environment at the Oxford
                           Street College   15

Chapter Three   **The Hofmann and Frankland Years, 1845–1865**   **27**
                     3.1. Introduction   27
                     3.2. Students, Assistants, and Instruction   28
                     3.3. Some Noteworthy Students and Staff   37
                     3.4. Hofmann's Research at the RCC   48

3.5. Frankland: his Earlier Career
     and his Work at the RCC   51
3.6. Applied and Extramural Work   57

Chapter Four   **T. E. Thorpe, W. A. Tilden, and**
                   H. E. Armstrong's Department at
                   the Central Technical College: 1885–1914   **79**
                   4.1. Thomas Edward Thorpe and some Staff
                        and Students of the Period 1885–1894   79
                   4.2. William Augustus Tilden and the
                        Founding of Imperial College, 1894–1909   83
                   4.3. Henry Armstrong's Department
                        at the C&GCTC   92
                   4.4. Thorpe's Return as Head of Department;
                        Departmental Reorganisation, 1909–1914   102

Chapter Five   **The Department During the First**
                   World War   **131**
                   5.1. Herbert Brereton Baker   131
                   5.2. The Department during the First World War 132

Chapter Six   **The Department Between the Wars,**
                   1918–1939   **155**
                   6.1. A Fresh Start after the War   155
                   6.2. Herbert Brereton Baker and Inorganic
                        Chemistry   160
                   6.3. James Charles Philip and Physical
                        Chemistry   171
                   6.4. Jocelyn Field Thorpe and Organic Chemistry 175

Chapter Seven **The Department during the Second**
                   World War   **207**
                   7.1. Introduction: Staff Members in 1939   207
                   7.2. War Preparations and Daily Life During
                        the War   211
                   7.3. Scientific Contributions to the War Effort 215
                   7.4. Some Notable Wartime Students   223

Chapter Eight   **New Research and Departmental Reorganisation after the Second World War, 1945–1965**   **241**

8.1. Departmental Governance   241

8.2. Vincent Briscoe as Mentor to Derek Barton and Geoffrey Wilkinson   243

8.3. Research: (a) Organic Chemistry; (b) Inorganic Chemistry; (c) Physical Chemistry   250

8.4. Departmental Reorganisation and Undergraduate Teaching   270

Chapter Nine   **Modernisation in a Changing Political, Economic, and Technological Climate: 1965–1985**   **303**

9.1. Some Political and Economic Problems of the 1970s   303

9.2. Departmental Administration, Reorganisation, and Planning for the Future   305

9.3. Two Nobel Prizes   312

9.4. Research: (a) Inorganic Chemistry; (b) Organic Chemistry; (c) Physical Chemistry   314

9.5. Undergraduate Teaching and MSc Courses   329

Chapter Ten   **A Period of Change, 1985–2000**   **357**

10.1. Introduction   357

10.2. Heads of Department and Section Heads, 1985–1993   358

10.3. Some Staff Changes, 1985–2000   359

10.4. Research into the 1990s: (a) Organic chemistry; (b) Inorganic Chemistry; (c) Physical Chemistry   360

10.5. Newcomers in the Later 1990s   368

10.6. BSc and MSci Courses; New Forms of Information Access; Social Life Among Students   369

	10.7. Departmental Reorganisation, 1992–2000	373
	10.8. Coda	377
Chapter Eleven	**Epilogue**	**399**
	11.1. Chemistry's Changing Situation	399
	11.2. Some Missed Opportunities	402
	11.3. The Importance of Origins	404
	11.4. Two World Wars	408
	11.5. Sociality and the Social Makeup of the Department	408
	11.6. Looking to the Future	412
Appendix One	**Liebig at Giessen; Some early 19th Century Chemistry**	**419**
	A. 1. Justus Liebig's Laboratory in Giessen	419
	A. 2. Some Chemical Ideas of the Early to Mid-19th Century	421
Appendix Two	**Chemistry Teaching at British Universities Before 1850**	**431**
Appendix Three	**IC chemistry and the Chemical Society (later RSC)**	**437**
	A.1. Foundation of the Chemical Society	437
	A.2. Related British Chemical Societies	439
	A.3. Presidents of the CS, RSC and RIC (Table 1)	440
	A.4. Women in the CS	440
	A.5. Journals of the Society and their Editors	444
	A.6. Awards of the CS and RSC	444
Appendix Four	**Chemistry Department Staff, at Ic, 1845–2000**	**447**
Bibliography		463
Abbreviations/Acronyms		513
Illustration Credits		517
Illustrations		519
Index		543

Acknowledgements

For their extended help we especially thank Eddie Abel, David Allen, Anne Barrett, Tony Barrett, Martin Bennett, Ian Gay, John Gay, David Goodgame, Malcolm Green, Anne Griffith, Paul Lickiss, Willie Motherwell, David Nicholson, David Phillips, Henry Rzepa, Ed Smith, Michael Spiro, David Widdowson, and Paul Wilde.

In particular we want to thank Ed Smith who read all the manuscript and all the proofs, pointing out a number of errors. For any remaining mistakes we are entirely responsible.

We are also grateful for the help given by Ray Anderson, Richard Andersen, Alan Armstrong, John Avery, David Baghurst, Jack Baldwin, Jack Barrett, Andrew Barron, the late David Bassett, Andy Bell, Chris Braddock, John Bradley, Bill Brock, John Cadogan, Brian Challis, David Cole-Hamilton, Ray Colton, Simon Cotton, Alan Cowley, Don Craig, Charles Cullis, Ieuan David, Alwyn Davies, Andrew DeMello, John DeMello, Andy Dengel, James Durrant, Phil Dyer, Paul Dyson, Russ Egdell, John Emsley, Alan Fersht, Julian Gale, John Gibson, Sue Gibson, Vernon Gibson, Ian Gillett, Margaret Goodgame, Jim Hanson, Catherine Harpham, the late David Hayward, Michael Hitchman, Bryony Hooper, Chris Howard, Fred Jardine, Sue Johnson, David E. H. Jones, Tim Jones, Angela Kenny, David Klug, Anthony Kucernak, Rob Law, Robin Leatherbarrow, Kenneth Leffek, Steve Ley, Nick Long, Philip Magnus, Chris Moody, Andreas Manz, Steve Marsden, Ron Mason, Martin Mays, Mike Mingos, Chris Moody, Peter Morris, Gerry Moss, Robyn Motherwell,

Paul O'Brien, David Otway, Ken Packer, Christopher Parkinson, Douglas Payne, Grace Payne, the late Tony Poë, Michael Pritchard, Elizabeth Rogers, Geoff Rayner-Canham, Marelene Rayner-Canham, Neil Robertson, Garry Rumbles, Michael Sammes, Peter Sammes, Jeremy Sanders, Mark Sebba, John Seddon, Andrea Sella, Sarah Shepley, Dick Sheppard, Andrzej Skapski, Alex Slawin, Michael Spiro, Patrick Stewart, Pete Sulsh, Richard Templer, David Turner, Ramón Vilar, David Waddington, Tom Welton, Andrew White, John Wilkinson, David Williams, Mary Williams, Derek Woollins, and Brent Young.

Thanks also to our editors Catharina Weijman, Mary Simpson, and Kalpana Bharanikumar, and to Elaine Lee and others at World Scientific Publishing for their help with the publication of this book.

Authors' Biographies

Hannah Gay was a professor in the history department at Simon Fraser University before joining the Centre for the History of Science, Technology and Medicine at Imperial College London in 2001. Now retired, she is an honorary research associate in the chemistry department. Her earlier work includes *The History of Imperial College London, 1907–2007: Higher education and research in science, technology and medicine* (2007) and *The Silwood Circle: A history of ecology and the making of scientific careers in late twentieth-century Britain* (2013), both published by Imperial College Press.

William P (Bill) Griffith is an Emeritus Professor and Distinguished Research Fellow of the IC Chemistry Department. He was an undergraduate in the Department, and went on to complete his PhD there with Geoffrey Wilkinson. He then went to Chicago under the Fulbright scheme as an assistant lecturer and postdoctoral fellow with Henry Taube, who, like Wilkinson, later became a Nobel laureate. He then attended Stanford, and finally returned to IC as a staff member. He has written eight books on platinum metal chemistry, some 300 research papers, and several publications on historical subjects.

Chapter One
Introduction

1.1 Historical Background

The chemistry department at Imperial College London (ICL) has a proud history.[1] Many of the world's outstanding chemists have worked in its laboratories, and many more have been educated in them. In writing this book our aim has been to recover the department's history in a way that will interest those who have connections to it, and those with general or specialist interests in chemistry and its history.

The department is the direct descendent of the Royal College of Chemistry (RCC), founded in 1845. However, as shown in subsequent chapters, it has important secondary roots in the Royal School of Mines (RSM), founded in 1851, and in the chemistry department founded at the City and Guilds' Central Technical College (C&GCTC) in 1884.[2] Origins matter in determining an institution's character and, because of this, we devote much space to the founding and early years of the RCC. The book covers the period 1845–2000 and includes material on the staff, students, chemical research, teaching, governance, and social life of the department. Much of what is discussed is placed in wider chemical, economic, cultural, and political contexts.

Histories can be written from the top-down or from the bottom-up. This is a top-down history in that much has been written about the heads of department and other leading figures. A very different, bottom-up history could be written. For example, a history tracing the lives of students both in and beyond the department might well tell us more about the department's wider influence than the one written here. However, more than gifted students and teachers are needed for a department to become as successful as the one at ICL. As we show, technical, administrative, and other supporting staff have also played important roles.

From the start, practical skills have been valued at ICL, and laboratory instruction has been emphasised over lectures. Because of this, a number of Oxbridge graduates came to the department in its early years to enhance their education by acquiring laboratory skills that were not taught at the ancient universities. Still today, the departmental ethos embraces the practical, just as it embraces both 'applied' and 'pure' research. The RCC's first Professor, A. W. (Wilhelm) Hofmann, encouraged this dual approach, emphasising chemistry's utility as well as its purely scientific interest. He encouraged students to both publish in chemical journals and to patent their work; and he tied chemistry's intellectual advance to industrial enterprise and the interests of the nation. However, although he was to make a small fortune from some of his dye discoveries, Hofmann was primarily interested in the discipline's intellectual development, and in having a voice in the academic world. This is also true of most who followed him.

We have written a largely chronological account, but the way in which we have divided the material into chapters fits our overall vision of different departmental eras. The early chapters include discussion of people, some of whom are today viewed as chemical heroes. Those who come to a discipline early and help to lay its academic and/or intellectual foundations are more likely to be remembered than those who come along later. It is not that pioneers are smarter or more gifted than their followers, it is more a matter of timing. Pioneers gain posthumous fame for having been prescient enough to choose a profession or occupation on the verge of becoming important, and for helping it become so. Further, the early professors and their students had the kind of freedom, and the opportunities that come when a discipline is still young, when institutions are small, and when people are waking up to the utility of their work. Because of their 'heroic' status, we give some of the early departmental figures marginally more space than is given to those who joined the department later. A few other professors, including two more recent heroes, the Nobel laureates Derek Barton and Geoffrey Wilkinson, also receive a fuller treatment. Since the 1990s the number of professors has risen dramatically. This is probably a good thing; but in a mature discipline, and as professorships multiply and become more run–of–the–mill, those holding them have to accomplish something truly spectacular to gain notice.

For many years Imperial College (IC) lived up to its name, seeing itself as an institution that promoted science of importance to the British Empire, and one that trained people for work not only in Britain, but also in the colonies and Dominions. The chemistry department was a part of that. The empire is long gone, but the college continues to attract both staff and students from around the world, and has a loyal, and international alumni body. Until the 1980s many students and some of the staff came from Commonwealth countries; today they are outnumbered by those from countries within the European Union. Further, from its start in 1907, the college brought students together from all classes of society, a legacy inherited from its constituent colleges, including the RCC. From its foundation in 1845, the RCC saw a type of class mixing that brought the children of landowners, manufacturers, professionals, civil servants, tradespeople, working people, and even a few aristocrats, together. The staff, too, came from a range of social backgrounds. The RCC was open to women from its inception, though in the early years of the department, there were few women students; today they make up a little over 40 percent of the undergraduates. There were some women on the staff from the early 20th century, but the number remained low until recently. The social mix resulted in a modern outlook, one in which intellectual, technical, and entrepreneurial values were all appreciated. It is also worth pointing out that IC's Royal Charter of 1907 stated that there be no discrimination based on religion, race or sex.[3]

Until recently most universities valued a liberal education above all else. Indeed, until fairly late in the 20th century many in the academic world, coloured by older aristocratic values, saw technical, entrepreneurial, or business ambition as decidedly second best. Today, universities still rightly place great value on intellectual advancement, but recognise also their broader role in society — something understood in the chemistry department since its foundation.

The RCC was purchased by the government in 1853 and became a part of the Government School of Mines (later, RSM). In 1873 the RCC, together with some departments from the RSM, moved from London's West End to South Kensington to form the Normal School of Science (NSS) which was renamed the Royal College of Science (RCS) in 1890. It occupied the building that is now the Henry Cole Wing of the Victoria and Albert Museum (V&A).[4] The development of the department first in Oxford Street, and then in South Kensington, is discussed in subsequent chapters.

The South Kensington location has been important to the identities of both students and staff. Already in 1873 chemistry students saw themselves as belonging to a local community that included some of the best science, art, and music students in the country and, of course, their outstanding teachers.[5] A little later some of the best engineers joined the mix; and, late in the 20th century, so did many excellent medical professionals and students. The department is located close to some of Britain's foremost museums and to the Royal Albert Hall. Many of London's other important sites are easily accessible, including some fine parks and the River Thames. This cultural geography has undoubtedly been influential in the lives of both students and staff, especially those with long departmental associations. Since the department is only a short bus ride from the centres of power in Westminster, its staff have often been called upon to give technical advice to members of the government and to civil servants. As we will see, this was especially the case during the two world wars when quick decisions on technical issues had to be made. It is probably fair to state that the experience of the wars helped to establish the identity of the department as an important national source of chemical expertise.

1.2 Some Organisational Points

The book is divided into chapters that reflect what we see as different eras in the department's history. Chapter Two covers the founding of the RCC, Chapter Three its foundational years under Hofmann and Edward Frankland. Chapter Four shows how Frankland and Thomas Henry Huxley, the biology professor at the RSM, successfully fought for the sciences at the RCC and RSM to be moved to South Kensington. It covers also the late Victorian and Edwardian periods, the renaming of the Normal School as the Royal College of Science (RCS) in 1890, the headships of Edward Thorpe and William Tilden, and the founding of IC in 1907.

It also includes a section on Henry Armstrong's chemistry department at the C&GCTC, its closure in 1911, and its merger with the RCS/IC department. Chapter Five covers the department during the First World War. It describes some of the important war-work carried out by both staff and students, focussing especially on the activities of the energetic head of department, Herbert Brereton Baker. Chapter Six covers the department during the interwar years when Jocelyn Thorpe, after a few years dedicated to helping the departmental war effort, put great effort into reinvigorating the organic chemistry section, and making it once again one of the best in the world. Chapter Seven covers the department during the Second World War under the joint headship of Vincent Briscoe and Ian Heilbron. Chapter Eight covers the difficult postwar years, and shows how the department functioned with three sections, constitutionally separate, and each under its own professor. This new constitution was the idea of Patrick Linstead who succeeded Heilbron as Professor of Organic Chemistry in 1949. After some difficulties, the late 1950s saw three long-term section heads in place: Richard Barrer followed Linstead as head of department, and was head of the physical chemistry section. Two former students, Geoffrey Wilkinson and Derek Barton, headed the inorganic and organic sections, respectively. Barrer expanded the physical chemistry section, Wilkinson was to build the inorganic section into one of the best in the country, and Barton advanced the high standards laid down by his predecessors.

By the late 1950s the postwar recovery was almost complete and, with government support, the department began to grow. In Chapter Nine we discuss a period of further, though interrupted, growth, 1965–1985. Following the 1963 Robbins Report on the future of higher education in Britain, the government decided to increase the number of university places, especially in science and engineering. IC was promised new funding for a major expansion. However, the 1970s saw a serious economic recession, and the expansionary plans had to be redrawn. By 1985 the economic problems, though relaxed, were not fully over. Chapter Ten, covering the period 1985–2000, gives an overview of how the department reoriented itself in light both of its financial difficulties and new developments in chemistry. One consequence was the end of the tripartite departmental structure and the formation of new sections; the period also saw considerable expansion in student and staff numbers. Our book ends in the year 2000, but we include a little information from the early 21st century so as to round out our stories. Like other historians we selected our data and put it together in a way that holds meaning for us. We hope that it will be meaningful also to our readers.

The book includes chapter endnotes, some of them extended. As is usual they include references to the sources used; archival sources are cited fully, full citations for published sources are given in the bibliography (in line with the University of Chicago style manual — preferred perhaps more in the humanities than in the sciences). The endnotes also include interesting information that would clog the main narrative were it to be placed there; much biographical and anecdotal material falls into that category. Our main narrative, however, can be enjoyed without much reference to the endnotes.

There are a few other technical points worth making. We acknowledge the decline in the use of the upper case for personal, as well as for book and paper, titles, and largely follow contemporary fashion, though not always consistently. In some chapters we begin with a discussion of organic chemistry, and in others with a discussion of inorganic or physical chemistry. As to the names of authors, following today's convention we use initials for the authors of chemical papers. For books and for all other papers we use first names or initials, depending on usage in the original publication. For place-names, British historical usage is adopted; for example, Ceylon before 1972 and Sri Lanka after.

The two final chapters were the most difficult to write. This is in part because many of the people mentioned in them are still alive, and in part because the number of people working in the department became far larger towards the end of the 20th century. We spoke with many people, and received stories from others via email; we are grateful to all who helped us. For the earlier period many more written sources are accessible because private and other papers have had time to reach the archives, and there is an extensive obituary literature. Whether written or oral testimony is more reliable is a matter for debate. What is undoubtedly the case is that temporal distance helps to place events, people, and their work, in perspective; distance allows for better judgements to be made. Perhaps we should have ended our book at an earlier date, but we believe that it was worth including the reorientation of the department in the

1990s, and to write a little about the late-century appointees who are helping to keep the department's outstanding reputation alive and well in the 21st century.

End Notes

1. The college's legal name was 'The Imperial College of Science and Technology' until 1988 when it became 'The Imperial College of Science, Technology and Medicine'. Until 2007, when it became an independent university, it was known simply as Imperial College (IC). Since 2007 its preferred name or 'brand identity' is Imperial College London (ICL). In this book, which covers the period up to 2000 we mainly use IC, but use ICL where appropriate.
2. This college was known as The Central Technical College, informally as The Central. After the founding of IC it was known as the C&G Technical College, informally as the C&G College.
3. This was unusual for 1907. The ICL Charter of 2007, the year ICL became an independent university, mirrors the culture of today and is yet more inclusive. Clause 8 states, '... the University shall not discriminate unlawfully against any person whether on the grounds of religion, race, ethnic origin, gender, sexual orientation, marital status (including civil partnerships), disability, social background, political belief or otherwise.' One interesting consequence of the 1907 Charter was that during the two world wars when both men and women took on special war work on college premises, work paid for by the government, the college asked that men and women be paid the same for doing the same work. The government was unwilling, so the Governing Body insisted that the difference be paid from college funds. In both cases it was not a large sum since the number of women workers was small. But the action was significant and says something important about the college. This is not to say that there was no discrimination against women at IC in the 20th century.
4. Henry Cole was the first head of the Government Department of Science and Art and, in that capacity, was responsible for the construction of many of the early education and museum buildings in South Kensington. Earlier he had been a major force in the creation of the Penny Post and the Public Record Office; and he had much to do with the success of the Great Exhibition of 1851, (Cooper, 2004).
5. Also located in South Kensington are the Royal College of Art and the Royal College of Music.

Chapter Two

The Founding of the Royal College of Chemistry

2.1 Justus Liebig's Following in Britain Before 1845

Justus Liebig (1803–1873), Professor of Chemistry at the University of Giessen, made several visits to Britain to see what was happening in the chemical world, and to promote his own ideas.[1] After his first visit in 1837, he wrote to J. J. Berzelius:

> I've been in England for a few months, where I saw a tremendous amount and learned little'. ... [England] 'is not a land of science and the chemists are ashamed to call themselves chemists, because the despised apothecaries have run off with the name.[2]

Liebig was prone to hyperbole. On this trip, he met several good scientists, including his friend Michael Faraday, and visited a number of industrialists. Among the other chemists were Thomas Thomson and Thomas Graham, both of whom sent students to Giessen. Among the industrialists was the Liverpool soda manufacturer, James Muspratt, whose three sons studied there.[3] Liebig encouraged his British students to translate his work and one of the first to do so was Graham's former student, Lyon Playfair who translated some applied organic chemistry and reported on it at the 1839 meeting of the British Association.[4] Liebig extended this work in a book translated by another of his British students, William

Gregory.[5] The translations paid off, and Liebig's ideas were soon taken seriously not only by chemists but also by progressive landowners, agriculturalists, and doctors. When Liebig returned to Britain in 1842, he was well received and, with Playfair as his guide, made a triumphal tour around the country.[6] After another visit in 1844, he made some comments that reveal something of his methodological outlook. Critical of British geologists whom he saw as having had too much say at the British Association meeting in York, he stated that they were mere empiricists and that their prestige was overly great as compared to that of the more deserving chemists, and that

> *only those works which have a practical tendency awake attention [in Britain] ... purely scientific works which possess far greater merit are almost unknown. ... Practice alone can never lead to a discovery of a truth or a principle. [In Germany,] in the eyes of the scientific men, no value, or at least but a trifling one, is placed on the practical results. The enrichment of [theoretical] Science is alone worthy of attention.*[7]

As Liebig must have known, this was an unfair judgement on British science. Although the Royal College of Chemistry (RCC), and by extension the early Royal College of Science (RCS) chemistry department, owed him much, they were also indebted to older ways of knowing. These included a proud mineralogical tradition inherited by, and extended in, the Government School of Mines.

On his return from Giessen, Playfair found work with a calico dye works near Clitheroe but was looking for an academic position. He held a part-time professorship at the Royal Institution in Manchester but, failing to find anything more, decided to take a professorship in Toronto. By the 1840s, however, it was thought important to keep chemical talent in the country. The Prime Minister, Robert Peel, intervened and paved the way for Playfair to become Chemist to the Geological Survey.[8] He also gave Playfair a number of chemistry-related tasks. They included reporting on the Irish potato famine, looking into coal-gas explosions, and sitting on the Royal Commission for the examination of the sanitary conditions in large towns (1843). Playfair also acted as guide to Robert Bunsen who was invited to England to investigate chemical change in blast furnaces.[9] As Chemist to the Survey, Playfair was given a laboratory near the Museum of Economic Geology, situated in Craig's Court (just off Whitehall).[10] Edward Frankland worked there as his assistant, and moved with him to Putney when he was appointed Professor of Chemistry at the Civil Engineering College in 1846. Five years later, Playfair was to become professor of chemistry at the Government School of Mines.

2.2 The Founding of the Royal College of Chemistry

> *In Oxford Street a college met the eyes*
> *of those who breathe the smoke of London skies,*
> *Grand was its structure, noble was the place*
> *Framed for the training of the rising race.*[11]

Liebig's reputation was such that many people thought it would be good for England to have a college like the one in Giessen (see Appendix One). Two who were determined to make the idea a reality were John Lloyd Bullock, a wealthy pharmacist and drugs manufacturer, and John Gardner, a medical practitioner with a licence from the Society of Apothecaries. Both were former Liebig students who saw the college as an opportunity for economic and social advancement, but they were careful to promote it in more noble terms. Gerrylynn Roberts has shown how they canvassed financial support among medical men, landowners and agriculturalists, claiming that the study of chemistry would lead not only to new scientific understanding, but also to improvements in 'medicine, arts, and agriculture.'[12] Thomas Wakley, editor of the *Lancet*, was a supporter. He persuaded some of his fellow surgeons, and some of his fellow MPs, to subscribe. Further, so-called 'high farming' or scientific agriculture was much in fashion around 1840, and among the new practices were the use of guano as a fertiliser, and the use of lime, a by-product of the coal-gas industry.[13] Edwin Chadwick, in his 1842 *Report on the Sanitary Conditions of the Labouring Population of Great Britain*, suggested that sewage be converted into manure, an idea favoured by Liebig and some other chemists, but one that proved largely impractical. Lord Ducie, owner of the Whitfield experimental farm near Stroud (visited by Liebig in 1842), and William Bingham Baring (later Lord Ashburton), owner of a large Hampshire farming estate, experimented with sewage.[14] Both were college subscribers.

The college won support because Bullock and Gardner gave voice to ideals that appealed to a broad constituency of landowners, medical men, academic scientists, chemical manufacturers, druggists, and politicians. They also piqued the interest of potential students and their parents by claiming that chemistry was an ideal field for 'young men with aspiration'. This and similar rhetoric was employed in their 1844 'Proposal for establishing a College of Chemistry for promoting the science and its application to agriculture, arts, manufactures, and medicine'. In it, they stated that major shareholders would have the use of a laboratory, a library, and a chemical museum, and that they would be assisted in any investigation that promised 'benefit to Great Britain its Colonies or Dependencies'.[15] All subscribers were to receive the biennial reports of the college which, it was claimed, would include much useful information. The proposal signed by 35 men received financial pledges from 760 others.[16] Lord Ducie, one of the signatories, lobbied Peel not only as Prime Minister, but also as someone interested in scientific farming.[17] Peel consulted his friend, the theologian and geologist William Buckland. Buckland, in turn, consulted other Fellows of the Royal Society and advised Peel to support the college. He stated that it should be situated in a large provincial town, that one of Liebig's assistants be invited as professor, and that only 'pure' science be taught.[18] Peel was interested in promoting chemical education but thought it best to do so in existing institutions, and did not think the college should receive government funding.[19] So, money was raised through private subscription, and the college was located in London where its promoters wanted it to be.[20]

Gardner and Bullock's first idea was to attach the college, with the name Davy College of Chemistry, to the Royal Institution (RI). They received the support of the RI's two Professors of Chemistry, Faraday and William Brande, but the RI managers declined, giving lack of space as their reason.[21] The shareholders then purchased a lease for a large house on Hanover Square with land bordering on Oxford Street to the north.[22] By 1845, enough money had been raised (and a roster of important names added to a provisional council) for a public meeting to be held. Prince Albert was elected President and the banker, William Baring, Chairman of the council. Also elected were 20 Vice Presidents several of whom, like Baring, were agricultural landlords. Prominent among the medical men on the council were Sir James Clark (Queen Victoria's physician), and Henry Bence Jones, Professor of Chemistry at St. George's Hospital, and a former Giessen student. The original idea was to use the large house for the college laboratories and administrative offices, for meetings of the council, and to accommodate the professor and college secretary. But the renovations needed were too costly. Hofmann lived in the house for a short period, but it was soon let commercially. Space was rented on George Street for temporary laboratories, and construction began on a college building, designed by the architect James Lockyer, on the part of the land that bordered Oxford Street.[23] Prince Albert, who donated £100 toward the building, laid the foundation stone on 16 June 1846. The stone is preserved in the chemistry department in South Kensington.[24] Present at the stone-laying ceremony were several dignitaries, including some foreign ambassadors, presidents of learned societies, the Lord Mayor of London and the Chancellor of the University of London. Students began working in the new building in October 1846.

Clark was engaged with the college from the start. He concerned himself with the financing and construction of the building, with college organisation, and consulted Liebig on who should be appointed Professor. Liebig suggested his former students, Carl Fresenius and Heinrich Will. When both refused, he suggested August Wilhelm Hofmann.[25] Hofmann, too, was reluctant to move since he had taken a position as *privatdozent* at the University of Bonn in 1844, and feared being left without an academic job should the London college fail. Prince Albert then intervened.[26] He arranged for Hofmann to be given a two-year leave of absence from Bonn, after which he could make a decision on whether or not to return. After negotiating a contract with Clark, Hofmann moved to London.[27] He was 27 years old and, as Colin Russell put it, during his 20 years at the college, he 'transformed the face of English chemistry.[28]

Hofmann was to be paid £400 per year with the possibility of annual increments of £100 up to a maximum of £700. In addition, he was to receive £2 for each full-time student and *pro rata* for part timers. He was to have a two-month summer vacation, and free accommodation. 'It seems like a fairy tale', he wrote to his brother, Fritz.[29] Indeed, the remuneration proved too generous and Hofmann soon lost his free accommodation and took a pay cut. The laboratory was open to students on weekdays from

9.00 am to 5.00 pm, and on Saturdays until 2.00 pm. In the German fashion, there were two semesters (October–February and March–July). The fee for full-time students was £15 per session and, as discussed in Chapter Three, 26 students, ranging in age from 16 to 40, enrolled in 1845.[30] Hofmann was to give three lectures a week, though most work was conducted in the laboratory. He was not allowed to take any outside work without the council's approval — readily given since it helped to promote the college.[31] He brought much chemical equipment with him from Germany and sold it to the college. On his marriage in 1846, he gave up the free accommodation and moved to a house in Fitzroy Square.[32]

Like Liebig, Hofmann held pure research above other pursuits, but encouraged those with entrepreneurial or vocational interests. As mentioned in Chapter One, he allowed students to take out patents on work carried out at the college.[33] Some students absorbed his ideal of pure research and dreamt of having a voice in the world of gentlemanly science, but few found academic work. Hofmann encouraged his early students to submit papers to Liebig's *Annalen*, but after helping to found the *Quarterly Journal of the Chemical Society*, he supported publication there. He negotiated well the various interests and, in his annual reports to the council, detailed the students' wide ranging achievements. In his 1851 report, he noted that those away helping their parents with exhibits for the Great Exhibition, were carrying out work of great national importance.[34]

National interests were stressed also by the college founders. Gardner, for example, wrote of 'an incalculable amount of mineral wealth exist[ing] in Great Britain and its Colonies, and also in India, concealed from its proprietors only for want of knowledge.'[35] Similarly, in the first of a series of evening lectures for the public, given in the theatre at the Museum of Practical Geology in Jermyn Street, the Earl of Clarendon, President of the Board of Trade, and a Vice President of the RCC, stated that young men would be helped into useful professions 'whereby not only would individual interests be promoted, but both in England and throughout her numerous dependencies, the national character of science would be raised and the natural resource developed.'[36] In another lecture, Gardner stressed pure learning, and that students at the college received as liberal an education as did those studying science at Oxford or Cambridge.[37] Others spoke on useful matters such as calico printing, the manufacture of glass, and agricultural chemistry. Liebig's brother-in-law, Friedrich L. Knapp, briefly a Professor in Giessen and later professor of chemical technology in Brunswick, gave a lecture entitled. 'The influence of science upon the progress of national industry.'[38]

Despite all the effort and enthusiasm, the college had financial troubles from the start. The cost of the Oxford Street building, completed in May 1847, was about £5000, leaving a debt of about £2000. This was partially met by donations of £50 from 28 members of the RCC council.[39] Further, questions were raised about the two founders having used the college name in promoting their business interests. Gardner was forced to resign as college secretary already in 1846.[40] In 1853, Playfair resigned his professorship at the Government School of Mines to join the government's Science and Art Department as Science Secretary. Hofmann was offered his chair and, fearing that the RCC would soon be bankrupt, considered accepting. This prompted the RCC council to broker a deal in which the government purchased the college from its shareholders, and amalgamated it with the School of Mines.[41] The name of the new institution was The Metropolitan School of Science Applied to Mining and the Arts. However, the older colleges retained their names and much of their separate identities. Chemistry teaching was consolidated at the RCC under Hofmann, and the government added some laboratory space, and a small lecture theatre to accommodate the larger student body. The curriculum changed because mining, geology, and metallurgy students needed more instruction in inorganic chemistry and mineralogical analysis than was typical at the RCC. This left its legacy. By 1907, and the formation of Imperial College, the chemistry department was strong in organic, inorganic, and analytical chemistry. It also retained some expertise in agricultural chemistry.

2.3 The Working Environment at the Oxford Street College

In 1846, after a year in temporary quarters, the college moved into its new, but not yet complete, building at 299 Oxford Street. The building no longer exists, but there are some first-hand accounts of it, including Jacob Volhard's of 1860.[42] A more comprehensive picture can be pieced together by including information found in the diaries of Herbert McLeod and

Charles Bloxam, in a number of letters, and in the memoirs of Frederick Abel and William Perkin.[43]

The lower-ground floor of the college housed apparatus that was used in common. This included distillation apparatus, oil and water baths, autoclaves, digesters, and charcoal furnaces. The latter were gradually replaced by gas burners during the 1850s. Also on the lower ground floor was a small room which doubled as kitchen and laboratory. It was used for the preparation of chemicals such as aniline in the quantities needed for experiments carried out on the upper floors.[44] The lab boy was expected to have a supply of fresh milk and bread in the kitchen, and to have lit the gas each morning so that members of staff could make breakfast when they arrived. His other duties included making blackboard chalk and carrying out carbon and hydrogen analyses for which students were charged the hefty sum of two shillings and sixpence.[45] McLeod, who studied at the RCC, was Hofmann's lecture assistant from 1860 to 1865, and Frankland's from 1865 to 1871. He records both chemical work and the preparation of meals in the kitchen/laboratory.[46] Next to the kitchen/laboratory was a mixing room and a small analytical laboratory. On the ground floor were a library, two balance rooms, one of which doubled as a reception room, a council room, the professor's office, and his laboratory. At the back of the building, contiguous with the lower-ground and ground floors, was the small lecture theatre built in 1853, and a preparation room for lecture demonstrations. On the top floor was a laboratory with 46 bench places for teaching and research. Hofmann's assistants had the prime spots, alongside the windows overlooking Oxford Street. The building's frontage was 34 feet long (10.4 m), and (before the lecture theatre addition) its depth was 53 feet (16.2 m).

In its early years, the laboratory was poorly equipped. Bloxam, later a professor at King's College, complained about a lack of corks and pneumatic troughs, and was pleased when a fellow student, Edmund Joynson, complained of a lack of reagents.[47] William Perkin also remembered there being little equipment, and that 'sulphuretted hydrogen [was made] in a small square chamber connected to the chimney flue. There were no stink closets except the covered part of a large sand bath heated with coke.'[48] Ventilation was a problem, various systems were tried, but the neighbours complained of bad smells and some procedures had to be stopped. Weather permitting, some experiments were carried out on the roof.[49] There was a pavement well at the front of the building, allowing light into the lower-ground floor. The well led to a store room under the street where the porter conducted a small business selling supplies to the students.[50] They had to provide much of their own equipment, including test-tubes and stand, funnels, porcelain dishes, flasks, beakers, watch glasses, platinum wire and foil, rubber tubing, crucibles, tongs, pestle and mortar, and some reagents.[51] Students were given a cupboard to store these items, and a key for which they paid a deposit. Cheap reagents such as the common acids and alkalis, as well as gas and fuel, were provided by the college. Students also had free use of communal equipment such as thermometers, burettes and graduated cylinders, but had to pay for anything they broke.

Hofmann brought Herman Bleibtreu (1821–1881) to London as his first assistant. Bleibtreu wore semi-military clothing in the laboratory and his English was poor, but the students liked him.[52] Hofmann's English was better, though he attended lectures by Brande and Faraday to help improve it further.[53] Bleibtreu stayed for only one year before returning to study in Germany. He was the first in a series of German assistants, most of whom appear to have been financially poor. Short-lived optimism concerning the college finances, and a corresponding short-lived tolerance by the council for German teaching assistants, meant that Bleibtreu was one of only a few Germans to be officially paid by the RCC.[54] For the others, Hofmann had to find outside sources of income.

Like Bleibtreu, some of the Germans came to earn some money before continuing their studies; others were seeking any chemical work they could find. One might imagine that the well-trained could have found something better in Germany, but it appears that laboratories like Liebig's were turning out more chemists than the market could bear.[55] Several of the Germans who came to the RCC were relatives of Hofmann or Liebig, or were former Liebig students.[56] The blooming of the coal-tar industry, and the success that some of them later achieved, can blind us to the rather poor prospects they enjoyed in the 1840s and 1850s. Britons who studied in Giessen had similar difficulty finding work. Augustus Matthiessen, for example, gained a PhD at Giessen (with Heinrich Buff) and then worked with Bunsen and Kirchoff in Heidelberg on the electrolytic isolation of alkali and alkaline earth metals from fused salts. He returned to London in 1857 without a job and helped Hofmann with his aniline research.[57] To keep things afloat at the college, Hofmann brought in some contract work, much of it related to public water and gas analysis, and to metal assaying. He was appointed a water examiner for London, a position created under the Metropolitan Water Act of 1852 and, after Thomas Graham became Master of the Mint in 1855, he was appointed an official non-resident assayer.[58]

When the college passed into government hands things became a little easier, though money remained tight. Poor, yet promising, students had their fees waived, but were expected to help out in their spare time. Hofmann set up an assaying laboratory in the basement of his Fitzroy Square house and, as an official assayer, was able to bring in enough funds to support his German assistants. Hofmann's older sister, Hanna, worked alongside the others until her fatal illness.[59] When not working on assays, the assistants helped by keeping up with the German literature, running errands, and acting as messengers. One or two lived with the Hofmanns and helped with household maintenance. In assigning the many tasks, Hofmann built a brotherhood of workers. He upheld morale, encouraged his assistants to carry out their own research, used inclusive language, speaking of his assistants and students as 'men of chemistry.'

Hofmann went to the college most mornings and made a round of the student benches. Like master classes, everyone was expected to listen also to instructions given to others. However, according to Henry Armstrong, Hofmann spent more time at his desk at home than at the college.[60] Perkin recalled that the German messengers were kept especially busy when Hofmann stayed in bed for six weeks with an eye injury suffered in a laboratory accident.[61] McLeod, too, recorded short periods when Hofmann, unwell, ran the college from his bed. He noted Hofmann's absences for consulting work, as an expert witness at trials, and his travels to Germany — not only during the summer vacation.[62] Some absences related to the illnesses and deaths of Hofmann's first two wives and sister. Clearly, Hofmann had set up a system that functioned well without his physical, if not his psychological, presence.

Endnotes

1. For a summary of Liebig's chemical ideas, and of work in his laboratory, see Appendix One. For a fuller treatment, and for Liebig's visits to Britain, (Brock, 1997).

2. (Read, 1958), p. 4; translation of quotation from (Carrière, 1893), p. 134.

3. Liebig's first British student was William Charles Henry (1804–1892), son of William Henry, the Manchester manufacturing chemist and friend of John Dalton. W. C. Henry was tutored by Dalton and later wrote his biography. The Henry family made its fortune from the manufacture of milk of magnesia. During his 1837 visit, Liebig was entertained by W. C. Henry at his country estate in Haffield, Herefordshire. For the Henrys, (Farrar, 1997); for W. C. Henry, (Greenaway, 2004). For Liebig's students associated with the RCC, Chapter Three. For a list of Liebig's British and American students, (Brock, 1997). Liebig toured Muspratt's soda factory, other factories making sulphuric acid, soap, steel, pottery and silk, and visited Charles Macintosh in Glasgow to see his method for waterproofing fabric. The Liebig and Muspratt families became friends. In 1851, Liebig visited the Great Exhibition, and Muspratt organised a tour for Liebig to see Ireland again, this time after the potato famine. On the same visit he met Queen Victoria and Prince Albert at Balmoral, (Muspratt, 1917). For James Muspratt, (Williams, 2004). Edmund, James Muspratt's youngest son, took over the family business and, in 1890, oversaw its amalgamation in the United Alkali Company. He was a founder of the Society of Chemical Industry and a major contributor to the University of Liverpool; (Williams, 2004b), (Clayton, 1924).

4. (Liebig, 1840). On leaving Graham in Glasgow, Playfair studied medicine in Edinburgh, but he left without a degree and rejoined Graham, by then in London, for a short period. He then moved to Giessen where he extended M. E. Chevreuil's work on the fatty acids, and where he gained his PhD in 1841. For more on the translation of Liebig's work into English, (Brock, 1997), Chapter Four.

5. (Liebig, 1964); this reprint of the first edition (1842) includes a fine introduction by F. L. (Larry) Holmes.

6. Liebig met many people, including the Oxford chemist, Charles Daubeny. William Buckland took Liebig and Playfair to several farming estates in his home county of Devon and, together with Daubeny, they visited Robert Peel at his country house, Drayton Manor, near Tamworth, Staffordshire. For this visit, (Brock, 1997), p. 99, and (Reid, 1899), pp. 68–72. Lyon Playfair's papers (ICL archives) contain several letters from Liebig reporting on work in agricultural chemistry at Giessen.

7. Quoted in (Brock, 1997), p. 100.

8. Peel consulted Buckland about the appointment and Buckland wrote glowingly about Playfair; (Reeks, 1920), p. 85. Playfair met Peel several times in the 1840s and was his guest on the day that Peel had the fatal fall from his horse (29 June

1850). Graham wrote to the chemist Thomas Andrews about Playfair, about the 'magnificent plans for a new Museum of Geology building on Jermyn Street, facing on Piccadilly', and grudgingly mentioned plans for the new college of chemistry building in Hanover Square; (SML, Thomas Andrews correspondence, 9 March 1845). Playfair was appointed professor of chemistry at the Government Scool of Mines and (later Royal School of Mines, RSM) in 1851. A good chemist, he is best remembered for his 1849 discovery of the first nitrosyl complexes, the nitroprussides $[Fe(NO)(CN)_5]^{2-}$, and some of their remarkable chemistry (the compounds are now used as vasodilators). For Playfair, (Scott, 1905), (Gooday, 2004), note Four and Appendix Two.

9. An official report on the work with Bunsen was presented at the British Association for the Advancement of Science (BAAS) in 1845. The furnaces were about 50 feet tall and the pair examined the mix at one foot intervals, from the top down to the hearth. As Playfair put it, they learned how to 'dissect a fiery furnace', (Chambers, 1920), p. 7.

10. The museum moved to a new building on Jermyn Street in 1851 and the Government School of Mines opened there in the same year.

11. This (rather poor but telling) verse is from a poem by Frederick Field, sent from Chile to Frederick Abel in 1858 (for Field and Abel, see Chapter Three). Copy in KCL archives, Charles L. Bloxam papers, Box 1.10.

12. (Roberts, 1973 and 1976); (Bud and Roberts, 1984), pp. 71–75. Roberts examined the backgrounds of the donors, noting that over half were either landowners or wealthy medical practitioners and that this group provided 71% of the funds needed for the construction and running of the college. For further details on donations see ICL archives, RCC minutes of annual general meetings, especially those of 31 August 1846.

13. For 'high farming', (Chambers and Mingay, 1966).

14. William Crookes, a student at the RCC in the 1850s, was later to experiment with sewage both with respect to recovering usable manure and to producing potable water. See also Chapter Three.

15. Hofmann was to assign students some problems sent in by college donors, few of whom made use of the college facilities themselves. From the Annual Reports (ICL archives) it would appear that Hofmann found such requests tiresome. After the government bought the college from its shareholders, he no longer had to accommodate them.

16. (Roberts, 1973), p. 1.

17. (Roberts, 1976), p. 468.

18. For Buckland, (Haile, 2004). For his advice, (Roberts, 1973), pp. 177–179.

19. (Roberts, 1976), p. 469. It should be noted that, with a few exceptions, the state did not support higher education anywhere in the country. Perhaps Peel did not wish to create a precedent.

20. Among the subscribers were Benjamin Disraeli and William Gladstone.

21. (Chambers, 1920), p. 47. Copy in ICL archives.

22. The first official address of the RCC was 16 Hanover Square, later 299 Oxford Street. The former building still stands though two storeys were added in the late nineteeth century. Sir James Clark (see below) lived at 10 Hanover Square; the Zoological Society of London, the Anthropological Society, three medical societies, and the Royal Agricultural Society occupied nearby buildings in the square; (Besant and Mitton, 1903). For more on the early history of the RCC and RCS buildings in Oxford Street and South Kensington, (Chambers, 1920), pp. 47–55; (Hofmann, 1871), pp. 145–153, (Forgan and Gooday, 1994).

23. The St George. building was owned by Bullock and rented from him for £100 per annum. His pharmacy was nearby at 29 Conduit St.

24. Although the stone made its way to South Kensington, it went unrecognised for many years. Indeed, in the 1950s it was being used to bend metal pipes until someone noticed that 'it had writing on it'! It is now displayed in RCS1.

25. Hofmann was born in Giessen, the youngest of six children. By the mid-1830s Liebig was attracting many students and Hofmann's father, an architect, designed a new, larger, chemical laboratory and a lecture theatre at the University. They opened in 1839. Hofmann began his studies in 1836, gaining a PhD in 1841 for work on the organic bases for which he later became famous. He isolated aniline from coal-tar while still at Giessen. In 1844 he moved to the University of Bonn but, as noted in the main text, stayed for only a few months before moving to London. Hofmann was raised to the Prussian nobility in 1888. For Hofmann, (Rocke, 2004), (Brock, 1972), pp. 461–464, (Brock, 2011), Chapter Three. For Clark, (Agnew, 2004). For more on Hofmann, Chapter Three.

26. Queen Victoria and Prince Albert visited the Prussian court at Brühl Castle during the summer of 1845. Accompanied by Clark, they looked in on Hofmann in his Bonn laboratory. He entertained them with some chemical demonstrations. (Hofmann, 1871).

27. (Chambers, 1920), p. 49 for the negotiation. Clark became something of a father figure to Hofmann. Fellow council member, Henry Bence Jones, had studied with Liebig. He became Hofmann's physician and a close friend; (Payne, 2004).

28. (Russell, 1992), pp. 65–75. Russell's sentiment was not new; as E. F. (Frank) Armstrong put it during the college's 1945 centenary celebrations, 'the choice [of Hofmann] was a happier one than anyone knew'; (Armstrong, 1945), 524. See also (Playfair, 1896), pp. 575–579. (Roberts, 1992), pp. 89–99.

29. (Volhard and Fischer, 1902), p. 28 (our translation).

30. After 1853, when the RCC joined the Government School of Mines, the semesters were replaced by three terms of three months each, and separate fees were charged for lecture and laboratory courses.

31. ICL archives, The Royal College of Chemistry, Reports and Research, p. 1 (1849). This issue covered the years 1845–1847. Together with some consultancy fees, Hofmann's salary and student fees gave him a comfortable income.

32. An English Heritage blue plaque was erected on the house at 9 Fitzroy Square in 1995. The German ambassador unveiled the plaque but then rushed off without saying the few words expected. Charles Rees, wearing a Perkin mauve tie, then stepped in and gave an excellent *ex tempore* speech about Hofmann and his contribution to British chemistry.

33. 48 students took out patents prior to 1865; (Roberts, 1973), p. 342.

34. IC archives: RCC Minutes of AGMs; 1847 and 1851 Annual Reports by A. W. Hofmann.

35. Gardner, quoted in (Roberts, 1973), p. 189.

36. Clarendon, quoted in (Roberts, 1973), pp. 287–88. As President of the Board of Trade he held the government portfolio for business interests.

37. (Gardner, 1846), p. 296. The idea that a liberal education could be obtained through the study of science was promoted by other scientists at this time. Gardner translated Liebig's *Familiar Letters*, as well as articles from German publications for *The Lancet*.

38. (Roberts, 1973), pp. 291–3. Henry E. Armstrong, 'Pre-Kensington History of the Royal College of Science and the University Problem,' delivered before the RCS Old Students Association, September 1920, p. 10 (ICL archives, RCS papers 22/3). Knapp sent his son to the RCC.

39. Earlier it had been estimated that the college could be run on about £1000 per year, that £650 would come from student fees and the balance from annual subscriptions. But this was too rosy an estimate.

40. Rumour has it that he was literally thrown out of his office in Hanover Square by Sir James Clark. The reasons for his forced resignation are complicated but had to do both with his leasing of Bullock's property on George St. for the temporary quarters of the RCC, and with improper financial speculation in a quinidine business he set up with Bullock — possibly with the collusion of Liebig and Hofmann. (Roberts, 1973); (Brock, 1997), pp. 134–135.

41. At that point Hofmann's salary was reduced considerably, but he was able make much up from student fees. A salary cap of £800 was applied for future reference.

42. (Volhard and Fischer, 1902), pp. 64–67; (Bentley, 1970), pp. 153–181; (Russell, 1992). In 2003, a RSC commemorative plaque was placed on the building that now occupies the site.

43. The diary of Herbert McLeod is held in the ICL archives, and that of Charles L. Bloxam in the KCL archives. (Abel, 1896), (Perkin, 1896).

44. Aniline was fundamental to Hofmann's research programme. In allowing its production in the laboratory/kitchen, he probably did not appreciate its toxicity. Later, after an accidental poisoning (from mercury compounds) in the laboratory at St. Bartholomew's Hospital in 1866, T. L. Phipson wrote an angry note about the dangerous conditions for assistants in both Hofmann's and Odling's laboratories. It appeared in several French and German publications. For Hofmann's response, *Chemical News* 13 (1866), pp. 7–8.

45. ICL archives; McLeod Diary, Aug. 4th, 1869. For the kitchen/laboratory, see also (Abel, 1896), pp. 583–589. Volhard records cooking sausages, bacon and eggs, and grilled cheese and that, during his time in London, the lab boy was J. T. Hadrell, whom he described as lanky and pious. Hadrell worked his way up to become a junior assistant; (Volhard and Fischer, 1902), pp. 66–67. Another, more successful lab boy, Alfred Tribe (1839–1885), studied with Bunsen and later worked for John H. Gladstone with whom he published several papers. Tribe obituary, (Anon., 1896), pp. 352–353.

46. On one occasion he combined both aspects by making a coffee extract from spent grounds — to make his small and costly coffee supply last longer. ICL archives; McLeod Diary, 28th November 1869.

47. KCL archives; Charles Bloxam Diary, Oct.7, 1850. Joynson joined his father's paper manufacturing business. For more on the laboratory's equipment, (Jackson, 2006).

48. Perkin, quoted in (Bentley, 1969) 21. The 'sulphuretted' hydrogen was converted to sulphurous acid before being vented so as to minimise complaints from neighbours. For this problem, see ICL Archives, RCC Minutes; Hofmann's Annual Report, 1848. (Abel, 1896) also records the lack of equipment.

49. ICL archives; McLeod Diary, May 22 and July 26, 1860.

50. Richard Coppins was the porter until his death in 1868. McLeod reports helping stock this shop by ordering from suppliers etc. For example, ICL archives, McLeod Diary, January 6, 1863.

51. ICL archives; Government School of Mines, prospectus and syllabus 1861–1862.

52. (Volhard and Fischer, 1902), p. 31. For other German assistants, see Chapter Three. See also note 56.
53. (Volhard and Fischer, 1902), p. 36; letter from Hofmann to his mother dated, 7 December 1847.
54. IC archives: financial details on assistants are in RCC Council minutes.
55. The number of chemists in Germany exceeded the demand in the period before 1860; (Wetzel, 1992), pp. 83–86.
56. Hofmann married Helene Moldenhauer, a niece of Liebig's wife, shortly after taking the London post. Among his German assistants with family or other personal connections was his friend Georg Merck (1825–1873) of the Darmstadt chemical/pharmaceutical family. In lieu of tuition fees, Merck worked as an unpaid assistant, mainly on water analyses. He moved to Giessen in 1848 where he gained a PhD. P. W. Hofmann, Hofmann's nephew, became an assistant in 1857. H. L. Buff, a Giessen student, arrived in 1854 later completing his studies in Göttingen. He reappeared in London as an assistant in the 1860s. Hofmann's sister Josephine was the first wife of Buff's father, Giessen physics professor, Heinrich R. Buff (1805–1878). Buff's second wife was the older sister of Liebig's first wife. Hofmann's first father-in-law died young and, after his death, his widow married the father of August Bopp, later an assaying assistant in London. On Hofmann's recommendation, Adolph Leibius, an assaying assistant in 1858, found work in the Mint in New South Wales. Adolf Geyger, a former Giessen student, was an assistant from 1856 to 1865. Returning with Hofmann to Berlin, he assisted him there before joining a chemical works in Lille run by C. F. Kuhlman. Peter Griess, a Liebig student, assisted Hofmann from 1858 to 1862 before finding work with the brewers, Allsopp and Sons, Burton-on-Trent. Carl Martius (1838–1920) was accepted as a student in 1860, paying no fees in exchange for a variety of services; he worked briefly with Roberts, Dale and Co., colour manufacturers in Manchester, before returning to doctoral studies with Liebig in Munich, and a major career in the chemical dye industry (a founder of AGFA, in 1871). Eugen Sell (1842–1896), a family friend, came in 1861, as did Maurice Holzmann; both admitted without fees. Holzmann later found work in the service of the Royal family and was knighted. (Volhard and Fischer, 1902), pp. 7,41,47,60; (Bentley, 1969). See also Chapter Three.
57. For Matthiessen, (Hartog, *revised* McConnell, 2004), (Anon., 1871). Augustus Matthiessen FRS (1831–1870) isolated calcium and strontium while working with Kirchoff and Bunsen in Heidelberg. He left Hofmann for work as a lecturer in chemistry, at St. Mary's Hospital, later at St. Bartholomew's Hospital. Elected FRS in 1861, he later won the Royal

Medal. He was known also for his 1860s work with George Carey Foster on the opium alkaloids. Partly paralysed from childhood and a depressive, Matthiessen took his own life in 1870. William Tilden presented samples of Li, K, Ca, and Sr, prepared electrolytically by Matthiessen, to the Science Museum (*inventory number* 1915–315).

58. Earlier Hofmann turned down this work. Hofmann to Liebig, 5th April, 1851, in (Brock, 1984); (Brock, 1976), p. 178.
59. (Volhard and Fischer, 1902), p. 61. Hanna Hofmann took over the household duties on the death of Hofmann's second wife in 1860. She (HH) died in the South of France in 1863; ICL archives, McLeod Diary, Mar. 2nd, 1863. In the early 1860s the rate for an assay of bronze, or of copper in gold coins, was 10 shillings. When Hofmann moved to Berlin the assaying was taken over by John Stenhouse. Stenhouse hired several former RCC students as assistants. (Stronach, *revised* Watson, 2004), (Anon., 1881), pp. 185–188.
60. Armstrong, *op. cit.* **38**, p. 6.
61. (Perkin, 1896), p. 602. The accident was caused by a student. Hofmann was cared for by Henry Bence Jones.
62. Hofmann was a frequent expert witness at trials involving chemical patents. See, for example, an Edinburgh case involving James Young and his paraffin business; ICL archives; McLeod Diary Oct 30, 1860. See also (Butt, 2004) and (Anon., 1884).

Chapter Three

The Hofmann and Frankland
Years, 1845–1885

3.1 Introduction

Shortly after arriving in London, Hofmann gave an inspiring open lecture at the college in which he tied his own ideals to those of his personal hero, Alexander von Humboldt. The 'venerable Humboldt', he stated, was correct in his view that a nation's prosperity comes from the intellectual endeavours of its citizens. The 'cultivation of natural science' was not only 'the unfailing source of the purest and highest intellectual enjoyment', it was also 'the mainspring both of individual and national prosperity.' According to Hofmann, the chemist 'enters the laboratory, where a new field of study opens to him which, when cultivated with zeal and assiduity, promises a rich and early harvest.'[1]

Hofmann was a fine rhetorician and persuaded his students that chemistry had a golden future, even though it was not yet clear what that future would bring or when, if ever, it would arrive. But arrive it did and, according to Henry Armstrong, 'no fairy tale could match' what actually happened. Hofmann's students were impressed by his enthusiasm and by his intellect, if not always by his manipulative skill. They admired the effort he put into teaching and research and appreciated that he published widely and encouraged them to do likewise. They were impressed by his international connections, that he was at home in Paris and Berlin, that he had the support of Queen Victoria and Prince Albert, and that he attracted famous and interesting visitors to the college. As Armstrong put it, he was 'cosmopolitan in speech, cosmopolitan in sympathies'. William Perkin recalled being amused by Hofmann's manner of speech, recording, for example, that when a student produced a scarlet salt of 'ortho-nitrophenol', Hofmann exclaimed, 'new bodies are floating in the air.' Frederick Abel, too was charmed by Hofmann's geniality and high spirits. Like other students, they were proud that this brilliant foreigner was living in their midst and adding lustre to their college.[2]

Frankland, too, was a brilliant chemist, but he lacked Hofmann's charisma.[3] The two first met when Hofmann made a return visit to Giessen in 1849, and Frankland gave him some glassblowing lessons. They became friends and Hofmann's later wish to have Frankland succeed him as professor was granted when, somewhat reluctantly and after many invitations, he decided to leave London in 1865 for a professorship in Berlin. Like Hofmann, Frankland was the professor at the college for 20 years. His contributions to chemistry were many and great, though much of his important work was carried out before his time at the RCC.

3.2 Students, Assistants, and Instruction

Twenty-six students enrolled in 1845, among them were Frederick Abel, Edward Nicholson, Henry How, Robert Galloway, Charles Bloxam, Frederick Field, and Thomas Rowney.[4] Another was Warren de la Rue, but he was atypical. Around 30 years old and already a good scientist, he was a college subscriber, on the RCC council, and of enormous help in getting the college up and running. He also translated German research papers for the students, thereby helping to keep their work up to date. He was elected FRS in 1850, one year before Hofmann.[5] As mentioned in Chapter Two, Hofmann brought Herman Bleibtreu from Germany as a teaching assistant. He also appointed John Blyth as assistant professor. Blyth had a PhD from Giessen and was looking for employment. After one year in London, Bleibtreu returned to Germany and, a year later, Blyth left for a professorship at the Royal Agricultural College in Cirencester. Their roles were then divided three ways. Nicholson became lecture demonstrator and research assistant and Abel became laboratory teaching assistant — not that this precluded him from helping also with Hofmann's research.[6] Both were paid £40 per year. Rowney was made a junior teaching assistant and was paid £20.[7] Assistants could earn more by giving private tuition to students and, from the mid-1850s, by marking school examination papers set by Hofmann, and later Frankland, for the government's Science and Art Department. In 1869, Herbert McLeod noted that he and William Valentin were paid £50 for marking a stack of 1000 papers 'that was over three feet high.'[8]

In the early days of the college Hofmann appointed two honorary assistant professors, James Sheridan Muspratt and David Price.[9] They set a pattern for other chemists happy to be given bench space in return for teaching or other duties. One who came to the college in 1862 was Hermann Sprengel. Originally from Hanover, he had been an assistant to Benjamin Brodie in Oxford. While at the college he developed his eponymous vacuum pump, achieving vacua not surpassed until James Dewar introduced charcoal cooled by liquid air as an absorbent. Sprengel pumps were widely used, including by William Crookes in his vacuum tube and radiometer work, and industrially by Edison and Swan for evacuating incandescent light bulbs.[10]

By the third session, and with the new Oxford Street building in place, the college could accommodate 46 people working at any one time.[11] Among those entering in 1846 were George Merck, Frederick Field, Charles Mansfield, Bransby Cooper, John Browning and Henry Noad.[12] Entering in 1848 was George Bowdler Buckton (1818–1905) who stayed for seven years and became Hofmann's research assistant. Together with Auguste Cahours they worked on allyl substitutions in organic bases. In his home laboratory Buckton carried out some work in organometallic chemistry and, in 1857, was elected FRS.[13] While at the college, he met William Odling and later married Odling's sister, Mary Ann.[14] Other early students include Frederick William Pavy FRS (1829–1911) and Thomas Hall (1818–1877). Pavy came to the college while studying medicine at Guy's Hospital. He was to become an eminent physician and physiologist.[15] Thomas Hall taught chemistry at the City of London School.[16] Over his years as a teacher he encouraged about 30 of his pupils, including Frank Clowes, Edward Divers, John Newlands, Alexander Pedler, William Perkin, the brothers John and William Spiller, and William Thorp, to attend the college. Another early student, John W. Reynolds, discovered propylene while at the college.[17] In addition to William Perkin (see below), at least four of the early students became independent chemical manufacturers. Henry B. Condy had a small business in Battersea and his name lives on in 'Condy's crystals' and 'Condy's Fluid'.[18] John Joseph Grossjean manufactured citric and tartaric acids and John Williams, together with a partner, W. K. Hopkin, founded the well-known firm of Hopkin and Williams, manufacturers of fine chemicals. He later became President of the Pharmaceutical Society. William Whiffen, too, was a successful manufacturer of fine chemicals. His grandson later donated money to build the Whiffen Laboratory in the chemistry department in South Kensington.

Abel left for a demonstratorship at St. Bartholomew's Hospital Medical School in 1851. By then Hofmann had trained others to take on the various assistantship roles. Henry Medlock and Charles Bloxam were appointed junior teaching assistants in 1849, followed by Abel's younger brother John S. Abel, William Crookes, John Spiller, and James Brazier.[19] Medlock and Bloxam soon became senior assistants, but in 1853 they left to work as analytical chemists. Bloxam married Abel's sister and was later professor of chemistry at King's College.[20] Other early teaching assistants include George F. Ansell, Augustus B. Northcote, Reginald Morley, and Edward Divers.[21] In 1853, John Spiller (1833–1921) moved to Jermyn Street where he taught metallurgy students for three years before leaving to work at the Woolwich Arsenal. In 1868 he joined his brother's firm of dye manufacturers, Brooke, Simpson and Spiller. Also attracted to metallurgy was William Gowland FRS (1842–1922), a medical student turned chemist. He worked for the Imperial Mint and Imperial Arsenal in Japan, returning to the RSM as professor of metallurgy in 1902.[22] The first head of the Imperial College chemistry department, William Tilden, was a part-time student in the early 1860s.

The fees for full time students were lower than at University College and other universities. As a result the RCC attracted not only students who lacked the classical education needed to matriculate at a university, but also those drawn by lower fees. Students came from all social classes and included old Etonians as well as the sons of tradesmen.[23] Ancillary sciences were not compulsory until later in the century. Some students chose to take mathematics classes elsewhere, or classes at the RSM — biology from Huxley, physics from Tyndall, or classes in geology, metallurgy or mining. Overall, fewer lectures were given at the RCC than at University College, and laboratory instruction was less structured. Hofmann encouraged self-education both in and beyond the laboratory. He also supported the formation of two evening clubs, one at which students read their own scientific papers and one for the discussion of political and literary subjects. Regular visits were organised to industrial sites such as breweries and gasworks. By the early 1860s students were making trips to the Woolwich Arsenal where Abel and several other former students were working on explosives.

The modern idea of progression through a syllabus does not describe well what went on at the college before it moved to South Kensington in 1873. Students came to the RCC in various states of preparedness, and were taught accordingly. Certificates were given for attendance or performance, the latter requiring completion of a small research project. For those starting from scratch, Hofmann recommended George Fownes' *Manual of Chemistry*. When Fownes died in 1849, Hofmann and Henry Bence Jones took over editorship of the book. New material was added, and they brought out six further editions.[24] During the first session of the academic year Hofmann gave about three lectures a week on general and inorganic chemistry, and in the second session, about two per week on organic chemistry. Before 1853, and the construction of a lecture theatre at 299 Oxford Street, lectures were given at the Museum of Economic Geology. As can be seen from extant student notes, and from syllabi that were published from 1853, Hofmann stressed both the intellectual aspects of chemistry and its uses in 'arts and manufactures.' Edward Matthey's sparse lecture notes from the mid-1850s show him listing metallic and non-metallic elements with notes on their chemical and physical properties. He also noted their natural abundance, distribution, and industrial importance, and appears to have learned something about the proportions of carbon, oxygen, hydrogen, and nitrogen in vegetable and animal matter. On leaving the college he joined his brother's firm, Johnson Matthey.[25]

From syllabi published in the late 1850s, we learn that 50 lectures on general and mineral chemistry were given annually — the use of the older name 'mineral' rather than 'inorganic' came from the School of Mines. The lectures began with discussion of the nature of matter, chemical combination, mixtures, solutions, and allotropes. Emphasis was on the physical and chemical properties of the more common elements, and on their uses. For example, when studying nitrogen, students were told about gaseous diffusion. With fluorine came instructions on the etching and engraving of glass; and with carbon there was a digression into coal mining and its dangers, the safety lamp, and coal-gas manufacture. Phosphorus was discussed in relation to the manufacture of matches, calcium to the manufacture of cements, mortars, and bleaching powder, and with silver came discussion of photography and the silvering of glass. Iron and its properties came with a digression into the uses of cast and wrought iron, and the manufacture of steel. Metal salts as paint pigments were discussed, as were the manufacture of sulphuric and hydrochloric acids, potash and its salts, borax, gunpowder, and other explosives. In the late 1860s, some lectures on spectrum analysis were given by J. Norman Lockyer.[26] After Frankland arrived in 1865 he cut some of the applied content and reduced the inorganic chemistry lectures to 40 a year. Both Hofmann and Frankland arranged short lecture courses during the summer, attended by science teachers from around Britain.

In the second half of the year Hofmann introduced students to Berzelian ideas and, by the late 1850s, to the theory of types (see Appendix One). In their organic chemistry lectures both Hofmann and Frankland appear to have progressed from a discussion of simple olefins to alcohols, acids and ethers; and anhydrides, fulminates and cyanates. The chemistry of the organic bases was a major topic. Natural alkaloids, especially pharmaceuticals such as quinine, were an important entry to some ideas that Hofmann asked the more advanced students to follow up in the laboratory. By the late 1850s aniline dyes came to the fore and, by 1860, the ways of preparing aniline had become an examination question.[27] Lectures were given also on natural products such as starches, sugars, oils, gums, resins and gelatine; on natural fibres such as flax, cotton and wool; on wood and peat, soaps and candles. Tannic and gallic acids were discussed in relation to the manufacture of leather.[28] There were lectures also on soil chemistry, on nutrition (one of Frankland's research interests), and on the chemistry of beer.

Several students came from the brewery town of Burton-on-Trent, among them John Gretton, later a partner in the Bass brewery, and the half-brothers Horace and Adrian Brown.[29] Horace Brown had learned some chemistry from Hofmann's former assistant, Peter Griess, before attending the college.[30] He and Henry Armstrong came to the college in Hofmann's final year and became lifelong friends. Brown left at the age of 17 to become a junior brewer at Worthington's brewery, where he was to find a major career.[31] Cornelius O'Sullivan, another important brewing chemist, was a Student Assistant who left with Hofmann for Berlin in 1865.[32] Some other students from the 1860s deserve mention. Frederick Douglas Brown FRS (1851–1922) was the founding professor of chemistry at the University of Auckland. George James Snelus FRS (1837–1906), the first to make pure steel from phosphoric pig iron in a Bessemer converter, won the Bessemer Gold medal in 1889. Percy Gilchrist FRS (1851–1935) and his cousin, Sidney Gilchrist Thomas (1850–1885), perfected the low phosphorus steel process.[33] Snelus, Gilchrist, and Thomas were all RSM metallurgy students who took chemistry as part of their studies.

Armstrong admired Frankland's laboratory skills but, as a teacher, compared him unfavourably with Hofmann. He complained of being 'fed' Frankland's *Lecture Notes*, which he thought 'thoroughly indigestible and forbidding,' and, claiming to know 'on what artificial lines structural formulae were built,' refused to take them 'too seriously'.[34] Clearly he failed to appreciate their considerable heuristic power. In the mid-1860s, aside from the professor, there was only one other full-time teacher, William Valentin. Valentin worked at the RCC for many years and, as Armstrong stated, the students saw far more of him than they did of Frankland.[35]

Lectures were accompanied by demonstrations, conducted at a level of practical competence not expected of the average student. Demonstrations were the responsibility of the lecture assistants who sometimes sought the help of local tradespeople. Hofmann would challenge his assistants to attend lectures elsewhere and to keep an eye out for good demonstrations they could borrow. Bloxam appears to have resented going on 'begging missions' for these, and for equipment that the college could not afford to buy.[36] By Frankland's time, apparatus could be borrowed from a collection held by the Science and Art Department in South Kensington. One long-serving lecture assistant was Herbert McLeod. McLeod was a brilliant manipulator and an outstanding demonstrator.[37] Among other things, and together with James Blakeman a tradesman who built equipment for the college, he constructed (and co-designed) Hofmann's molecular models of 1865. The atoms were represented by coloured table croquet balls, and were connected by metal tubes — the term 'bond' was introduced by Frankland only in 1866. In introducing the models during a farewell lecture at the Royal Institution in 1865, Hofmann amused his audience by saying:

> *I will on this occasion, with your permission, select my illustrations from the most delightful game of croquet. … Let the croquet balls represent our atoms, and let us distinguish the atoms of different elements by different colours. The white balls are hydrogen, the green ones chlorine atoms; the atoms of fiery oxygen are red, those of nitrogen, blue; the carbon atoms, lastly, are naturally represented by black balls.*[38]

The models represented empirical formulae and were not envisaged in stereochemical terms. They did, however, prompt speculation on how atoms attach to each other. For Hofmann the atoms had 'valence,' a term he introduced in his 1865 textbook, *Introduction to Modern Chemistry*.[39] Valence replaced a term that he did not care for, namely Frankland's 'atomicity.' Although he appreciated Frankland's theoretical ideas, 'atomicity', he stated, was

> *a vague and rather barbarous expression … we shall escape this evil by substituting the expression quantivalence … and designating the elements univalent, bi-valent, tri-valent and quadrivalent.*

Manufacturers were given licences to make and sell Hofmann's models, as well as other pieces of equipment made at the college. The models were popular and were shown at the front of many a lecture hall. From there it was only a short step to thinking more stereochemically, as Frankland, Williamson, Kekulé and others were beginning to do.[40]

By and large, learning by doing was valued over lecture and book learning, and the laboratory was the focal point of student life. Success there meant more than success in the examination room. In their first year students carried out basic qualitative and quantitative inorganic analysis. Beginning with simple compounds, by the end of the year they were able to analyse complex solid mixtures, and some simple gas mixtures. Students who showed promise were given small research problems already in their first year, though this practice faded with Frankland, and more routine instruction took over. Hofmann, however, assigned projects such as analysing mineral waters, assaying ores, and determining the minerals present in the ash of cereal seeds. If successful, students were encouraged to publish their results.[41] Organic chemistry lectures were given in the second session, but students gained experience in practical organic chemistry only in their second year. As mentioned in Chapter Two, Hofmann gave verbal instructions in the laboratory, often in the form of master classes.[42] Included were instructions on Liebig's *kaliapparat*, on nitrogen analysis (Dumas' method), and on the analysis of simple organic compounds. Much of this material appeared in Hofmann's 1865 textbook, as did the new atomic weight system (C=12, O=16, and S=32). Hofmann adopted it even before the 1861 Karlsruhe Congress (Frankland, shortly after). According to Herbert McLeod, the new system caused much confusion.[43] Frankland's notation introduced a little later was similarly confusing. John Cargill Brough made fun of it in a poem that he illustrated:

> *Though Frankland's notation commands admiration.*
> *As something exceedingly clever,*
> *And Mr. Kay Shuttleworth praises its subtle worth,*
> *I give it up sadly forever:*
> *Its brackets and braces, and dashes and spaces,*
> *And letters decreased and augmented*
> *Are grimly suggestive of lunes to make restive,*
> *A chemical printer demented.*[44]

Acid sulphate of ammonium, NH_4HSO_4.

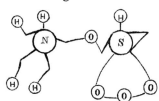

According to Guthrie.　　　　According to Frankland.

[N = △　H = ·　S = ⁓⁓　O = −]

[Here N is seen to be a pentad and S a hexad.]

Advanced students took on some complex analyses, and the more gifted joined in Hofmann's research programme (see below). An article published in the Chemical Society's journal, or in Liebig's *Annalen*, was a mark of maturity, as was admission to fellowship of the Chemical Society. The latter entailed presenting some good work at a meeting, a practice that made fellowship 'better than a degree,' according to James Campbell Brown.[45] Perkin proudly remembered giving papers to the Chemical Society when it met at Dr. Pepper's house in Cavendish Square.[46] Advanced students and assistants were expected to help also with the writing of papers and books, and with translating and proof reading. In one grumbly diary entry, McLeod states that Hofmann gave him a paper by Peter Griess already translated by Valentin, 'which has to be put into English.'[47] When Hofmann became editor of *Churchill's Manual of Chemistry,* he invited his assistants to dinner, after which they worked until 2 a.m., on the index and table of contents.[48] Such work was also part of Frankland's regime. His assistants worked on the revision of Brande's *Dictionary,* and helped with Frankland's own manuscripts. McLeod recorded sending corrected proofs, etc. to wherever Frankland happened to be, frequently at distant meetings or giving invited lectures.[49] His assistants prepared the demonstrations and transported them to the various lecture sites. When Frankland gave the Royal Institution Christmas lectures for children in 1866, he asked McLeod to devise all the experiments, and bribed him by saying that he would ask the college principal, Roderick Murchison, to raise his salary.[50] Frankland was not happy when McLeod was given work at the 1867 Paris Exhibition, organising the displays of the British contingent of chemists, and was away for several weeks.[51]

When Hofmann left for Berlin in 1865 he was given a grand farewell dinner with many speeches. Warren de la Rue spoke of 'a glorious brotherhood' of chemists that had derived 'enlightened pleasure … [and] a powerful means of effecting good from the study of so glorious a science.'[52] It is hard to find similar rhetoric connected to Frankland, even though he was much admired. As a teacher he was not in the same class as Hofmann, but he was recognised as the better research chemist. When Frankland became Professor at the RCC, not only was he often away, he continued to spend time in his laboratory at the Royal Institution where he retained his professorship until 1868. This was because Hofmann was given the option of returning to the college, and only formally resigned in 1868.

Frankland soon complained of cramped conditions at the college. The opportunity to move came as a result of the 1870 Royal Commission on Scientific Instruction and the Advancement of Science, chaired by the Duke of Devonshire. Frankland and some of the RSM professors made presentations to the Commission arguing for a move — the mining and metallurgy professors argued against. Frankland stated that 'the college has been constantly overcrowded with most urgent and diligent students who, for lack of space and the appliances of modern chemical laboratories, have received very inadequate instruction.'[53] Together with Thomas Henry Huxley he promoted the RSM and RCC as twin nuclei for a new national school of science and technology. The Commission was sympathetic and suggested that the RSM and RCC be accommodated in a building that was under construction in South Kensington for the Royal School of Naval Architecture and Marine Engineering. The building (today the Henry Cole Wing of the Victoria and Albert Museum — henceforth V&A) was intended both for the naval architects (already housed in South Kensington, but poorly), and for a general science college to complement the college of art (later RCA). Since there were only a few naval architecture students, the Commission suggested dropping the idea of a new science college, and allowing the RCC and RSM to move. The government agreed, and the westward migration began.[54]

3.3 Some Noteworthy Students and Staff

Frederick Field FRS was the college poet.[55] He wrote many comic poems and song lyrics recording the happenings of his generation of chemists. They enlivened many a social gathering. Here are some examples:

> *A stands for ABEL, of Arsenal renown,*
> *As great a gun as Armstrong in famous Woolwich town:*
>
> …
>
> *F surely stands for FARADAY, and F should stand alone*
> *The letter of the alphabet, the chemist of the throne*
>
> …

H stands for HOLZMANN, who resides in circles high and great,
Yet leaves sometimes his castle halls, for men of low estate;[56]

…

[And] for HOFMANN, who, they say, intends to quit his old domaine;
I for one, most heartily, still trust he will remain,
And that in future years, as now, each warm admiring B
May hail the great Professor at the famous RCC.[57]

…

Of NICHOLSON I now must sing, for he's of aniline the king,
He medal gold from Paris won, presented by Napoleon.

…

Of purple PERKIN next we sing, a very clever cove,
Whose name in every nation is identified with mauve.[58]

F did not stand entirely alone; in another poem we find,

Thrice welcome Frankland, every one will say
Hail to the rising chemist of the day!…
Father of Ethyl! that portentous birth
Which to its very centre shook the earth.

And,

Thallium! we hail thee and we owe to Crookes
More for thy happy birth than for his books;[59]

3.3.1 Sir William Crookes FRS (1832–1919)

William Crookes entered the college in 1848 and performed brilliantly. In his second year he was awarded the Ashburton Scholarship giving him free tuition. He was also appointed a Junior, later Senior, Teaching Assistant, and stayed at the college for six years. His teaching speciality was the chemistry of metals. While at the college he carried out several interesting research projects. The most important were in two areas; first, the chemistry of photography where he undertook work with his friend and fellow student,

John Spiller; second, the analysis of a sample of soot, and all that followed from it. Hofmann was sent a large quantity of chimney soot from a sulphuric acid works in Tilkerode, in the Harz Mountains. Illustrative of his extraordinary ability to meld his own interests with those of his students, Hofmann told Crookes that the soot probably contained selenium. Ammonium sulphocyanide (thiocyanate) was used as a toner in photography. Perhaps, Hofmann suggested, its selenium analogue would prove just as, or even more, useful. Crookes found that, indeed, the soot had a high selenium content. He isolated the selenium, fusing it with potassium ferrocyanide to make a series of selenocyanides and presented his results to the Chemical Society in 1851. It was the first of his work to appear in print.[60]

Crookes was introduced to Faraday while still a student and, inspired by him, was drawn toward the physical chemistry interests that were to occupy so much of his later life. Already at the RCC, Crookes took photographs of some refraction patterns displayed by crystals held between tourmaline plates in polarised light, and was the first to detect such patterns beyond the visible spectrum. Even before Bunsen and Kirchoff published their work on spectroscopy in 1859, Crookes had studied the flame colours associated with different elements as a means of qualitative analysis. Also important to his future career was Hofmann's 1852 appointment as a water examiner for London. Crookes assisted with the analyses, something that proved useful when he later went into the sewage treatment business.

Crookes discovered thallium after he left the college, and after a short period of photographic work at the Radcliffe Observatory. The discovery came after Kirchoff and Bunsen had made clear the significance of emission spectra to chemical analysis. Crookes understood that spectroscopy could help in the discovery of new elements, something Bunsen had already demonstrated with his discovery of rubidium. (When Hofmann wanted to demonstrate some of Bunsen and Kirchoff's work at the college, he had to borrow Crookes' equipment.) Crookes had kept about three pounds of the soot he had analysed earlier, planning to look for tellurium at some future date. Working in his home laboratory, he noted that the soot's spectrum did not show tellurium lines. As expected, it showed those of selenium. It also showed a bright green line, not previously recorded. Crookes' problem was to show that it was not associated with any known element. When he found no evidence for that, he isolated the cause of the spectral line and discovered a new element. For much of this painstaking work he had the help of an assistant, Charles H. Greville Williams. Crookes announced the new element in 1861, naming it thallium (Gr. green shoot).[61] The discovery brought him fame, but was just the start of a varied and highly productive career. A successful entrepreneur and a brilliant scientist, Crookes was elected President of the Chemical Society, 1887–1889, and President of the Royal Society in 1913.[62]

3.3.2 *John Alexander Reina Newlands (1837–1898)*

Newlands, the son of a Congregationalist minister, came to the RCC in 1856.[63] He left one year later, becoming assistant to J. T. Way at the Royal Agricultural Society. Newlands was a social and political activist and, in 1860, he joined Garibaldi's forces in the south of Italy (his mother was Italian). On his return he set up a chemical consulting business with his older brother, Benjamin E. R. Newlands, also a former RCC student, and taught chemistry part-time in some London schools. During the years 1860–1863, Newlands published several short articles in *Chemical News* that anticipated the ideas of J. Lothar Meyer and Dimitri Mendeleev. He recognised that elements with similar properties occurred at definite atomic weight intervals, and focussed especially on the interval eight. He called his finding the 'law of octaves'. He presented on this to the Chemical Society in 1866 and published it in *Chemical News*; but this was not seen as a serious academic journal and his work was ignored. When the Royal Society awarded the Davy Medal to both Mendeleev and Lothar Meyer in 1884, Newlands published a book in an attempt to establish his priority.[64] Finally, the Royal Society acknowledged his earlier contribution and, in 1887, Newlands, too, was awarded its Davy Medal; but he was never elected FRS.

3.3.3 *Sir William Henry Perkin FRS (1838–1907),* *Charles Mansfield, and Perkin's Three Sons*

Perkin, the son of a builder, entered the RCC in 1853 at the age of 14 and, at 17, he became Hofmann's research assistant.[65] Hofmann was engaged in isolating complex hydrocarbons from coal-tar, and making organic bases by reduction of their nitro-derivatives. Perkin was asked to isolate anthracene (then called paranaphthalene) from coal-tar. He failed in this, so some anthracene was purchased from Bethel's Tar Works. Perkin was unable to nitrate the anthracene but he did produce anthraquinone. However, he did not recognise this since Dumas and Laurent, the discoverers of anthraquinone, had given it an incorrect formula. More successful was his assignment to study the action of cyanogen chloride on some organic bases. It was the subject of his first publication in 1857.[66]

Hofmann was interested in the chemical synthesis of natural compounds. The formula of quinine had been determined by Liebig in 1831. Crystalline 'naphthalinidine' (today, naphthylamine), with an empirical formula that differed only slightly, had recently been synthesised. Hofmann thought that the synthesis of quinine was therefore possible; indeed he referred to 'the artificial formation of quinine as a great desideratum.'[67] During the Easter vacation of 1856 Perkin, with the help of his friend Arthur Church, set out to see whether he could make quinine in his home laboratory. Many years later, in his Hofmann memorial lecture, Perkin reminisced that he thought the best way forward was to start with toluidine, substitute an allyl group for a hydrogen to produce allyltoluidine; and that two 'equivalents' of that compound, by taking up oxygen and by losing hydrogen as water, would result in quinine.[68] (As mentioned, at this time Hofmann and George Buckton were working on allyl substitutions, together with Auguste Cahours who was visiting from Paris.) Perkin reasoned as follows:

$$2 \ C_{10}H_{13}N + 3O = C_{20}H_{24}N_2O_2 + H_2O \quad \text{(Perkin used C=12 in his 1896 reminiscences).}$$

He oxidised a salt of allyltoluidine with potassium dichromate only to get a 'dirty reddish brown precipitate', but no quinine. He then decided to repeat the experiment with the simpler base, aniline, and this time produced a precipitate that was almost black but which, when dissolved in 'methylated spirit' (methanol), turned purple. Because the solution stained a mopping-up cloth it looked interesting — at least to Perkin. Hofmann did not know about this experiment until later but, like other organic chemists of the period, was suspicious of colour and regularly used animal charcoal as a decolourising agent. Perkin, however, recognised that he had made a purple dye, one that he found was especially good at colouring silk. Church urged him to patent it, which he did. It was the first coal-tar dye (though not the first artificial dye) and Perkin named it aniline (or Tyrian) purple.[69] After a favourable report from the dyers Messrs. Pullars of Perth, and against Hofmann's advice, Perkin embarked on the risky path of becoming a chemical manufacturer.[70]

Financed and supported by his father, and with business help from his brother Thomas, Perkin built a factory at Greenford Green in Essex. By 1857 it had produced enough of the dye, at a cost of £120 per kilogram, to supply a London silk dyer. The dye was a great hit in France where it was given the name 'mauve' (Fr. colour of the mallow flower), a name that stuck. Indeed, it was praise from France, and an award from the Société Industrielle de Mulhouse in 1859, that helped Perkin's factory to take off and to manufacture also other aniline dyes. However, mauve's first serious competition also came from France, with the production of magenta by Renard Frères of Lyons. Derivatives of magenta (named for the French victory of 1859) later displaced mauve.[71] Perkin was elected FRS in 1866 and President of the Chemical Society, 1883–1885. He was also a founder member of the Society of Chemical Industry.

The raw material needed in the manufacture of aniline dyes is benzene. Hofmann had isolated aniline in 1843 and benzene in 1845, both from coal-tar.[72] He demonstrated that he had, indeed, recovered benzene by using it to make nitrobenzene and aniline. A systematic investigation of the content of coal-tar was later carried out by one of his RCC students, Charles Mansfield. Mansfield devised a good method of fractional distillation and was able to isolate relatively pure benzene. Hofmann asked him to move this work away from the college because it was dangerous. Mansfield then rented his own premises in St. John's Wood and continued with the distillation, isolating also toluene and xylene. By 1855 he had isolated 13 compounds from coal-tar, and was on his way to isolating more, when he was severely burned in a laboratory explosion. He died nine days later at the age of 35.[73] By then he had patented a method for producing nitrobenzene on a large scale. Perkin was to use the patent; his early source of benzene was a coal-tar distillery in Glasgow. Later he relied on Simpson, Maule and Nicholson's factory at Locksfields in South London for nitrobenzene. Simpson, Maule and Nicholson were to take over the Atlas Chemical Works in Hackney Wick where they, too, began manufacturing dyes. Like Perkin, both Maule and Nicholson retired early, and wealthy, from the dye business. Hofmann's student, William Spiller, joined with Simpson and, in 1868, the company became Brooke, Simpson, and Spiller. It was to take over Perkin's factory and later joined with others to become British Alizarin Ltd.

Perkin's three sons all studied at the RCC.[74] William Henry Perkin, Jr., FRS (1860–1929), the elder son from his first marriage, arrived in 1877. He was taught mainly by A. J. Greenaway, and W. R. E. Hodgkinson, and his talent was soon recognised.[75] Perkin, Jr., left in 1880 to study with Johannes Wislicenus in Würzburg and then, for four years, with Adolf von Baeyer in Munich. He went to Germany despite his father thinking it 'a dangerous centre of free thought.'[76] By several accounts, Perkin Sr., was deeply religious, politically conservative, and abstemious in his habits. He was also generous, and from the sale of his Greenford dyeworks he set up New Hall, an interdenominational church hall for his largely German workforce. It is now the Sudbury Neighbourhood Centre. Perkin, Jr., profited from his German exposure and became the leading British organic chemist of his generation. He held chairs at Heriot–Watt College, Owens College (later the University of Manchester), and the University of Oxford. While in Munich, he met Frederick Stanley Kipping with whom he formed a close professional and personal relationship. Kipping married his own first cousin, Lilian Holland. Perkin then married her sister Mina. Kipping followed Perkin to Edinburgh as his demonstrator, and together they wrote a series of important textbooks: *Practical Chemistry* (1890), *Organic Chemistry* (1894–1895) and the less successful *Inorganic Chemistry* (1909). Kipping soon moved to London as Henry Armstrong's demonstrator at the City and Guilds College (C&G). Arthur Lapworth, Kipping's assistant at the C&G, married Kathleen, the youngest of the Holland sisters.[77] We will return to Kipping, Lapworth, and the C&G chemistry department in Chapter Four.

William Perkin's younger son from his first marriage, Arthur George Perkin FRS (1861–1937), came to the RCC in 1878.[78] From there he won a Clothmakers scholarship to study colour chemistry and dyeing at the Yorkshire College of Science. After a period in the colour industry he rejoined the Yorkshire College just before it became part of the University of Leeds and, in 1916, he succeeded Arthur Green as professor of Tinctorial and Dye Chemistry. Frederick Mollwo Perkin (1869–1909), the son of Perkin's second marriage, was a student at the Normal School of Science (NSS) in the mid 1880s. He then studied briefly in Edinburgh, before following in the footsteps of his older half-brother and moving to Würzburg where he took a PhD with A. R. Hantzsch. He was appointed Head of the Chemistry Department at the Borough Polytechnic Institution (today, London South Bank University), staying a few years before setting up as a private consultant on fuel oils derived from coal and peat. Like their father, all of Perkin's sons were musical. The cellist, Leo Stern, another student at the college, worked at a bench next to Arthur Perkin. Stern joined the brothers in trios and quartets, but is best remembered as the soloist in the 1896 premiere of Antonin Dvorak's cello concerto, performed in London under the composer's baton.

3.3.4 *Herbert McLeod FRS (1841–1923) and Some of His Friends*

> *Their passes o'er my view another shade;*
> *Of somewhat smaller form and slimly made,*
> *With slight moustache and beard this one appears,*
> *And hair extended sideways o'er his ears;*
> *His name you know, for he, in lecture-weeks,*
> *Does all the work, while Frankland only speaks.*[79]

Herbert McLeod came to the college in 1857, having studied chemistry for one year with former RCC student, George Ansell, at the Royal Panopticon. Hofmann was so impressed with McLeod that he soon waived his fees and appointed him lecture assistant. Indeed, McLeod's competence was such that Hofmann negotiated a permanent position for him with a salary of £100 per year. One of McLeod's duties was to carry out analyses for all the professors but, since those in the School of Mines made little use of his services, he became an all-round assistant to Hofmann, and then to Frankland. In 1871, he moved to a professorship at the Royal Indian Engineering College at Cooper's Hill (near Egham, Surrey). Hofmann and Frankland gave McLeod all kinds of tasks, not all of them chemical. For example, he was asked to deal with the porter, Richard Coppins, when Coppins was drunk and disorderly. McLeod briefly lodged with the Coppins family and managed these incidents well.[80] He was also asked to deal with troublesome and troubled students.[81] He kept accounts of the laboratory expenses and sometimes paid for things out of his own pocket, settling later with an often reluctant Hofmann, or with a more compliant Frankland.[82] He was also asked to fix things in Hofmann's house.[83] McLeod attended parties at both homes, preferring the more casual atmosphere in the Hofmann household. Parties at the Franklands entailed hiring suitable clothing.

McLeod succeeded with both Hofmann and Frankland because he could deal with all kinds of problems, and could make sense of their perfunctory instructions. In order to have things ready in time for the lectures he was sometimes helped by his friends. One from his early years at the college was Charles Groves FRS (1841–1920) who became an assistant to John Stenhouse, and was later a lecturer at Guy's Hospital.[84] Groves was also the official chemist to the Thames Conservancy Board, and editor of the *Journal of the Chemical Society*. Another friend who left to work for Stenhouse was Edmund J. Mills FRS (1840–1921), later Professor of Technical Chemistry at Anderson College in Glasgow. David Howard (1839–1916), a friend of both Groves and McLeod, entered the college in the same year as McLeod while an apprentice with the family firm in Stratford, East London.[85] Howard studied only general and inorganic chemistry, a little surprising given that the firm, founded by his grandfather, Luke Howard FRS, sold quinine and other natural products. David Howard became president of the Society of Chemical Industry and was a founder member and President of the Institute of Chemistry.

Another friend who helped McLeod was Alexander Stewart Herschel FRS (1836–1907), the son of Sir John Herschel.[86] Herschel, a Cambridge graduate, came to the RCC/RSM to enhance his education with some practical experience and was enrolled from 1861–1865.[87] Another friend and part-time student was Lord Sackville Cecil (1848–1899), the younger half-brother of the Marquess of Salisbury. He, too, was a student at Cambridge where he took a degree in 1869. But, with a practical bent and the need to earn a living, he came to the college while trying to decide whether to pursue a career in chemistry or telegraphy. The latter won out and provided him with a very good income. In 1878 he became director of the Metropolitan and District train line where McLeod helped with a range of practical problems.[88] McLeod recorded the few occasions when he had to prepare demonstrations for the lectures that Hofmann gave to the royal family at Osborne and Windsor. After one lecture, Hofmann reported that despite the royal servants complaining about 'stinks and bangs', the Queen 'approved.' Of another he wrote, 'I cannot think of a better assistant than McLeod, it is a pleasure to see his work.[89]

When McLeod became a professor at the Royal Indian Engineering College, he took along one of Frankland's lab boys, George Scott then aged 14, and one of his research assistants, Francis E. Matthews (1862–1929). Matthews had spent some time in Bonn where he was said to have been a favourite of August Kekulé. A prodigious calculator, he had races with McLeod's calculating machine (an Edmondson) which he often won. Later Matthews joined the firm of Johnson Matthey.

McLeod invented the eponymous gauge for which he is best remembered while at the Royal Indian Engineering College. A low pressure gauge, it has long been used because it is an absolute standard, can be used for calibration, and does not interact with gases.[90]

3.3.5 *Raphael Meldola FRS (1849–1915)*

Raphael Meldola came from a Jewish family that included some eminent scholars and rabbis in its ranks.[91] His Italian grandfather was haham to the Sephardi community at the Bevis Marks synagogue in the City of London.[92] His father, less successful, was unable to pay for a university education, and Meldola entered the RCC in 1866. Some of his student notebooks survive.[93] He was an orderly note taker, but did not shine in the laboratory and Frankland did not appoint him an assistant. A fellow student gleefully wrote to Henry Armstrong, who had recently moved to study in Leipzig, that Meldola had broken two glass Sprengel pumps during the course of analysing some gases dissolved in water.[94] Clumsiness aside, Frankland would have had little sympathy for a student who devoted so much time to his natural history interests.

Meldola found employment as an assistant assayer in John Stenhouse's laboratory where he worked under Charles Groves and improved his laboratory skills. He returned to the RCC in 1872 as a demonstrator in inorganic chemistry, soon also as an assistant to J. Norman Lockyer in the solar physics laboratory. Lockyer had asked Frankland whether he should appoint Meldola or Oliver Lodge. Frankland told him to appoint Meldola.[95] By then Meldola was described as a 'careful and painstaking observer and experimentalist.'[96] He also had interest in the chemistry of photography and Lockyer was seeking evidence for the presence of various elements on the sun, something that required taking many plates of the solar spectrum. In 1874 the 23 year old Silvanus Phillips Thompson FRS (1851–1916), already well educated in the classics, came to the college on a bursary. He and Meldola became close friends. Frankland appears to have taken Thompson under his wing and given him tickets to the Friday evening discourses at the Royal Institution. Thompson wrote to his mother that he learned more about lecturing there than he did at the college; 'I have learned a good deal of the method and "technic" of lecturing … of seeing what we do not get at all in Guthrie, and very little in Frankland, the swing, the ease, the dash, that makes all the difference between the easy and tedious lecturer.'[97]

Although he had a slow start as an organic chemist, Meldola made a name for himself as an entomologist. Both Charles Darwin and Alfred Russel Wallace were his mentors. Shortly before his death in 1882, Darwin promoted Meldola's election to the Royal Society and gathered some signatures for the certificate, but was unable to persuade Frankland to sign.[98] After Darwin's death Frankland changed his mind and Meldola was elected FRS in 1886. Perhaps Frankland's change of heart was related to Meldola's recent success as a dye chemist. Meldola left the college in 1877, to work at the Atlas Colour Works of Brooke, Simpson, and Spiller.[99] While there, he discovered the first oxazine dye, known as Meldola's Blue, as well as some other dyes. His chemical reputation was growing, especially in Germany, and in 1885 he was appointed professor of chemistry at Finsbury Technical College. A few months earlier his friend Silvanus Thompson had been appointed professor of physics and college Principal. Meldola was President of the Chemical Society (1905–1907) and of the Institute of Chemistry (1912–1915). After his death the Society of Maccabaeans donated money to the Institute for a prize to be named in his memory. It was first awarded in 1921 to Christopher Ingold (see Chapters Five and Six).[100]

3.4 Hofmann's Research at the RCC

Hofmann brought the Giessen ideal of group research to London. Students and staff worked well together and, although Hofmann was recognised as the leader, compared with other institutions there was less sense of hierarchy. Hofmann recognised that his research could not be carried out without many enthusiastic helpers and he treated them well.[101]

Many organic bases were being synthesised in laboratories during the 1830s and 40s. Since some had empirical formulae close to those of useful chemicals derived from plants, Hofmann believed that, before long, chemists would

> *imitate, for our own special purposes, the formative forces of nature. Every new reaction with which we become acquainted, is a step nearer to the solution of this grand problem.*[102]

Hofmann was not alone in thinking that synthetic compounds would one day outdo plant-derived pharmaceuticals such as the febrifuges quinine and cinchonine. This vision fuelled two types of research at the college. First, the extraction of chemicals from plants, and the determination of their formulae; second, organic synthesis carried out in a theoretically informed manner. Aniline was central to the synthesis programme, and the fact that it had been derived first from a plant (anil, Portuguese for indigo) was significant. It was the starting material for a range of compounds with possible medical or other potential. What Hofmann did not foresee was the aniline dye industry.

Several of Hofmann's students and assistants worked with plant materials. For example Bleibtreu isolated coumarin from tonka beans. Nicholson worked with caffeine, first isolated by F. F. Runge, and confirmed an earlier empirical formula suggested by John Stenhouse. Together with Abel, he worked also on strychnine. Nicholson, Abel, Field, and Noad all studied chemicals extracted from cumin oil.[103] Thomas Rowney and Henry How were put to work extracting compounds from the orange plant, and Arthur Church was to become more generally renowned as an expert on chemicals derived from plants.

In 1845, Hofmann published a paper with J. S. Muspratt in Liebig's *Annalen* on 'the production of organic bases which contain chlorine and bromine'. In 1848, they delivered a paper to the Chemical Society on nitraniline.[104] These papers led to further work on the substitution of hydrogen also by 'alcohol radicals' and to the synthesis of compounds such as ethylaniline and diethylaniline. With Nicholson, Hofmann explored the action of cyanogen on aniline, toluidine and cumidine and, beginning in 1848, began delivering papers on this to the Chemical Society.[105] Hofmann was puzzled because cyanogen did not substitute in the way that the halogens did. Rather it appeared to add to the bases, without affecting their saturation capacity. Hofmann gave the products formulae analogous to those for conjugated acids, For cyaniline the formula Cy, $C_{12}H_7N$, (the comma after Cy (C_2N) was a way of describing what he saw as a loose attachment, analogous to the way we today describe hydrates such as $CuSO_4.H_2O$). He called such compounds conjugated bases. This way of thinking fitted with Berzelian radical theory (see Appendix One). Hofmann also believed that the formula for strychnine, the composition of which was under study by Abel and Nicholson, was similar, namely $Cy,C_{42}H_{23}NO_4$. But his students sided with Fresenius and gave it the formula $C_{44}H_{23}N_2O_4$.[106] In his 1848 paper Hofmann introduced a conjugated ammonia theory of organic bases, stating that organic bases were compounds composed of ammonia and a conjugated organic radical. Using C=6, and the nomenclature, NH_3 = ammonia; Cy = cyanogen = C_2N; and An = $C_{12}H_4$, bases were given formulae such as: aniline = (NH_3.An); cyaniline = (NH_3.AnCy).

A year later Hofmann moved from his Berzelian outlook to a more Parisian one — toward the type theory of Laurent and Gerhardt (see Appendix One). Indeed, his new work supported their ideas. The full articulation of his ammonia type was published in *Philosophical Transactions* in 1850, the first of his papers to appear in that journal. He stated that the salts of organic bases were analogous to the salts of ammonia. Understandably, aniline was his principal example.[107]

H	$C_{12}H_5$	R^1
NH	NH	NR^2
H	H	R^3
ammonia	aniline	amines, R^1, R^2, R^3 hydrocarbon radicals

Hofmann's continued use of the term 'radical' suggests his still having one foot partially in the Berzelian camp.[108] However, from about 1850 onward, work at the college was guided by type theory even though aniline did not exactly behave like ammonia. Research became focussed on the molecular constitution of the volatile organic bases and on their properties.

Today we see the ammonia type as implicit recognition of the trivalency of nitrogen. Similarly, we see the work that Alexander Williamson published on ethers and alcohols at roughly the same time as implicit recognition of the divalency of oxygen.[109] Williamson believed his compounds were variants of the water type. For example:

H	C_2H_5	C_2H_5
O	O	O
H	H	C_2H_5
water	ethanol	diethyl ether

Despite his shift toward type theory, the earliest impetus for Hofmann's work came not so much from Paris as from Berzelius who, already in 1837, expressed the view that the natural alkaloids were peculiar ammonia compounds. Berzelius claimed that there was much in common between ammonium and alkaloid salts, something that Hofmann demonstrated in great detail.[110]

What this meant for the assistants at the college was that they were asked to carry out combustions using charcoal furnaces (later gas burners), and to use digesters for heating aniline and other bases at various temperatures, and with a range of chemicals.[111] (Frankland had pioneered the use of digesters earlier in Germany.) The idea was to produce as many ammonia type compounds as possible, and in a logical fashion. But the digesters were not without their problems; 'the new leaden digester has burst again … the apparatus flew up to the ceiling then bounded across the room and fell at Richard's feet.'[112]

Perkin's work led to a diversion. After 1856 Hofmann, too, became engaged with colour chemistry. Together with Edward Nicholson, by then a manufacturing chemist, he developed some successful rosaniline dyes known as Hofmann violets. Both he and Nicholson became wealthy as a result. Coal-tar chemistry had led to a colour industry; it would soon lead to a pharmaceutical industry and, as illustrated by these lines from an amusing 1888 poem in *Punch,* the world at large took notice.[113]

> *There's hardly a thing that a man may name*
> *Of use or beauty in life's small game,*
> *But you can extract in alembic or jar*
> *From the "physical basis" of black coal tar.*
>
> *You can make anything from a salve to a star,*
> *If you only know how, from black coal-tar.*

Hofmann was to become president of the Chemical Society (1861–1863).[114] In 1875 he was awarded the Royal Society's Copley Medal. He continued as a successful chemistry professor in Berlin. There, too, he made new discoveries and had many successful students.

3.5 Frankland: His Earlier Career and his Work at the RCC

Sir Edward Frankland FRS (1825–1899) was born near Garstang, Lancashire.[115] He attended eight different schools before being apprenticed to a Lancaster pharmacist at the age of 14. In 1845, after six years as an apprentice, he moved to London and found work as an assistant to Lyon Playfair (see Chapter Two). Playfair's first laboratory was in the underground kitchen of a house on Duke Street.[116] When Frankland arrived, Playfair was focussed mainly on the problem of gas explosions in coal mines. But he was absent briefly because Robert Peel had asked him to examine the potato famine in Ireland. Playfair's assistant, Thomas Ransome, took Frankland under his wing and taught him much.[117] When Playfair was appointed professor of chemistry at the Civil Engineering College in Putney, Frankland became his lecture assistant. What determined Frankland's future path, however, was his friendship with Hermann Kolbe who was working with Playfair on gas analysis. Six years older than Frankland, he had studied with Friedrich Wöhler in Göttingen, and with Robert Bunsen in Marburg. When, in 1847, Bunsen invited Kolbe to return as his assistant, Kolbe persuaded Frankland to join him.[118] Frankland worked in Bunsen's laboratory for two separate periods. Between them he spent a year teaching chemistry, geology, and botany at Queenwood College, Hampshire, where he met John Tyndall also teaching there. Queenwood was a progressive school, and Tyndall and Frankland were encouraged to set up a laboratory — possibly the first school laboratory in England. They taught experimental science, and Frankland's further research begun in Marburg. When he returned to Marburg, Tyndall joined him. Frankland was the first Briton to gain a PhD under Bunsen. For a brief period, he worked also at Giessen where he met Hofmann in 1849.

In 1850, Frankland returned to Putney as Playfair's successor and carried on with the Marburg research (see below). His growing reputation won him the professorship at the new Owens College in 1851, and election to the Royal Society in 1853. However, financial and other difficulties at Owens College (later the University of Manchester), together with its remoteness from the centres of scientific and professional life in London, prompted Frankland's return to the metropolis six years later. In London he put together a living by teaching at various colleges, including the medical school of St. Bartholomew's Hospital.

Frankland and Tyndall shared a love of mountains and, in 1859, they carried out some scientific experiments on Mont Blanc. It is said that they were the first to sleep in tents on the summit. The experience led Frankland to experiment in how the body burns food, a topic he later lectured on at the RCC. In 1863, he was appointed to a professorship at the Royal Institution (not the Fullerian Chair which was occupied by Odling) where Tyndall was the Professor of Natural Philosophy. Tyndall also taught at the RSM and, in 1864, together with Huxley and six others, he and Frankland formed the influential X-Club.[119] Frankland's expertise in gas analysis drew one of Hofmann's students, Frank Baldwin Duppa, to work with him. For 10 years, until Duppa's death, theirs was a fruitful partnership.[120] They built on Frankland's foundational work in organometallic chemistry (see below); and they began to determine how best to analyse organic matter and gases dissolved in water, work that was important to the provision of safe water supplies in Britain.

At Marburg, Frankland began working on some aliphatic compounds with the aim of isolating the radicals methyl, ethyl, and amyl. In this he was in part inspired by Bunsen's isolation of cacodyl, then viewed as a possible radical (see Appendix One). Frankland and Kolbe thought of releasing 'ethyl' from ethyl cyanide and, using C=6, they thought along the following lines:

$$C_4H_5CN + K = C_4H_5 + KCN.$$

Their work was intricate and dangerous, but Frankland was always a fearless experimentalist. They isolated something that they thought was the radical 'ethyl', reporting both a major explosion, and that they were slightly poisoned.[121] Frankland carried out similar experiments at Queenwood, replacing potassium with less reactive metals, notably zinc, and replacing ethyl cyanide with ethyl iodide. He continued these experiments after returning to Putney, claiming to have produced both the methyl and ethyl radicals. In 1864, Carl Schorlemmer showed that Frankland's 'methyl' was ethane, a compound discovered by Faraday in 1834.[122] Frankland had made the dimers ethane and butane, not the radicals he claimed.

In his experiments with methyl iodide and zinc, Frankland noticed a white residue in the tube. It reacted with water producing 'a brilliant flame'. After subjecting it to some analytical tests he claimed to have produced 'zincmethyl' and, after looking again at the ethyl iodide reaction, also 'zincethyl.'[123] In a postscript to his 1850 paper, Frankland stated that Hofmann demonstrated the 'spontaneous flammability' of 'zincmethyl' at a meeting of the Chemical Society.[124] This was exciting and led to work with other 'radicals' and other metals, notably tin. Frankland first used the term 'organometallic' in what is perhaps his best-known paper, one delivered to the Royal Society in 1850, but published only in 1852.[125] The paper also hints at future valence ideas.

> *I had not proceeded far in the investigation of these compounds in Putney before the facts … began to impress upon me the existence of a fixity in the maximum combining value or capacity of saturation in the metallic elements which had not before been suspected … no matter what the character of the uniting atoms may be, the combining power is always satisfied by the same number of these atoms.*[126]

Frankland called this the law of atomicity. As we have seen, Hofmann disliked the term 'atomicity', and introduced the term valence. But Frankland's idea, by whatever name, was enormously fecund.[127] After

Frankland's death, Stanislao Canizzaro wrote to Ludwig Mond, stating 'the discovery of zinc-ethyl and zinc-methyl of Frankland had been the starting point of my theory on the atomic weights of metals'. He claimed that using density measurements of the volatile compounds of zinc and other metals led to the final acceptance of Avogadro's Hypothesis, and to a standard system of atomic weights, with C=12.[128] Frankland began using the new system of atomic weights in 1862, about 18 months after Hofmann. His research into organometallic chemistry continued at the Royal Institution where, together with Baldwin Duppa, and using zinc ethyl, he synthesised a range of new ethers leading to speculation on the constitution of those and of the related ketones. Duppa retained his position as lecture assistant at the RCC until his death in 1873.

Looking back at papers that Frankland published from about 1850 one can see that, like Hofmann, he was at first tied to the Berzelian idea of radicals but increasingly came to accept type theory. It was by recognising the strengths and weaknesses of both approaches, that Frankland arrived at his own theoretical position. Much of his work on organometallic compounds, and on valence theory, was published by the time he came to the RCC. He was awarded the Royal Society's Copley Medal in 1863; his fame was secure.[129]

After moving to the RCC in 1865 he continued to work with Duppa, including some pioneering work in organo-boron chemistry. In 1866, in a paper on the notation of chemical compounds, Frankland introduced the term 'bond', not yet 'chemical bond.'[130]

> By the term bond, I intend merely to give a more concrete expression to what has received various names from different chemists. ... It is scarcely necessary to remark that by this term I do not intend to convey the idea of any material connection between the elements of a compound ... their nature [in all probability is] much more like those which connect members of our solar system.

In 1868, J. Norman Lockyer came to the college to work with Frankland on gaseous spectra. There was a fair bit of disagreement between them, especially when Lockyer's attention moved to sunlight, and Frankland at first questioned his claim to have found a 'non-terrestrial' element on the sun, namely helium.[131] However, Frankland's most important work at the college was, perhaps, in the area of water analysis. It will be discussed in the next section.

As with Hofmann, Frankland had many student assistants. Henry Armstrong, perhaps the best known, is discussed in Chapter Four. Others who later did well as chemists include Sir Alexander Pedler FRS (1849–1918), and Arthur Liversidge FRS (1846–1927). In 1873, Pedler was appointed professor of chemistry at Presidency College, Calcutta and had a major career in Bengal.[132] Liversidge had a major career in Australia and is remembered in the RSC Liversidge Award.[133] Others who deserve mention: George S. Newth (1851–1936), the son of the biblical scholar Samuel Newth, was the author of several chemistry textbooks.[134] He had a teaching career at the college until 1909. Edward Kinch (1848–1920) became an assistant to Arthur Church at the Royal College of Agriculture in Cirencester.[135] He was professor of chemistry at the National Agricultural College in Komaba, Japan, before returning to Cirencester as professor of agricultural chemistry. Thomas Mather FRS, a student from 1880 to 1882, turned from chemistry and later joined the City and Guilds College as professor of electrical engineering. Thomas Humpidge was professor of natural science at Abertstwyth, and Thomas Purdie FRS, Professor of Chemistry at St. Andrews.[136] William J. Sollas left the college for Cambridge where he specialised in geology. He became professor of zoology and geology in Bristol. Frankland had just one female research student, Mary E. Owens, who came from Cincinnati.

Aside from his own son, perhaps the best known of Frankland's appointees was Francis R. Japp FRS (1848–1925). Japp studied law in Scotland. After a period of ill health, and travel in France and Germany, he decided to study chemistry. He did so first with Bunsen in Heidelberg, and then with Kekulé in Bonn. Returning to Scotland, he became an Assistant to Alexander Crum Brown. In 1880, Frankland appointed him to take charge of the research laboratory in South Kensington.[137] One year later Japp was promoted to assistant professor and continued in that position under T. E. Thorpe. He carried out research on ketones and on the structure of phenanthraquinone and, together with Frankland, wrote a notable textbook on inorganic chemistry.[138] In 1889, he moved to the chair in Aberdeen.

Frankland appointed his son Percy Faraday Frankland FRS (1858–1946) to a demonstratorship in 1880, and to a lectureship soon after.[139] Percy Frankland was a student at the NSS, and had wanted to study medicine. Overruled by his father, he dutifully set out for Würzburg where he worked on the diazo coupling of naphthalene derivatives with salicylic acid and gained a PhD. On his return he developed an interest in bacteriology and left his mark by reviving work in agricultural chemistry. The field had languished since the early days of the college when landowner subscribers had demanded it be part of the curriculum. As discussed in Chapter Six, an MSc in agricultural chemistry was introduced in the 1920s. One of Percy Frankland's assistants at the college was Frederick Gowland Hopkins FRS (1861–1947). Hopkins had been a student at the City of London School where two of his classmates were the older sons of William Perkin. Hopkins lost his father when he was a child and his father's cousin, Frederick Abel, advised him to study at Cambridge. He did not follow this advice and, after a few false starts, became a chemistry student first in South Kensington, and then at UCL, before returning as Percy Frankland's assistant. He later studied medicine at Guy's Hospital and became the first professor of biochemistry at Cambridge. In 1929, he won the Nobel Prize in medicine/physiology.[140]

Edward Frankland was of medium height, and was athletic. People remarked on his speed of movement, that he was someone who never wasted a minute, that he began speaking before reaching the front of the lecture room, and that when the lecture was over, he 'streaked off.' He rarely used the blackboard, relying instead on diagrams, drawn on huge pieces of calico cloth, that were hung at the front of the lecture theatre. He often carried out the lecture demonstrations himself. For a demonstration of the explosion caused by mixing hydrogen and oxygen, he used ginger beer bottles as gas containers. The demonstration was still in use in the 1960s.[141] In the 1880s Frankland's lecture assistant was George Newth. Daylight entered the lecture theatre through a glass roof. When Newth wanted the room darkened he would signal to two men who were on duty during lectures. They would then pull on ropes to draw blinds across the ceiling. If electricity was needed, it came from 40 Grove cells. Late in the century a dynamo was installed outside the building with leads running to the inside.[142] Newth remembered Frankland for his 'extreme courteousness' but stated that 'he came very little in contact with his students many of whom were personally unknown to him.'[143]

Frankland was president of the Chemical Society, 1871–1873. He retired from the department in 1885 at the age of 60 and moved to Reigate. During the years 1896–1899 he dictated an autobiography 'for the amusement of my children and grandchildren'. It was published posthumously in 1901, but was almost immediately withdrawn and a version, edited by his two daughters, appeared a year later.[144] A reason for this may be that the first edition, which includes some harsh and dismissive remarks on the Christian religion, proved divisive within his family. Frankland died in Norway, a country he often visited and where he enjoyed both the mountains and the salmon fishing. As mentioned in Chapter Three, Herbert McLeod wrote his obituary for the Chemical Society. McLeod rightly made much of Frankland's experimental skill. Indeed, when reading Frankland's papers one is struck not only by his intelligence, but also by the care and time he took in carrying out his work, much of it dangerous. Frankland was a complex person and undoubtedly one of the best chemists the college has ever had. He was the founder of organometallic chemistry, coiner of the terms 'organometallic' and chemical 'bond,' a major contributor to the idea of valence, and to the theory of structural chemistry more generally.[145] The discipline owes him much. Consistent with Newth's remarks above, McLeod wrote that Frankland interacted little with students and that he had a 'retiring character … so marked that even those who were in frequent contact with him heard very little from his lips of what he had previously accomplished.'[146]

3.6 Applied and Extramural Work

Hofmann and Frankland both took on outside work. Hofmann, as mentioned in Chapter Two, was a water examiner for London and a non-resident assayer for the Mint. He was also an industrial consultant, an expert witness in the law courts, and he took on some occasional assignments for the government. For example, in the late 1850s and early 1860s the newspapers were full of stories of people being hit by small stones and crumbling dolomite, falling from London buildings. With Faraday, Hofmann was asked to advise on air pollution, and on structural decay including at the Palace of Westminster.[147] When the Albert Memorial was about to be built, the Queen asked him to report on how marble statues were standing up to the acidic London atmosphere. Hofmann had scaffolding placed around Marble Arch, and sent Herbert McLeod and Alec Gilman to examine the stones.[148] They were also asked to examine some of the statues and tombs in Westminster Abbey. According to McLeod they removed 'some black encrustations from old royal tombs' with a mixture of hydrochloric and nitric acids.[149] Hofmann gave his views on coatings that could be used to harden the marble. Later the Queen sought advice on the conservation of some old-master drawings that were being attacked by mildew. Frankland sent McLeod to remove the mildew with 'chloride of lime'![150]

Hofmann took on some work related to the contamination and adulteration of foods. In the early 1850s he worked with Thomas Graham on lead contamination in sugar. They were also asked to examine beer samples because it was claimed that some British pale ale, much admired in Continental Europe, derived its bitter taste from strychnine and not from hops. The accusers were some German brewers unable to replicate the taste, and the accused were the Burton-on-Trent firms of Allsopp and Bass. Hofmann and Graham analysed many samples of the ale, stating that the accusations were false.[151] Their findings were published in a widely distributed pamphlet. According to Hofmann, 'what started originally as a rejection of a ludicrous insinuation, had finally served as popular publicity; one could not climb into any railway carriage, into any omnibus, in any cab, without finding our report attached'. Liebig published a German translation of their work in his *Annalen*. Hofmann also noted that many samples of best Burton Ale became the property of his laboratory (Graham did not drink) and that 'they did not last long.'[152]

Perhaps the most important of the applied work was that related to the safety of the national coal-gas supply, and to the safety of drinking water. Hofmann began work at the college in both these areas, especially on the latter after he was appointed Water Examiner for London in 1852. When Frankland came to the college in 1865 he inherited this work and, with the help of student assistants, continued to monitor the London water supply.[153] He also carried out work for the Metropolitan Board of Works on the deodorisation of sewage. Water analysis truly took off in 1868 when Frankland was appointed to replace John T. Way on The Royal Commission inquiring into the rivers and domestic water supplies of Great Britain. At that point Frankland took over the direction of the Commission's laboratory on Victoria Street and spent about one day a week there.[154] Many students were given work in Victoria Street, including James Day, Frank Clowes, Robert Warington and William Thorp.[155] On taking over from Way, Frankland commissioned two 15 foot long tubes, each three inches in diameter from the Whitefriars Glass Company. The tubes were filled with sand, and used to filter sewage. They were prototypes for large scale sewage works (glass was used so as to see what was going on). The glass tubes were then the longest ever made in London, and many people came to view them.

McLeod did not work in Victoria Street, but he was asked to devise a new method for determining the amount of nitrogen in the solid residues of drinking water samples, and to build an apparatus for determining water turbidity. He made improvements to the college's Sprengel pumps and eudiometers, and was asked to copy a water exhauster that Frankland had seen in Zurich.[156] Today McLeod is not as widely acknowledged for his contributions to water analysis as are some of Frankland's other assistants — Thorp, Armstrong, and Clowes for example, but for a few years he played as important a role as they did. McLeod sold his apparatus to Frankland and the Rivers Commission. He also developed an apparatus for the analysis of gases given off in coal mines, known as the Frankland–McLeod apparatus. Joseph W. Thomas, who learned how to use it while a student at the college, later collected and analysed gases from several collieries in South Wales. He became the first public analyst for Cardiff, Newport, and the County of Glamorgan.[157] Perhaps more than any other chemical department of the period, the one that was to become a department of Imperial College in 1907, was evenhanded when it came to pure and applied research. Both were valued and the legacy was lasting.

Endnotes

1. A. W. Hofmann, Remarks on the importance of cultivating experimental science in a national point of view, reprinted in *Reports of the Royal College of Chemistry and researches conducted in the laboratory, 1845–1947*, (London, 1849), pp. 23–63. Copy in ICL archives.

2. Hofmann Memorial Lectures: (Armstrong, 1896), quotations, 638, 729. Armstrong's extensive lecture gives what may be the best summary of Hofmann's research; (Abel, 1896), (Perkin, 1896), quotation, 602, (Playfair, 1896). Armstrong mentions, as did Herbert McLeod in his diary, things that went wrong when Hofmann took over the lecture demonstrations; for example, McLeod noted that Hofmann burned his hand badly when trying to show the combustion products of gunpowder; ICL archives, McLeod diary, 9 March, 1860.

3. After Frankland's death it was difficult to find anyone willing to write the Chemical Society obituary. Armstrong agreed to do so and then changed his mind. William Tilden, the CS President, was embarrassed that there had been no obituary by 1904 and tried, unsuccessfully, to persuade Francis Japp who had written one earlier, to write another. In the end he persuaded a reluctant Herbert McLeod; ICL archives, McLeod diary, 15, 29 June and 20 July, 1904. McLeod's obituary (McLeod, 1905) appeared six years after Frankland's death in 1899. There were two timelier obituaries but none in the Royal Society's journals despite Frankland being a fellow and Copley medallist. (Wislicenus, 1900), (Japp, 1900).

4. For Nicholson, (Goodall, 2004), (Anon., 1891). Before attending the college Nicholson was an apprentice with one of the RCC founders, J. L. Bullock. In 1853 he joined George Simpson, a paint manufacturer who had attended the college in 1846, and another student, George Maule, in opening a fine chemicals business in South London, named Simpson, Maule and Nicholson. Henry How (1828–1879) later worked as an assistant to Thomas Anderson in Glasgow. He became professor of chemistry, later principal, at King's College, Nova Scotia (the college, then in Windsor, is now in Halifax); (Blakeley, 1968). Robert Galloway (1822–1896) became the chemistry teacher at Queenwood College, a position held earlier by Frankland. Later he was professor of chemistry at the Royal College of Science, Dublin. For the others see below.

5. Warren de la Rue FRS, the son of Thomas de la Rue, founder of the well-known stationery firm, had a PhD from Giessen. He was a founder of the Chemical Society, and twice its President, 1867–1869 and 1879–1880. He attended the college to learn about colours useful to the family business. An early success was the extraction of the red (carmine) colouring agent from cochineal insects that feed on *Opuntia* cacti. He named it carminic acid; (De la Rue, 1845). With his employee, Hugo Müller, De la Rue worked also on dyes used in the printing of postage stamps, and developed the silver chloride cell. They made a battery with 14,400 cells which they

demonstrated at the Royal Institution. De la Rue later experimented with celestial photography at the Kew Observatory. For de la Rue, (Hartog *revised.* A. J. Meadows, 2004), (Daus., 1971), (Anon., 1890).

6. Frederick Abel, fluent in German, acted as clerk to John Gardner in the period leading to the opening of the college. When Gardner was forced out, Abel took on the role of college secretary. During his six years at the RCC he published several papers, including some on strychnine with Edward Nicholson. He left to become demonstrator under John Stenhouse at St. Bartholomew's Hospital and, together with Charles Bloxam, who married his sister, wrote a textbook (Bloxam and Abel, 1851). Hofmann wrote the preface and the book went into many editions. Abel succeeded Faraday as lecturer in chemistry at the Royal Military Academy at Woolwich, and had a major career as an ordnance chemist. Together with James Dewar, he invented cordite, something that led to a prolonged legal dispute with Alfred Nobel who patented dynamite a year later (Nobel's objections to the earlier patent were rejected by the High Court). Abel was also an expert on coal dust explosions. He was elected FRS in 1860 and knighted in the same year (and made a baronet in 1883) and later became Chemist to the War Department and Scientific Advisor to the War Office. He was President of the Chemical Society (1875–1877) and of the Institute of Chemistry (1880–1883). Abel came from a musical family and entertained gatherings of chemists with performances on his zither. (Steele, *revised.* Watson, 2004), (Spiller, 1905).

7. Thomas Henry Rowney (1817–1894) left the RCC to take a PhD at Giessen. He was later Professor of Chemistry at Queen's College, Galway.

8. ICL archives, McLeod Diary, May 31, 1869. In 1870 Frankland needed yet more help with grading the chemistry exams in South Kensington and McLeod managed to get the much desired work for his friend Charles Groves.

9. David Price had a PhD from Leipzig where he studied with O. L Erdmann. He left the RCC in 1850 and later worked for Simpson, Maule and Nicholson. Muspratt, the son of James Muspratt and older brother of Edmund (see Chapter Two), had earlier studied with Graham and Liebig. He left for his home town of Liverpool in 1848 and set up his own chemistry college. (Hartog *revised.* Williams, 2004). Obit. J. S. Muspratt, (Anon. 1871).

10. Hermann Johann Philipp Sprengel FRS (1834–1906). Later Sprengel worked on explosives for John Hill's powder works in Faversham. He was elected FRS in 1878; (Schaffer, 2004), (Messel, 1907). For his pump, (Sprengel, 1865), (Webb, 1965), (Sella, 2008).

11. (Chambers, 1896) l. In the eight years of its existence as a private institution the college enrolled 356 students. For a contemporary account, (Abel, 1896).

12. Noad, a mature student, had worked in the area of electricity. However, it was mainly for his work on cymol that he was elected to the Royal Society in 1856, (cymol or cymene was discovered by Charles Gerhardt in cumin oil). In 1847 Noad was appointed professor of chemistry at St. George's Hospital, (Boase *revised*. Morus, 2004), (Anon., 1878). John Browning was an apprentice in his father's instrument shop. In 1856 he took over the family firm and built it into one of the foremost scientific instrument makers in London. His spectroscopic equipment was widely used — for example, by Henry Roscoe, (Meliconi, 2004), (Gay, 2008). Bransby Cooper followed other members of his family into medicine. George Merck (see also Chapter Two, note 56) came from Darmstadt where his family owned a pharmacy that was the first to introduce accepted standards for the purity of pharmaceutical chemicals. Merck's younger brother, Wilhelm, attended the college a little later. Both returned to work for the Darmstadt firm which grew under their management. Wilhelm's son, George, founded an independent branch of the firm in New Jersey in 1894. It was to become the major pharmaceutical company of today, (Brock, 2000), 175–76. For the others mentioned, see below.

13. For Buckton, (Buckton and Hofmann, 1856), (Buckton, 1861), (Steele *revised*. Foote, 2004), (Spiller, 1907). After his marriage, Buckton built a large house in Haslemere with a laboratory and an astronomical observatory. His later interests were mainly entomological.

14. William Odling FRS (1829–1921) studied only briefly with Hofmann. He followed his father into the medical profession and, as medical officer for health in Lambeth, worked with Frankland on drinking water. Cholera was still a problem in London. Their work helped in its eradication, and that of other waterborne diseases. Odling translated Laurent's *Méthode de Chimie* into English, and was a contributor to the development of Type Theory (see Appendix One). He was Fullerian professor of chemistry at the Royal Institution, 1868–1872, before moving to Oxford. He was President of the Chemical Society (1873–1875), and of the Institute of Chemistry (1877–1880), (Russell, 2004b).

15. For Pavy, (Power, *revised*. Coley, 2004).

16. For an obituary of Hall, (Anon., 1878).

17. (Reynolds, 1851). A captain in the Royal Engineers, Reynolds later became a Major General and worked with Abel at the Woolwich Arsenal. His son followed him as a student at the college.

18. The crystals are crystalline potassium permanganate in a form used by horticulturalists and gardeners; the fluid is an alkaline solution of manganates and permanganates used as an antiseptic.

19. As a student James Smith Brazier (1825–1889) published papers on the flax plant and the types of soil it favoured. He was described by Hofmann as 'one of the finest analysts in the laboratory.' Later he was appointed professor of chemistry at the University of Aberdeen. Quotation, ICL Archives; RCC Council Minutes, 13th December, 1848. For Brazier obituary, (Anon, 1889). John Sangster Abel later managed a copper mining company in Chile. For Crookes and Spiller see below.

20. For Bloxam, (Spring, 2004). Henry Medlock (1825–1875) became laboratory manager for the General Apothecaries Company on Berners Street. Later he was chemist to the brewers, Ind. Coope, where he became known as a specialist in water purity and analysis, (Anon., 1875). In 1859 he patented a process for the manufacture of magenta. Edward Nicholson discovered the same process a little later at his firm Simpson, Maule and Nicholson. The firm purchased Medlock's patent, manufactured the dye profitably, but were successfully challenged in court by yet another manufacturer who claimed that the patent was invalid. Aniline dyes were being developed in many places at this time, so the situation was complex; see Peter J. Morris and Anthony S. Travis. 1992. 'A History of the International Dyestuff Industry, *American Dyestuff Reporter*' http://colorantshistory.org/ HistoryInternationalDyeIndustryRev1/HistoryInternationalDyestuff IndustryFirefox/dyestuffs.html.

21. George Frederick Ansell taught chemistry at the Panopticon in Leicester Square before joining Thomas Graham at the Royal Mint. He criticised what he saw as waste and inefficiency at the Mint and, after 10 years, was dismissed as a troublemaker. His daughter, Gertrude, was a well-known suffragette. (Ansell, 1870), (Courtney *revised*. Brown, 2004). Augustus Beauchamp Northcote (1831–1869) moved to Oxford where he took a degree, and was a lecturer at Exeter College. He was later a consulting chemist in London. Reginald Morley (1826–1860) was a promising organic chemist who died young. Edward Divers left the RCC to work with John Stenhouse at St. Bartholomew's Hospital (where he met August Kekulé). Divers gained an MD in Ireland and then joined several Western scientists and engineers in helping to set up the new Imperial Engineering College near Tokyo. The laboratories he designed for the college were modelled on those of Liebig and Hofmann. Divers became principal of the college in 1882. He published on the chemistry of selenium and tellurium and was elected FRS in 1885, (Davis, 2004), (Sakurai, 1913).

22. For Spiller, (Anon., 1922); for Gowland, (Curthoys, 2004), (Anon., 1922). Gowland carried out some important archaeological work while in Japan and introduced the Japanese to Western-style rowing.
23. The student body included some deposed French royals: Phillipe d'Orléans, Comte de Paris, his brother and his cousin were occasional students at the college.
24. Other books used at the college in the early period include Liebig's various publications and those of Fresenius and Will (see Chapter Two); also, the fourth edition of Gmelin's *Handbuch* which began appearing in 1843, Thomas Graham's *Elements of Chemistry* (1843), W. A. Miller's, *Elements of Chemistry* (1855), Charles Gerhardt's *Précis de chimie organique* (1845) and his *Traité de Chimie* (1854), J. Pelouze and E. Frémy's *Traité de Chimie Générale, analytique industrielle et agricole* (1853), Kolbe's *Lehrbuch der organischen chimie* (1860) and, later, Henry Watts' *Dictionary of Chemistry* (5 vols. 1868). (Hofmann, 1865) was a compilation of material used in his teaching at the college.
25. For Edward Matthey's notebooks, Wellcome Library (Western manuscripts collection, 3495–3497). For George Matthey, (Griffith, 2013).
26. For Lockyer, (Meadows, 2004). At the time of these lectures Lockyer worked at the War Office. In 1881 he was appointed lecturer in astrophysics. Lockyer collaborated with chemists in his spectroscopic work but came into conflict with many by claiming that his solar spectra showed that atoms in the sun were breaking down. Alfred Fowler, his student and successor as professor of astrophysics, 'explained' the abnormal spectra by invoking the new theory of ionisation. Together with Alexander Macmillan, Lockyer founded *Nature*.
27. Examinations were introduced only after the RCC became part of the Metropolitan School of Science. Hofmann insisted that if there were to be written examinations, then there would also be a practical analysis examination. The written examinations were heavy on analytical methods and industrial processes.
28. One of Frankland's assistants, Henry R. Procter FRS (1848–1927), became a specialist in leather tanning and was later the First Professor of Applied Chemistry at the Yorkshire College in Leeds, (Anon., 1928).
29. Adrian Brown (1852–1919) studied with Kolbe, and then with Frankland at the RCC. After a brief period as assistant to William J. Russell at St. Bartholomew's Hospital, he returned to Burton-on-Trent as Chemist to the brewers Messrs Salt and Co. Later he was professor of Brewing and Malting at Mason College and, when the University of Birmingham was founded, was named professor of the Biology and Chemistry of

Fermentation, and Director of the School of Brewing, (Armstrong, 1922).

30. (Armstrong, 1937). According to Armstrong, Griess was a 'rough diamond' but very engaging. Griess discovered some diazo-compounds while working with Hermann Kolbe in Marburg. Hofmann was interested in this and, in 1858, offered him laboratory space in exchange for assistance. But Griess soon needed a paying job and, in 1862, Hofmann found him one as Assistant to Henry Bottinger, a former Liebig pupil and major brewing chemist, who worked for Allsopp and Sons, Burton-on-Trent. For Griess, (Williams, 2004d).

31. For Henry Armstrong, Chapter Four. Horace Tabberer Brown FRS learned about water purification at the college, something he took to the brewery. Later he established the first laboratory at the Guinness brewery in Dublin. He promoted Pasteur's ideas and carried out fermentation research in a home laboratory and at the Royal Botanic Gardens in Kew, work for which he received the Copley Medal. For biographical memoirs/obits., (Armstrong, 1928), (Anon., 1925). Another of their contemporaries, Ernest Theophron Chapman (1846–1872), attended school in Heidelberg where he heard Bunsen lecture. After studying at the RCC, he worked with Kolbe in Marburg, but was later killed in an explosion at a factory in the Harz mountains while attempting to upscale the manufacture of ethyl nitrate. Brock has speculated that Chapman was the author of some amusing satirical pieces on chemists and their theories. The anonymous author claimed to be an inmate of the Hanwell Asylum, (Brock, 2011), Chapter 39.

32. O'Sullivan was a scholarship student, described in (Armstrong, 1937) as 'a genial Irishman'. In 1866, after Hofmann recommended him to Michael T. Bass, O'Sullivan moved to Burton-on-Trent to work for the Bass brewery. He published work on the hydrolysis of starch and, while studying the action of malt enzymes on starch, discovered maltose. He was elected FRS in 1885; (James *revised*. Sharp, 2004), (Anon., 1922).

33. The Thomas and Gilchrist process was used first at the South Bank (London) steelworks of Bolcrow and Vaughan. For Snelus, (Bone, *revised*. St. John, 2004).

34. Frankland's *Lecture Notes for Chemical Students, embracing mineral and organic chemistry*, (Frankland, 1866) used modern formulae and laid out his 'valence' theory. (Armstrong, 1937), p. 378.

35. William George Valentin (1824–1879) was born in Nürnberg, (Anon., 1880), (Armstrong, 1937). He came to study at the RCC in 1855 and stayed on at the college. His textbooks were used there. For example, (Valentin, 1872) and a laboratory manual, (Valentin, 1879).

36. In his diary Bloxam mentions borrowing equipment from various sources; (KCL archives, Charles Bloxam Diary, entries from the 1850s). By the 1860s, Henry Bence Jones, William Crookes, Augustus Matthiessen, William Barrett and John Stenhouse were good sources of equipment. William Fletcher Barrett FRS was a student at the RCC but turned from chemistry to physics after working with Tyndall. He held various positions in London, and later became professor of experimental physics at the Royal College of Science, Dublin; (Gauld, 2004).

37. For McLeod, (James, 2004c), (Morley, 1924) and (Thorpe, 1924). Herbert McLeod was elected FRS in 1881. His diary with daily entries from 1860–1923 describe activities at the RCC, as illustrated in (Gay, 2000).

38. Lecture at RI, 7 April, 1865, (Hofmann, 1865b). Hofmann's colour convention has survived, notably in published reports of X-ray crystallographic studies. The original coloured croquet balls are kept at the Royal Institution. The retort-type stands supporting the models were made by Blakeman.

39. (Hofmann, 1865).

40. (Meinel, 2005).

41. For example, (Abel and Rowney, 1849), (Merck and Galloway, 1845) and (Rowney and How, 1845). The dates for the second two papers are a little misleading. Papers given over the period 1845–1847 were combined in a single volume dated 1845. The papers were delivered in the years 1846–1847.

42. Formal lectures were given only in the first year. Second year lectures came only late in the century.

43. ICL archives, McLeod Diary, several entries in October 1861. W. A. Tilden recalled how confusing he and other students found the switch at the time, (Tilden, 1904). Much later McLeod wanted to find out exactly when Hofmann adopted the new atomic weights. He pinned the date down to between 14 December, 1859 and 5 April, 1860. (ICL archives, McLeod diary, 1 October, 1892).

44. From a poem 'Modern Chemistry' (1868) by John Cargill Brough; copy with signed illustration in the RSC library, B-Club files. The Kay-Shuttleworth referred to was the son of the more famous James Kay-Shuttleworth, and was the author of a chemistry textbook, (Kay-Shuttleworth, 1868). John Cargill Brough (1834–1872) was not a student at the RCC. Self-taught, he was editor of both the *Chemist and Druggist* and *Laboratory*; the latter was a competitor to Crookes' *Chemical News*.

45. James Campbell Brown, 'Reminiscences of August Wilhelm von Hofmann,' in (Brown, 1914), p. 64.

46. (Perkin, 1896), p. 601. John Henry Pepper (1821–1900) was an analytical chemist and lecturer at the Royal Polytechnic Institution. He was famous for an optical illusion known as Pepper's Ghost.

47. ICL archives; McLeod Diary, April 22nd, 1864.

48. (Brown, 1914) p. 68. Churchill's *Manual*, successor to (Fownes, 1844) went into many editions.

49. For example, ICL archives; McLeod Diary, entries for Aug. 3rd. and 4th., 1865.

50. ICL archives; McLeod Diary, Nov 30th, 1866. In 1869 McLeod's salary was raised from £105 to £110 per year.

51. There are some interesting diary entries on this exhibition. McLeod was paid £52.10s for his services.

52. Report in *Chem. News*, **11** (1865) pp. 210–216.

53. Frankland, quoted in (Reeks, 1920b), p. 111.

54. The naval architects moved to Greenwich. Both Hofmann and Frankland had earlier been asked to advise on the design of the chemistry laboratories for the general science college; the laboratories were used by the Normal School of Science (NSS). The mining and metallurgy departments of the RSM did not move at this time.

55. For Field, (Usselman, 2004b), (Anon., 1886). On leaving the RCC, Field worked for a copper mining company in Chile. On his return he was appointed professor of chemistry at the London Institution. He later joined the firm Simpson, Maule and Nicholson where, together with Nicholson, he made the first azo dye, named Field's Yellow. He was elected FRS in 1863. His family firm, which he joined later, also had metal mining interests in Chile. Like Bloxam, he married one of Abel's sisters.

56. Sir Maurice Holzmann (1835–1909) was a student at the RCC, and later Personal Assistant to Prince Albert. After Albert's death he was appointed Secretary to the Duchy of Cornwall and Librarian at Marlborough House.

57. The reference is to Hofmann's forthcoming departure to Berlin in 1865. The B-Club was a social, fraternal, chemists' club, not restricted to the RCC. Its members were known as B's or bees (after section B of the BAAS). For the B-Club and fraternal life among chemists, (Gay and Gay, 1997), (Gay, 2000).

58. King's College London (KCL) archives, Charles L. Bloxam papers, Box 1.10. 'A Chemical Alphabet.'

59. For the verses on Frankland and Crookes, RSC Library, B-Club papers. F. Field, 'A Chemical Review.' (Field writes of himself in the third person, but we think he was the author.) It is a long poem and names 78 chemists.

60. (Crookes, 1852).
61. Thallium was discovered independently, also in 1861, by C. A. Lamy. Lamy isolated the metal one year later by electrolysis. For Crookes and Greville Williams, (James, 1981). Crookes' samples of thallium salts (*inv.* 1915–162, 1919–389), and the metal (*inv.* 1915–314) are held in the Science Museum, London.
62. For details of Crookes' work on thallium and his many other achievements after leaving the RCC, (Brock, 2008); see also, (Brock, 2004b). Crookes won the Royal, Davy and Copley Medals of the Royal Society, was knighted in 1897, and was made OM in 1910. In 1967 an English Heritage blue plaque was erected on the house at 7 Kensington Park Gardens, Notting Hill, where Crookes lived and worked from 1880 until his death.
63. For Newlands, (Sutton, 2004). This *ODNB* entry includes details also on his brother, Benjamin Edward Reina Newlands (1842–1912).
64. (Newlands, 1884). Newlands read his paper 'The Law of Octaves, and the Causes of Numerical Relations among the Atomic Weights' to the Chemical Society on 1 March, 1866. It never appeared in *J. Chem. Soc., Trans.,* but was published in *Chem. News.* 13 (1866) 113–4. It is rumoured that publication in the Chemical Society journal was blocked by a rival theorist, William Odling. In a later review of his papers, however, (Newlands, 1882), Newlands mentions that in 1877 Odling pointed out the primacy of his (Newlands') work. In 1998, on the centenary of Newlands' birth, and to rectify the shabby treatment he received in 1866, the Royal Society of Chemistry erected a blue memorial plaque to Newlands in West Square, Southwark in 1998.
65. For Perkin, (Meldola, 1908, 1908b), (Travis, 2004), (Eisenstein, 1974). The Stepney Historical Trust erected a memorial plaque to Perkin at the site of his home laboratory in Cable Street, Shadwell; the RSC erected two plaques at the site of his factory in Greenford Green, Essex. The William Perkin Church of England High School in Oldfield Lane, North Greenford, opened in 2013 (see Chapter Ten). Perkin came to the college from the City of London School where his teacher was Thomas Hall (see above).
66. (Perkin, 1857).
67. (Perkin, 1896), p. 603.
68. (Perkin, 1896); (Perkin, 1869).
69. Tyrian purple was a classic colouring agent made from a Mediterranean sea snail. Perkin's dye was similar in colour. The exact formula of Perkin's dye (both the one made in his laboratory and the mauve from his factory) is a matter of dispute. His starting materials were far from pure. For some

recent work on the complex structures of mauve see (Sousa *et. al.*, 2008). The Science Museum, London, holds a sample of Perkin's mauve, probably from his original preparation, and of some dyed material. They also hold a sample of his synthetic alizarin.

70. Perkin and Church experimented further with colour chemistry; for example (Church and Perkin, 1857). They explored a number of azo-compounds and, later, Perkin manufactured some azo dyes. Perkin and Church also had artistic interests in common and went on painting expeditions together. While a student Church had a painting exhibited at the Royal Academy and considered becoming an artist. Later he became professor of chemistry at the Royal Agricultural College in Cirencester and then professor of chemistry at the Royal Academy where he directed work on the cleaning and restoration of paintings. Church believed that he had discovered a new element that he named *nigrium*, in 1869. It was associated with zircon, Perhaps he found some hafnium, not properly identified until 1925, (Fontani, Costa and Orna, 2015), pp. 112–3, 486. Church was elected FRS in 1888; For Church, (Greenaway, 2004b). See also an obituary of Church by another RCC student, (Laurie, 1916).

71. Perkin's patent for aniline purple (named mauve in England from 1859) was not valid in France. From around 1860 magenta, also known as roseine, fuchsine and some other names for what was basically the same dye, took over. Hofmann named the mix of aniline and toluidines from which they were made rosaniline. Collectively, with an aniline blue and Hofmann's aniline violet (1863), they were known as rosaniline dyes. A collection of Hofmann's dyes was kept in the department and the dyes were used as demonstration samples into the 1930s. The collection is now in the Science Museum, London, (inv. 1936–593). In the 19th century the purple/mauve dyes were worn by both the Empress Eugenie and Queen Victoria and became very fashionable — too fashionable for some. The bright new colours were 'poisoning taste' according to John Ruskin, and William Morris made a point of using natural dyes such as indigo, and madder for his fabrics. Perkin kept up with changes in demand and later manufactured some 'natural' dyes, beginning with alizarin by the mid 1860s.

72. Faraday discovered benzene in 1825.

73. For Mansfield, (Brock, 2004c), (Travis, 2008). Mansfield was seriously burned while carrying his still out of the laboratory — to save the building. Brock's *ODNB* entry includes some interesting details on Mansfield who, despite ill health, lived his short life to the full. See also (Ward, 1970 and 1984).

74. (Robinson, 1956).

75. Alfred John Greenaway (1852–1938) studied under Hofmann, and was appointed demonstrator by Frankland. In 1881, he became an assistant to the physician F. W Pavy FRS at Guy's hospital (see note 15 above). Greenaway was a close friend of William Perkin, Jr., and wrote a memoir included in (Thorpe, Robinson and Greenaway, 1932). Greenaway was editor of the Chemical Society's *Journal*, and editor of George Kamensky's translation of (Mendeleev, 1891). On a visit to the department in 1936, Greenaway noted that some apparatus brought to South Kensington from Oxford Street in 1873 was still in use (see *Record of the Royal College of Science*, June 1936, 27); for Greenaway, (Gibson, 1939). William Richard Eaton Hodgkinson (1851–1935), a student at the college who went to Würzburg for a PhD, was in charge of the teaching laboratory. He edited some later editions of Valentin's *Practical Chemistry*. In the early 1880s he was appointed lecturer in Chemistry and Physics at the Royal Military Academy in Woolwich where he later became Professor, (Anon., 1935).

76. Quotation from (Morrell, 2004). Perkin may have chosen to study with Wislicenus because Hodgkinson had done so earlier.

77. (Rochow and Krahé, 2001). This book is a biographical historical novel of the three Holland sisters who married Perkin, Kipping and Lapworth.

78. For Arthur Perkin, (Morrell, 2004b), (Robinson, 1936–1938) and (Robinson, 1938).

79. F. N. Jewsbury, 'Herbert McLeod FRS,' reprinted in *Phoenix* **12** (5) (1927), p. 150. Copy in ICL archives.

80. Hofmann appears to have been more tolerant of Coppins' drunken behaviour than was Frankland who, according to McLeod, wanted to sack him. In any event, Coppins died on the job in February, 1868. ICL archives; McLeod diary, Jul 6, 1863, Nov 1, 1865, Jan 4, 1868, and Feb 12, 1868.

81. ICL archives; McLeod diary, Feb 14–17, 1865. McLeod helped Henry C Reynolds, who had some mental health problems, and had sent 'an extraordinary production to Hofmann [titled] "My Life"'. Reynolds, educated at Eton College, was the son of John H. Reynolds (see above). He followed his father into the Royal Engineers, left with the rank of Lieutarant. Colonel, and returned to chemistry at University College, Bristol.

82. See, for example, ICL archives; McLeod diary, Nov 24, 1860, Jan 19, 1861 and May 30, 1863.

83. McLeod had a special interest in clocks and was often asked to fix Hofmann's. See, for example, ICL archives, McLeod Diary, Oct 25th, 1860.

84. For Groves, (Tilden, 1920). John Stenhouse FRS had a long connection to the college and lent it much equipment. He had a PhD from Giessen (1839) and taught at St. Bartholomew's Hospital until suffering a stroke. After a three year recuperation in Nice he returned to London and set up a private consulting laboratory where Groves and many other former RCC students found employment. See also, (Stronach *revised*. Watson, 2004).
85. For Howard, (Williams, 2004c), (Thomson, 1917).
86. For A. Herschel, (Hollis, *revised*. Meadows, 2004)
87. Later Herschel was a professor of physics, first at Anderson College, then at Newcastle. But he retired early to his boyhood home, Observatory House in Slough, where he furthered his work on meteors.
88. (Gay, 2003).
89. (Volhard and Fischer, 1902), 81-9 (quotations, our translation). For some royal demonstrations, ICL archives, McLeod diary, 4, 5 February 1863, January 27, 1864, March 13–20th, 1865. McLeod notes that some demonstrations were the same as those used by Hofmann in his lectures to working men.
90. (McLeod, 1874). A large volume of gas at unknown low pressure is compressed into a much smaller known volume by means of a mercury column. The pressure in the small volume is read by using a mercury manometer and the original pressure is then calculated, using the gas law. Simple in conception, the design of a workable gauge was an important technical achievement; (Sella, 2011). McLeod also invented a widely used sunshine recorder.
91. For Meldola, (Poulton, 1917), (Webb *revised*. Travis, 2004), (Gay, 2010). Meldola claimed that his Sephardic family came from Toledo. That is possible, but the family name came from the Italian town of Meldola where the family settled.
92. Haham, religious teacher — the term rabbi is not used in this Sephardi synagogue.
93. ICL, B/MEL/1/1–3; Meldola was a student 1866–1868.
94. ICA, Henry Armstrong correspondence, letter 242 from James Day, 14 December 1867.
95. (Meadows, 1972), pp. 131–134. Meldola had just published his first book on non-metals, (Meldola, 1873). A later edition included the metallic elements.
96. (Eyre and Rodd, 1947), p. 99.
97. Quotation, (Grieg, 1979) 7. The Guthrie mentioned was Frederick Guthrie FRS (1833–1886), who had studied chemistry under Graham at University

College and had taught in several places before coming to the RSM as professor of physics in 1868, (Gooday, 2004b). For Thompson, (Gay and Barrett, 2002), (Smithels *revised*. Gooday, 2004). As noted in Gay and Barrett, Thompson discovered the radioactivity of uranium in 1896, but hesitated to publish. When he did send a paper to *Proc. Roy. Soc.,* The Editor, George Stokes, informed him that Becquerel had published three weeks earlier.

98. Cambridge University Library, Darwin correspondence, letter 13674, Frankland to Darwin, 9 February 1882.

99. It is worth noting that Otto Witt was later an employee at this firm. He suggested a theory connecting colour to chemical constitution, and convinced others by successfully predicting that chemicals of the type of the yet unknown azo dyes would be highly coloured. They were made soon after. Some see this as the beginning of designer synthesis, central to much modern chemistry. But Hofmann was thinking in designer terms even earlier as, for example, with quinine, thus setting Perkin off on his hunt for quinine, and the accidental diversion into dye chemistry.

100. The Meldola Prize, combined as the Harrison–Meldola Prize since 2000, is one of the most prestigious awards of the RSC. Until 2000 it was given for original chemical research in any area except physical and theoretical chemistry. Since 2000 it has been given for the most meritorious and promising original investigations in chemistry.

101. Reactions that carry Hofmann's name, such as the Hofmann degradation (the conversion of primary amides $RCONH_2$ to amines RNH_2) and the Hofmann elimination (conversion of amines to alkenes using methyl iodide and silver oxide), are from the later Berlin period.

102. ICL archives, A. W. Hofmann, 'Introduction to the Researches Conducted in the Laboratory of the College,', *Reports of the Royal College of Chemistry and Researches Conducted in the early Years, 1845–1947,* (1849), **60**.

103. For example, (Nicholson, 1845); (paper read in 1847; for date anomaly see note 41). (Abel, 1845).

104. (Muspratt and Hofmann, 1848). Muspratt worked also with natural indigo while at the college.

105. (Hofmann, 1849). This was the first in a series of papers on the volatile bases. For an earlier anticipatory paper, (Blyth and Hofmann, 1845).

106. (Modern empirical formulae used here.) Abel and Nicholson did not go along with him in thinking strychnine was a conjugated base, hence their different formula. Abel and Nicholson presented their strychnine work at a meeting of the Chemical Society and were elected fellows; (Abel and

Nicholson, 1850). Hofmann soon recognised that many bases resembled aniline in only certain respects, and that there were different classes of alkaloids.

107. (Hofmann, 1850 and 1851), in which he discusses some non-volatile bases. For further discussion of Hofmann's ammonia type (Keas, 1992); see also (Hofmann and Cahours, 1857). Hofmann's former student, G. B. Buckton helped with this work.

108. Hofmann switched definitively from C=6 to C=12 in 1860 (see note 43). He also introduced the modified atomic weights introduced by Gerhardt and Cannizzaro to his students.

109. For a good summary of Williamson's work, (Brock, 2000), pp. 233–40.

110. (Hofmann, 1849 part 3) mentions the Berzelian influence.

111. Hofmann acknowledged Nicholson and Abel's 'unremitting zeal and remarkable experimental skill with which, during several years these gentlemen have assisted me in the prosecution of the researches on the volatile organic bases'; (Hofmann, 1850), quotation, 320.

112. ICL archives; McLeod Diary, March 13, 1860. 'Richard' was Richard Coppins, the college porter.

113. *Punch*, 15 Sept., 1888.

114. In 1867 Hofmann, together with A. von Baeyer, founded the *Deutsche Chemischer Gesellschaft zu Berlin*, established along the lines of the Chemical Society of London. Hofmann was elected its first president.

115. For Frankland, (Russell, 1996, 1999, 2004, and 2008), (Brock, 1972b), (Halton, 2015). For Frankland's early life, (Russell, 1986). Frankland's own memoir as edited, and with additions, by two of his daughters: W. M. N. and S. J. C. (Frankland, 1902). See also note 3.

116. This was before the founding of the Government School of Mines in 1851.

117. Ransome, grandfather of author Arthur M. Ransome, carried out mineral analyses for the Geological Survey.

118. For A. W. H. Kolbe (1818–1884), (Rocke, 1993).

119. For the X-Club, (Barton, 1998). The club members had influence in science politics. Interestingly, what prompted its formation was the so-called 'Declaration of Students of the Natural and Physical Sciences', issued by some students and assistants at the RCC, led by Herbert McLeod. Their religious zeal upset Huxley and Frankland; (Brock and Macleod, 1976), (Gay, 2007).

120. Baldwin Francis Duppa FRS (1828–1873), the son of a well known landowner and educationist, came from a far wealthier background than Frankland. His father, a follower of P. E. von Fellenberg, had sent him to

Fellenberg's Hofwyl School in Switzerland. He then studied briefly at Cambridge, did not stay for a degree, and became a student at the RCC in 1855. Duppa had a large private income, a country estate, and was a JP. Nonetheless he acted as secretary and assistant to William Perkin before joining Frankland at Barts Hospital, and then at the Royal Institution. For an obituary, (Anon, 1874).

121. (Kolbe and Frankland, 1849), (Frankland, 1850).

122. (Schorlemmer, 1864).

123. It was hyphenated zinc–ethyl only in later publications. Organometallic, on the other hand, was earlier hyphenated.

124. For a fine review of Frankland's work in this area, (Seyferth, 2001).

125. It is often said, though never claimed by Frankland, that zinc–methyl, etc. were the first organometallic compounds. In fact the first such species was 'Zeise's salt', now formulated as $K[Pt(C_2H_4)Cl_3]$, made in 1830 by the Danish pharmacist W. C. Zeise and first noted in a paper published in Latin by the University of Copenhagen, and then in German translation in 1831, (Zeise, 1831). See also (Hunt, 1984). For Wilkinson and Zeise's salt see Chapter Nine.

126. (Frankland, 1852). Quotation from the paper, (Russell, 1996), p. 109. Russell states that Frankland read the paper in 1850 but that its publication was delayed because the journal editor, George G. Stokes, mislaid the manuscript. For a later articulation of Frankland's ideas see his Bakerian Lecture, (Frankland, 1859).

127. Frankland was not alone in thinking along these lines. His friend Kolbe, and Kekulé, were doing so.

128. (Russell, 1996), 107–108. The settlement came after the 1860 Karlsruhe Conference, not so much as a direct outcome of the conference since the problem was already well recognised and was addressed by Kekulé who stated that 19 different formulae for acetic acid were in use — clearly an unsatisfactory situation, (Kekulé, 1857).

129. Later, Frankland published an edited collection of his early papers, (Frankland, 1877). His editing confused people about when he actually adopted the C=12 atomic weight convention. He did so in 1862.

130. (Frankland, 1866b). This paper includes many ideas on notation that have survived to this day.

131. Terrestrial helium was first detected by Luigi Palmieri in 1881, among the volcanic gases of Mount Vesuvius. Frankland also questioned Lockyer's claim that elemental atoms were disintegrating on the sun. See note 26.

132. For Pedler, (MacLeod, 2004), (Tilden, 1919). Pedler was a benefactor of the CS and the Pedler lectureship (later Pedler award) was established in his memory in 1929.

133. For Liversidge, (MacLeod, 2004b and 2009).

134. George Newth's inorganic chemistry textbook, used at the RCS in the 1890s, appears to us very good; it provided an early, and systematic, treatment of the elements according to Mendeleev's table. The woodcuts illustrate apparatus used at the college, (Newth, 1895). For an obituary of Newth, (Anon., 1936).

135. Kinch edited and partially rewrote Church's textbook on agricultural chemistry, (Church and Kinch, 1906).

136. Thomas Samuel Humpidge (1853–1888) left the college in 1876. He studied the chemistry of the rare earths with Bunsen in Heidelberg and gained a PhD before becoming science master at the Hofwyl School, near Berne (where Frankland's assistant Baldwin Duppa was educated). Later Humpidge held the Chair of Natural Sciences at the University College of Wales (Aberystwyth) and, before his premature death, worked on the atomic weight of beryllium (perhaps there was a connection between this work and his early death; the toxicity of Be was recognised only later), (Anon., 1888). Thomas Purdie FRS (1843–1916) worked on a farm in Argentina before entering the college in 1874 at the age of 29. In his second year he was appointed as a demonstrator. He left for Würzburg where he studied for a PhD alongside W. H. Perkin, Jr., At St. Andrew's University Purdie was known for his work on stereochemistry and optical activity; (Irvine, 1917). Another student, George E. Davis (1850–1906), worked in the chemical industry in Manchester. He was a major figure in the founding of the Society of Chemical Industry in 1881 and is credited with being the first to think of chemical engineering as a separate discipline, (Anon., 1907).

137. Huxley wanted the main function of the NSS to be the teaching of science teachers and, for that reason, copied the French (École Normale) in naming the college. Others objected and the name Royal College of Science was adopted in 1890. For obituaries of Japp, (Philip, 1925), (Anon., 1926) and (Thorpe, 1928). For more on the buildings of the period, (Forgan and Gooday, 1994, 1996).

138. (Frankland and Japp, 1884). The book had mixed reviews. From today's perspective it looks remarkably good; perhaps it was too forward looking for its time. Japp was awarded the CS Longstaff medal in 1891. In 1929,

when Imperial College became part of the University of London, Assistant Professors became Readers.

139. His father wanted him to gain a British credential (he gained a BSc from the University of London), before being appointed Lecturer. Percy Frankland left the RCC in 1888 for a chair in Dundee. Later he became professor of chemistry at Mason College (later the University of Birmingham). His relationship with his father was strained. (Garner, 1948 and 1948b), (Garner *revised*. Russell, 2004).

140. For Hopkins, (Dale, 1948 and 2004), (Sutton, 2011). Hopkins was the father of the archaeologist Jaquetta Hawkes.

141. E. R. Roberts (ed.) 'Chemistry department history', p. 73; typescript dated 1963 in ICL archives.

142. Information in this paragraph and quotation, from notes on Frankland sent by Sidney Young, his former student and laboratory demonstrator, to A. A. Eldridge in 1958. ICL archives, KC\1 Eldridge correspondence.

143. G. N. Newth (brief memoir with no official title), *Royal College of Science Journal*, pp. 11–12 (1888–1889), pp. 178.

144. (Frankland, 1901, 1902). One of the few extant copies of the original edition is in the British Library and includes a handwritten dedication to H. G. Wells from Frankland's son, Frederick William Frankland. Frederick worked with his father in the South Kensington laboratory for just one year (1874–1875) before emigrating to New Zealand where he entered the civil service. He became an actuary, returned to London in 1890, and ended his career in New York. For more on this version of Frankland's autobiography, (Russell, 1986, 1996). See also note 115. The autobiography mentions Frankland's great interest in opera and gardening, that he fitted his Hampstead house with electricity, and that he built an astronomical observatory in the garden.

145. (Russell, 1982).

146. (McLeod, 1905), p. 589.

147. Crookes reported on this; (Russell, 1982). See also, Report of the Committee on the decay of stone in the New Palace of Westminster, *Parliamentary Papers* **486** (1862), p. 14.

148. Alexander William Gilman (1843–1903) left the college to work in a London brewery. Known as Alec, he remained a close friend of Herbert McLeod until his death.

149. ICL archives, McLeod Diary, 8 Mar, 16 Apr, 27, 28 Jun, 1860; 9 Feb 9, 1861, 7–9 Jun, 1862; for Westminster Abbey quotation, 28 Aug, 1863.

150. ICL archives, McLeod Diary, 29 July, 1869.

151. T. Graham, A. W. Hofmann and Henry Allsopp, 'Report on the alleged adulteration of pale ales by strychnine' (1852). For a report on the Report, see (Graham, Hofmann and Allsopp, 1853).

152. (Anderson, 1989), quotations, 341.

153. See, for example, (Frankland, 1866c). For Frankland and coal gas, (Russell, 1996), 162–163.

154. For details, (Hamlin, 1990). For Frankland's one-day-a-week schedule see ICL archives, McLeod diary.

155. Frank Clowes (1848–1923) left to teach at Queenwood College where Frankland had taught earlier. In 1881 he became the first professor of chemistry, then principal, at University College, Nottingham. He returned to London in 1897 as Chief Chemist to the London County Council, (Baker, 1924). Robert Warington, the son of a founder of the Chemical Society with the same name, left the college to work for John Lawes at Rothamsted. He was later a professor of agronomy at Oxford, (Goddard, 2004). William Thorp stayed at the Commission's laboratory until it closed in 1877, (Clowes, 1900). One of his college friends was Capel Berger who died young of chemical poisoning. After Berger's death Thorp was invited to join the family firm of Lewis Berger where he became chief chemist.

156. For example, IC archives; McLeod Diary; 24 Feb, 9 Mar, 1866; 11–18 Mar, 1867; several entries in March and April, 1868; 13-14 Oct, 1869. McLeod used Crookes' photometer in determining turbidity (12–17 Nov, 1869). McLeod also designed a collecting bottle for water samples (4 Jan, 13 July, 1869). June and July, 1867, May, 1868, Oct 13 and 14th, Nov, 12, 17, 1869.

157. Joseph William Thomas (1846–1914), (Anon., 1915).

Chapter Four

T. E. Thorpe, W. A. Tilden, and H. E. Armstrong's Department at the Central Technical College: 1885–1914

4.1. Thomas Edward Thorpe and Some Staff and Students of the Period 1885–1894

Thomas Edward Thorpe FRS (1845–1925) succeeded Frankland as head of department in 1885.[1] He came to the college having already achieved much. Born and raised near Manchester, he studied chemistry at Owens College. He worked there with Henry Roscoe whom he assisted in research on photochemistry and on the chemistry of vanadium.[2] In 1866 Thorpe travelled to Pará, Brazil, and then to Lisbon. While away, he carried out a study on the relation between the sun's altitude and the chemical intensity of daylight. During the sea voyage he measured the amount of CO_2 in the air, claiming it to be constant day and night, a result inconsistent with data published by the Danish chemist, B. C. Lewy, which showed seasonal, diurnal, and nocturnal variation.[3]

On his return, Thorpe received the Dalton Scholarship, allowing him to study with Bunsen in Heidelberg where he gained a PhD.[4] He then spent a few months with Kekulé in Bonn before returning to Owens College in 1870 when the Franco–Prussian War broke out. In the same year he was appointed to a professorship at Anderson College where he worked with James Young on paraffin, and began research on phosphorus chemistry. His synthesis of PF_5, was evidence for the pentavalence of phosphorus.[5] In 1874, he moved to a professorship at the Yorkshirse College of Science and, while in Leeds, he designed new chemical laboratories in an old bankruptcy court. He added to his solid list of publications on phosphorus chemistry, and his other work included a study of coal dust explosions.[6] In 1874, he published his *Manual of inorganic chemistry* — later editions appearing into the 1890s.[7] He was elected Fellow Royal Society (FRS) in 1876, won the Royal Medal in 1889 and, in 1881, was the first recipient of the Chemical Society's Longstaff Medal. He was the Society's President, 1899–1901.

Thorpe had two periods as head of the chemistry department in South Kensington, the first from 1885 to 1894.[8] During that period he continued his research on phosphorus chemistry, determined the atomic weights of silicon and gold, and carried out some research in physical chemistry.[9] His principal coworkers for the research on phosphorus, Alfred Tutton, Frederick Hambly and James Rodger, were all students at the college.[10] Earlier Tutton had taken evening classes at the Stockport Mechanics Institution and at Owens College. He came to the Normal School Science (NSS) with a Royal Exhibition scholarship in 1883. A brilliant student, he won the Tyndall (physics) and Hatton (chemistry) prizes, and the Murchison Medal (geology).[11] He was appointed a demonstrator, then Lecturer, but left in 1895 to take up the position of Government Inspector of Schools for the Oxford District. He was elected FRS in 1899.[12]

Thorpe and Tutton isolated phosphorous oxide by burning phosphorus in a limited supply of air.[13] The oxide had a garlicky smell, similar to the one reported by workers in match factories. Thorpe claimed that pure phosphorus was odourless. He speculated that the health damage suffered by workers, including necrosis of the jawbone (phossy jaw), was due to phosphorous oxide, not phosphorus as was then claimed. The physician Sir Thomas Lauder Brunton FRS had fed animals small quantities of 'pure' phosphorus (red phosphorus, made industrially from around 1850) and reported no ill effect.[14] In 1898, Thorpe was asked to head a government panel to look into match manufacture. The panel visited match factories in Britain and abroad and, in 1899, issued a report making recommendations for a safer workplace.[15] By then it was recognised, not only in Britain, that by using red phosphorus rather than the cheaper, reactive and volatile white allotrope, and by manufacturing safety matches, rather than 'strike anywhere' ones, the working environment could be made safer. The Berne Convention of 1909 led to an international ban on the use of white phosphorus in the match industry.[16]

With Rodger and Hambly, Thorpe continued his earlier work on the fluorides and oxyfluorides of phosphorus. With Rodger he prepared the novel gas PSF_3 and with Hambly he measured the vapour density of hydrogen fluoride.[17] No wonder that, when Tutton looked back at his time in the laboratory with its inadequate ventilation and poor fume hoods, he stated 'we lived dangerous days.'[18] With Rodger, Thorpe also carried out a series of studies on the viscosities of organic compounds — the subject of a Bakerian Lecture.[19] Further, he took part in four eclipse expeditions organised by J. Norman Lockyer (the first, well before his time at the college) and collaborated with Arthur Rücker on a magnetic survey of the British Isles.[20] One of Thorpe's best known publications from his time in South Kensington is his *Dictionary of Applied Chemistry*. The first volume was published in 1890, but work on the *Dictionary* really took off during his second period as head of department and is discussed briefly below.

Already in the department when Thorpe arrived was Henry Chapman Jones (1855–1932). Known as Chappie, he had studied chemistry at the Birkbeck Institution (College from 1907) before coming to the NSS as a student in 1874. He became Frankland's assistant and then demonstrator. Just before Frankland's retirement he was given a lectureship and placed in charge of the analytical laboratory, a position he held until 1914. Chapman Jones was said to be very short-sighted; he 'virtually rubb[ed] his nose with a book when reading it.'[21] But he wrote several books, was an expert in photographic chemistry, and taught a course in that field.[22] His long tenure, and the fact that students spent much time in the analytical laboratory, meant that Chappie was remembered by generations of students. Another teacher of this period was Frederick Guthrie. He was a demonstrator, and the son of a former professor of physics in the NSS who had the same name.[23]

According to E. F. (Frank) Armstrong, Thorpe 'quickened the spirit of a band of devoted students and staff.'[24] Others saw Thorpe as forbidding, and were made anxious by his daily tours of the laboratory — in morning dress with a 'silk hat perched rakishly over his left eye.' While lecturing he wrote formulae on the blackboard, 'followed a yard behind by his assistant, Coppen, who carried a duster.'[25] During Thorpe's first period as head of department the number of students grew to about 145, including about 12 research students and 35 summer students, the latter mainly school teachers. About 30 students gained their associateship each year. A few took the University of London BSc examinations performing better than average, indicative of the high level of instruction at the Royal College Science (RCS). Gilbert Morgan (see) graduated at the top of the BSc chemistry list in 1896.[26] Clarence Smith, a long-time editor of the *J. Chem. Soc.*, was a student, 1894-1897.[27] Jocelyn Thorpe, came to the college for the academic year 1892–1893, and then moved to Heidelberg where he gained a PhD.[28] He later returned as professor of organic chemistry and is discussed in Chapters Five and Six.[29]

Thorpe increased the number of lectures in inorganic and general chemistry (cut back earlier by Frankland), adding more also in organic chemistry. He asked Rodger to give the first lecture course in physical chemistry. Rodger had given some lectures earlier, but the compulsory course began in 1894. Students remembered Thorpe's own lectures as being heavy on industrial chemistry, and that he displayed large charts illustrating things such as sulphuric acid manufacture, and Bessemer steel plants. He also spent much time on Prout's Hypothesis, and on the ideas of Lothar Meyer and Mendeleev. George Newth was the lecture demonstrator when Thorpe decided to demonstrate Henri Moissan's preparation of fluorine.[30] Thorpe and Newth thought they were following Moissan's procedure, but failed to produce fluorine in several attempts. A rumour then spread that Moissan, too, must have failed. Moissan had to send an assistant from France to show Thorpe how to do the electrolysis properly. This story illustrates not only the difficulty of replicating novel procedures, but also that in the late 19th century undergraduates were exposed to dangers of a kind unthinkable today.[31]

Chemistry shared many of the RCS facilities, including the lecture theatres, with the other departments. There were two teaching laboratories, named North and South, running along the sides of the main and first floors of the building. A research laboratory ran, corridor-like, along the front of the building. It had the large windows (which are still there) opening on to the loggia facing Exhibition Road — a good thing since the laboratory was poorly ventilated. The three laboratories soon became overcrowded and there was insufficient storage space for chemicals and apparatus. Much was stored in underground passages, and in the Western Galleries of the South Kensington Museum (rebuilt and renamed the V&A in 1899). In 1896, an appeal for more space was made to the Department of Science and Art, and one year later the government announced the construction of a new building to house the RCS administration and the physics and chemistry departments. By then Thorpe had left the college, having been appointed Director of the Inland Revenue Laboratory at Somerset House in 1894. He had the task of merging it with another small laboratory run by the Customs Department, and moving both to a new Government Research Laboratory being built at Clements Inn.[32] Thorpe stayed as director of the laboratory until 1909 when he returned to IC. He received a knighthood in recognition of his government service.

4.2 William Augustus Tilden and the Founding of Imperial College, 1894–1909

William Augustus Tilden FRS (1842–1926) succeeded Thorpe as professor of chemistry in 1894.[33] Tilden was a Londoner. At the age of fifteen, and after some patchy schooling, he began a five-year apprenticeship with Alfred Allchin, a Barnsbury pharmacist. Allchin's friend, John Stenhouse (see Chapter Three), recognised Tilden's talent and encouraged him to carry out research, and to study for a University of London BSc. Allchin paid for Tilden to attend lectures at both the Pharmaceutical Society and the Royal College of Chemistry (RCC). Tilden was a part-time student at the RCC from 1860 to 1862. He later wrote that Hofmann's lectures 'came like a ray of light from heaven, and just at the time when the changes in notation and atomic weights introduced by Gerhardt and Cannizzaro began to cause much perplexity among students.'[34] On completing his apprenticeship, he worked for a year as a junior assistant to Stenhouse and was paid £20. From 1863 to 1872 he was John Attfield's demonstrator at the Pharmaceutical Society.[35] Tilden continued to study on his own: Latin, French and German for matriculation at the University of London, and the sciences for his BSc which he gained in 1868.[36] Awkwardly, though perceptively, Martin Forster wrote that Tilden 'was one of an abundant upward-struggling community to whom the prospect of a definite academic hall-mark offers an elevating incentive to self-improvement.'[37] In 1871, Tilden was awarded a DSc; his examiners were William Odling and Heinrich Debus. Debus, who had gained a PhD in Marburg under Bunsen, was then the senior science teacher at Clifton College.

One year later, Tilden succeeded Debus at Clifton College where he taught both physics and chemistry and helped to develop a modern side to the public school curriculum.[38] Accompanying him to Bristol was William A. Shenstone (later FRS), a pharmacy student who came as his assistant. In 1874, Tilden prepared nitrosyl chloride and used it to great effect in his subsequent work.[39] During the summer holidays he and Shenstone distilled turpentine and some other essential oils, separated out what they thought were the terpenes, and used the nitrosyl chloride to convert terpenes into their more easily identifiable nitrosochlorides.[40] In this way Tilden helped to lay the foundation of terpene chemistry, for which he was elected FRS in 1880. In the same year, Mason College opened in Birmingham and Tilden was appointed its first professor of chemistry. Given the college's location, he was expected to teach also metallurgy, and to know about blast furnaces. With the help of some Birmingham iron masters, and yet more self-education, he gained much metallurgical knowledge, but the terpenes remained his research focus.[41] In a landmark paper published in 1884 (which included possibly the first use of the term 'cracking,' and which paved the way for the manufacture of artificial rubber), Tilden wrote that he had passed turpentine vapour through an iron tube heated to about 550° C, and isolated a number of compounds. One was isoprene which he stored in some sealed bottles. Describing this work eight years later in a lecture given to the Birmingham Philosophical Society, he stated, 'I was surprised a few weeks ago at finding the contents of the bottles containing isoprene from turpentine entirely changed in appearance.' Floating on the surface were 'large masses of solid of a yellowish colour … that turned out to be india-rubber.'[42]

In 1894, Tilden was invited to apply to become Thorpe's successor — he was told that were he to do so he 'would probably be appointed,' as indeed he was.[43] When he arrived in South Kensington the college was overcrowded with 123 students, not counting the research and summer students. However, as mentioned, a new building for the RCS was soon to be approved. In 1897, Tilden began working with Aston Webb, the architect for the new building. He had a major say in the design of the chemistry department, and its laboratories.[44] The RCS building was constructed on a site purchased from The Royal Commissioners for the Exhibition of 1851; it opened in 1906.[45] Chemistry shared the new building with the physics department, the college bookstore, the Science Museum library, a refectory, and the impending IC administration.[46] The main chemistry lecture theatre had room for 150 students. It had two screens for lantern slide projection, blackboards, and places for hanging diagrams.[47] Wide pipes were fitted to the demonstration table so as to evacuate fumes — fumes had bothered students in the old building. The theatre had connections for water, gas and electricity, and it had a vacuum pump. Next to the theatre was a preparation room with a large storage area for apparatus and chemicals, and nearby was a freezing room and a machine for making liquid air. There were also smaller lecture theatres for physical and organic chemistry.

The laboratory for first year students was on the ground floor. It was about 28 m long and 23 m wide, and had an 11 m ceiling reaching to the upper floor of the building.[48] It had room for 144 students (some of the students came from other disciplines, such as geology and metallurgy). Island workplaces were organised in groups of four with shared sink and cupboard space. Hydrogen sulfide cabinets were installed on the benches and supplied by a generator (and gas holder) in a neighbouring room.[49] In other neighbouring rooms there were balances, reagents, and instruments of various kinds. In addition there were teaching laboratories for physical and organic chemistry each with places for 40 students, and a large advanced analytical laboratory on the top floor with 130 places. The physical chemistry laboratory was on the ground floor, and had an adjoining room for gas analysis, facilities for electrochemical experiments, and a large rotary vacuum pump. After WW1, a larger physical chemistry laboratory was set up in space that had earlier been used for a refectory.[50] The organic chemistry laboratory was on the first floor, and its work spaces were twice as large as those in the other teaching laboratories. There were some adjacent rooms for combustions, balances, an air compressor, and there was a dark-room. There was no teaching laboratory for inorganic chemistry, but it was taught in the advanced analytical laboratory on the top floor. This laboratory also doubled as an examination hall. It is interesting that the department placed so much emphasis on analytical chemistry. One possible explanation has to do with the earlier unification of the RCC and RSM. Students at the Royal School of Mines (RSM) had to spend many hours on mineralogical and metallurgical analysis. Hofmann had to accommodate that kind of work after becoming responsible for the chemical education of RSM students (something that the department continued to provide in South Kensington). Unlike the situation in the old RCS building, where the long corridor-like research laboratory belonged to the professor alone, the new RCS building had space for the assistant professors to have their own laboratories. Lecturers and demonstrators worked either in one of the professors' laboratories, or carried out their research in the teaching laboratories alongside the students. Some space was left unassigned until after WW1.

By Tilden's period, undergraduates were given 65 lectures in 'theoretical and systematic' chemistry in their first year. These included basic inorganic chemistry. Over their second and third years students could take 60 lectures in organic chemistry. For those wanting the Associateship of the Royal College of Science (ARCS), introduced in 1890, 30 of the organic lectures were compulsory; also compulsory were 20 in analytical chemistry and 20 in physical chemistry. Courses in mathematics, mechanics, geology and botany were then optional. As before, students were taught the nature of chemical combination, and the chemical and physical properties of the common elements. By the 1890s, the theory of valency was central to instruction and modern nomenclature was used. In their fourth year, students were expected to work with a member of staff on a specialised topic. Optional courses were given on a range of topics such as fermentation and photographic chemistry. The syllabus was more structured than 20 years earlier, but it was to become even more so after the return of Thorpe in 1909.

Indicative of the new, Wilhelm Ostwald gave the address at the first ARCS graduation ceremony to be held in the new building. Ostwald, van't Hoff, and Arrhenius were the big names of the day, and their physical chemical ideas were slowly being incorporated in the curriculum. However, the college's strength still lay in its organic chemistry. When Thorpe returned in 1909 he moved to strengthen inorganic and physical chemistry, something resented by the organic chemists. They believed that there was much new material in their field that the students needed to know; added to the basic aliphatic, and aromatic chemistry were ideas in stereochemistry and isomerism, organometallic chemistry, the chemistry of ethers and thioethers, phosphines, arsines, stibines, aldehydes, ketones, cyanogen compounds, terpenes, camphor, and so on. However analysis had also modernised and this, along with inorganic and physical chemistry, were the fields that Thorpe favoured.

During the 1890s the lecture fees per term were £3 and the laboratory fees £13. They remained the same up until WW1. Students with the most prestigious scholarships, the Royal Scholarships, had their fees waived and were awarded £50 per year. National Scholarships were means tested, college fees were paid, and students were allowed up to 30 shillings per week for living expenses. Students still had to supply much of their own apparatus. Included in a long list were a blow pipe, platinum foil, test tubes, various flasks and beakers, funnels, a retort stand, sand bath, Bunsen burner, and crucibles.[51] As earlier, visits to industrial sites were organised. In the period 1903–1905 students visited Bovril, the Whitefriar's Glass works, Idris Minerals (shown around by Mr. Idris himself)[52], the Barclay and Perkins brewery, the Beckton gas and coke works and Brin's oxygen works in Westminster. In 1909, H. S. Wellcome invited students to visit the Dartmouth works of Burroughs and Wellcome.

In 1905, the geologist John W. Judd retired and Tilden was appointed Dean of the RCS. He was also a member of the University of London senate. In 1907, one year after the new building opened, the RCS, the RSM, and the City and Guides Central Technical college (C&GCTC) joined to form the Imperial College of Science and Technology and Tilden became a member of its governing body.[53] The new college entailed some rationalisation of resources. In so far as chemistry was concerned, most important was the closure of Henry Armstrong's department at the Central, and the accommodation of some of its staff and resources within the RCS department. Planning for this began after the 1907 Wolfe Barry Committee submitted its report.[54] The actual merger began in 1911 and was completed in 1913. However, because of the war, the reorganised department had its true start only in 1919.

Although much of Tilden's attention was directed to the design of the new laboratories, and to the newly founded IC, he managed to carry out some research. One has the impression that, like others of his generation, he inherited Hofmann and Frankland's intrepid approach in the laboratory and some of his terpene work illustrates that. He heated his sealed tubes in tin cans filled with water and on one occasion, while bending down to adjust a burner, a tube burst with a 'terrific bang.' Boiling water sprayed over his head and 'he ran through two rooms without straightening up.'[55] During the 1890s, prompted by the debate over the atomic weights of nickel and cobalt, Tilden worked with John Perry on the relation between the specific heats of metals and their atomic weights. Their early results were reported in the Bakerian Lecture of 1900.[56] The audience for this lecture was, however, small, few could make their way to the Royal Society because of the large crowd celebrating the turn of events in the South African War; many people were hoping to get a glimpse of Queen Victoria.[57]

In the late 1890s, Tilden published on helium, and other gases occluded in minerals, but his main interest remained the terpenes.[58] Several of his research students had careers in the rubber industry; some of them are mentioned in two memoirs written by George Stafford Whitby.[59] Whitby, a brilliant student, entered the college in 1903 at age 15 with a National Scholarship. Three years later he graduated with the Hatton prize and was appointed demonstrator. In 1910, he joined the exodus of organic chemists following Tilden's resignation. The first decade of the 20th century saw a boom in the rubber industry due to the demand for automobile tyres. Tilden helped Whitby find a position as chemist to some rubber companies with plantations in Malaya.[60] After a few years in Malaya Whitby moved to McGill University where, in 1920, he gained a PhD and was appointed as assistant professor. In 1929 he became Director of the Chemistry Division of the National Research Council of Canada and, in 1938, returned to England where he succeeded Gilbert Morgan as

Director of the Chemical Research Laboratory in Teddington. After WW2 he returned to North America as Professor and Director of the Institute of Rubber Research at the University of Akron. Herbert Wright, a botany student who studied chemistry with Tilden, made a fortune from rubber. A major college donor, he later served on IC's governing body. Harold Hibbert came to work with Tilden in 1908 and, like Whitby, seeing little prospect for advancement after Tilden's retirement he left for North America.[61]

Two notable students of this period, Mary Boyle and Hilda Judd, were winners of the Hatton Prize in 1901 and 1904 respectively. Boyle published on the iodosulphonic acids of benzene and gained a DSc. She became a lecturer at Royal Holloway College. Judd, the daughter of J. W. Judd, Dean of the RCS, represented the college at the British Associate for the Advancement of Science (BAAS) meeting in South Africa in 1905. She was Martin Forster's assistant for a short period before joining the professor of botany, John B. Farmer, with whom she worked on the cold storage of food during WW1. In 1908, the Hatton prize was won by Victor Little. He joined the staff, but left in 1915 for Thorium Ltd. where he became Chief Chemist. Little contributed to the nine-volume *Textbook of inorganic chemistry* edited by the University of Birmingham chemist, J. Newton Friend. Other departmental contributors include Vincent Briscoe who came to the college as a student in 1906, and Arthur Eldridge who joined the staff in 1910. Eldridge and Little were close friends, known in the department as Dulong and Petit.[62] Briscoe and Eldridge are discussed in later chapters.

Five other important figures of this period were William Wynne, Martin Forster, Gilbert Morgan, Martha Whiteley, and James Philip. Forster who was Tilden's assistant at Mason College came with him to London and was appointed demonstrator in 1895.[63] In 1902, he succeeded Wynne (discussed below) as assistant professor of organic chemistry. He lectured on a wide range of topics and clearly made an impression.[64] G. W. Himus, a student from 1910 to 1914, and later a Reader in fuel technology in the chemical technology and chemical engineering department, stated,

one of my very vivid recollections is the terrifying appearance of M. O. Forster, when one first saw him. His immaculate silk hat, morning coat, striped trousers, patent leather boots, jet black hair and moustache with not a single whisker out of place, ... an appalling manifestation of assistant professorial magnificence... [Even in the laboratory] he wore a spotless white shirt, starched cuffs turned up ... an impressive reminder to the untidy student that flannel slacks and pullover are not the correct dress for all occasions ...[Also of note were]... his sarcastic remarks at any interruption during a lecture.[65]

However, Himus stated that by the time students were in their third year Forster would come into the lab and chat with them in a friendly and helpful manner. Forster took an interest in student affairs and by several accounts was very popular.[66] He continued to work with Tilden for a while but his research developed in a direction informed more by work begun during his year at the Central. It is discussed briefly below.[67] Forster was another organic chemist to leave after Thorpe's return to the department. He considered making a political career, but failed to get elected. When he left in 1913, a departmental dinner was held in his honour at the Royal Adelaide Galleries in the Strand. The guests were entertained by Eldridge at the piano, and by songs from Philip and Albert King. King sang:

I am the very pattern of a modern man political,
I've information physical, organic, analytical,
I know the law of octaves and the table periodical,
Can find the metals in a spot, by ways the most methodical.[68]

Forster was appointed Director of British Dyes in 1915. The country was paying the price for letting the dye industry pass largely into German hands. Imports had ceased, the government took control of Read Holliday and Co., and some smaller dye manufacturers, and formed a consortium tasked with producing a steady supply of colouring materials.[69] Forster left England after the war, appointed Director of the Indian Institute of Science in Bangalore in 1922.

Like Forster, Gilbert Morgan studied at Finsbury Technical College under Raphael Meldola. He then worked for Read Holliday in Huddersfield before coming to the college in 1894 as a mature student. He performed brilliantly, coming top of the university's BSc list.[70] He was described as witty, vivacious, and as having a remarkable memory. Tilden was keen to appoint him to the staff. A hard worker, Morgan stayed in the laboratory well into the night and was soon promoted from demonstrator to assistant professor. He worked on diazo reactions, and the synthesis of aromatic diazonium salts, as well as on organo-phosphorus, -arsenic, and -antimony compounds. Together with Forster, he synthesised some new camphor derivatives. Both had the assistance of Frances Micklethwait who gained her ARCS in 1901.[71] She helped Morgan further his work on diazo reactions, and to develop some arsenical bactericides which were submitted to Henry G. Plimmer for testing on animals.[72] Today Morgan is remembered as a founder of coordination chemistry. In 1912, he left for the Chair of Chemistry at the Royal College of Science, Dublin. He was elected FRS in 1915 and, after Meldola's death in 1916, he returned to Finsbury Technical College as professor of chemistry. In 1919, he was appointed Mason professor of chemistry at the University of Birmingham and, in 1925, became the first Director of the government's new Chemical Research Laboratory in Teddington. Morgan was elected President of the Society of Chemical Industry in 1931, President of the Chemical Society in 1933–1935, and was knighted in 1936. In his will he left money to the Chemical Society for the creation of the Corday–Morgan medal and prize.[73] Derek Barton was the first recipient.

Martha Whiteley came to the college in 1898, one of a few 'scholar teachers' to be appointed in this period.[74] She carried out research under Tilden — mainly on tautomerism in oximes, on caffeine derivatives, and on barbiturate compounds.[75] After gaining her DSc in 1902, she was appointed demonstrator in organic chemistry. In 1904, she organised a petition that was sent to the President and council of the Chemical Society seeking the admission of women to the fellowship. Thorpe and Tilden proposed a motion to that effect but it was defeated.[76] Whiteley stayed on the staff and was promoted to assistant professor in 1920, the first woman to achieve that rank at Imperial College.[77] She will be discussed further in the following two chapters.

After Rodger's early death in 1897, physical chemistry was taught for a couple of years by John Shields. A former RCC student working with William Ramsay at University College, Shields came to his old college just to give the lectures. In 1899, Tilden invited James Philip to take over.[78] Philip was then working with Armstrong at the C&GCTC, known as the

Central, but he moved to the RCS in 1900 as demonstrator. He was soon promoted to lecturer, and then assistant professor. In 1906, he set up an office and research laboratory on the lower ground floor of the new building. The same office and laboratory were used by future professors of physical chemistry until the demolition of much of the RCS building in the 1970s. Philip helped Tilden in promoting the new RCS Chemical Society. He is discussed further in Chapters Five and Six.

Like Thorpe, Tilden wrote several textbooks, the most enduring being (Tilden, 1876). Late in life he published a number of works in the history of chemistry.[79] He played a major role in the Institute of Chemistry and was elected President, 1891–1994. He was active also in the Chemical Society and was elected President, 1903–1905. He was awarded the Royal Society's Davy Medal in 1908 and was knighted in 1909, the year that ill health forced his retirement. The Mendeleev memorial lecture that Tilden delivered to the Chemical Society in the same year was said to have been 'outstanding.'[80] He retained a laboratory at the college and continued his terpene research for a few more years. His widow left money for an award in his memory. Founded in 1939, the RSC Tilden Award is awarded annually for advances in chemistry.

4.3 Henry Armstrong's Department at the C&GCTC

As noted in Chapter Three, Henry Armstrong FRS (1848–1937) came to the RCC as a student in 1865.[81] Earlier he had been a pupil at Colfe's Grammar School in Lewisham. The school was endowed by the Leathersellers Company which later supported the chemistry department at the C&GCTC.[82] Armstrong was a child naturalist, and 'a naturalist, he remained.'[83] He much enjoyed walking in the countryside and making observations. While at the RCC he attended physics, geology and natural history lectures at the RSM. One of his obituarists who thought him insufficiently focussed, stated, 'he did not belong to the August order of the Olympians but was one of the Titans. He had all the spare parts of genius but not the long patience to put them together.'[84] It is perhaps true that Armstrong spread his considerable energy too thinly to reach the pinnacle of success. Nonetheless he led a successful life, and lived it to the full. He published over 60 papers on naphthalene substitution, and many others on aromatic ring systems, heterogeneous catalysis, metal corrosion, colour in organic molecules, fermentation, combustion, hydrolysis, and plant enzymes. Although not keen on new electronic theories, he recognised that the deep colour associated with quinones was related to whatever was being represented by the double bond.[85] He was interested in colour, enjoyed colour in flowers and speculated on their chemistry. He often wore brightly coloured clothing, including coloured lapels (a different colour for each) on his dinner jackets. This was seen as eccentric, but Armstrong claimed that if his example were to catch on, it would help the dye industry.[86]

After studying at the RCC, Armstrong moved to Leipzig to study with Hermann Kolbe — gaining his PhD after working on what he later recognised was an isomeric mix of phenol derivatives. In 1870, he returned to London and a lectureship at St. Bartholomew's (Barts) Hospital Medical School where he worked with Augustus Matthiessen on alkaloids.[87] A few months later he was appointed Professor at the London Institution and began some research of his own in a small cellar behind the lecture theatre.[88] At the time, chemists were struggling with the properties of camphor for which no satisfactory formula based on the benzene model had yet been suggested. With some of his students, Armstrong took up the problem, and began the work on camphor chemistry that occupied him for many years. In 1874, he published an introductory textbook on organic chemistry.[89]

Armstrong was ambitious and applied for several jobs before his appointment as the first professor of chemistry at Finsbury Technical College. The college was founded in 1875 by the City and Guilds of London Institute for the Advancement of Technical Education (CGLI).[90] After nine years there, Armstrong moved to South Kensington, to the CGLI's Central Institution (renamed the Central Technical College in 1893). He was one of four founding professors, and gave the very first lecture in the new building in 1884.[91] The City and Guides Central Technical College (C&GCTC) was the only university-level technical college of its kind in the country. The professors carried out research and the students were admitted by examination.[92] The following question was on the very first entrance examination. It is a typical Armstrong question, in that there is no reference to established ideas, and because it forced prospective students to think things through for themselves.

How would you show that water which has been freely exposed to the atmosphere contains 'air' in solution? What apparatus would you employ in order to extract and collect a quantity of dissolved air?

As to instruction, the CGLI council decided to follow the *École Centrale des Arts et Manufactures*, with its motto '*la Science est une.*' This meant that students at the C&GCTC were given a similarly broad scientific education, and had to study mathematics, chemistry, physics, and mechanics before being allowed to specialise. Specialisation in the different engineering fields began only in the third year (of a four-year programme), and was research based. Armstrong approved of this pedagogical approach and is remembered for his ideas on science education for both university-level technical colleges and schools.[93]

Once in South Kensington, Armstrong was free to build the kind of department he wanted, but with a serious limitation.[94] Most of his students were future engineers who had to take chemistry as part of their training. Some of them later became leaders in the chemical industry but, unlike at the RCS, there were few who wished to pursue careers as research chemists.[95] Armstrong addressed this problem in three ways. First, he appointed some promising young chemists to the staff. He collaborated with them, and encouraged them to carry out research that could lead to more senior appointments elsewhere. Second, he developed chemical technology expertise within the department so as to attract engineering students into applied chemical research. As a result some students specialised in chemistry or chemical technology in their third and fourth years. This area of study formed a nucleus for the later chemical technology and chemical engineering department at IC.[96] Third, Armstrong was interested in how compounds were held together spatially.[97] Believing that crystallography was the key to understanding this, he decided to make it a serious field of study in his department. In 1886, he invited Henry Miers, who worked in the mineralogy department of the Natural History Museum, to give lectures and practical instruction in crystallography.[98] Miers was a Lecturer at the C&GCTC from 1886–1895. Among those attending his classes were three well-known mature students: William Barlow, Sir William Phipson Beale and Bernard Harrington.[99] Miers also attracted younger enthusiasts, notable among them William Pope, Martin Lowry, and Arthur Lapworth. When he left in 1895, he was succeeded as lecturer in crystallography by Pope. In 1901, Pope was succeeded by Lowry.

William Jackson Pope FRS (1870–1939), was another of Raphael Meldola's students at Finsbury Technical College. He came to the C&GCTC as Armstrong's research student, and was appointed a demonstrator soon after.[100] Pope's period at the Central was formative. Highly intelligent and multilingual, he learned much from those around him, especially from Armstrong with whom he worked on terpene chemistry, and from Frederick Kipping (see following paragraph) after becoming his assistant. Inspired also by Miers, Pope's research moved toward optical activity, crystal structure, and the stereochemistry of organic compounds. As Kipping later noted, 'the happiest hours of [Pope's] life were spent in the dark room with his goniometer, in calculating the results of his measurements, and in drawing the crystal figures.'[101] Kipping, in turn, was to learn from his assistant, such that optical activity, and crystal structure became his interests too.[102] Some impressive crystallographic work was carried out also by another of Armstrong's research students, Clare de Brereton Evans. She made mirror image crystals of ethylpropylpiperidinium iodide, but found that neither form exhibited optical activity in solution. She continued to work on this problem, not resolved until it was recognised that asymmetry can be associated with pentavalent nitrogen.[103] More generally the C&GCTC became known for its crystallographic expertise, and chemists sent in samples for crystallographic analysis. As one of Armstrong's obituarists noted, many German papers included the acknowledgment, 'Mitteilungen aus dem Krystallographischen Laboratorium des Central Technical College.'[104]

When Pope first arrived at the C&GCTC, he was given the task of testing one of Armstrong's many theories. It was commonly held that turpentines from different sources contained different terpenes, but Armstrong thought otherwise. He believed, that different turpentines contained the same mix of terpenes, and that any difference was due to the proportion of optical isomers present. Pope studied pinene extracted from French and American oils of turpentine. French pinene, for example, showed high *laevo* rotation whereas that of the American pinene was low. Further research on terpenes from other turpentines, entailing much crystallographic work, appeared to confirm Armstrong's theory, though not conclusively.[105] After Kipping's appointment (see below), Pope spent several years working with him. One of the problems they set themselves was explaining the realignment of elements, or groups of elements, in molecules undergoing racemisation. Together they also uncovered several series of isopolymorphous compounds. Pope's crystallographic work also came into play in his realising that, in camphor, the carbonyl group can migrate between positions 2 and 6.

Pope succeeded Miers as lecturer in crystallography, a position he retained even after becoming head of the chemistry department at the Goldsmiths' Institute (later College) in 1897. In 1901, he was appointed to the chair of chemistry at the Manchester School of Technology. William Barlow joined him in Manchester to work on their short-lived 'valency-volume theory.'[106] In 1908, Pope succeeded Edward Liveing as professor of chemistry at Cambridge where he extended his work on optical activity.[107] He was elected FRS in 1902, won the Longstaff Medal in 1903, the Davy Medal in 1914, served as President of the Chemical Society, 1917–1919, and was President of the Society of Chemical Industry, 1920–1921. In recognition of his many contributions to the war effort he was made KBE in 1919.[108]

When Pope left the C&GCTC in 1901, Martin Lowry was appointed lecturer in crystallography and Physical Chemistry.[109] Lowry had come to the C&GCTC on a Clothworkers scholarship in 1893 and, in 1896, he became Armstrong's assistant. Together they carried out work on the terpenes, and on camphor.[110] Lowry, too, caught the excitement of the crystallography section. He learned much physical chemistry and, like Pope, began to speculate on the dynamic nature of isomerism and on the nature of optical activity. One of his ideas was that hydrogen ions migrate during isomeric conversion. He considered also the migration of radical cations and anions leading to an extended definition of acids and bases. This definition, advanced independently by the Danish chemist, J. N. Brønsted (and later known as the Brønsted–Lowry theory), was one in which acids were defined as proton donors, and bases as proton acceptors. Lowry first presented his ideas to Section B at the BAAS meeting in 1904.[111] While at the C&GCTC he also laid the foundation for his lifelong study of optical rotatory dispersion and coined the term 'mutarotation.' When the department at the C&GCTC closed down, he worked for a brief period in the

RCS department before his appointment, in 1913, as head of the chemistry department at Guy's Hospital Medical School. He was soon made a professor at the University of London, the first (non-physician) chemist at a medical school to achieve that rank. While retaining his position at Guy's, he returned to South Kensington during WW1 and worked alongside Martha Whiteley and others, as part of the trench warfare unit (see Chapter Five). In 1920, he was appointed the first professor of physical chemistry at Cambridge, where he continued his important work in crystallography, and optical rotatory power. At Cambridge, Lowry's ideas were taken up by N. V. Sidgwick. Given that Pope had earlier been appointed head of department, it can be said that much early 20th-century chemical work at Cambridge had its start in Armstrong's department at the Central.[112]

A future Rector of IC, the chemist Sir Patrick Linstead, rightly saw Armstrong as 'one of the outstanding personalities of British chemistry.' In his day Armstrong was possibly chemistry's greatest booster, and probably the most frequent attendee at Chemical Society meetings. Very convivial, he revived the Chemical Society's dining club and its functions were well managed by his wife.[113] Armstrong gave many papers at the Chemical Society and was elected President, 1893–1995. Although he enjoyed theoretical speculation, he was on the conservative side when it came to other people's ideas. As noted in Chapter Three, he had been hesitant to accept some of Frankland's ideas and, in his 1895 Presidential address to the Chemical Society, he challenged those of Ostwald, Arrhenius, and van't Hoff.[114] However, his own view of things led to some interesting work on hydrolysis, and on the nature of plant enzymes, a topic that occupied him during his long period as an Emeritus Professor in the RCS. Even then Armstrong was reluctant to accept the reaction mechanism ideas of Robert Robinson. As to Robinson's diagrammatic curly arrows showing electrons moving around molecular bonds, Armstrong was dismissive. As he put it, 'a bent arrow never hit the mark.'[115]

In some ways the two departments in South Kensington can be seen as contiguous since there was much movement back and forth, and a fair bit of cooperation among the members of staff.[116] Armstrong gathered a gifted group of young chemists at the C&GCTC, and their research output was remarkable. As he envisaged, many of his appointees were to have major careers. One person who chose a different path was Gerald T. Moody who came to the C&GCTC from Finsbury Technical College with Armstrong. Already as a young Finsbury student, Moody was included in gatherings at Armstrong's home, and joined family members on their long country walks. He became a lifelong friend. He did not carry out much research but he was an important teacher, and was said to have been 'a pastmaster in the art of organizing dances.'[117] Appointed demonstrator when the new college opened, he was later promoted to lecturer. For first-year engineering students, he was the embodiment of Armstrong's 'heuristic' pedagogy. The students were taught largely without textbooks and, guided by Moody, they spent much time in the laboratory 'learning by doing.'[118] Armstrong gave some lectures to the first year students with tips on how to learn for oneself. Martha Whiteley attended both Tilden's lectures at the RCS, and Armstrong's at the C&GCTC. Her notes make interesting reading. It appears that Tilden had a more historical approach to his subject and, as one might expect given his heuristic ideas, Armstrong a more philosophical one.[119]

Another student who moved from Finsbury with Armstrong was William Heller. He later took Armstrong's heuristic method to Ireland.[120] There were a few women students at the C&GCTC. One, L. E. (Edna) Walter, became a school inspector for the Board of Education in England, and was another exponent of the heuristic method. Ida Smedley (see Note 76) had studied chemistry at Newnham College, Cambridge before coming to London as Armstrong's research student. She soon picked up on the optical activity work, and took it back to Cambridge when appointed demonstrator. In 1906, she became an assistant lecturer at Manchester University, the first woman to be appointed to the academic staff of its chemistry department. She returned to London in 1913, to a research position at the Lister Institute of Preventive Medicine.[121]

Shortly after arriving at the C&GCTC, Armstrong appointed a third demonstrator, William Palmer Wynne FRS (1861–1950).[122] Wynne was a scholarship student at the NSS School (1881–1885) where he won several prizes and gained both his associateship and an external BSc from the University of London. Like Moody he became one of Armstrong's regular walking companions, but he was also a close chemical collaborator. In

1890, after five years at the C&GCTC he returned to what, by then, had become the RCS when appointed to succeed Francis Japp as assistant professor. Even after this appointment Wynne continued to work with Armstrong at the C&GCTC on the structure of naphthalene and its derivatives; together they synthesised as many mono-, di-, tri-, and tetra-substituted compounds as they could.[123] This work, of growing importance to the dyestuffs industry, was interrupted by the authorities at the C&GCTC who objected to Wynne working in their laboratories where he was no longer an employee. They were especially annoyed that Armstrong had given him a master key to the building. Armstrong tried to smooth things over, but was not fully successful. Wynne's research activity became restricted and his output waned; it never fully recovered. In 1902, he was appointed to a chair at the Pharmaceutical Society, and in 1904 he became professor of chemistry at the University College of Sheffield (University of Sheffield from 1905). He was elected President of the Chemical Society, 1923–1925 and, on his retirement from Sheffield in 1931, Pope invited him to Cambridge and gave him a research laboratory. Wynne worked there for 15 years, returning to his work on naphthalene and toluene, and cataloguing the many specimens prepared earlier with Armstrong — purifying many of them in the process. The collection was donated to the Dyestuffs Division of ICI. When the Division closed the samples were about to be thrown into a skip, but they were rescued and are conserved in the chemistry department at IC.[124]

As mentioned in Note 63, Forster worked at the C&GCTC for a year before Tilden was able to find him a position at the RCS. Armstrong tried to persuade him to stay on, claiming that at the RCS he would be under Tilden's thumb, would be unable to carry out his own research, and would find it difficult to find a more senior position elsewhere.[125] But Forster appears to have been more independent minded than Wynne. He was able to carry out his own research in the RCS department and, with a private income, supported a large research group. It included nine Swiss chemists; one, H. E. Fierz later changed his name and became Professor Hans Fierz-David of the ETH in Zurich. But Forster did not escape Armstrong's influence altogether. It was Armstrong who encouraged him to take up camphor chemistry, something that became his lifelong work.[126] He was also influenced by the work being carried out at the C&GCTC on optical activity and, like Lowry, combined synthetic work on camphor chemistry with physical chemical measurement. He also worked on organic tri-azo compounds, many of them explosive.[127]

Although Wynne carried out his research at the C&GCTC, his teaching duties were at the RCS. To replace him, Armstrong added to an already strong group of organic chemists by inviting Frederick S. Kipping to come from Edinburgh as senior demonstrator in 1890.[128] Kipping had already accomplished much, and his famous textbook, *Modern organic chemistry*, coauthored with Perkin, would be published in 1894.[129] One of his first tasks at the C&GCTC was 'to examine a crude sulphonation product of bromocamphor prepared by W. J. Pope.'[130] It was the start of his interest in camphor. Like others, Kipping contributed to what his obituarist described as 'the assiduous cultivation of the camphor field in South Kensington at the turn of the century.'[131] He was soon promoted to lecturer. His very successful seven year partnership with Pope was briefly described earlier. It is probably fair to say that Kipping was the more accomplished synthetic chemist, but that Pope was the more adventurous scientist. Together with Lowry, Pope brought crystallography and physical chemistry to the study of aromatic compounds. His work was outstanding, and he would have set an impossibly high standard for Kipping's future assistants. According to Kipping's obituarist, 'to work with [him] was no easy thing. He believed with Jeremiah that "it is a good thing for a man that he bear the yoke in his youth."'[132]

Kipping was fortunate in having yet another assistant at the C&GCTC willing to 'bear the yoke', namely Arthur Lapworth.[133] Of Lapworth Kipping later stated, 'although he was considerably my junior in age we soon became fast friends; perhaps it would be truer to say that our relationship, even in those early days, was rather that of congenial brothers.'[134] As mentioned in Chapter Three, they were to become brothers-in-law. Lapworth's father, Arthur, was the first professor of geology at Mason College, and Lapworth was educated there. When he moved to the C&GCTC as a Royal Exhibitioner in 1893, he joined the camphor research circle as Kipping's research student. Lapworth was to reconcile much of the conflicting data on the structure of camphor. He recognised that it must contain a cyclopentane ring, paving the way for the acceptance of Julius Bredt's 1893 formula.[135] As mentioned, Lapworth attended Miers' influential course in crystallography. He worked also with Armstrong on the sulphonation of β-naphthol ethers and gained a DSc at the young age of 23.[136]

In 1897, Kipping was elected FRS and left the C&GCTC for the Chair of Chemistry at University College, Nottingham — in succession to Frankland's former student, Frank Clowes.[137] Lapworth left soon after, working for a short period at the School of Pharmacy in Bloomsbury, and then at the Goldsmith's Institute in New Cross where he preceded Pope as head of the chemistry department. In 1908, he became senior lecturer in Inorganic and Physical Chemistry at the University of Manchester, later succeeding Perkin as professor and head of department. Lapworth was elected FRS in 1910, and was awarded the Davy medal in 1931. In Manchester he developed the subject of reaction mechanism, taken up by his assistant (and later Nobel Laureate) Robert Robinson. As mentioned, Armstrong was critical of some of their ideas. It is, however, remarkable that the professors of physical chemistry at two major universities had their start as organic chemists in the department built by Armstrong at the Central. The future professor of physical chemistry at IC, J. C. Philip, was similarly trained as an organic chemist, under Japp at the University of Aberdeen. He, too joined Armstrong at the C&GCTC, but by then he had spent two years in Göttingen with W. H. Nernst learning about the ionising power of solvents.[138] Philip is discussed in more detail in subsequent chapters.

Robert Robinson wrote that 'all one's memories of Henry E. Armstrong are vivid, ... [He was] 'colourful' 'provocative' [and] 'with an intense interest in the advance of mankind in general and the science of chemistry in particular.'[139] It was a fair comment. Armstrong was a man of many parts: a good chemist, a pioneer in higher technical education, and a promoter of science education in schools. He wanted industrialists to take chemistry seriously and was instrumental in making chemical technology a university discipline. A touch dogmatic, he was nonetheless a quick learner. A family man, he had a patriarchal (and paternal) attitude not only toward members of his family but also toward his staff. He was an outstanding mentor to younger chemists, and built a remarkable department. It must have been a bitter blow to see it close. However, he continued his research in the RCS department, working there for many years with his son, E. F. (Frank) Armstrong, and with several research students, and assistants. The topics he chose for his later work were hydrolysis, and plant enzyme chemistry. As can be seen from the index of the *Proceedings of the Royal Society*, he read many papers at the Royal Society during this

period. He was elected FRS as a young man in 1876, and was awarded the
Davy Medal in 1911. His 61 years as an FRS contributed to his being a
mover and shaker in the larger world of science, and he was still influential as an Emeritus professor. Throughout his life he devoted much time to
the Chemical Society, was Secretary, 1875–1893, and President, 1893–
1895. Like many people brought up in the Victorian period he publicly
acknowledged his intellectual debts. It was he who organised the Hofmann
memorial conference in May 1893. A banquet was held in Armstrong's
honour in May 1911.[140]

4.4 Thorpe's Return as Head of Department; Departmental Reorganisation, 1909–1914

Tilden resigned in 1909 due to ill health, but he kept his research laboratory for a few more years. Thorpe returned as head of department and set
about modernising the curriculum. The first year, labelled the intermediate
year, was for students who had received little scientific instruction at
school. Now they had to study mathematics and physics as well as chemistry. In the second year they were joined by students with high school
certificates in the sciences and studied mainly chemistry. In addition
students took short courses in any two of botany, zoology, mechanics, and
geology. The final two years were devoted exclusively to chemistry.
Examinations were taken at the end of each of the first three years.
Students who passed the third year examinations gained their associateship (ARCS). As before, the fourth year was devoted to working with a
member of staff on a short research topic, and to attending short specialist
courses. Students who completed their fourth year were now awarded the
Diploma of Imperial College (DIC).

Thorpe was keen to strengthen inorganic, physical, and analytical
chemistry. He also had to find someone to give chemistry lectures to first
year engineers since the chemistry department at the C&GCTC was
closed to new entrants from 1911.[141] He promoted Philip to assistant professor in physical chemistry, and appointed Arthur Bramley, who had just
completed his ARCS, as demonstrator in physical chemistry.[142] He
brought in some outsiders as demonstrators, causing upset among the
students. Tilden had given all vacant demonstratorships to top graduating

students, but Thorpe saw this practice as 'inbreeding.'[143] Among those still on the staff when Thorpe returned were Morgan and Forster, both assistant professors in organic chemistry, and Chapman Jones Lecturer in analytical chemistry. Whiteley and Whitby were demonstrators in organic chemistry, and Little and Newth were demonstrators in General and Inorganic chemistry. Sidney Young was the first year lecture demonstrator. Of these only Whiteley, Young, and Little were still on the staff in 1914. Little left during the war. One of Thorpe's new demonstrators was Cyril Edgar Sladden, appointed in 1912. He joined the army in 1915, had a distinguished war record, and resigned in 1919 to become the chemistry master at Eton College.

Vincent Briscoe graduated with his ARCS 1909 and was then employed by Thorpe to work on the *Dictionary of Applied Chemistry*. He later remarked that the experience taught him 'to read and write and to cope with tyrants.'[144] When Newth retired in 1910, Briscoe was appointed assistant demonstrator and carried out some research of his own, including a precise measurement of the atomic weight of vanadium.[145] He stayed in the department until 1921, though from 1916 only as a part-time lecturer. Briscoe's war work is discussed in Chapter Five and his later return to the department in Chapters Six, Seven, and Eight. His view, that Thorpe was difficult to work with is backed up by a story told by Arthur Eldridge who came to the college in 1910 as Thorpe's research student. On arrival he located another research student and asked where to find the professor. He received the indirect reply, 'good God, Edward, here's a bloke who actually *wants* to see old Tommy.'[146] Eldridge was given work in an area that Thorpe had brought from the government laboratory, namely the analytical chemistry of food and drugs. He stayed in the department for 50 years as student, demonstrator, lecturer, and senior lecturer in inorganic chemistry. It was he who was given the assignment of lecturing to the approximately 130 first year engineering students. Eldridge is discussed further in subsequent chapters.

Another of Thorpe's appointees, Henry F. Harwood, was expected to bolster analytical chemistry in the department — which he did. Harwood had studied chemistry in Manchester and Heidelberg and was appointed demonstrator under Chapman Jones. He, too, is discussed in subsequent chapters. Three other members of staff deserve mention, Philip Robertson,

Norman Haworth, and Albert King. Robertson was an organic chemist who moved from the C&GCTC when its department closed. A New Zealander, he won a Rhodes scholarship to Oxford in 1905, then gained a PhD under A. R. Hantzsche at Leipzig. He worked in the department until 1920 when he returned to New Zealand as professor of chemistry at Victoria University in Wellington.[147] Haworth, also an organic chemist, was appointed senior demonstrator in 1911. However, since Thorpe did not allow him sufficient research space, and wanted him mainly as a teacher, he did not stay long. He moved to a lectureship at the University of St. Andrews in 1912, and was later a Nobel Laureate.[148] King, appointed a demonstrator in 1911–1921, was treated in much the same way as Haworth, but stayed until after the war. He was later Professor of Textile Chemistry at Leeds.[149]

Although new students were no longer admitted to the C&GCTC department, Armstrong and a few of his staff stayed on until those enrolled earlier had completed their studies. In 1913, Armstrong was made an Emeritus professor and moved to the RCS with a small group of research students. A section of his old department, chemical technology, moved with him. Earlier, both Armstrong and Thorpe had pushed for the creation of a separate chemical technology department. The governing body of IC agreed, but it took some years for this to become a reality. The first idea was to house the new department in a building contiguous with the RCS, but after a decision was made to leave that area to the Science Museum, a new building was constructed behind the Royal College of Music.[150] Chemical technology (later chemical technology and chemical engineering) remained in the RCS until its transfer to the C&G in 1939.

From 1909, students in the RCS chemistry department could take fourth year lecture courses in both chemical technology and chemical engineering. The lectures focussed primarily on the coal and coal-gas industry. H. G. Colman, who taught also at the C&GCTC, gave a course on gas manufacture in 1909–1910 and, one year later, William Bone FRS, professor of Fuel and Gas industries at the University of Leeds, was invited to give a course of 16 lectures.[151] A course on 'the design of plant required for chemical engineering' was offered by John W. Hinchley, a former prize-winning chemistry student at the NSS and a lecturer at the Battersea Polytechnic. In 1912 Bone was appointed Professor of Fuel and

Refractory Materials — a close thing since he cancelled a planned voyage on the *Titanic* at the last moment. He became head of what, at first, was a sub-department of chemistry named chemical technology. It was located in the basement of the RCS building. Bone soon appointed two demonstrators, George Finch, a specialist in refractory materials, and Geoffrey Himus, the former chemistry student who was so impressed by Forster's appearance. In the interval, Himus had run a power station in Shanghai. Both Finch, and Himus stayed on at IC. Finch became a professor, an FRS, and a famous mountaineer.[152] In 1914 chemical technology became an independent department, and moved into its new building (completed only after the war, and later named for Bone). After WW1, there was a perceived need for more chemical engineers and the department planned to expand. However, there was competition from UCL. When William Ramsay died in 1916, Frederick G. Donnan succeeded him as head of the UCL chemistry department. Donnan was keen for UCL to have a chemical engineering department built in Ramsay's honour. UCL went ahead and opened its department in 1923, even though an agreement existed to allow IC alone to expand in that area. IC responded to the UCL plans by appointing Hinchley assistant professor of chemical engineering in 1917, he was given a full chair in 1926.[153] However, until 1957, undergraduate students in chemical engineering, and chemical technology received instruction in the chemistry department for the first two years of their degree programme. When the Roderic Hill building opened in 1957, there was room for the chemical engineers to teach a full undergraduate programme of their own.

As mentioned, Armstrong continued his research as an Emeritus professor. He also continued his political battle with the University of London. Earlier, he had stated that the university, 'breaks faith with us and declines to help us in educating our students in such a manner that they may become efficient chemists able to enter works and appreciate the numerous problems demanding the constant exercise of the reflective and analytical habit of mind.'[154] He wanted the university to allow a research option as an alternative to the examination route to a degree. In making his case, he pointed out that some of his students had failed the BSc examinations but had nonetheless published valuable work in the chemical journals, and many had succeeded in industry. He argued more successfully, that degree examinations should be weighted more towards the practical.

During his second term as head of department Thorpe carried out little research. Aside from reorganizing the department, his main project was the *Dictionary of Applied Chemistry*. He continued to work on it after retiring to Salcombe in 1912 — to pursue his passion for yachting. As mentioned, the first volume of the *Dictionary* appeared in 1890. Two further volumes were published in 1893.[155] Whiteley continued working on the *Dictionary* after Thorpe's death in 1925. She and Jocelyn Thorpe became coeditors of the fourth edition. After Jocelyn Thorpe died in 1940, Whiteley continued as sole editor, working on the *Dictionary* into her seventies with the help of an Assistant Editor, A. J. E. (John) Welch.[156]

When Thorpe retired as head of department in 1912 he was succeeded by Herbert Brereton Baker. Baker is discussed in subsequent chapters but, like Thorpe, he was somewhat antipathetic toward organic chemistry. Tilden and Armstrong continued their research in the department, but the younger organic chemists felt beleaguered and there was a general exodus in the years following Tilden's retirement. The most senior to leave was Forster who, as a productive assistant professor, had hoped to inherit Tilden's chair, and then to succeed Thorpe as head of department. With Baker's appointment his prospect even of a chair looked slim. Had he stayed a few months longer he would perhaps have been promoted to professor — but he may have left knowing that this was not to be. Whatever the case, the decline in organic chemical expertise prompted a change. A decision was taken to have three professors, one each for inorganic, physical, and organic chemistry, and to give them some independent powers. In 1913 Philip was promoted to professor of physical chemistry and, in 1914, Jocelyn Thorpe was appointed professor of organic chemistry.[157] Baker made one other pre-war appointment of note. His friend and former Dulwich College pupil, Bernard Mouat Jones, became an assistant professor. He is discussed in the following chapter.

The RCS chemical society, founded by Tilden in 1895, remained active until the start of the war. It continued to organise talks, and industrial visits. In the 1913–1914 academic year, Tilden, himself gave a talk to the society, as did two students, Samuel Sugden and Alfred G. Pollard.[158]

End Notes

1. For Thorpe, (Hammond, 2004), (Bedson, 1926), (Kopperl, 1976), (Halton, 2015). As a young man Thorpe was known as Tom. Later he used his second name, Edward. Behind his back the students called him Tommy. Thorpe's literary skills are evident in his chemical publications, but also in books that he wrote on yachting (he was an enthusiast) and the history of science, (Thorpe 1896, 1902, 1905, 1906, and 1909). In the same year as Thorpe published his biography (1906), he unveiled a statue of Joseph Priestley in Birstall.

2. Owens College was recognised by the University of London. Many of its students, including Thorpe, gained external BSc degrees from the university. Thorpe helped Roscoe to correct some of Berzelius' earlier work on vanadium chemistry, and they were the first to isolate the metal.

3. For a report on Thorpe's paper given to the Manchester Literary and Philosophical Society (28 November, 1865), and on the science carried out on the voyage, (Smith, 1865). Lewy spent much of his working life in Paris where the classical work on carbon dioxide levels in air had been carried out by Théodore de Saussure and J. B. Boussingault. For a late 19th century discussion of CO_2 levels, see the entry 'Atmosphere' in (Watts, 1890).

4. This scholarship for postgraduate study (£50 a year for two years) was awarded by Owens College.

5. (Thorpe, 1876).

6. (Thorpe, 1875, 1878).

7. (Thorpe, 1874).

8. Thorpe lived at 61 Ladbroke Grove. Herbert McLeod described a number of chemists' dinner parties and other social events at Thorpe's home; McLeod diary, ICL archives.

9. For example, (Thorpe and Laurie, 1887). Thorpe was not the first in determining the atomic weight of gold (or of other elements) but, like others, he was attempting greater accuracy.

10. Frederick John Hambly (1868–1960) was to make an industrial career in Canada where he became President of the Electric Reduction Co. He was also President of the Canadian Institute of Chemistry and among the original appointees to the National Research Council. James Wyllie Rodger (1867–1897), a Scot, joined the college in 1885 and carried off all the major prizes. Appointed a demonstrator, he was placed in charge of the South Laboratory. Sadly he died at the age of 30 from pulmonary tuberculosis; obituary, (Anon., 1897).

11. The Hatton Prize was named for a former chemistry student, Frank Hatton (1860–1882) who was accidentally shot and killed while on an elephant hunting expedition in Borneo. Hatton worked with Frankland with whom he published three papers; for his obituary, (Anon., 1883).

12. For A. E. H. Tutton, (Spencer, 2004), (Anon., 1939). For an interesting note on Tutton, (Brock, 2012). Later Tutton became an Inspector of Schools for the Southwest of England and, in 1924, retired to Cambridge where he occasionally taught in the mineralogy department. Tutton's successor at the RCS was an American, Arnold Eilort, author of a guide to stereochemistry, (Eiloart, 1892). His stay was brief; he came into an inheritance and left to cofound a Tolstoyan religious commune in Purleigh, Essex; (Holman, 1978).

13. (Thorpe and Tutton, 1890); Barker North's assistance is acknowledged in this paper. North, a Thorpe assistant, became a Professor at Bradford Technical College. The paper is wonderfully detailed and demonstrates much knowledge of the history of phosphorus chemistry. It includes also crystallographic detail. Tutton had taken instruction in crystallography from Henry Miers (see (98)) and began a programme of research on the crystalline forms of chemically related compounds when he moved to Oxford. He characterised many salts, among them some double salts, $R_2[M(SO_4)_2].6H_2O$, (where R is a monovalent metal or ammonium cation and M is a divalent metal cation), named after him Tutton Salts. He also published several books, including one on crystallography, (Tutton, 1911). While at the NSS, Tutton contributed several articles to the student journal, including a speculative paper inspired by the ideas of Mendeleev, 'The new atomic theory,' *Science Schools Journal*, 1 (1887), p. 34 (copy in ICL archives).

14. (Brunton, 1885), p. 638. Today, phosphorus is recognised as highly poisonous. The elimination of white phosphorus in the match industry has a complicated history. Thorpe and Tutton contributed to its elimination, but may have been credited with a greater role than they actually played. The problems were being addressed in many countries. For more, (Emsley, 2000), Chapter Six.

15. T. E. Thorpe, T. Oliver, and G. Cunningham, 'Report to the Secretary of State for the Home Department on the use of phosphorus in the manufacture of lucifer matches,' (London: HM Stationery Office, 1899).

16. In Britain the White Phosphorus Prohibition Act of 1908 came into effect on 1 January, 1910. To help with its enforcement, Thorpe wrote a paper on how to detect white phosphorus in matches, (Thorpe, 1909b).

17. (Thorpe and Rodger, 1889), (Thorpe and Hambly, 1889). For these experiments they had platinum apparatus made by Johnson Matthey. Another student who worked with Thorpe in this area, Walter Kirman, entered the college in 1886 and was appointed Thorpe's assistant in 1891.

18. A. E. H. Tutton, 'Memories of the college half a century ago,' *The Record*, December, 1936, pp. 42–45; quotation, 43: (ICL archives).

19. (Thorpe and Rodger, 1894) for Bakerian Lecture, 1 January, 1894. Rodger gave the lecture and, to that date, was the youngest person ever to have done so.

20. Thorpe's first eclipse expedition was to Sicily in 1870, the first of eight such expeditions organised by Lockyer. The boat they were sailing on from Naples to Catania hit a rock, but all made it to shore and the instruments were saved. However, clouds covered the sun at the time of the eclipse. On some of the later eclipse expeditions Thorpe collaborated with Sir William de Wiveleslie Abney FRS (1843–1920). Abney taught chemistry and photography at Chatham before retiring from the army in 1881. He began working in South Kensington at the same time as Thorpe, when appointed Director of Science in the Government Science and Art Department. Later he became assistant secretary to the Board of Education. Although a busy bureaucrat, Abney carried out scientific work in photography, and was a founder of infrared spectroscopy, (Morris, 2004). For a report of eclipse work carried out in Senegal, (Abney and Thorpe, 1896). They claim to have used methods similar to those they used in Grenada for the eclipse of 1886. As to the magnetic survey, Thorpe had carried out work of that kind too, notably with Arthur Rücker his colleague both at the Yorkshire College and at the RCS.

21. E. R. Roberts, 'A History of the Chemistry Department at Imperial College' (1963), p. 89. (ICL archives, typescript.)

22. For an obituary of Henry Chapman Jones (1854–1932), (Philip, 1933). Chapman Jones' notes on Frankland's lectures given in the academic year 1875–1876, and a transcribed laboratory notebook for the years 1889–1907, are held in the ICL archives. He wrote several books, including (Chapman Jones, 1881, 1895, 1898). His 1881 textbook went into many editions and sold well also in the United States. He was President of the Royal Photographic Society, 1912–1914, worked with W. de W. Abney on photographic procedures, and his 1895 book on the science of photography also went into many editions.

23. Frederick Bickel Guthrie (1861–1927) had a PhD from Marburg. He was a demonstrator, 1888–1890, before emigrating to Australia to become a

demonstrator under former RCC student, Archibald Liversidge (see Chapter Three), at the University of Sydney. Guthrie had a major career in Australia as an agricultural chemist.

24. (Armstrong, 1945). Edward Frankland Armstrong (1878–1945), named after Frankland and known as Frank, was the son of Henry Armstrong. A student under Thorpe, he later joined his father at the C&G. After working in Germany, and some further research with his father, he joined Huntley and Palmer and moved to Reading as their Chief Chemist in 1906; for his book on carbohydrate chemistry, (Armstrong, 1910). During WW1 he held a government contract for the manufacture of acetic acid and acetone by the catalytic oxidation of ethanol. From 1925 he was Managing Director of the British Dyestuffs Corporation, (Russell, 2004c), (Gibson and Hilditch, 1948).

25. ICL archives, KC\1–3; C. K. Ingold to Eldridge, 25 March, 1958. See also A. A. Eldridge, 'Diamond Jubilee Lecture' delivered to the Imperial College Chemical Society in 1956, (ICL archives, B\Eldridge; typescript). According to Eldridge, the lecture demonstrator, Sidney Young, claimed that Herbert Brereton Baker was the first professor to clean his own blackboards. As to Coppen, he had the misfortune to resemble the infamous poisoner, Dr. Crippen, and was given the nickname Crippen. (He was described by Kenneth Hickman as 'a wispy, undernourished little man with tobacco-coloured moustachios waxed to two beautiful upturned tips.' (Retrieved from http://solarsaddle.wordpress.com/2012/01/06/classic-kit-kenneth-charles-devereux-hickmans-molecular-alembic/) J. N. Lockyer acknowledged 'Mr. Coppen' for help with several astrophysical papers. Unhappy with working conditions at the college, Coppen tried to start a technicians' union, and for that lost his job; see, F. W. L. (Les) Croker's, memoir, incorporated in Bernard Atkinson, 'Department of Chemistry: Recent history, 1960–1989' (typescript on CD, ICL archives).

26. ICL archives; Reports of the NSS/RCS Div. III (chemistry) for the period 1885–1900.

27. Clarence Smith (1875–1945), briefly on the staff, gained his DSc in 1903 before moving to the East London Technical College. In 1915 he joined the Department of Explosives Supply. He was editor of the *J. Chem. Soc.*, 1924–1945, (Hewitt, 1946).

28. J. F. Thorpe was not related to T. E. Thorpe. However, there was a connection. The reason JFT went into chemistry was because he was unhappy as an engineering student at King's College. As mentioned, TET was a keen yachtsman. He spent much time sailing off the Devon coast, close to JFT's

family home. TET was a friend of JFT's father, a barrister, and advised him that his son could make a good career in chemistry. So, after two years as an engineering student, Jocelyn Thorpe turned to chemistry at which he was to excel. Roberts, *op. cit.* (21), p. 82.

29.   Some other students of the late 19th century: Robert E. Barnett, a student from 1890–1993, became principal of Leeds Technical School; John Samuel Strafford Brame (1871–1953), a student 1892–1996, and on the staff 1896–1997, was professor of chemistry at the Royal Naval College, Greenwich, 1914–1932. A specialist in petroleum chemistry, Brame was President of the Institute of Petroleum, 1921–1923, (Dunstan, 1954). William Burton (1863–1941), a student from 1885–1887, worked at the Wedgwood pottery and was later manager of Pilkington's Tile and Pottery Co. He contributed an entry on pottery and ceramics to the fourth edition of Thorpe's *Dictionary*. Charles Samuel Garland (1887–1960) was a student, 1905–1909, and demonstrator, 1909–1912. Active in college affairs, he founded a company that made equipment for the radio industry. For a short period he was MP for Islington. He joined the governing body of Imperial College in 1923 and was made FIC. William Godden (1884–1954) graduated in 1907 and became an assistant to the former RCC student, physician and physiologist, F. W. Pavy FRS (see Chapter Three). Godden's interests were biochemical and he became an expert in animal nutrition, (Cuthbertson,1956). Elizabeth G. Hagerty, a student from 1889–1992, became headmistress of the Higher Grade and Organized Science School, Cardiff. John T. Hewitt FRS (1868–1954), a student from 1884–1887, was professor of chemistry at the People's Palace Polytechnic, forerunner of the East London Technical College, later Queen Mary College, (Anon.,1946). George Thomas Holloway (1863–1917) entered the college in 1881, and was an assistant to both Frankland and Thorpe. He then worked in Newfoundland on mineral resources, returning to London to start a business as an analyst and assayist in Limehouse. In 1915 he was appointed Chairman of the Royal Ontario Nickel Commission. John Holmes (1871–1919) was a Student Assistant with whom Thorpe published several papers on measuring the quantity of methyl and ethyl alcohols in mixtures. Holmes devised a set of alcoholometric tables published in 1912. Sir Albert Howard, a student 1893–1896, was an Advisor on Agricultural Chemistry in India. Sir Thomas Kirke Rose, a student 1883–1887, was Chief Chemist and Assayer at the Royal Mint. Walter Henry Watson, a student 1891–1894, became head of the chemistry department at Portsmouth Municipal College.

30. ICL archives; KC\1 Eldridge, notes sent to Eldridge from Sidney Young, former student and lecture demonstrator. Moissan made solutions of potassium fluoride in hydrogen fluoride and isolated fluorine by electrolysis at sub-zero temperatures. He first isolated fluorine in 1886.

31. One former student reported that Newth had 'made the students' day' when one of his demonstrations got out of control and the lecture theatre windows were blown out. ICL archives, B\E. J. Wayland.

32. This was one of the old inns of chancery, phased out by the late 19th century. Many cases of lead poisoning had been reported and one of Thorpe's major concerns at the new laboratory was the elimination of lead from pottery glazes and paints. He also had to deal with food adulteration and other problems. He continued with his work on atomic weights, including the confirmation of Marie Curie's atomic weight of radium.

33. For Tilden, (Morris, *revised* 2004), (Forster, 1927), (Philip, 1928), (Hekke, 1976).

34. Tilden left a handwritten memoir (1917) of his life as a chemist to the Chemical Society; quotation, 4; RSC library.

35. Tilden's earliest papers show signs of his association with both pharmacy, and Hofmann's laboratory. They include papers on the constitution of aloes and the synthesis of derivatives of methylanthracene.

36. In his memoir (*op. cit.* 34), Tilden claims to have studied both French and German. Only one modern foreign language was required for matriculation.

37. (Forster, 1927), p. 3192.

38. (Pippard, 2002).

39. The preparation of the highly reactive and toxic NOCl was complicated and dangerous; (Tilden, 1874).

40. The name 'terpene' was coined by Kekulé for substances containing the isoprene unit, C_5H_8. For nitrosoterpenes see, for example, (Tilden, 1875), (Tilden and Shenstone, 1877). Oils extracted from pine tree resin (turpentine), juniper, sage, citrus fruit skins, caraway, bergamot, and other natural sources, were heated in iron tubes. This produced a range of hydrocarbons and much time was spent sorting out the terpenes. Examination of the nitrosochlorides allowed a major advance: the division of the terpenes into the 'orange' and 'turpentine' classes. Tilden made terpineol, $C_{10}H_{17}OH$, and the hydrocarbon $C_{18}H_{16}$, later shown to be dipentene. Noting that the essential oils of many plants have the formula $C_{10}H_{16}$, Tilden speculated that they were composed mainly of terpenes.

41. Tilden was a friend of Henry Armstrong and wrote several letters to him about his terpene work. In 1881 he wrote about the distillation of rubber, and theories of its constitution. He was distilling as many resins as he could get hold of, and was examining the resulting hydrocarbons. He asked Armstrong for some Russian turpentine. ICL archives, Armstrong papers, letters 556 and 561, Tilden to Armstrong, 7 March, 25 December, 1881.

42. (Tilden, 1884, 1892), quotation, 1892, 183. Isoprene, a liquid at room temperature, was discovered as a result of the destructive distillation of india rubber (caoutchouc) by the chemist C. H. Greville Williams in 1860. Williams found that isoprene had the same empirical formula as india rubber — but then so do many other compounds, (Williams, 1860). For Tilden's review of his work on the natural and artificial terpenes, (Tilden, 1888). Later, he stated that Perkin had examined his 1892 rubber samples, confirming that they were indeed rubber. The samples were exhibited at the BAAS meeting in York in 1906, and then deposited at the V&A Museum in South Kensington (The Science Museum was built later and took over the science-related materials from the V&A). (Tilden, *revised* S. Glasstone, 1936). Samples of Tilden's isoprene and rubber are held also at the Birmingham University archives. The sample of isoprene has degraded, but the rubber sample, labelled 'artificial rubber,' was analysed in 1997 and shown not to be polyisoprene, but the related poly(2,3-dimethyl butadiene) ('methyl rubber'), (Bate *et al.*, 1997). The London sample, presumably the original, has yet to be analysed.

43. Claim and quotation from Tilden's handwritten memoir (Note 34). That Tilden was invited to apply upset Henry Armstrong. The two were friends, but Armstrong had hoped to succeed Thorpe at the RCS. In a letter to Lockyer before the appointment, he wrote that he would apply if he were given a guarantee of being appointed, and that his salary would not be lower than the one he was receiving at the Central (£1000 per year). ICL archives, Armstrong papers, Armstrong to J. N. Lockyer, 30 March, 1894. Armstrong did not receive a guarantee and did not apply. In another letter to Frederick Abel he wrote, 'for some reason known to himself, Thorpe has been very antagonistic to me of late' and that he did not want him as his successor. Armstrong thought that this was because he had been openly critical of Thorpe for leaving some signed (but unfilled) Chemical Society cheques with one of his assistants while away on an eclipse expedition. ICL archives, Armstrong papers; letter to Sir F. A. Abel, 30 March, 1894.

44. Tilden included some of these plans in his book (Tilden, *revised* S. Glasstone, 1936). Sir Aston Webb also designed the RSM building and the Cromwell Road section of the V&A, (Dungavell, 2004). Tilden's son, the architect Philip Armstrong Tilden (1887–1956), was given the name Armstrong after his father's good friend. P. A. Tilden was a pupil of T. E. Collcutt, architect for the Imperial Institute. Its central tower is all that remains at IC's South Kensington campus. Philip Tilden later redesigned Churchill's country home, Chartwell, (Waymark, 2004). For the South Kensington buildings, (Forgan and Gooday, 1994, 1996).

45. This was one of the few college building sites sold by the Royal Commissioners (most are leased). The government paid £70,000, far below the valuation of £200,000. There was much debate over the use of the south side of the Imperial Institute (now Imperial College) Road. Many people wanted it for the Tate Gallery (see discussion in *Nature*, (Anon., 1892). Lord Kelvin, Lord Rayleigh, and other FRSs, successfully lobbied for the entire site surrounding the Imperial Institute to be devoted to scientific education.

46. Webb included a building at the north-eastern corner of the site. The ground floor was for a post office, and the upper floors for the Meteorological Office (located there until after WW2). *Reports of the Commissioners of the Exhibition of 1851* (8th Report, 1911, in ICL archives). The bookshop, run by Lamley and Co., was located in the RCS until the end of WW2 after which textbooks were sold at Lamley's in South Kensington until the late 1970s.

47. Many diagrams and slides were prepared by Margaret Reeks, daughter of an earlier registrar of the RSM. She began working for the RSM in 1893 but, after the formation of IC, worked also for the RCS. She had an office in the basement of the chemistry department and was still working there in the 1920s.

48. We suspect that this high ceiling was a response to the poor ventilation in the old building. After WW2 the laboratory was redesigned; see Chapter Eight.

49. (Morris, 2015), pp. 104–105.

50. The refectory moved to the new student union building.

51. The full list can be seen in RCS calendars of the period.

52. T. H. W. (Howell) Idris (1842–1925), was a Welshman, an MP, a London County Councillor, a Fellow of the Chemical Society, and a mineral water manufacturer. An Idris advertising slogan was 'I like Idris when I's dry'.

53. For the founding of the college, (Gay. 2007b). Geology was part of the RCS (though located in the RSM building), until 1966, when it joined the RSM.

54. The committee was appointed by IC's Governing Body. Its chairman, Sir John Wolfe Barry (1836–1918), was a civil engineer whose work included Tower Bridge and numerous docks. Asked to make suggestions for rationalising the resources of the three colleges, he recommended closing the C&G chemistry, physics and mathematics departments, and merging them with the RCS departments. For Barry, (McWilliam, 2004).

55. Roberts. *op. cit.* (21), p. 77. Tilden was not seriously harmed.

56. (Tilden and Perry, 1900). This work was related to testing the ideas of Dulong and Petit. Tilden, assisted by Sidney Young, used a Joly calorimeter for temperatures in the range of solid CO_2 to the boiling point of oxygen. His later papers, reporting work on gold, platinum, copper, iron, silver and aluminium, noted the influence of temperature on specific heats. John Perry (1850–1920) FRS was professor of mathematics and mechanics at the RCS (1896–1913). Like Tilden, though earlier, he had been a science master at Clifton College.

57. Ladysmith was relieved on 28 February, 1900 after a long siege, and the relief of Mafeking (now Mafikeng) was expected soon. On March 8th, the day of the Bakerian, Queen Victoria made a public appearance. ICL archives, McLeod diary, for report of the lecture.

58. Having been sent a buttery solid, a by-product in the manufacture of lime juice, Tilden showed that one of its constituents, limettin, was present also in lemon oil, and was identical to 4,6-dimethoxycoumarin, (Tilden and Burrows, 1902). Harry Burrows (1871–1911), a Hatton Prize winner, went to Heidelberg, gained a PhD under Karl von Auwers, and returned to the department as a demonstrator.

59. (Whitby, 1960). See also his 'Recollections of the Royal College of Science' (1958); typewritten manuscript, ICL archives; KC\1 Eldridge correspondence. Whitby mentions fellow students, N. S. Grace, chief chemist for Dunlop Tire and Rubber Goods Ltd. in Toronto; and Lancelot Owen, a Welshman with the 'gift of the gab' who spent much time on a soap box at Speakers Corner in Hyde Park. Owen was editor of the student magazine *Phoenix* and, during WW1, was stranded on Ocean Island in the Pacific, the site of a major phosphate mine. The only other European on the island was a German. After the war he made a career in the oil industry in Trinidad and Venezuela. For Owen, see also ICL archives B\Boswell, typewritten memoir, pp. 105–106. George Stafford Whitby (1887–1972) continued his

illustrious career in the United States where he carried out some pioneering studies on polymerisation.

60. Several students from this period found work in Malaya with the rubber industry; for example, Sydney Morgan who graduated in 1905. Whitby and Morgan worked alongside some RCS graduates in botany and zoology.

61. For Hibbert, (Wolfrom, 1958). Before coming to the RCS Hibbert studied chemistry in Manchester and then in Leipzig where he gained a PhD under Arthur Hantzsch. On leaving the department he worked for DuPont, returning to academic life first at Yale University and then as Professor of Industrial and Cellulose Chemistry at McGill. He was a major figure in cellulose chemistry as well as in the larger worlds of United States and Canadian science.

62. (Friend, 1914–1919); Briscoe contributed the much praised entry 'the inert gases' (in part II of volume I). Henry Vincent Aird Briscoe (1888–1961) was another former pupil at the City of London School. He returned to the department as Professor of Inorganic Chemistry in 1932 and is discussed further in the following chapters. For 'Dulong and Petit,' Roberts, *op. cit.* (21), 1980. Harry Frank Victor Little, known as Victor (nicknamed Petit), returned often to the college from the works at Ilford. He joined the IC Freemasons' lodge when it was founded in 1923.

63. Sir Martin Onslow Forster FRS (1872–1945), known as Onslow to his friends, was a student of Raphael Meldola at Finsbury Technical College. In 1892 he gained a PhD at Würzburg under Emil Fischer. He was Tilden's private assistant in Birmingham and came with him to London in 1894. However, his first year in London was at the C&G on a Salters Company fellowship working under Armstrong. One year later William Tate, who taught qualitative inorganic analysis at the RCS, resigned to take the chair of chemistry at the Bengal Civil Engineering College, and a position opened up. Forster was awarded the CS Longstaff Prize in 1915. (Simonsen *revised* Watson, 2004); obituaries, (Armstrong and Simonsen, 1945 and 1946).

64. In his memoir, (Whitby, 1960), Whitby states that when he was putting his own lectures together, he recognised that many of Forster's lectures were cribbed 'to the letter' from Victor Meyer, Paul Jacobson, *et al., Lehrbuch der organischen chemie* (Leipzig: Veit and Co., 1908). On a different topic, Forster wrote an article in *Phoenix* (1908–1909), pp. 5–8, on the Quebec tercentenary which could well have been cribbed from a Quebec nationalist.

65. ICL archives; KC\1 Eldridge; letter from Himus to Eldridge, 17 April, 1958. Perhaps Forster was emulating his mentor since Tilden was also remembered for his 'magnificent appearance.'

66. ICL archives, *RSC Journal* XVI (November, 1903), p. 35.
67. For work with Tilden see, for example, (Tilden and Forster, 1895).
68. Typescript, 'Complimentary dinner to Dr. M. O. Forster FRS, 11 December, 1913'; ICL archives B\Forster. For Philip and King, see notes (79) and (149) respectively.
69. British Dyes contracted out some work to universities, including IC.
70. For Morgan, (Irvine, *revised* Watson, 2004), (Irvine, 1941), (Wardlaw, 1941). The birth date given in Irvine's obituary is incorrect. Morgan was born in 1870 and was educated at the Central Foundation School on Cowper Street. A fellow pupil was William Pope (see below). Forster, two years younger, also attended the school, and all three moved on to Finsbury Technical College. While working at Read Holliday, Morgan made use of an autoclave and, on one occasion, made some phenol formaldehyde resin. Looking back, he said, 'I often think of the contents of that bottle which contained the potentialities of fortune.' He failed to recognise the resin's utility, something Leo Baekeland was to do a little later. Quotation in (Wardlaw, 1941). Two graduates of the IC department later worked for Bakelite Ltd. in the United Kingdom. G. W. Hodd who gained his ARCS in 1923 became Managing Director, and R. F. Hunter who gained his ARCS in 1929 became Research Manager. In 1907 Morgan was offered the chair of chemistry at the University of Sydney. At first he accepted but then changed his mind, (Morgan, 1939).
71. (Burstall, 1952). Micklethwait was educated at Swanley Horticultural College before entering the RCS in 1898. She left in 1918 for a job in Nottingham with Boots Pure Drug Co., returning to Swanley as Principal in 1921; for an example of her work with Morgan, (Morgan and Micklethwait, 1905). According to Morgan (Morgan,1939) about 14 senior students published papers with them, including W. R. Moore who left to work with ICI (Nobel Division), G. S. Whitby (see above), Arthur Clayton, W. O. Wootton, and Mary Alcock. The last two sadly died young. Clayton (1878–1954) was a student from 1903–1905, and on the staff, 1905–1910. He then joined the dye manufacturers Read Holliday and Sons before moving to the United States in 1920 to work for another dye manufacturer, Calco Chemicals, in New Jersey; for a short obituary, (Anon., 1955). A prize, named after Micklethwait, is awarded to the undergraduate who has shown outstanding performance for their degree and research project. For more on Micklethwait, Chapter Five.
72. Salvarsan (arsphenamine) was first used by Paul Ehrlich at around the same time. For Morgan and bactericides, ICL archives, *Annual Reports ICL*

(1910). Henry George Plimmer FRS (1856–1918) had studied under Pasteur. He was Director of the Cancer Laboratory at the Lister Institute and an outstanding microscopist. At the start of the war he was appointed professor of comparative pathology at IC — a personal chair endowed by a benefactor. For Plimmer, (Anon. 1918).

73. Morgan's parents were servants in a country house. His mother was a house maid whose name before her marriage was Corday. Morgan, thankful to his parents for helping him to get an education, made the bequest in their memory. Like some others in this story Morgan had to struggle to get an education and make his way in life. Morgan was interested in industrial chemistry and wrote a few books on the subject, for example (Morgan and Pratt, 1938).

74. Scholar teachers were research students who were given some teaching responsibilities. Martha Annie Whiteley studied chemistry at Royal Holloway College where she gained a BSc. She came to the RCS department in 1898, having taught science at Wimbledon High School for Girls for seven years, (Eldridge, 1957), (Creese, 1997), (Barrett, 2004), (Horrocks, 2011), (Rayner–Canham and Rayner–Canham, 2008), (Nicholson and Nicholson, 2012).

75. For example, (Whiteley, 1900), (Whiteley and Mountain, 1909). Harold Mountain died before this paper was read at the Chemical Society.

76. This was not the first such motion put to the Chemical Society. Vernon Harcourt proposed the admission of women in 1880 and there was a further attempt in the 1890s. In 1904 Marie Curie was given an honorary fellowship which may have prompted Whiteley's petition. Whiteley made another attempt in 1908, helped by Ida Smedley, then a research student at the C&GCTC. Smedley was the first woman to be granted full fellowship in 1920 and was on the Chemical Society's council (1931–1934). For more on Smedley see below.

77. When IC became part of the teaching University of London in 1929, assistant professors were given the university title of Reader.

78. James Philip, the son of a Church of Scotland minister, was a graduate of Aberdeen University in mathematics and natural philosophy. After deciding to study chemistry, he spent a further two years at the university with Francis Japp before moving to Göttingen where he gained a PhD under Walther Nernst. In 1897 he joined Armstrong at the C&GCTC, but spent time also at Cambridge with C. T. Heycock and F. H. Neville working on the structure of metal alloys. Philip wrote several books intended for children; for example, (Philip 1910). For Philip, (Egerton, 1942).

79. For textbooks, (Tilden, 1876, 1880,). His historical books include (Tilden, 1910, 1918).
80. (Tilden, 1909).
81. For Armstrong, (Wynne, 1937), (Rodd, 1940), (Keeble, 1941), (Rodd *revised* Brock, 2004). The Henry E. Armstrong Memorial Lecture was endowed in 1943 by some of Armstrong's children and the Society of Chemical Industry. John Vargas Eyre, a student, then demonstrator, at the Central moved with Armstrong to the RCS and later worked at Finsbury Technical College. For his biography of Armstrong, (Eyre, 1958); see also (Hartley, 1971). Ernest H. Rodd entered the Central in 1906 and worked with Armstrong on crystal morphology. He was Armstrong's assistant at the RCS and later worked for ICI Dyestuffs. He wrote a seminal series, *The Chemistry of Carbon Compounds* (a series known as 'Rodd' to countless students); the first edition appeared in 1951. For the second edition, (ed. Samuel Coffey), (Rodd, 1964). There were further editions. For an by obituary of Rodd, (Coffey, 1971). Armstrong's papers, including much correspondence and a list of his published papers, are in the ICL archives.
82. Armstrong was made a freeman of the Leathersellers in 1907.
83. (Rodd, 1940). Armstrong was interested in natural history and rural affairs and was a member of the management committee of the Rothamsted Experimental Station. A proponent of vitamins (advitants as they were then known), like Hofmann he advocated the study of plant chemistry for medical purposes.
84. (Keeble, 1941), p. 245.
85. Armstrong was the first to develop the quinonoid theory, (Armstrong, 1888).
86. (Keeble, 1941), pp. 232, 233.
87. Matthiessen committed suicide one year later (see Chapter Two), but Armstrong continued to work part-time at St. Bartholomew's for 12 years. He was paid £50 per year for lecturing to medical students.
88. For this and other details of Armstrong's early life, (Eyre, 1958). An earlier Professor at the London Institution, William Grove, left several of his (eponymous) electrochemical cells behind in the laboratory. These and Grove's memoirs sparked Armstrong's interest in electrochemistry.
89. (Armstrong, 1874). This organic chemistry textbook went into several editions. Armstrong and Charles Groves edited the organic section of Miller's textbook, (Miller, 1880).
90. Armstrong applied for the position at the Yorkshire College of Science taken by Thorpe. Thorpe later applied for the chair at the C&GCTC, won

by Armstrong. Armstrong also applied for the Jacksonian Chair at Cambridge but the position went to James Dewar. Dewar, six years older than Armstrong, was to become a close friend.

91. The lecture was on methods of teaching science, especially chemistry, (Eyre, 1958), p. 85. The building was designed by the architect Alfred Waterhouse. He had earlier designed the Natural History Museum.

92. For more on the Finsbury Technical College and the C&GCTC, (Gay, 2000b). Entrance by examination was unheard of in most technical colleges at that time. Matriculation examinations existed for university entrance, but those wishing to study science did not always need to take examinations in the sciences. They had, however, to pass examinations in other subjects, including mathematics and Latin. In a draft for an 1896 report on progress at the C&GCTC, Armstrong wrote that the college should not worry about the entrance examinations discouraging applicants. It was possible, he stated, to use discretion and admit those who were able even if they failed parts of the examination. As an aside he noted that the chemistry department at University College had no entrance exams and 'the number of "wasters" who enter ... [is] considerable'. ICL archives; Armstrong papers, 1st series, 203.

93. Armstrong wrote much on scientific and technical education, (Brock ed., 1973). This collection of Armstrong's essays has a fine introduction by Brock; see also (Brock ed., 1996), Chapters Seven and Nineteen. Armstrong played a significant role in developing the curriculum at Christ's Hospital School. He advised on the design of laboratories, and proposed that a farm and market garden be attached to the school — to supply both healthy food and sites for instruction. Armstrong's former student, Charles E. Browne, was senior science master at the school.

94. H. E. Armstrong, 'Personal notes on the origin and development of the chemical school at the Central,' *The Central,* V. 13, (1916), pp. 84–96; (copy in ICL archives).

95. Some examples of Armstrong students who were successful in industry: W. R. Woodbridge and A. J. Cook were sought-after specialists in the manufacture of Portland cement; F. F. Renwick, a specialist in photographic materials, was Chief Chemist at Ilford Ltd. Several entered the brewing industry, among them C. G. Jones and H. B. Mole. T. H. Pope became a demonstrator under Adrian Brown at the Birmingham School of Brewing, and, in 1927, was appointed Senior Chemist at the research department of the Distillers Company. Edmund C. Rossiter (1867–1937), with whom Armstrong published papers on the naphthalene series, was possibly the

first person to have produced urea formaldehyde resin. He worked for Albright and Wilson, becoming Chief Chemist at the company's offshoot, British Cyanide. S. S. Napper was chief chemist at Courtauld's Coventry works. Francis Howard Carr (1874–1969) was chief manufacturing chemist at Burroughs Wellcome, 1898–1912, and later chairman of British Drug Houses (later BDH Chemicals). He was on the governing body of IC from 1940–1965.

96. Fourth year students specialising in chemistry were mostly supported by scholarships donated by the Salters and Leathersellers Companies.

97. Armstrong speculated on the mechanics of the ring structure of benzene and came up with a centric formula not unlike the one suggested by A. von Baeyer, (Armstrong, 1887).

98. For Miers, (Tizard *revised* 2004), (Holland and Spencer, 1943). Henry Alexander Miers FRS (1858–1942) was educated at Eton and Trinity College, Oxford, where he studied mathematics, classics and science. He then studied crystallography and mineralogy in Germany, later finding work in the mineralogy department of the British Museum (Natural History) with Nevil Story Maskelyne. In 1895 he left both the museum and the C&GCTC, succeeding Maskelyne in the Waynflete chair of mineralogy at Oxford. He was elected FRS in 1896 and, in 1908, became principal of the University of London. In 1915 he was appointed Vice-Chancellor of the University of Manchester, and given a personal chair in crystallography.

99. William Barlow FRS (1845–1934) was educated at home. When he met Armstrong in 1888, he was a largely unrecognised prodigy and, with a private income, had no need for employment. Armstrong appreciated his mathematical ability and encouraged his scientific ambition. He introduced Barlow to Miers. Barlow made a major contribution to the geometrical theory of crystallography and was elected FRS in 1908, (Pope, 1934). Sir William Phipson Beale (1839–1922) was a baronet and, by profession, a barrister. As a young man he worked in his uncle's steelworks and became interested in chemistry. He attended some of Hofmann's lectures and spent some time in Bunsen's laboratory in Heidelberg. Many of his friends were chemists. Armstrong was an occasional guest at Beale's Scottish estate where he enjoyed the salmon fishing. Bernard James Harrington (1848–1907) was a Canadian with a BSc from McGill. He was the first recipient of the PhD degree in chemistry from Yale University, and was professor of chemistry and mineralogy at McGill. Harrington attended Miers' lectures as a Professor.

100. For Pope, (Gibson, 1941), (Gibson *revised* Watson, 2004), (Moody and Mills, 1941), (Mann, 1975). William Jackson Pope FRS (1858–1942) was a student at the Central Foundation School on Cowper Street School before moving to Finsbury Technical College where, contrary to (Gibson, 1941) he studied under Raphael Meldola (not Armstrong). He did not perform well in his final examinations, but was admitted to the Central on a Mitchell scholarship because Meldola wrote that he was exceptionally gifted. (For Pope's examination record, and Meldola's report, Guildhall Library, CGLI papers, Ms 21, p. 826; minutes of Board of Study, 1 October, 1887). Pope became one of Armstrong's closest friends, but his life was changed by Miers. In 1893 he applied for a position in the mineralogy department of the Natural History Museum (see ICL archives, Meldola papers, Pope to Meldola, 18 January, 1893). Perhaps luckily, he was not appointed, but crystallographic ideas informed his later work. Pope was awarded the CS Longstaff prize in 1900. According to G. T. Moody (see below), Pope belonged to the Garrick Club and had many friends in the theatre.

101. Kipping, quoted in (Moody and Mills, 1941). Miers devised an improved goniometer for measuring the angles of growing crystals, as well as one for work under the microscope.

102. (Pope, 1892, 1896), (Kipping and Pope, 1898). Assisting this work were students, S. J. Peachey, E. M. Rich and A. W. Harvey. Peachey and Harvey moved with Pope to the Goldsmiths' Institute and then to Manchester. Rich was later Senior Education Officer at the London County Council, and another voice for Armstrong's heuristic method. Pope and Peachey published several joint papers. For example, they prepared the first compound in which the centre of asymmetry was a sulphur atom; (Pope and Peachey, 1900). Peachey was appointed a Lecturer in Manchester. He was the father of the astrophysicist E. Margaret Burbidge.

103. (Brereton Evans, 1897). De Brereton Evans was educated at Cheltenham Ladies College, taking the London University BSc examinations from there. She enrolled at the C&GCTC as Armstrong's research student and was a proponent of his educational ideas, (Brereton Evans, 1898). Later she joined William Ramsay's research team at University College and signed Martha Whiteley's petition to have women admitted to the Chemical Society.

104. (Rodd, 1940), p. 1429.

105. See, for example, (Armstrong and Pope, 1891). Sobrerol (in the title of this paper) was named for the former Liebig student, Ascanio Sobrero, who discovered that terpenes exposed to sunlight formed solids.

106. (Barlow and Pope, 1906).

107. The selection committee for the appointment at Cambridge included Thorpe, Tilden and W. H. Perkin Jr. ICL archives; Meldola papers, Pope to Meldola, 3 July, 1908. Meldola was one of Pope's referees.

108. Pope allowed much war work to be carried out in Cambridge. After hearing of the German gas attacks he synthesised mustard gas to see how it could be countered or protected against. As we will see in the following chapter, parallel (and coordinated) work was carried out at IC.

109. For Martin Lowry FRS (1874–1936), (Pope, 1938), Russell (2004d). Lowry was a serious Methodist and lay preacher.

110. See, for example, (Armstrong and Lowry, 1902). The sulfonic acid of camphor was first prepared by A. Reychler.

111. In this connection Lowry carried out some work with an amateur chemist who worked in the department in his spare time. Sir William Robert Bousfield was a Cambridge educated lawyer and MP. Armstrong communicated one of their papers to the Royal Society, (Bousfield and Lowry, 1905).

112. For the ideas of Lowry and Lapworth, (Nye, 1993), pp. 173–177. Armstrong was dismissive of Lowry's view that crystals of sodium chloride did not contain NaCl molecules but were simply geometrical arrangements of sodium and chlorine ions. Lowry's progressive view, shared later by Lawrence Bragg, was one of many new physical ideas with which Armstrong took issue. See his letter to *Nature* (Armstrong, 1927b), p. 478 in which he wrote, 'it's time chemists took charge of chemistry once more'.

113. Linstead, quoted in Roberts, *op. cit.* (21), p. 77. For the dining club, (Gay and Gay, 1997).

114. (Armstrong, 1895); this presidential address is interesting and ranges widely over problems current at the time. Armstrong wrote two essays (Armstrong, 1909) and, in a humorous way, he tried to make a case against ionisation. He gave the name 'hydrone' to a single water molecule, H_2O, and speculated that it combined with HCl such that the oxygen atom formed two separate bonds with the HCl, one with the hydrogen, the other with the chlorine atom.

115. (Eyre, 1958), pp. 138, 139. Armstrong believed that solution was a manifestation of chemical activity. At the time there was debate over the role of water and whether it was an active agent. H. B. Dixon and H. B. Baker both held views similar to Armstrong's for a time. Armstrong published a series of over 30 papers with the general title, 'Studies of the processes operative in solutions' in *Proc. Roy. Soc.* between 1906–1914. Frederick P. Worley

was his student and co-author for some of these; he also wrote several of his own papers in a similar vein. Worley was later professor of chemistry in Auckland. Quotation about Robinson's bent arrows, Roberts, *op. cit.* (21), p. 77.

116. Armstrong was on good terms with Thorpe (but see Note 43). They did not publish together but cooperated in South Kensington. Thorpe, who never married, enjoyed entertaining Armstrong's children on his yacht. Edith Armstrong met the chemist Stephen Miall at one of Thorpe's yachting parties and they later married.

117. (Armstrong, 1944). Moody's few publications were on the controversial topic of the rusting of iron. He gained a DSc from the University of London by examination — examination was the norm (not rule) until the introduction of the PhD (see Note 128 below). Moody left chemistry for the City in 1907 and became a director of several investment trusts. He managed his mother's finances, made a fortune, and left a substantial sum to the Worshipful Company of Dyers for the construction of housing for old people connected to the dyeing trades. He was elected Prime Warden of the Dyers Company in 1936 and served on the Delegacy, part of the IC governing body devoted to the interests of the C&G college. Quotation on dances, *The Central*, 4 (1907), p. 153 (ICL archives).

118. See Note 93.

119. ICL archives, B\Whiteley.

120. (Gregory, 1949). William Mayhowe Heller (1868–1949) became Senior Inspector of Technical and Scientific Education in the Irish Free State. Armstrong was a founder of section L of the BAAS in 1901. It was devoted to 'educational science,' and Heller was active in it. For more on Heller, and on Armstrong's heuristic method of science instruction in Ireland, see Julianne Gallagher, 'Elementary science in Irish primary schools from the late 1800s to the present day,' MSc thesis, Dublin City University, 2007; also Note 93.

121. For Smedley, (Creese, 2004). Smedley married a professor of medicine, took his name (Maclean) and turned toward biochemical research. She became an expert in fat metabolism; (Maclean, 1943).

122. For Wynne, (Rodd 1951 and 1951b). After gaining his ARCS and BSc, Wynne worked for a year as a lecturer at Rutherford College, Newcastle-upon-Tyne before joining Armstrong at the C&GCTC. In 1897, he succeeded Groves as editor of *J. Chem. Soc.* In 1902 Gilbert Morgan took over as editor.

123. Much of their work was presented to the Chemical Society in series of short papers on the mono-, di- and tri- derivatives of naphthalene. See the *Proceedings*, from the late 1880s to the early 1900s.

124. According to (Rodd, 1951 and 1951b) there were 460 specimens in the original Cambridge collection, but only 263 came to IC. Some of the samples have been examined to see whether they were classified correctly. On the whole they were and, as Henry Rzepa remarked, this was just as well given the many dye patents that relied on the classifications; Retrieved from http://www.ch.imperial.ac.uk/rzepa/blog/.

125. For Forster, (Armstrong and Simonsen, 1945, 1946).

126. For an early paper, (Forster, 1896). Like Armstrong, Forster published a few long series of papers. They included, for example, (Forster and Micklethwait, 1902) and (Forster and Fierz, 1905).

127. His assistant, J. C. Withers, lost several fingers in an explosion and the work was brought to an end. Eldridge lecture, *op. cit.* (25), p. 3.

128. For Frederick Stanley Kipping FRS (1863–1949), (Challenger, 1950–1951), (Challenger, 1951), (Kopperl, 1973) and (Challenger *rev* Shorter, 2004). The date given in the latter for when Kipping went to the C&GCTC is incorrect. It should be 1890 not 1900. In 1887 Kipping was the first person to gain a DSc from the University of London on the basis of research papers, a pattern that gradually became the norm for the DSc (few candidates) after the introduction of the PhD in 1920.

129. (Perkin Jr. and Kipping, 1894). Pioneering work that Kipping began in Munich contributed to his becoming FRS already in 1897. His first publication was selected for mention in his FRS certificate, (Kipping, 1888). He continued this line of synthetic work with Perkin in Edinburgh, focussing especially on the preparation of aromatic ketones.

130. Kipping, quoted in (Challenger, 1951), p. 854.

131. (Challenger, 1951), p. 855.

132. (Challenger, 1951), p. 862.

133. For Arthur Lapworth FRS (1872–1941), (Robinson, 1947), (Coley *revised* 2004), (Farrar, 1973).

134. Quotation, (Robinson 1947), p. 555. Kipping lived close to the college at 7 Milborne Grove in South Kensington. His home was a popular meeting place for chemists from the RCS and the C&GCTC.

135. Lapworth outlined his ideas in a paper, 'The constitution of camphor' presented to Section B of the BAAS meeting in Bradford, 1900. See also (Kauffman, 1983).

136. Herbert McLeod was one of Lapworth's DSc examiners. In connection with the exam, McLeod wrote in his diary that Lapworth, 'is a sharp fellow but careless.' Armstrong, fearing that Lapworth would be failed, wrote a couple of strong letters in his defence. McLeod wrote that these were unnecessary since he and the other examiner were not intending to fail Lapworth. ICL archives, McLeod diary, 18–26 June, 1895.

137. In Nottingham Kipping developed his interest in silicon-organic compounds and prepared forerunners to the polymeric silicones. He was awarded the Longstaff Medal in 1909.

138. According to the Nernst–Thomson rule, the greater the dielectric constant, the greater the ionising power of the solvent.

139. Robinson, quoted in (Eyre, 1958), p. 9. Robinson was a research student of W. H. Perkin Jr. in Manchester. He claimed to have learned organic chemistry from Perkin's research assistant, Jocelyn Thorpe. According to Robinson's obituarists, Lapworth had a major impact on his thinking, having brought crystallographic and physical chemistry ideas to Manchester when he moved there as senior lecturer in inorganic and physical chemistry. (Lapworth's first research student in Manchester was J. R. Partington.) For Robinson, (Todd and Cornforth, 1976).

140. For a good description of this banquet held at the Cecil Hotel, (Eyre, 1958), pp. 168, 169. W. J. Pope presided and there was a distinguished guest list of 238 people.

141. Armstrong received his salary for another three years until all his students had graduated.

142. For Bramley, (Philip, 1935). Bramley, born in Yorkshire, became a mill worker at age 15. He had to support his mother and the younger children in the family. He took evening classes at Halifax Technical College and also taught there for some years. At the age of 28 he won a national scholarship to the RCS. He worked with Philip until 1919 and was later appointed head of the department of pure and applied science at Loughborough College.

143. For a discussion of this dispute, and quotation, see ICL archives, *Phoenix* (1910–1911), p. 119. Many outraged students wrote angry letters to the editor; one wrote 'the fact that Sir Edward Thorpe will not trust his own students is an amazing admission of the bankruptcy of the teaching in his department,' 155. One external student appointed as a demonstrator in 1910, Hugh Griffiths (1891–1954), moved to work for Nobel's Explosives Co. in the war. He was elected President of the Institution of Chemical Engineers in 1945; for a brief obituary (Donald, 1954). Another outsider was Oscar Lisle Brady (1890–1968), a graduate of the University of the

Cape of Good Hope who came to IC in 1912 as a research student and demonstrator. During much of the war he worked at the Royal Arsenal, Woolwich, returning to the department briefly in 1919 before moving to UCL as a lecturer in organic chemistry. Later he was a consultant to the Windmill Theatre in Soho, and known by the Windmill girls as 'Uncle Oscar,' (Ingold, 1968).

144. Briscoe, quoted in an unsigned memoir dated 17.04.1959. (We think the author was Geoffrey Wilkinson). Copy in ICL archives B\Briscoe.

145. As noted, Thorpe carried out such work earlier. Thorpe was an inaugural member of the International Committee on Atomic Weights in 1902. Briscoe followed him on subsequent international committees. Briscoe had published earlier with the organic chemist, P. W. Robertson (Mare, 1969) but when Thorpe returned to the department, he moved toward inorganic chemistry.

146. Eldridge lecture, *op. cit.* (25), p. 2.

147. (Mare, 1969).

148. For Haworth, (Bircumshaw *revised* Horrocks, 2004), (Kopperl, 1972), (Halton, 2015). The rank of senior demonstrator was dropped in 1930 and was replaced by a new rank, assistant lecturer. Haworth was to succeed Gilbert Morgan as professor of chemistry at the University of Birmingham. He was a specialist in carbohydrate chemistry and paved the way to the synthesis of vitamin C for which he was awarded the Nobel Prize in 1937. He was elected FRS in 1928, was president of the Chemical Society, 1944–1946 and, in 1968, the CS established the Haworth memorial lectureship in his memory. For the claim that Haworth and King were not given research space, Eldridge lecture, *op. cit.* (25). However, Haworth and King did publish one paper while in the department, (Haworth and King, 1912).

149. Albert Theodore King (1865–1939) worked in J. F. Thorpe's 'drugs factory' during WW1, (Chapter Five). He was given a lectureship in inorganic chemistry in 1920, but left one year late to become chief chemist at the Wool Research Association, and was later Professor at Leeds, (Burrit, 1939). Three undergraduates of note in this period: J. A. Hanley (1907–1911), professor of agricultural chemistry at King's College, Newcastle, F. M. Potter OBE (1910–1913), Director of Scottish Tar Distillers, and B. B. Dey (1911–1915), Director of the Central Electrochemical Institute in Madras.

150. Like Tilden earlier, William Bone, the head of chemical technology, had to work with the architect Aston Webb. Bone, a proud no-nonsense Teessider, hated Webb's designs for the RSM and RCS, and claimed that too much

money had been spent on elegant frontages. In 1914 he got what he wanted — a plain box-like two-storey building. Two further storeys were added later and the building was accessed by a bridge from Prince Consort Road. The bridge has long gone, but the building, named after Bone, still stands.

151. For Bone, (Finch and Egerton, 1938), (Egerton *revised* Watson, 2004). Bone was educated at Manchester University and was a research student under H. B. Dixon. He built an important fuel technology section within his department at IC.

152. Finch, an Australian educated at the ETH in Zurich, was appointed Professor of Applied Physical Chemistry in 1936. He pioneered the use of oxygen by mountaineers during an expedition to Mount Everest in 1924, (Finch, 1924). See also (Osborne, 2004) and (Blackman, 1972). Geoffrey Wilfred Himus (1894–1964) ran the coal and fuel laboratory in the RCS basement. The department has had several names since its beginning as a sub-department of the chemistry department. M. de Reuck, 'History of the department of chemical engineering and chemical technology' (typescript in ICL archives).

153. (Hoblyn *rev*, 2004). John W. Hinchley (1871–1931) founded the student Chemical Engineering Society. Its first president, H. A. Humphrey, later designed the Billingham works for ICI. Hinchley's widow wrote a short biography: Edith Hinchley, *John William Hinchley, chemical engineer*. It was privately printed by Lamley and Co. in 1935. Copy in ICL archives.

154. CGLI, Ms 21,868/8; memorandum addressed to Mr. Soper of the CGLI, 12 June, 1889. The row over examinations is discussed in *The Times*, 23 February, 1910. Many on the University senate would have cringed at the mention of the word 'works.'

155. Among the RCC/RSM/RCS/C&GCTC contributors to the first, 1890, volume were: C. O'Sullivan, R. Warington, W. H. Perkin jr., R. Meldola, W. C. Roberts Austen, F. R. Japp, A. E. H. Tutton, and W. P. Wynne. A second five-volume edition was published between 1916–1919. For this Thorpe received editorial help from Briscoe and Whiteley. They and other department members, notably Philip, were also contributors. Thorpe was working on a third edition at the time of his death in 1925. The editorship was then taken over by Henry Foster Morley. The first two volumes of this edition appeared in 1927–1930, and later ones in 1934–1935. They were published simultaneously in Britain and the United States.

156. After her home in Roland Gardens was bombed in 1940, Whiteley moved all the papers connected to the *Dictionary* to Cambridge. After the war she was helped by an editorial board that included I. M. Heilbron, H. J.

Eméleus and, from outside the department, Alexander Todd, (Thorpe *et al.*, 1941–1956).

157. Baker wrote to the Rector that Forster was a man of 'considerable private means' and that he had spent about £200 a year of his own money on equipment and support for research students. J. F. Thorpe, he wrote, cannot be expected to do the same. He asked the college to supplement Thorpe's Royal Society grant (£60) with an additional grant of £50. (Rector's correspondence, 17 February, 1914).

158. Samuel Sugden FRS (1892–1950) joined the department as a student in 1912. He was the Hatton prize winner in 1914 and, during the war, worked at the Woolwich Arsenal. He was later professor of physical chemistry at Birkbeck College, and then at University College, (Sutton, 1951). Pollard will be discussed in later chapters.

Chapter Five

The Department During the First World War

5.1 Herbert Brereton Baker

Herbert Brereton Baker FRS (1862–1935) became the head of department in 1912 and was to lead the departmental war effort.[1] His father, an Anglican curate, was determined that Herbert and his brother Charles would go to Oxford. Fearing that they would not win scholarships in the classics, he moved them from Blackburn Grammar School to Manchester Grammar School where they were taught by the renowned science teacher, Francis Jones. The move turned out well and both sons won scholarships in the natural sciences. On graduating they became science masters, Charles Baker at Shrewsbury School and his younger brother, Herbert, at Dulwich College. At Balliol, Herbert Baker's chemistry tutor was Harold Baily Dixon from whom he learned the experimental skills for which he later became known. Among other things Baker was an excellent glass-blower, and he knew how to dry gases. Indeed, extreme drying became his speciality — obsession one could say — and the effect of moisture on chemical change was a topic that engaged him throughout his life. Already at Oxford, he managed to impress others. When Henry Roscoe paid a visit to the Balliol laboratory, he was astonished when Baker demonstrated the distillation of phosphorus in dry oxygen. It proceeded uneventfully, unlike a similar distillation using damp oxygen. Three years later he published a paper on the subject.[2]

Baker taught at Dulwich College from 1884–1901, where he continued his research on the effects of drying.[3] He was elected Fellow of Royal Society (FRS) in 1902. In 1903, after a year as headmaster of Alleyn's School (affiliated to Dulwich College), he was appointed Lee's Reader at Oxford and began work on the atomic weight of tellurium. It was to bring him much attention.[4] At Oxford he also carried out experiments on the oxides of nitrogen together with his wife, Muriel Baker (1875–1944). She, too, had studied chemistry at Oxford.[5] When Baker moved to Imperial College (IC) in 1912, they continued to work together in a laboratory at their home at Gerrards Cross. In the same year he was awarded the Chemical Society's Longstaff Medal. At IC Baker was popular with students, though behind his back they referred to him as Dry Baker and His Royal Dryness.

5.2 The Department During the First World War

When war was declared many students volunteered for military or other types of service. Enrolment dropped in 1914 but, when conscription was introduced in 1916, the number of students plummeted to about six in the first and ten in the second year. Several of the technical staff volunteered to work in munitions factories, and some of the academic staff joined the army. Perhaps they were inspired by the college Rector, Sir Alfred Keogh, who became Chief Commissioner of the Red Cross Society in 1914 and, shortly after, agreed to Lord Kitchener's request that he rejoin the army as Director-General of the Army Medical Services.[6] The students and staff remaining in the department joined the war effort in ways that are described here.[7]

The First World War (WW1) has been called 'the chemists' war' because it saw the first time use of chemical weapons on a large scale. Then, as now, the use of such weapons was viewed with horror. The number of soldiers killed or seriously injured by chlorine as a result of its use at Ypres in April and May, 1915, was a great shock.[8] In 1917 William Pope stated, 'the unhappy events of the last two years have given rise to a widespread belief that the science of Chemistry is largely responsible for the accentuation of the horrors associated with war.' In his view scientists were not responsible for the consequences of their discoveries, but he recognised that chemistry, 'so potent an agent for good becomes a powerful weapon in war.' As Pope also wrote, once war was declared 'practically every chemical technologist and every academic chemist in the country' contributed to the war effort.[9] Our discussion begins with departmental work on poison gases and then moves to some other topics.[10]

Early in April 1915, British intelligence reported that Germany was planning an imminent attack with poison gas. It was rumoured that the gas was either arsine or arsenic trichloride. Baker and Jocelyn Thorpe were summoned to meet Keogh at the War Office. Baker advised Keogh that the use of arsenic gases was unlikely since, in his view, they could not be released safely by hand and, if delivered by shells, they would decompose when the shells exploded. Further, he claimed, the gases would not spread well.[11] Nonetheless he agreed to ask members of his department to design a respirator that could protect against them. A model for arsine was constructed using cloth soaked in silver nitrate and work on it was proceeding when Baker was summoned back to the War Office on the 28 April, 1915. News had reached London of an actual gas attack, begun on the 22nd.[12] Lord Kitchener ordered Baker and J. S. Haldane to rush to the Front to investigate.[13] Members of the department were asked to evacuate glass globes, pack them, and send them to the army headquarters at St. Omer with instructions on how to collect gas samples. A few weeks later a group of about 20, mainly junior members of staff and research students, went to the front to act as temporary instructors in the defence against gas attacks, and to show soldiers how to use and look after their respirators.[14]

Baker's account of his journey to the Front is interesting. Neither he nor Haldane had passports; both were fingerprinted and travelled with officially stamped copies. Baker described the complicated manoeuvres required to exit Dover Harbour which was netted and boomed so as to catch enemy submarines. On reaching Dunkirk, they were driven to army headquarters at St. Omer where they were given a description of the gas. It was greenish, and floated above the ground to a height of about 1–1.5 m. and had progressed toward the Canadian troops at 3.7 m/sec. Baker immediately suspected chlorine, though because the gas remained low-lying for some time, he wondered whether it included also something denser.[15]

One of the first things that Baker did was to ask for Bernard Mouat Jones to be taken out of the trenches and given the job of assisting him in the gas inquiries.[16] Jones appeared the next day wearing a kilt (he had enlisted as a private in the London Scottish regiment). Haldane stayed in St. Omer carrying out postmortems on gassed soldiers whose bodies had been brought there from the front, while Baker and Jones were driven by ambulance across the border to a nursing station near the front at Ypres where some of the Canadian survivors were being treated. Baker interviewed a soldier who 'gave a full account of how the cloud of gas came, how the French territorials ran away and how the Canadians ... had stuck it out. He was [in] very bad [shape] ... [and] was a hero if ever there was one'. Baker also noted young children playing outside the nursing station, seemingly oblivious to the dangers nearby. Baker and Jones gathered verbal evidence from the survivors, and medical evidence from the staff. They cut some tarnished metal buttons off the Canadian uniforms for analysis, and smelled the uniforms for evidence of chlorine. On their return, Haldane listened to what they had to say before returning to London to report to Prime Minister Asquith. Sir Arthur Sloggett, Director of Medical Services on the Western Front, commandeered the laboratory of a lycée in St. Omer and further testing began. Baker asked that Jones be kept in the laboratory, suggesting he be made an officer so as to avoid night-time curfews. Sloggett replied 'Oh, you want a commission for him, do you? We'll make him a general if you like'. Jones was made a captain. Shortly after, Keogh appointed another IC scientist, William Watson, as Director of what was named the Central Laboratory at GHQ. Jones was appointed assistant director. Watson, an assistant professor in the physics department, inspired by the Royal College of Science's (RCSs) fire extinguishers, came up with an idea for their use as a defence against gas warfare. He was given the rank of Lt. Colonel and was later made CMG. Sadly, exposure to poison gases led to his premature death in 1919.[17]

Baker and Jones analysed material scraped from the tarnished buttons, and confirmed that the gas was chlorine, though Baker wondered whether some phosgene might also have been used. The two men set to work devising some temporary respirators using 'washing soda, hypo, and glycerine.'[18] Baker soon returned to London to work on a respirator that could be mass-produced, while Jones remained in France to monitor future attacks and to test for the gases used. He witnessed Britain's use of both chlorine and lachrymators at Loos and Auchy in September 1915.[19] Jones was not only Baker's junior colleague in the chemistry department, he had been his pupil at Dulwich College.[20] It is therefore not surprising, that in their subsequent correspondence Baker displayed paternal concern, frequently warning Jones not to expose himself to high concentrations of gas.[21] Theirs is an interesting correspondence which includes Baker's descriptions of some experiments carried out in the chemistry department's trench warfare unit. Trenches were dug both behind the department in South Kensington, and more extensively at the recently opened Royal Engineers Experimental Station at Porton Down, Wiltshire. Animals were tested to see how they fared when attacked by chlorine and other gases. Some pigs were fitted with experimental respirator helmets and, overall, fared better than sheep and dogs. This was the case even without the helmets, since they buried their snouts in the soil — some were able to dig fast and bury almost their entire bodies.[22]

On his return from France, and in line with Kitchener's request, Baker made the chemical aspects of gas mask design a priority in the department, focussing especially on protection against chlorine and phosgene. The Ministry of Munitions equipped a laboratory in the department with the help of Sir George Beilby, the managing director of the Castner-Kellner Co. and a member of the Admiralty's Board of Inventions and Research. The laboratory, which after the war was converted into an agricultural chemistry laboratory, was used in part for the analysis of spent German shell fragments so as to detect the gases being used. In his diary, Baker gleefully noted that Kitchener told him that he had discussed respirators with Haldane, complaining that Haldane was 'too philosophical.' 'You are the sort of man I want,' he said.[23] Work on the respirators entailed measuring the rate of penetration of chlorine, phosgene and other gases through various fabrics soaked in chemical solutions and then dried out. Initially flannelette was the favoured fabric and the early respirators were basically bags made from chemically impregnated flannelette and fitted with celluloid windows. When using the masks, soldiers were told to dampen them down so as to increase protection against chlorine.

James Philip, the professor of physical chemistry, worked on increasing the absorptive properties of activated charcoal. He showed that plant charcoal was a better absorbent than animal charcoal, and was the first to design a box mask with a wood charcoal filter.[24] The small box respirator, widely used later in the war, was based on his work. Oscar Brady, a demonstrator at the time, remembered being put to work testing the structural soundness of the various designs. He and others ran up and down the corridors to see whether they could breathe easily while wearing the flannelette bags and other prototype masks. He also noted evacuating and sealing glass globes to be sent to the front for the collection of gas samples.[25] Arthur Eldridge remembered Vincent Briscoe putting his excellent glass-blowing skills to use in making the globes.[26]

An early respirator designed for chlorine and phosgene was in part due to Muriel Baker. She cut up women's stockings and black veiling (the kind that Edwardian women wore to funerals) and wrapped the material around cotton waste that had been soaked in concentrated solutions of sodium carbonate, sodium phenate (today sodium phenoxide) and hypo, and then dried.[27] The veiling package seemed to work well and was made into a face mask attached to a helmet designed in France by Jones, Watson, and Cluny MacPherson, a medical officer in the Newfoundland regiment. The helmet had a tube valve to keep the expired CO_2 from reacting with the phenate, and was fitted with goggles to protect against tear gas. Baker was asked to personally test the new respirator in front of army personnel at the Royal Army Medical College at Millbank (RAMCM).[28] Haldane did not like the new model and claimed that one of the older respirators worked better. He was asked to test it alongside what became known as the Newfoundland helmet. Both men entered a gas chamber filled with air and some chlorine. In his diary, Baker proudly noted that Haldane:

> *retired in four minutes and had not stopped coughing when I came out twenty minutes later. The helmet was a bit stuffy but no chlorine came through ... [But] Haldane, intent on crabbing it, said no one could move in it, so I ran up and down the passage with it on. I must confess I was a bit pumped but I made as light of it as possible.*[29]

The army decided to test the Baker/Newfoundland model in the field and soon asked for it to be mass-produced. In his diary Baker later noted that it performed successfully, and that it had saved many lives. As to phosgene, it was used by the French and British as well as by the German armies. One student in the department, Alexander Barclay, a future keeper of chemistry and photography at the Science Museum, joined the army in 1916 and was posted to the Royal Engineers Special Brigade (the Gas Corps). He wrote that, when in France, he and others 'let off phosgene in cylinders in a rather primitive way when the wind was right' and that getting to the front line was difficult and that he often fell 'through wet and rotten duckboard.'[30]

Early in 1916 Baker became worried about arsine since traces were said to have been found in some spent enemy shells. Shell fragments brought to the department showed no evidence of arsine. Nonetheless, Baker asked his research students, James Sugden, John Dowdall and John Ross to experiment with the liquefaction of arsine and to seal some in steel tubes.[31] This work was carried out on a cart located outdoors, behind the department. When Baker went to observe what was going on, he found:

> *a tube lying on the ground for every passerby to go and smell. There was supposed to be 10 cc of liquid in it, and if it had exploded it might have done considerable damage. We took it up on the roof and put it in a bucket of water. Bubbles came out showing it was leaking.*[32]

While no arsine was found in German shells, mustard gas was detected. Its properties, how to detect it, and how to counter it, then became a serious research project in the department — as it did under Pope at Cambridge and Perkin in Manchester.[33] Frances Micklethwait worked on mustard gas both as chemist and guinea pig. Eldridge remembered her and her coworkers 'popping into the corridor every now and then to see how the experimental blisters on their arms were getting on.'[34] One of her coworkers was Christopher Ingold, then a research student under Jocelyn Thorpe. Ingold spent much of the war on poison gas research and, early in 1918, was sent to the Cassel Cyanide Company in Glasgow to run an industrial plant for the manufacture of the SK lachrymator.[35] After the war he returned to the college as a demonstrator in industrial chemistry. He is discussed further in Chapter Six.

In May 1916, Baker was asked to meet King George V, who was coming to inspect work at the RAMCM. Also present were Keogh, Sir David

Bruce (the famous microbiologist who was the college commandant), and some other senior army officers. Baker was asked to explain the research being carried out on respirators. At the time it was feared that respirators would be needed also for civilians. Some conventional bombs had been dropped during Zeppelin raids and civilians had been killed. William Ramsay alarmed the authorities by stating that large numbers of Londoners would be killed were there to be an aerial gas attack. Baker was sceptical. He had supervised some experiments in the marshes at Shoeburyness during which different gas bombs were dropped from towers, and gas shells were fired from guns. Most of the gases were either destroyed or dispersed quickly. Baker told the King about this, and explained what was being done at IC. The Prince of Wales who accompanied his father seemed rather bored so, to liven things up, Baker demonstrated the effect of the lachrymator SK on the willing prince — 'just enough to make him weep.'[36]

Until he was killed in 1916, Kitchener kept asking for different types of respirator. New models were tested at Porton Down and gas attacks were staged on Salisbury Plain. Baker's diary entry for 16 April, 1916 describes a visit to Porton made together with William Pope, Jocelyn Thorpe and Percy Frankland. Before giving advice, they watched different types of shells being filled with different gases. They observed the shells exploding and how the military guinea pigs, some on the open plain, others in trenches, fared in their various gas masks. They also noted the methods used to sample the air after the explosions. Baker's student, James Sugden, spent time at Porton, collecting gas samples after test explosions. Further experiments in dropping shells from an airship were carried out at an air station at Hoo in Suffolk. Baker noted that on one occasion some of the shells fell 'too close for comfort.'[37]

Jocelyn Thorpe was appointed to the chair of organic chemistry in 1914. Like Baker, Thorpe was a member of the Ministry of Munitions trench warfare committee. He was made Director of both the Chemical Laboratory at Porton Down and of a small trench warfare unit at IC. After looking at some of the trenches being dug in France, Thorpe had similar ones dug at Porton, and two also behind the chemistry department in South Kensington. A small laboratory was built next to them for gas analysis. With so many other duties, Thorpe delegated leadership of the college unit to Martha Whiteley. Under her direction people worked on small prototypes of the larger-scale experiments conducted on Salisbury Plain. Gases were synthesised in the college laboratories, and experiments were carried out on how best to fill shells and hand grenades with gases under pressure (some of them liquefied). The grenades were then thrown near the college trenches. Gas dispersion through the air and in the trenches was monitored. Different respirators were tested and, as mentioned, animals were used in some of the experiments. Martin Lowry returned to the department to work with the unit during the war. He became expert in filling shells and was much consulted by the army. The most widely used gas prepared in the department was the lachrymator SK, already mentioned.[38] Martha Whiteley's procedure for making this gas was used in industrial production. When news of her activities reached the press, she was labelled 'the woman who makes the Germans weep.'[39]

Whiteley was also involved in developing various incendiary mixtures to be used for flares or smoke bombs. When Kenneth Hickman graduated in 1916, he was employed by the government to work on flares, at first under Whiteley. He described an experimental flare bomb, made of magnesium ophorite (a mixture of potassium perchlorate and magnesium), that he was instructed to take to the airbase at Orfordness. He was taken up in an airplane with an open cockpit, with instructions to light the fuse and heave the bomb overboard. Exhausted and scared, he forgot the further instruction — to observe the result. On Thorpe's advice the government set up an experimental station in Wembley Park (on a site where the stadium now stands); work on smoke bombs and flares was carried out there. Hickman was posted to Wembley for the rest of the war. Most of his coworkers were army personnel, but they included at least one other student from the department, James N. E. Day. One of the incendiary mixtures developed at Wembley was named DW for Dr. Whiteley.[40]

Jocelyn Thorpe's widow left a memoir in which she tells a little of her husband's involvement in the war effort. In it she wrote that after the gas attacks of April 1915 Lord Kitchener asked her husband to work on chemical warfare agents with Lt. Colonel Crossley, the commandant at Porton Down. He returned home saying 'I am going to dislike myself; I am going to be ashamed of being British and I don't know how many friends we shall lose.' He was not allowed to explain to his wife why this was so: 'I shan't be able to talk to you for a long time on anything to do with these matters'. She also noted that when Lloyd George became Prime Minister he sent for Thorpe offering to make him a Lt. Colonel, but Thorpe refused. Having been placed in charge of the chemical laboratory at the military establishment at Porton, he believed that he would have more control over how things were done as a civilian.[41] On one occasion he was visited at Porton by two German spies, one disguised as a Russian general, the other as his aide. The 'aide' told Thorpe that the 'general' spoke only Russian and French and that he would act as interpreter. Thorpe asked whether the general spoke any German and was told that he did not. Later, however, when shown around Salisbury Cathedral, the 'general cried out *"sehr schön"* — it's beautiful.' Lady Thorpe claimed that the spies were shown no secrets and were soon apprehended. She also noted that her husband probably saved the life of J. S. Haldane who, along with his son J. B. S. Haldane, was taking part in an experiment at Porton. It was to determine the altitude airmen could reach before needing oxygen. Her description of the experiment is vague, but it appears that J. S. Haldane was in a chamber from which oxygen was slowly being depleted (possibly by the inflow of nitrogen). He began acting a little strangely and, although J. B. S. claimed that his father was alright, Thorpe insisted he be taken out — which he was, just in time.

On another occasion, Thorpe was himself taken for a German spy. He had been asked to go and look at some trenches being constructed at the military experimental station at Dungeness, but he missed the special train that was supposed to be taking him there. Since Thorpe had his 'white pass' he was able to persuade the driver of the next train to stop at an appropriate spot. As he was walking toward the trench site he was stopped by soldiers calling 'halt or we shoot.' He was arrested and taken to a guard post where one of the guards phoned the local army headquarters. Asked what his prisoner looked like, he replied 'rather short, rather stout, round [and] red-faced.' This made Thorpe even angrier, but the description was deemed accurate enough to have him escorted to the trenches where he carried out his inspection. Thorpe also made trips to France to inspect the trenches there, and to look into cases where gas use was suspected. On one occasion he was standing outside the town of Amiens, close to where a gas attack had occurred. He was accompanied by two army officers and a servant when a shell burst about 150 metres from where they were standing. Thorpe and the servant went to retrieve it. While doing so another shell landed near the officers, killing them both and destroying the car that had brought them to the front. On another inspection visit, Thorpe stopped to give a chemistry lecture in Paris. He spoke in French and was invited to return, but with the request 'next time, would you please speak in English.'[42] Despite his poor French Thorpe was made an Officier de la Légion d'Honneur after the war.

Lady Thorpe occasionally visited the department. On one occasion she was in Whiteley's laboratory when there was a small explosion, and her leg was hit by the iron door of a small furnace that flew open and knocked her to the ground. She reported that 'brandy was fetched which was had by Dr. Whiteley, not by [me],' that 'Dr. Kon saved my leg' by pouring alcohol over it, and that she was 'laid up' for three months.[43] George Kon, a Cambridge MB, but not yet a DSc, was Thorpe's research student at the time. At the time of the accident he was working on drug production under Frances Micklethwait. Kon was to join the army as a lieutenant in 1916. He was made liaison officer between the department and a number of respirator factories, and reported to the War Office. When the United States entered the war in 1917, he was sent to consult with American gas mask experts and liaise with United States military personnel. He ended the war as a captain. Kon is discussed further in Chapter Six.

Thorpe had other concerns aside from his work with poison gases. James Philip had been appointed chairman of the Royal Society's Committee on Synthetic Drugs, with the task of organizing pharmaceutical production in university laboratories throughout the country. The idea was to find suitable methods for the production of pharmaceuticals that, before the war, were imported from Germany. University scientists then shared their methods with manufacturers able to prepare the drugs in bulk. Thorpe went further, allowing the organic chemistry teaching laboratory be given over to the production of some local anaesthetics, and analgesics, for use in naval hospitals. Frances Micklethwait was put in charge of this small drug factory. But before it could get off the ground she, together with some research students, had to figure out some German patents. The departmental 'factory' made about forty pounds of phenacetin ($4\text{-}CH_3CONHC_6H_4OC_2H_5$) and a small range of other products, including about twelve pounds of the local anaesthetic β-eucaine, and sixty pounds of hexamethylenetetramine. The governing body of IC was unhappy that international patent laws were being broken in its laboratories, but war trumped their concerns which were further eased by the fact that the pharmaceuticals were being used by the navy. In a note to Baker, Thorpe wrote that they gave 'complete satisfaction to the medical officers concerned.'[44] However, he complained to the Board of Trade that he was not a manufacturing chemist and, in late 1916, his team passed on their synthesis methods to pharmaceutical manufacturers. Whiteley, an expert in barbiturates, also developed procedures for their production. According to Lady Thorpe, her husband was sometimes annoyed with Whiteley. He 'thought her a woman in a thousand. Said she was a wonderful woman, but irritating.'[45]

Baker gave space in the department to some other wartime activities. He put one laboratory at the disposal of the Marquis de Chavelay Laubat, an official of the French Government who worked on explosives.[46] Baker, himself, was working also with the Whitefriars glass company on making a type of glass resistant to chemical agents and to changes in temperature. Before the war, it was purchased from a manufacturer in Jena. The geologist Percy Boswell helped by finding sands for that, and for high-grade optical glass that, similarly, could no longer be imported. In an undated report to Alexander Gow, the college secretary, Baker reported that Whitefriars was making about five tons of the new chemically resistant glass per week. In the same report he noted that Professor Bone was working on coal and oil resources, and on ways to make gas fires more efficient.[47]

William Bone was a pacifist. He drew the line at poison gas work and would have nothing to do with it. He was appointed chairman of the British Association committee on fuel economy. More than other professors, he worked hard to have his students exempted from military service, but this led to some compromises. For example, he agreed to train a few students for senior positions in munitions factories. To help students avoid conscription when it was introduced in 1916, Bone asked them to sign a form stating that they were working on matters of national importance and that 'I hereby undertake for the duration of the war to place my services unreservedly at your disposal.' This seems to have worked, and Bone's grateful students spent long hours at the college working for him.[48] George Finch, more in line with the national mood, gave a course on explosives and then joined the army along with five of his students. Four others who had taken his course joined the Admiralty cordite factory at Holton Heath, Dorset. In connection with fuel economy, John Hinchley carried out some pioneering work on the dewatering of peat, but problems with this remained unresolved by the end of the war. Bone appointed two women lecturers in chemical technology because of staff shortages.[49]

Baker also set up a departmental group to work on mobile water purification units under the direction of Colonel (later General Sir William) Horrocks of the army medical services. The team drew on departmental expertise in water purification developed earlier by Frankland. It was a subject with which the department still engaged, and one that was taught to undergraduates. In his diary Baker noted that both small and large water purification units were made. The smaller ones were sent by lorry and ferry to France, and the larger ones were moved by barge. Some went as far as Mesopotamia and Persia. Each large unit consisted of smaller units for sedimentation, alum injection, and filtration. The water could also be chlorinated or dechlorinated. Eric Rideal, who was not on the college staff, joined the water purification team as a captain in the Royal Engineers. He was responsible for supplying drinking water to Australian troops on the Somme.[50] Baker's student, James Sugden, who joined the Royal Engineers as a Lieutenant in 1915, was also a member of the team. One year later he was sent to the Middle East to supervise the setting up of about 60 of the large water purification plants.[51] He left the army as a captain, rejoined the department after the war, and became something of a legendary figure, we will return to him in Chapter Six. Also discussed in Chapter Six are Arthur Eldridge and Alfred Pollard, both of whom joined the water purification work. Eldridge was an all-rounder. Not only did he help out with water purification, he also engaged in gas mask design, conducted experiments with the trench warfare unit, helped Boswell with his glass research, and worked in Thorpe's pharmaceutical factory. Earlier he had studied some Arabic, but his dream of being sent to Mesopotamia with the water purifiers was never realised.[52] Two young students, Harold T. (Tom) Ellingham and John W. Baker were sent there. Ellingham graduated in 1916, winning both the Hatton Prize and the Murchison Medal. He and Baker enlisted in the Royal Engineers, joined the Mesopotamian Expeditionary Force as chemical officers, and served in the Middle East for the rest of the war. After the war Ellingham joined the staff; Baker completed his undergraduate studies and then became a research student under Thorpe. They are discussed in subsequent chapters.

One of Professor Baker's achievements late in the war was a device for ventilating carbon monoxide from pillboxes after the firing of guns.[53] It allowed for much greater efficiency in their use. Two other departmental projects are worth mentioning. One made use of a small plant for the manufacture of butyl alcohol that had been built in connection with Tilden's work on the synthesis of artificial rubber. The alcohol was made by the fermentation of maize mush using *Bacillus butylicus* and acetone was a by-product. In 1914, the government became interested in the production of acetone since it was used in the manufacture of cordite. However, departmental work in this area moved only slowly, and the project was taken over by the Manchester chemist (and future first president of Israel), Chaim Weizmann. He found some more efficient bacilli, and some other mashes, and developed a successful procedure for acetone production. The other project involved Vincent Briscoe, then a highly energetic junior member of the department. Together with Victor Little (see Chapter Four), he designed a prototype factory for the production of thorium oxide. Little left in 1917 to join Thorium Ltd. where he became chief chemist. Thorium oxide can be safely heated to high temperatures and, at such temperatures, is luminescent. It was used in the manufacture of mantles for various types of military lantern. Briscoe also engaged in some secret wartime activity, developing invisible inks; as we will see, he returned to this work in the Second World War (WW2). He also acted as wartime caretaker of the organic chemistry section at the Sir John Cass College, continuing to lecture part-time in the IC department. In 1921, he was appointed professor of inorganic and physical chemistry at Armstrong College, Newcastle. He returned to IC as professor of inorganic chemistry in 1932 and will be discussed further in subsequent chapters.

We have found no separate statistics on wartime casualties for the chemistry department. For the college the toll was high, especially given that students were not encouraged to enlist prior to conscription in 1916. About 2200 students and 103 members of staff served in the armed forces. There were about 675 casualties including 309 deaths. The names of the dead were inscribed on three memorials, one in each of the federated colleges.[54] Baker was critical of poor government recognition for the work carried out in his department. He and Thorpe were made CBE; Philip, Whiteley and Hickman OBE, and Micklethwait MBE.[55] Mouat Jones was awarded the military DSO. Whiteley was also given a monetary award of £100, and Ingold was awarded the British Empire Medal. The medal citation read 'for great courage in carrying out work in a poisonous atmosphere, and risking his life on several occasions in preventing serious accidents.'[56] Baker, however, thought that more people should have been recognised. He was not alone in his resentment. Complaints came from around the country, including from other universities. The somewhat haphazard system of recognition may have been partly due to reputed turmoil within the Ministry of Munitions after Winston Churchill took over in 1917.

Thorpe was more forward-looking and delivered lectures on the future of scientific research and industrial development. Together with others at the Royal Society, he was active in planning for the postwar period. People at the Board of Trade, believing that Britain had been too dependent on German imports for some technical, medical, and chemical goods, asked the Ministry of Education to plan for increased technical and scientific training after the war, so that Britain would be in a better position *vis-à-vis* its competitors. An advisory council was set up by the Minister of Education in 1917 to which Thorpe was appointed. The council, forerunner of the Department of Scientific and Industrial Research (DSIR), played a major role in planning for the postwar period. The DSIR was to direct and fund scientific research for many years after the war.

End Notes

1. For Baker, (Thorpe, 1935), (Jones *rev*, 2004).
2. (Baker, 1885). For Roscoe's astonishment, (Thorpe, 1935), p. 523.
3. (Baker, 1894, 1898). In his 1898 paper Baker claims that NH_4Cl sublimes but, when very dry, does not dissociate below 350°C. Later, some doubt was cast on Baker's intensive drying work but it has not been totally dismissed. In his obituary, J. F. Thorpe (Thorpe, 1935) tells an interesting story about Baker having hit upon a form of colour photography while at

Dulwich College. He quotes Baker as having been 'struck by the fact that the colours of the oxides of tungsten are in the order of the colours of the spectrum, I gave an albumen print of a photograph to two boys to tone with a solution of sodium tungstate in hydrochloric acid. They presently appeared from the dark room with the photograph in true natural colours. A golfer in scarlet jacket on a green lawn ... darker green shrubs ... blue sky ...[etc.].' The photo was observed by about 50 pupils but it quickly faded and the results could not be repeated.

4. (Baker, 1907). Tellurium, an apparent anomaly in Mendeleev's table since its atomic weight is slightly greater than that of iodine, was the subject of discussion before atomic numbers were distinguished from atomic weights.

5. Women who completed the degree examinations at Oxford were not awarded degrees. However, they were permitted to apply for MA degrees from Trinity College, Dublin. We do not know whether Muriel Baker did so. Her father, H. J. Powell, had also studied chemistry at Oxford. He was the grandson of the founder of the Whitefriars Glass Company, and a partner in the business. In the early 20th century the RCS chemistry department purchased glassware from Whitefriars.

6. Lord Kitchener was Secretary of State for War. Keogh was Rector of IC, 1910–1922. He had served in the army earlier as Surgeon-General. Unlike at most other universities, and despite Keogh's example, students and staff were not encouraged to volunteer, though many did. When conscription was introduced in 1916 it was widely opposed at IC where most people went along with the former Normal School student, H. G. Wells, in arguing that people trained in science and engineering could serve their country best in scientific and technical capacities, and that military leaders needed to be more scientifically informed. The 'memorandum from men of science' sent to the national press in 1916 made much the same points. It was signed by 36 eminent scientists including the IC chemists T. E. Thorpe, H. E. Armstrong, W. A. Tilden, and J. C. Philip. For Keogh, (Harrison, 2004). For an account of IC in the First World War, (Gay, 2007b), Chapter Five.

7. Some of the people discussed in this chapter are mentioned in *Pro Patria — Remembering the First World War*, (RSC, 2014).

8. The statistics on deaths and casualties from poison gas are not very reliable. It is estimated that about 3 percent of all combat deaths on the Western Front were due to poison gas and that the first attack at Ypres in April–May, 1915 with chlorine resulted in 4000 French and Algerian casualties, including about 2000 deaths. The long 48 hour attack on Canadian troops that began two days later resulted in about 6000 casualties, including about

2000 deaths. In May British troops, too, were attacked with chlorine at Ypres, (Haber, 1986).
9. (Pope, 1917). Seward's book, which includes Pope's chapter, is an anthology of essays on science and WWI by 'Cambridge graduates.' Pope may have been an honorary graduate. His chapter gives a good account of the state of applied and industrial chemistry in Britain and Germany at the start WW1.
10. For a full account of poison gases during WW1, (Haber, 1986); see also (MacLeod, 1993), (Freemantle, 2014).
11. National Archives, Kew; H. B. Baker, diary 1915–1916 (PRO WO 142281); entry, 29 April, 1915. Earlier in 1915 the Germans had used a toxic tear gas (xylyl bromide) against Russian troops.
12. Chlorine gas, a by-product of the German dye industry, was released 22–25 April, 1915 in two waves. See Note 8.
13. John Scott Haldane FRS (1860–1936), a leading authority on the physiology of respiration, and a Copley medallist, was known for having explained divers' bends. He plays a greater role than Baker in many accounts of chemical warfare defence. But that may be due to his having written many memos on the subject, because he was an outspoken critic of some senior army officers, and because he came from a Scottish family with links to the British establishment. His brother, Richard Burdon Haldane was a member of the government. Although Haldane carried out some work on poison gases, and advocated the use of oxygen in battlefield therapy, it would appear that Baker had the confidence of both Keogh and Kitchener when it came to defence against chemical weapons. Perhaps this was because Keogh was loyal to the college, and because he and Kitchener were friends. Both were Irish and had served together in earlier campaigns, notably in the South African War. Kitchener was killed in 1916 when the ship carrying him to negotiations with his Russian counterpart was hit by a torpedo, but Keogh continued to rely on Baker. Baker was antipathetic towards Haldane. They shared a hotel room while in France. Baker wrote in his diary that Haldane's bedtime reading was Herbert Spencer's *Moral Philosophy*, commenting 'it takes all sorts to make a world.' For Haldane, (Sturdy, 2004).
14. (Haber, 1986), p. 51.
15. About 6000 canisters of chlorine (about 350 metric tons) were released by hand at Ypres. The Germans relied on the prevailing winds but were not without casualties of their own.
16. Bernard Mouat Jones (1882–1953), educated at Dulwich College and Balliol College, Oxford, taught chemistry at Government College, Lahore,

before joining IC in 1912; for Jones, (Hartley *revised* Watson, 2004), (Howell, 1955).

17. Quotations, Baker diary, *op. cit.* (11). The RCS fire extinguishers were 50 gallon open water tanks mounted on trolleys and fitted with hand pumps and hoses. Watson thought that, if filled with hypo, they could be used in the trenches and their contents sprayed into the air when needed, (Callendar, 1920). Watson, educated at the RCS, had earlier collaborated with the physical chemist J. W. Rodger (see Chapter Four). For a good account of the work carried out at the Central Laboratory at General Head Quarters (GHQ), Thomas R. V. David, 'British Scientists and soldiers in the First World War with special reference to ballistics and chemical warfare,' Chapter Four; PhD thesis (2009), Centre for the History of Science, Technology and Medicine, ICL; copy in ICL Library. CMG (Companion of the Order of St. Michael and St. George).

18. In this they were not alone, temporary gas masks were being made by all the belligerents. Hypo was sodium thiosulphate, so named because it was originally thought to be a hyposulphite.

19. Only a few canisters of chlorine were used, possibly because of fickle winds resulting in many British troops being gassed. The flannelette masks designed at IC (see below) gave only limited protection. The term 'mask' seems not to have been much used at the time, 'respirator' was more common. Jones had a supervisory role in the filling of shells with the lachrymator, ISK (Imperial South Kensington), so named because it was developed at the college. Later it became known simply as SK. The gas (ethyl iodoacetate mixed with some ethanol) was made in both Glasgow and Calais by the Cassel Cyanide Co. Shells were filled in Calais. Jones reported the 'effective' use of ISK/SK at Loos and Auchy; National Archives, PRO 142/ CL 18/15; Jones to Baker, 18 October 1915.

20. Toward the end of the war Jones succeeded Watson as head of the Central Laboratory and was promoted to Lieutenant (Lt) Colonel. After the war he was in charge of dismantling the laboratory and moving the equipment to Porton Down. He resigned from IC in 1919 when appointed professor of chemistry at Aberystwyth. Shortly after, he became Principal of the Manchester College of Technology. In 1938 he was appointed Vice-Chancellor of the University of Leeds, returning to Porton Down during WW2 as Director of the laboratory. Jones was said to have been charming, witty, and a very good administrator. Given the nature of his career, his scientific output was small. Interestingly, he was another young chemist to have come under the spell of Henry Miers who taught him at Oxford; his

few publications are on the application of physical chemical methods in mineralogy. Another of Baker's former Dulwich pupils, with whom he also collaborated during the war, was Harold Hartley (later Sir Harold Hartley FRS). Hartley worked briefly with Jones at the Central Laboratory. In 1918 he became Controller of the Chemical Warfare Department.

21. National Archives, Kew; PRO 142/CL 28/15. Baker also corresponded with Watson.

22. The experiment with pigs is mentioned in Lady Thorpe's memoir, 'Anecdotes,' written after her husband's death; typewritten copy in ICL archives, B\Jocelyn Thorpe. For Thorpe see below. One of Baker's research students who worked in the trench warfare department was Arthur Barker Hatton MBE (1892–1945), (Anon., 1945). Hatton came to the department in 1914 with a Manchester BSc; he was on the staff 1916–1919. He also had a commission in the Royal Naval Volunteer Reserve (RNVR) and, late in the war, worked back in Manchester on materials used in aircraft.

23. Baker diary *op. cit.* (11), undated entry, but probably some time in May, 1915. No doubt Baker was unfair to Haldane who also worked hard throughout the war.

24. Kenneth Hickman (1896–1979), a student at the time, remembered experiments continuing day and night to find the plant charcoal that best absorbed chlorine. 'Cherry pits, peach kernels, coconut shells, chips of mahogany' were among the things charred and tested. He claimed that coconut shells made some of the best active charcoal.   http://solarsaddle.wordpress.com/2012/01/06/classic-kit-kenneth-charles-devereux-hickmans-molecular-alembic/

25. ICL Archives; B\Eldridge, O. L. Brady to Eldridge, 26 March, 1958. For Brady see Chapter Four, Note 143.

26. ICL archives, A. A. Eldridge, 'Diamond Jubilee Lecture' delivered to the Imperial College Chemical Society, 21 February, 1956. Printed internally, copy in the ICL archives. For Briscoe see below and subsequent chapters.

27. The sodium phenate was used to protect against phosgene with which it reacts to give diphenyl carbonate. Muriel Baker and some assistants carried out much of this work at the Bakers' home laboratory. They tested various cloths soaked in a range of protective chemicals before settling on sodium phenate. As Tom David notes (*op. cit.* 17), at this early stage the chemical war was based on very basic chemical knowledge. What was needed was drive, leadership and organizing ability — skills that both Baker and Thorpe possessed in abundance.

28. Today the Millbank buildings are occupied by the Chelsea College of Art and Design. MacPherson worked with Jones and Watson in the St. Omer laboratory. The tube valve appears to have been his idea.
29. Baker diary *op. cit.* (11), 20 May, 1916.
30. ICL archives B\Eldridge; Barclay to Eldridge, 3 June, 1958. See also (Foulkes, 2001). After the war, Baker recommended Barclay for a job at the Science Museum.
31. For Sugden see below. John Patrick Mitchell de Courmaceul Dowdall won the Hatton Prize in 1915. He enlisted in the army medical corps in 1917 and was later principal scientific officer at the Chemical Defence Establishment at Porton Down. John David McBeath Ross returned to Scotland after the war, to a lectureship at Dundee.
32. Baker diary *op. cit.* (11), 6 March, 1916.
33. Mustard gases are a class of compounds, the commonest being $(ClCH_2CH_2)_2S$, *bis*-(2-chloroethyl)sulphide. Unlike chlorine, but like phosgene, they are not visible and can be odourless when pure. Most are vesicants, are less lethal than phosgene but, as volatile liquids, they tend to hang around, thus adding to their danger. Early detection of mustard gases and phosgene, so that signals could be sent to soldiers in time for them to cover up and put on their masks, was a major problem addressed by some in the department. On the battlefront various hooters, bells and rattles were used to sound the alarm. In Manchester, W. H. Perkin supervised the fairly large-scale production of mustard gas. For a history of the discovery of mustard gas, (Duchovic and Vilensky, 2007).
34. Eldridge, *op. cit.* (26).
35. For SK see Note 19. George Beilby was on some of the same wartime committees as Thorpe and Baker, he asked for their help and Thorpe sent Ingold to Glasgow.
36. Baker diary, *op. cit.* (11), 6 March, 1916. For the production of this gas see Note 19. For a history of the gas and its use, J. F. Thorpe, 'History of SK', typed manuscript dated 10 February, 1919, National Archives, Kew; PRO/MUN5/385/1650/7.
37. Baker diary *op. cit.* (11), 3 May, 1915.
38. According to Simon Jones, when the SK lachrymator (see Note 19) was tested in the departmental trench, its effect on a tall War Office official was inconclusive. A short boy was paid a shilling to be the next guinea pig and he suffered, (Jones, 2007), 3. Jones' story sounds apocryphal, but his book includes some details on gas attacks, and on a range of protective

equipment. SK had the advantage over some other compounds in that it did not corrode metal containers.

39. ICL archives; A. A. Eldridge, 'Martha Annie Whiteley, 1866–1956', *The Record* (September, 1956), pp. 13, 14.

40. Hickman, *op. cit.* (24). Major Lister, who was in charge at Wembley, wrote a report on some of these devices in the War Office's *Proceedings of the Trench Warfare Unit*: National Archives, Kew; WO 142/208.

41. At roughly this time Thorpe was appointed to the Advisory Council of the Privy Council Committee for Scientific and Industrial Research.

42. Lady Thorpe's memoir, *op. cit.* (22).

43. Lady Thorpe, *op. cit.* (22). It is not clear whether Lady Thorpe declined the brandy because she did not drink, or whether she was offended that it went to Martha Whiteley and not to her. Her tone makes us believe the latter.

44. ICL archives; KC/9/6, H. Brereton Baker's correspondence files. The chemicals were prepared for the Admiralty. Hexamethylenetetramine is not an anaesthetic. It was used along with sodium phenate in gas masks to combat phosgene. Professor Tilden attended a college chemical society meeting and complimented those who, under Thorpe's direction, were working on synthetic drugs for the Navy. Specimens were displayed at the meeting. Report in *Phoenix* (new series) 1 (1915), p. 9. Another β-eucaine factory was set up by W. P. Wynne, then at the University of Sheffield.

45. Lady Thorpe memoir, *op. cit.* (22).

46. ICL archives; KC/9/8, Baker correspondence file; Baker to A. Gow (College Secretary), 23 February, 1915.

47. Helping with this, and fuel efficiency more generally, was M. G. Christie, manager of the British Otto-Hilgenstock Coke-Oven Co. He was made an assistant professor during the war and lectured on carbonisation, including the manufacture of coke from coal.

48. It is worth noting that the average working week before WW1 was 56 hours, so the students were probably working more hours than that. After the war, legislation limited the work week to 48 hours.

49. Miss Sinkinson was the sister of a demonstrator in the department. She left during the war after an incident in which she and her brother, afraid of Bone, failed to report some damage to the gas holder of the department's pilot gas-producing plant. Beatrice Butler left at the end of the war. M. de Reuck, 'History of the department of Chemical Engineering and Chemical Technology, 1912–1939' (1960), pp. 36–38; typescript copy in ICL archives.

50. Sir Eric K. Rideal FRS (1890–1974) was a Cambridge educated physical chemist. His father, Samuel Rideal, had been one of Frankland's students at the Normal School and had developed an interest in sewage treatment and water purification. Before the war, Rideal worked with his father on water purification in Ecuador. Later, working along the Somme, he was injured and invalided out of the army. He spent the latter part of the war trying to replicate the Haber–Bosch process with a team at UCL. After the war he joined T. M. Lowry at Cambridge, had a varied and successful career, before returning to IC as a Senior Research Fellow on retiring from his chair at King's College London in 1955. For more on Rideal including obituary references see Chapter Eight.

51. In one of his diary entries, 19 October, 1916 (*op. cit.* 11), Baker wrote that he and Horrocks went to see one of the large units destined for Mesopotamia after it had been loaded onto a barge. He noted that Sugden was in 'high glee' since the unit was 'working like a charm, producing beautifully clear water.'

52. Eldridge *op. cit.* (26) p. 5. Together with Briscoe, Eldridge wrote a first aid manual, (Eldridge and Briscoe, 1915). It had a foreword by Sir Alfred Keogh.

53. During the last year of the war, concrete shelters were established along the front in France and Belgium, each with a Vickers' maxim machine gun and two gunners. The shelters, named 'pill boxes,' proved difficult to ventilate and carbon monoxide accumulated. Several casualties occurred, but Baker's device, when attached to the machine guns, helped improve the situation. At the same time, Hertha Ayrton (1854–1923) developed a ventilation fan. Ayrton, the wife of William Ayrton, a former Professor of Physics at the C&GCTC, was a good physicist in her own right. She may well have designed a better ventilator than Baker's but it was less developed at the time, and she was not as well connected to the military as he was. (Ayrton, 1919–1920).

54. Among the dead was Captain Ivan R. Gibbs (1891–1916), a demonstrator in the department, killed at Loos. He is recorded also on the RSC memorial at Burlington House. (Chapman, 1916).

55. In 1913 the Rector, Sir Alfred Keogh, wrote a letter to Henry Miers in which he was full of praise for Whiteley's many contributions and that 'it has always seemed to me that the position she holds on our staff is not equal to her efficiency … [and that he has] no intention — of allowing her … to remain in her present position. … She is fitted to fill far higher posts and … her upward progress will not be restrained by any consideration of sex.' KC\9\8, Keogh to Miers, 18 April, 1913.

56. (Leffek, 1996), p. 40, states that Ingold won this medal for brave and rapid action under pressure. In one instance, shells were being filled with HCN and the pipe feeding them became loose. Ingold, holding his breath, rushed to tighten the pipe up. He then walked quickly upwind, so that any lingering gas would quickly evaporate from his hands and clothing. In later life Ingold never mentioned the award and was reticent about his work at Cassel Cyanide.

Chapter Six

The Department between the Wars, 1918–1939

6.1. A fresh start after the war

Imperial College (IC) was beginning to find its way when the 1914 war started. By war's end there was some doubt as to whether it would survive as a federal entity. There had been a massive drop in income from student fees, and runaway inflation took its toll on both endowments and grants. However, thanks to the efforts of its staff and members of the governing body, the college was able to make a fresh start. professors Baker and Philip were among those who worked especially hard in this regard. Typically, in a speech given at the Royal College of Science (RCS) Chemical Society dinner in 1924, Baker emphasised the need for students to identify with the new college,

> *we shall never attain the University status which we all so ardently desire so long as we remain three separate and distinct Colleges with but little mutual interdependence. We must try to build up* Imperial *College loyalty until it is as high an order as our college loyalty.*[1]

Baker was active in support of student affairs and in bringing students from the three older colleges together. A strong advocate for student accommodation, he was appointed chairman of the IC hostel committee, and helped to raise funds for the first hostel which opened in 1926. Muriel

Baker chose the furnishings. On his retirement Baker donated the clock that can still be seen in the Beit Quadrangle.[2] Philip was chairman of the IC war memorial committee which raised funds for a college sports field on land purchased in Wembley.[3] He was elected chairman of the Athletic Ground Committee, was also chairman of the Refectory Committee from 1931–1936, and secretary and treasurer of the Student Finance Committee from 1919–1937. Thorpe put much of his energy into building a research group, and into restoring the department's reputation, diminished since the retirement of Tilden, as a major centre in organic chemistry.

In 1919, after low enrolment during the war years, student numbers swelled to over double the prewar figure. This reflected both the return of those who had served in the armed forces, and the many others seeking an education that had been delayed or interrupted. Further, the annual fees were £39, lower than those at more established universities. Together with a distinguished staff, this attracted students to the department.[4] Many appear to have won scholarships or received grants of one sort or other, including the special grants given to returning servicemen. Overcrowding lasted well beyond 1919, and many school leavers had to delay their studies because of a shortage of places nationwide. It took about seven years for all the qualified applicants to be accommodated. As before, entry to the first year course was open to promising students without the Higher School Certificate (HSC) in mathematics and science.[5] Those with the HSC in the appropriate subjects entered in the second year. In 1920 there were 126 students (including students from the Royal School of Mines — RSM) in the first year, 76 (chemists only) in the second year, and 85 in the third year.[6] In 1923, when numbers had not yet stabilised, 68 chemists were enrolled in the first, 76 in the second, 78 in the third, and 72 in the fourth year. By 1928 numbers had declined to a level that remained roughly stable until Second World War (WW2), about 20 chemists enrolled in the first year, about 50 in the second and third years, and about 40 in the fourth year.[7] Completion of the third year led to the ARCS but, increasingly, students also sat the external University of London BSc examinations. Fourth year students carried out short research projects and were eligible for the DIC.[8] A few stayed on to carry out further research; after 1920 this could lead to a PhD as well as a DIC.[9]

As head of department, Baker organised instruction for the large postwar student intake and appointed new teaching and technical staff.

Many demonstrators came and went in this period.[10] Despite the government's intention of expanding scientific and technical education, the economic situation was uncertain and new funding slow to arrive. By and large, chemistry fared better than other academic disciplines because its industrial importance was recognised. When IC applied to the Ministry of Reconstruction for funds, the chemistry department's request for £4,000 was granted. This seemingly small sum for repairs and refurbishment was seen as all that could reasonably be expected in difficult times. However, the new Department of Scientific and Industrial Research (DSIR) provided research funding, and grants came from the chemical industry. The 1920s saw a number of industrial mergers leading to the formation of major companies such as ICI and Unilever, and to the chemically-based production of many consumer goods. The department responded well to these developments both in seeking new research funding, and in helping many of its graduates to find industrial employment.[11]

Training undergraduates in the kinds of technical processes used in the chemical industry was seen as important. The governing body of the college requested that the department build a new industrial chemical laboratory and provided £7,000 toward its construction. The laboratory was equipped with the help of a £9,000 donation from a former student, William Whiffen, owner of a family business that manufactured fine chemicals. The business was founded by his grandfather, also named William Whiffen, who was a former Hofmann student at the Royal College of Chemistry (RCC). Named for Whiffen, the laboratory housed a pilot-scale chemical manufacturing plant, but getting all the machinery to the top floor of the building where the laboratory was located was not easy. Cranes were used to lift some of the heavier items through an opening in the roof. Arthur Balfour, the former Prime Minister, came to open the laboratory in 1920 and stated, 'now, instead of performing their experiments in test tubes and-er-that kind of machinery, the students will be able to carry out their tests in-er-er-retorts and the like mechanism.'[12] In fact students were to learn how to use 'machinery' such as vats, autoclaves and filter presses. Christopher Ingold was in charge of the new laboratory. Under his direction, all third year students spent some time working on semi-large-scale production. Ingold recalled that one of the first procedures they carried out was the oxidation of 1½ tons of castor oil and the preparation of suberic acid.[13] The industrial Whiffen Laboratory was closed in 1938 when Ian Heilbron succeeded Jocelyn Thorpe as professor of organic chemistry. The Whiffen name was retained, but the laboratory and some neighbouring rooms were re-equipped as an organic chemistry research laboratory with places for 24 students. It was to become renowned.

In 1929 the college joined the University of London. In anticipation the chemistry department, like some others at IC, ventured in new directions so as to make use of the university's internal MSc degree. Two vocational postgraduate courses were introduced, one in agricultural chemistry under Alfred Pollard, the other in the chemistry of food and drugs under Arthur Eldridge. The agricultural chemistry course was timely since, in 1925, the college purchased its first field station at Hurworth, near Slough. Pollard and his students carried out field studies there.[14] The new degree courses were recognised by the Royal Institute of Chemistry (RIC) and attracted many students, including some from the Dominions and colonies. Undergraduates, too, could choose to spend their fourth year specialising in these areas. New staff members were appointed to cope with the demand.[15]

Undergraduates still had to provide much of their own apparatus which was sold in a store run by an external company. Incoming students could buy starter sets for five guineas (£5. 5s.) — no small sum at the time.[16] One student, Eric Thurston, remembered each student having a large box of equipment which had to be packed each vacation and hauled up two flights of stairs for storage.[17] Memoirs of the period mention Solomon, the man in charge of the store, almost as often as they do the professors. Solomon, probably his surname, was described by Arthur Eldridge as 'rather short and shuffling, a little bent, a shiny black apron under his jacket, [always wearing] a Charlie Chaplin bowler.' He wandered around the department carrying a box of apparatus, offering bargains.[18] Many students were poor and in need of bargains. What today would be considered a modest lunch was a luxury that few could then afford.[19] Coffee, beer, and buns were the staple foods for many. Proper clothing was a further expense. Male students were forbidden to enter the Science Museum Library (where the chemistry and other scientific journals were kept) without jacket and tie. Things were no easier for the staff. Aside from the professors, most were poorly paid and there was little technical or secretarial assistance. F. W. L.

(Les) Croker, who started as a lab boy in 1926 at 15 shillings per week, remembered there being only one departmental secretary, Miss Hornsby, who was employed from 1932.[20] As Croker also recalled, before WW2 there was only one telephone in the department. It was located in the messenger's box in the main hall, and most members of staff had no access to it. Croker told an interesting story of an event that must have occurred during the 1930s. He was making decimolar silver nitrate in a 20 litre bottle while wearing a suit and no lab coat. The bottle broke while he was shaking it, and his grey suit became covered in brown stains. He asked the new professor of inorganic chemistry, Vincent Briscoe, for some money towards a new suit and was told, 'you know what I would do if I were you Croker, try washing it in potassium cyanide, I think you will find that will clean it.' With no safety regulations preventing him, Croker followed Briscoe's advice. When the suit 'was rinsed and dried and sent to the cleaners it came out perfectly alright.'[21]

After the war an attempt was made to broaden undergraduate education. Harry Riley, who enrolled in 1919 and was later on the staff, remembered having to attend history lectures and classes in essay writing. He stated that the latter were given 'not very satisfactorily' by Philip Bull.[22] Bull, a former student with a distinguished war record, joined the staff in 1919. The new classes were experimental. Indeed, it is perhaps best to see the first half of the period covered in this chapter as one of making a new start by trying new things. Most significant was the tripartite departmental structure. Separate sections in inorganic, organic, and physical chemistry made their formal appearance in 1914, each under a professor; but they got their true start after the war. A similar departmental model was adopted elsewhere — at Leeds for example. However, both University College and King's College retained general departments, with just two professors at this time. Also significant was the introduction, in 1920, of the external University of London PhD. It led to an increase in the number of research students staying beyond the fourth year. Some came from outside the college, including several from India and the Dominions. A few Russian students also arrived, keen to leave their country during the revolutionary period.[23]

Baker encouraged students to take an active role in the RCS (later IC) Chemical Society when it resumed in 1922. Both staff and students gave papers, and some eminent people were invited. In 1922 Christopher Ingold gave a paper titled 'Some aspects of quantum theory,' illustrating his grasp of matters well beyond organic chemistry, and J. J. Thomson spoke on 'Electrons in chemistry.' In 1923 W. H. Perkin spoke on 'The formation of rings in the o- and p- position' F. W. Aston gave a talk on 'Atomic weights and isotopes,' and F. G. Donnan one on 'Surface actions in relation to chemistry.' Later in the decade J. C. Irvine spoke on 'Polymerization problems in carbohydrate chemistry' and H. B. Hartley on 'The association and dissociation of electrolytes.' In 1929 the new Rector, Henry Tizard, gave a physical chemistry talk, and Ian Heilbron, visiting his future place of work, spoke on 'The fat soluble vitamins — A and D.' Several former students gave talks, including Lowry and Lapworth. A few of the talks were historical, and some of the evenings were given over to films on industrial chemical processes. In 1924, the *Revised* C. W. Howell spoke on 'the chemical proof for the authenticity of the Turin Shroud,' and Marie Stopes, who had a BSc from UCL, spoke to a packed lecture theatre on birth control. However, it is unlikely that any of the talks were as amusing as the one given on photography by Kenneth Hickman (see subsequent paragraphs).

Illustrating a need for fraternal conviviality, a group of students founded the Hofmann Society in 1933. Membership was by election and restricted to 'non-abstaining gentlemen who have carried out research in organic chemistry.' The purpose was for senior students — excluding women — to discuss organic chemistry, for the 'upkeep of the index of melting point specimens, ... the operation of a research chemical exchange bureau,' and for keeping a 'blacklist of unrepeatable work.' In 1939 the society created a book prize, named after Hofmann, to be awarded to the best student in the organic chemistry final examinations. The department took it over in 1958.[24]

6.2. Herbert Brereton Baker and Inorganic Chemistry

Herbert Brereton Baker was known well beyond the chemistry department for his sense of decorum. Those reaching adulthood in the 'roaring twenties' saw him as decidedly old fashioned. According to the college secretary, Baker was 'horrified' to hear a female student utter the words 'not bloody likely' in a college production of G. B. Shaw's *Pygmalion*.[25] When the student union building was completed in the early 1920s, Baker opposed the inclusion of a bar. But the new Rector, Thomas Holland, persuaded him that it was better that students drink at the college than in the neighbourhood pubs — not that this was ever prevented.

Baker was supportive of women students, but thought it only proper they be denied entry to the union bar. And, always the schoolmaster, he was strict with male students with regard to the kind of language they used in the presence of their female peers. Nonetheless, he was kinder and more popular with the students than T. E. Thorpe had been.[26] Kenneth Hickman, who entered the second year course in 1913, left an amusing memoir in which he wrote that Baker's 'lectures were famous. He was a remarkable little man with a massive black moustache, a diminutive figure but impressive presence ... he made elementary science live for us ... and I was soon his favourite.' Perhaps it was as well that Baker was not told that the exuberant Hickman had set off a small firework composed of magnesium turnings and potassium chlorate during his first week at the college. The demonstrator, Arthur Eldridge, was shocked. He came over to Hickman's bench and recorded his name and address in a small notebook. Later, when Hickman asked why there had been no reprisal, Eldridge told him that, still new to the job, he had no idea how to report the incident. He thought, rightly as it turned out, that the formal recording of Hickman's details was sufficient intimidation.[27] It is perhaps not surprising that Hickman was sent to work on flares and smoke bombs during WW1 (see Chapter Five).

Hickman was far from alone in enjoying Baker's lectures.[28] Baker believed that new students should not be taught solely by the junior staff and, despite carrying a heavy administrative load, he gave the first term lectures to new entrants in both the first and second years. Not surprisingly his postwar research output was limited, but his reputation as an experimentalist remained high. His glassblowing skills were renowned, and he continued to help students build their apparatus. His technical skills were evident also in his favourite leisure activity, woodcarving. As we will see, he attracted some very good research students despite his disapproval of advanced degrees.[29] According to Alexander King, Baker denounced the PhD as 'a new-fangled and unnecessary German invention.' He approved of students spending some time in German laboratories, but held that they should do so for the sake of science, and their own edification, not for some external accreditation. As Harry Eméleus put it, 'the last thing one could say was [that one] wanted a PhD. Baker would have thrown me out if I had said that.'[30] Baker's work on the effects of the long term drying of chemicals still drew considerable interest. In 1923 he was invited by the Dutch Royal Institute of Science to give a set of lectures on 'the catalytic effect of traces of water.' He also made a synthetic breakthrough in preparing selenium trioxide.[31]

Four members of staff from this period played important roles in undergraduate instruction: Arthur Eldridge, Henry Harwood, James Sugden and Alfred Pollard. The first two joined the department shortly before WW1. Sugden, whose contributions to the war effort were mentioned in Chapter Five, was appointed a demonstrator shortly after the war, as was Pollard. Eldridge continued to give general chemistry lectures to first year engineers, and supervised the second year chemistry students in the main laboratory. In 1926, by then a lecturer, he introduced the earlier mentioned MSc course. Later he was to become a senior lecturer and assistant director of the Inorganic and Physical Chemical Laboratories. Eldridge engaged in both student and college affairs. Called 'uncle' by many students, his retirement party in 1960 drew a large crowd.[32]

James Sugden had overall responsibility for the first year students. He completed the course begun by Baker with lectures on the metals and non-metals, and supervised the first year laboratory. Tom Ellingham wrote that 'from his desk ... [Sugden] gazed dispassionately for a quarter of a century at successive generations of students ... always ready to give personal advice when the situation warranted it.'[33] One of those students, Eric Roberts, later joined the staff. According to Roberts, Sugden was a 'notable eccentric,' the students gave him a hard time, and his attitude toward them 'was a curious mixture of disillusionment, frustration, and tolerant amusement.'[34] This is supported by the fact that Sugden collected student questions, and listed them together with his answers in the Course of Study booklet. That way he could respond to almost any question by saying 'you'll find the answer on page ... go and read it.' Roberts also noted that Sugden was a creature of habit who arrived and left the college at exactly the same times each day. And that he left for lunch at a given time, walking along Exhibition Road to his preferred lunch spot in South Kensington. Sadly, on the 11 July, 1944, he departed from this routine so as to avoid debris left by a flying bomb that had landed near the post office. Taking the slightly longer route along Queen's Gate, he was fatally injured when another flying bomb landed near the main gates of the Natural History Museum.[35]

Henry Francis Harwood (1886–1975) studied chemistry at Manchester University before moving to Heidelberg for a PhD. He came to the department as a demonstrator in 1911, and was put in charge of the analytical laboratory. A noted expert on rock analysis, he gave a fourth year course on the subject. He also lectured on the history of chemistry. Harwood, who became a reader, was described as shy and retiring, yet strict with students. On one occasion, unobserved, he watched a student scoop some spilled material back into a crucible and then asked, 'is this quantitative Mr. ...?.'[36] Perhaps he had a misanthropic streak. According to Roberts, he occasionally invited junior members of staff to his home in Buckinghamshire where he kept some Fell ponies, and gained much pleasure from the fact that anyone attempting to ride one invariably fell off. Harwood worked closely with geologists at the college, and received the Geological Society of London's Wollaston Fund Prize in 1938.[37] Some years after he retired the department renamed a laboratory, and named a student prize in analytical chemistry, after him.

Alfred Pollard was a student in the department during the war and helped in building the water purification units. After the war he worked with Albert Chibnall, professor of biochemistry and a specialist in plant proteins.[38] Although not strictly an inorganic chemist, Pollard taught within the section for over 40 years, retiring in 1961 as Senior lecturer. Knowing that Pollard owned a smallholding in Sussex, Baker, encouraged him to lecture on agricultural chemistry and to develop the above mentioned MSc course. According to Kitchener, the smallholding accounted for Pollard's healthy complexion and for his arriving late and departing early each day.[39] Pollard became an expert in soil chemistry, carried out analyses of agricultural soils, and analysed the soils brought back by the 1939 Imperial College expedition to Jan Mayen Island.[40] One of his collaborators, Stanley Jacobs, came to the department as an undergraduate in 1923. Jacobs won the Hatton Prize in 1925 and took the

MSc in agricultural chemistry before joining the botany department as a demonstrator. Later he became Reader in bacteriology, and was Editor of the *Journal of Applied Bacteriology*.[41]

Baker did not build a research school. He allowed his students to go their own way, and his appointees to the inorganic chemistry staff followed a wide range of interests. This pattern continued under Briscoe and Wilkinson. Writing in the mid-1960s, Eric Roberts wrote, there was 'a welcome tolerance of a wide variety of researches under individual members of staff that has, in the main, characterised inorganic chemistry throughout its history.'[42] However, two members of the staff did work with Baker on extreme drying, namely Margaret Carlton and Ronald Purcell. Carlton came to the department at the end of the war, to complete undergraduate studies begun at Birkbeck College. She gained her ARCS and BSc in 1919, PhD in 1924, and became Baker's private assistant. She was his principal collaborator on the work relating to the catalytic influence of traces of water.[43] On his retirement she was appointed assistant lecturer and assisted Briscoe in his research. Purcell was more independent. An undergraduate in the department, he became Baker's research student in 1925. Baker suggested that he spend a year in a German laboratory, a sensitive issue in the postwar period. Purcell decided to go to the University of Amsterdam where he worked with Andreas Smits for a year in 1927. On his return he continued to work with Baker but, inspired by Smits, began research in physical chemistry. He was soon given a lectureship in that section.[44] Aside from Carlton, Baker's postwar students moved away from his interests in extreme drying and were encouraged in their independence. One of Baker's students was Samuel Francis (Frank) Boys (1911–1972) who was to become an eminent theoretical chemist. Boys graduated with his BSc in 1932, was awarded a Beit Research Fellowship, and began working for a PhD on cadmium complexes. However, he also took courses in the mathematics department, and began some theoretical work on optical rotatory power. In this he was encouraged by professor Philip who recognised his ability in theoretical chemistry. Boys left cadmium chemistry behind and moved to Cambridge in 1935.[45]

Some of Baker's students joined the staff in the 1920s, others in the 1930s. Among the earlier appointees were Kenneth Hickman, Douglas Spencer, Henry Lister (Harry) Riley, and Leslie Theobald. As mentioned in Chapter Five, when Hickman graduated in 1916 he worked first under Martha Whiteley, and then at the Wembley Experimental Station on flares and smoke bombs. In 1919, with a grant from the Photographic Research Association, he became a research student in the department. The Association was one of several bodies supported by the government with the mandate to assist young scientists seeking work or further education during the postwar period. Baker gave Hickman a small room and allowed him to go his own way. More an inventor than a chemist, Hickman was trying to make a name for himself in the world of photography, but he was something of an all-rounder. When his grant ran out Baker offered him a demonstratorship under Harwood in the analytical laboratory. One of Hickman's inventions was an all-glass toilet system which he mounted on a bench in the lab. It was, perhaps, a forerunner to his important work with syphons.[46] He also had a private consultancy in technical photography and published several papers in photographic journals.[47] He gained an external PhD from the University of London, was promoted to lecturer, and stayed in the department until 1925.

Douglas Spencer entered the college as an undergraduate after the war. As a research student under Baker he was drawn to Hickman's photographic work. Baker was unhappy about this and told him not to be 'beguiled by Hickman and photography. You've got the makings of a really good chemist.' But Spencer was beguiled and, in 1925, gained both his PhD and the Williamson Medal for the best research in Britain on photographic chemistry.[48] Spencer wrote a memoir in which he tells an amusing story about assisting Hickman in a lecture demonstration for the RCS Chemical Society.[49] Hickman announced in advance that during the lecture he would photograph Christopher Ingold, chairman for the evening's session, and boasted that he would project the photograph on the overhead screen within one minute of having taken it. He asked Spencer for his assistance, and that he persuade Ingold to wear his academic cap and gown for the occasion. The lecture theatre was crowded with people coming to witness what they thought an impossible feat. Wearing his regalia, Ingold faced the audience alongside a large seconds timer. The timer started when the photographic flash went off. Hickman then developed the photograph in the darkened theatre and, fifty seconds later, handed a plate to Spencer whose job was to dry and then project it. Hickman knew in advance that he couldn't quite make his one-minute claim. Ever the prankster, the plate he handed Spencer showed a donkey dressed in academic robes. This caused much laughter, allowing time for the photograph of Ingold to be washed, partially dried, and projected moments later. Amused and suitably impressed, the audience forgot about the timer.

Spencer was a gifted cartoonist as well as an excellent chemist and photographer. Using the pen name 'Grey Moon' he contributed many cartoons to the student journal, *Phoenix*. Two are reproduced in this book. When Hickman left the department for a job with Eastman Kodak in Rochester, New York, Spencer inherited his photographic business and set up a small consulting firm on the Fulham Road together with Bull and Humphrey Murray.[50] Spencer became a lecturer but left the department in 1933.[51] His successor, Thomas Pearson, was assigned to teach in the analytical laboratory under Harwood. Pearson published papers on the polysulphides of the alkali metals and, in collaboration with Purcell, some papers on the free radicals formed by selenium and tellurium in photochemical reactions.[52] Together with Harry Eméléus (see below) they studied a number of malodorous compounds of selenium and tellurium which left a residual smell in the department long after they had all left.[53] In the late 1930s Pearson was Assistant Warden of the student hostel; the warden was Eldridge. On one occasion Pearson invited the journalist Philip Gibbs to a hostel dinner. In his book, *England Speaks*, Gibbs wrote that he was surprised that 'the warden spoke a Latin grace.' After dinner Pearson showed Gibbs around the department where he met a young man who said that he was 'measuring the atomic weight of radioactive lead'; another told him 'this place is lousy with organics.' The organic chemistry section was the largest of the three, but Gibbs did not understand the reference.[54]

Henry Lister (Harry) Riley (1899–1986) was a Hatton Prize winner. Awarded a Beit Fellowship, he was a research student under Baker, 1921–1923. He was then appointed a demonstrator and became a lecturer soon after. Together with Baker, he determined the atomic weight of silver, though why they repeated the work of Theodore Richards is unclear. When Briscoe returned in 1932, Riley moved to Newcastle where he succeeded Briscoe as professor.[55] Theobald, known as Theo, was a postwar student who joined the staff in 1925. He worked under Harwood, taking over the directorship of the advanced analytical laboratory when Harwood resigned in 1940. He was appointed reader in 1945.[56] According to Kitchener, Theobald lived almost entirely in the advanced analytical laboratory (now converted to the Barton laboratory in RCS1) and gave few, if any, lectures. When he succeeded Harwood and was given the keys to the laboratory safe where the platinum crucibles were kept, he said 'I have waited twenty years for this.'[57] Like Harwood, Theobald was remembered by generations of students as strict and rigorous; one student recalled that 'duplicates had to agree to 1 part in 500 for volumetric analysis and 1 part in 1000 for gravimetric analysis.'[58] He was also remembered for his huge collection of references listed on three by five inch index cards that occupied 50 drawers in his office. After he retired in 1963, the heavy emphasis on gravimetric analysis ended, and, as will be discussed in subsequent chapters, more attention was paid to instrumental procedures. In the early 1930s, Janet Matthews, the Pedler Research Scholar of the Institute of Chemistry, was on the staff. She worked with Briscoe on air-borne dusts in relation to work place disease, notably silicosis. Together they set up the department's first microanalytical laboratory.[59]

Joining the staff in the 1930s were Harry Eméleus and Stuart Anderson, perhaps the best known of Baker's research students. Eméleus (known as Emmy) entered the college as an undergraduate in 1921. In 1923, after what he described as 'just about the toughest assignment I ever had,' he passed the two sets of examinations needed to gain his ARCS and BSc. He decided to carry out research in inorganic chemistry because 'I knew myself to be weak in maths and was not greatly interested in organic chemistry.'[60] Baker appears to have had difficulty coming up with good projects for his students, preferring them to find their own. He gave Eméleus the curious task of finding out whether iodine would react with platinum under the influence of radium radiation. On Eméleus's first day in the laboratory someone turned off the water and his evacuated reaction vessel was flooded. Although Eméleus recovered the radium, Baker was annoyed and from then on left him to his own devices. No doubt this served him well — as it had Hickman and Spencer.[61] Eméleus, however, did pick up Baker's practical glassblowing skills.

After the radium fiasco, and inspired by some of Baker's lecture demonstrations, Eméleus carried out research on the luminescence of phosphorus. He won the Dixon Fund Essay Prize for his 1925 paper, 'The inhibition of the glow of phosphorus.'[62] A Royal Commission of 1851 senior studentship allowed him to spend a year in Karlsruhe with Alfred Stock where he learned about silicon and boron hydrides, and how to handle volatile, flammable, and explosive compounds.[63] After his return to London in 1928 he gained his PhD and, in the same year, was awarded a Commonwealth Fund Fellowship by the Harkness Foundation. This enabled him to spend two years (1929–1931) at Princeton with Hugh Stott Taylor.[64] His time there coincided with the opening of the new Frick Laboratory, and a series of lectures by some of the foremost physical chemists of the day. Inspired, Eméleus made what he called 'an excursion' into physical chemistry and carried out some experiments in photochemistry.[65] He returned from the privileged Princeton environment to an IC that, though improved since the war, was struggling with the consequences of the Great Depression. Baker appointed him a senior demonstrator (renamed assistant lecturer when that rank was introduced one year later), and Eméleus built a small research team. A flow of publications followed, some engaging with the photochemistry that he learned at Princeton. More generally, however, his papers show him using the expertise picked up in Stock's laboratory. He published papers on the hydrides of non-metals, including several on silane.[66] When Briscoe returned to the department as professor of inorganic chemistry, Eméleus collaborated with him on the isotopic composition of water from different sources.[67]

Eméleus lectured on inorganic chemistry to second and third year students and taught practical inorganic chemistry in the analytical laboratory. Together with his younger colleague, Stuart Anderson, he modernised the curriculum. They introduced recent research findings, and encouraged students not to rely solely on their out-of-date textbooks. Interestingly it was James Philip, General Editor of the Routledge series, *20th-Century Chemistry*, who invited Eméleus and Anderson to write a new inorganic chemistry textbook aimed at students who already knew some basic chemistry. As Greenwood noted, their book, *Modern Aspects of Inorganic Chemistry* (1938), was 'a runaway success which was to change the perception of the subject throughout the world.'[68] It went through many editions, was widely translated, and became the most influential inorganic chemistry textbook until F. Albert Cotton and Geoffrey Wilkinson published their *Advanced Inorganic Chemistry* in 1962.

Eméleus's work in WW2 is discussed in Chapter Seven. After the war he was offered the chair of physical chemistry but, given his weakness in mathematics, wisely declined.[69] Instead he left IC in 1945 for a Readership, soon professorship, in inorganic chemistry at Cambridge.[70] There he worked on fluorides (an offshoot of some of his war work), and on transition metal chemistry. He was elected Fellow of Royal Society (FRS) in 1947, won the Davy Medal in 1962, was President of the Chemical Society, 1958–1960, and President of the RIC, 1963–1965.

Eméleus' coauthor, John Stuart Anderson, known as Stuart or JS, was a Londoner. His father, a cabinet maker, died when he was eight years old leaving the family in extreme poverty. A county scholarship enabled him to enrol at the Northern Polytechnic (today University of North London) and, on winning a Royal Scholarship, he moved to IC in 1926. Two years later he came top of both the ARCS and BSc examination lists and was awarded the Hatton Prize.[71] He was wooed by several members of the staff who wanted him as a research student. Later he wrote that although he was more impressed with the department's organic chemists, 'some perverse streak made me decide that inorganic chemistry must present areas of neglected opportunity, and I decided to enter professor H. B. Baker's laboratory.'[72] Given Anderson's retiring nature, it was a wise choice. As we have seen, Baker preferred that his students choose their own research topics. He also cultivated a friendly and collaborative group of students and junior staff in his laboratory. He expected the senior ones to help the newcomers, and it appears that they did.

With the help of Baker, Purcell and Geoffrey H. Cheesman (later a professor at the University of Tasmania), Anderson learned what was essential for those working in Baker's laboratory, namely how to blow and manipulate glass. He decided to work on the chemical and physical properties of nickel carbonyl. After gaining his PhD in 1931, he won a travelling scholarship and spent a year in Walter Hieber's laboratory at the University of Heidelberg where he learned more about metal carbonyls. Hieber had published widely but held a low-ranking position at the university. Since he refused to join the Nazi Party, and did not condone its activities, he remained in a low position until after WW2 and his 1947 appointment to the chair of chemistry in Munich.[73] Before leaving for Heidelberg, Anderson made an important discovery relevant to Hieber's work. At the time, chemists debated whether carbonyl was a carbon monoxide molecule that somehow tacked on to metals, or whether the carbonyl bond was like the one in CO_2, namely covalent. The physics department had recently acquired a Raman spectrometer. In 1930, just two years after Raman spectroscopy was discovered, Anderson showed that the carbonyl group in the complex was little altered in wave number (and therefore in its nature) by attachment to the metal.[74] This was a remarkably prescient observation. Anderson learned much practical chemistry in Hieber's laboratory, including work on nitrosyl compounds. He continued to work on carbonyl and nitrosyl ligands, and discussed them in the textbook he wrote with Eméleus. Also mentioned in the textbook was a paper he published on the preparation and reaction of Zeise's salt, $K[PtCl_3(C_2H_4)]$, the first organometallic compound to have been discovered (by W. C. Zeise in 1827). As discussed in Chapter Nine, Geoffrey Wilkinson was inspired when reading about this compound in their book.[75]

Anderson was a keen outdoors person. Before returning as a demonstrator in 1932, he made a canoe trip down the Neckar and Danube to Budapest, and a hiking trip in Greece. Eméleus had returned from Princeton one year earlier, so the department now had two young and very talented inorganic chemists on the staff. Early on Anderson decided to learn some crystallography. Largely self-taught, he built his own X-ray apparatus realising only later the dangers to which he had exposed himself. Unlike Eméleus, it took the more retiring Anderson some time to build a research team; but he was a collaborator and worked with Lawrence Brockway on electron diffraction.[76]

Even as a young man Anderson was held in awe. He was seen as erudite, as an outstanding experimentalist, and as having a remarkable memory. Later his Australian colleagues said of him, 'he knew bloody everything twice over.'[77] Like Eméleus, Anderson was drawn to Briscoe. He engaged with Briscoe's isotope studies, something not without benefit since he was to use deuterium in his own work on the kinetics of isotopic exchange among transition metal complexes.[78] Anderson collaborated also with some organic chemists, including on a study of the absorption spectra of the phthalocyanines.[79] Ambitious, but seeing little chance for advancement in the department, he left for a lectureship in Melbourne in 1937.[80]

Looking back, it is clear that Baker attracted many good students.[81] His allowing them to follow their own interests largely unsupervised worked well for the more gifted. Although there was little room for the ambitious to advance within the section, it provided an excellent jumping off point for major careers elsewhere. Those who stayed were devoted more to teaching than research. Some, like Eldridge, took a serious interest in student affairs and provided the continuity and cohesion that made the department a congenial place of study. According to Les Croker, Eldridge 'had a wonderful unifying effect on the department.[82]

Baker was elected President of the Chemical Society, 1927–1928.[83] When he retired in 1932, Thorpe and Philip became joint Heads of Department and Briscoe returned as professor of inorganic chemistry.[84] Briscoe was seen as progressive. In taking over from the Edwardian Baker, he brought the department into the modern age. He approved of the PhD, admired professionalism, and encouraged the prompt publication of research findings. As noted, his strong personality drew others to his own lines of research. He is discussed further in the following chapters.

6.3 James Charles Philip and Physical Chemistry

Philip was one of the most loved and respected professors, not only in the history of the department, but of IC. He was remembered for 40 years of outstanding service, and for joining in many student activities. He played tennis with students into older age, formed a student Glee Club, and sang at student and departmental functions. In a pastoral role he cared for the intellectual development of the young, encouraged students to think about their future careers, and helped them in their personal lives. As Alfred Egerton, professor of chemical technology, noted

> *Throughout his time he made a point of getting to know every undergraduate in the chemistry department, and for many years it was his custom to invite every third-year student to his house, where Mrs. Philip helped them to feel at home. ... When old students visited the college after many years absence, Philip seldom failed to remember their names and their careers.*[85]

Philip was a good lecturer. He taught physical chemistry mainly to third year students, gave a few lectures also to those in the second year, to physics and chemical engineering students, and to students from the RSM.[86]

After First World War (WW1) he built a small physical chemistry research section.

Philip's research interests were mainly in the behaviour of solutions, work he began before the war and which led to his being elected FRS in 1921. With one of his early students, Arthur Bramley (see Chapter Four), he compared the influence of the presence of electrolytes and non-electrolytes on the solvent power of water, and demonstrated a wide range of solute behaviour. After the war he turned to the study of electrolytes in non-aqueous solutions and continued his war work on the absorptive properties of charcoal. Late in his career he began a study of fog particles. Egerton likened all this work to 'a collection of études' rather than 'a finished symphony, it lay more in the application of a wide knowledge of physical chemistry to the elucidation of specific problems rather than pioneering work in a special field.'[87] No doubt études best fitted the working life of someone who took on many tasks beyond the laboratory, including serving as honorary secretary of the Chemical Society for many years.

Some of the research in the physical chemistry section during the 1920s and 30s was inspired by the photochemical work of Purcell and Emeléus. However, new appointees brought new interests with them, notably in electrochemistry, surfaces, colloids and radiochemistry. Joining the section before the start of WW2 were Alex King, Tom Ellingham, Joe Kitchener, and Fritz Paneth. Henry Tizard, appointed college Rector in 1929, was a physical chemist who took a keen interest in what was going on. Like Philip, he had worked with Nernst in Berlin.

As mentioned in Chapter Five, Ellingham was a prize winning student who joined the Royal Engineers and the Mesopotamian Expeditionary Force. After the war he visited the Anglo–Persian oilfields (using river and mule transport), and travelled also in parts of India and Egypt.[88] On his return he organised support for ex-servicemen at the college, many of whom had difficulty returning to civilian life. Appointed a demonstrator, then lecturer, he assisted Purcell in running the undergraduate physical chemistry laboratory.[89] He lectured on both thermodynamics and electrochemistry, covering the blackboard with notes written in advance so as not to waste time while lecturing. According to Roberts, he lectured very slowly, 'with an almost perpetual smile that charmed the dullest student through the most intricate backwaters of the subject.' He failed, however, to charm one of his brightest students. Geoffrey Wilkinson added a marginal note next to this quote in his own copy of Roberts' history. Ellingham's lectures of 1940, he wrote 'put me off thermodynamics for life' and 'King's lectures on kinetics were just as bad.'[90]

Ellingham's research was on electrode reactions. He thought seriously about fuel cells and learned much from Arthur Allmand FRS, professor of physical and inorganic chemistry at King's College, whom he assisted in rewriting the *Principles of Applied Electrochemistry*. Ellingham, in turn, was assisted by Hubert Britton who later joined Allmand at King's.[91] Ellingham's name lives on in Ellingham diagrams, used in extraction metallurgy to evaluate the thermodynamic feasibility of reducing different metal oxides and sulphides.[92] Known more generally for his diagrams and charts, Ellingham designed some to make sense of the activities and business transactions of a number of chemistry-related learned and professional societies. Very much a joiner, Ellingham claimed that he was 'probably known personally to more British chemists than anyone else of [his] generation.'[93] His colleagues saw him as a confirmed bachelor, but shortly before leaving the department in 1945 he surprised them by marrying the owner of a South Kensington antique shop.

Wilkinson's other nemesis, Alexander (Alex) King had been a lively undergraduate. Active in the literary and debating society, he had also founded the short-lived student journals *The Muckrake* and *Monochrome*, was an Editor of *Phoenix*, and a regular attendee at Edith Sitwell's literary salon in Bayswater.[94] As a research student he worked under what he called Baker's 'eccentric ideas of apprenticeship,' gaining an MSc before leaving to work with Kasimir Fajans at the Institute for Physical Chemistry in Munich.[95] He took Baker's questionable advice not to stay for a PhD and, in 1932, accepted Baker's offer of a demonstratorship in physical chemistry at a salary of £175 per annum — about £50 lower than that of demonstrators with a PhD. King carried out research in colloid and surface chemistry. He also gave a course on chemical calculations and, together with Anderson, published a successful book on the subject. He inherited Philip's course in technical German and, with Hans Fromherz, published a German–English technical handbook.[96] King wrote that he missed the 'kindly but largely out of date' Baker. However, he recognised

that Briscoe helped to bring the department into the modern age by insisting that, at the postgraduate level, its role was 'the training of highly
efficient research scientists.'[97] King's leadership of the highly challenging
college expedition to Jan Mayen Island in 1938 so impressed Tizard that,
as will be discussed in Chapter Seven, he was given a number of important
tasks during WW2.[98] By the start of the war King was a senior lecturer.

Joseph (Joe) Kitchener arrived in 1938. Students held a dim view of
his lecturing ability but he became one of the foremost colloid chemists of
his generation. As discussed in subsequent chapters, he had a long association with IC — with the chemistry department until 1961, and as a
reader in the department of mining and mineral technology until 1985.[99]
Friedrich (Fritz) Paneth arrived in 1933, and stayed in the department until
appointed head of department and chair of physical chemistry at Durham
in 1939.[100] Born and educated in Vienna, he worked for some years with
Stefan Meyer at the Institut für Radiumforschung and, in 1929, was
appointed professor of chemistry at the University of Königsberg. There
he carried out research on the chemistry of free radicals and managed
what Frankland had failed to accomplish earlier; namely he showed that
free methyl and free ethyl can exist in the gas phase. He also worked on
the detection of helium, developing analytical methods for measuring very
small quantities of the gas, including its detection in radiochemical reactions. He brought this work to the department where he detected the presence of helium in meteorites, estimating their ages by using theory on
helium's origin in cosmic radiation.[101] His work on free radicals influenced also those in the inorganic chemistry section — notably Pearson
and Eméleus.[102]

Fluent in English, Paneth was on a lecture tour in Britain when Hitler
came to power and he decided not to return to Germany. A highly respected
chemist, the department was happy to give him space; and, with a number
of external grants, he set up a small and lively research group. At first a
visiting lecturer, he was soon made Reader in radiochemistry. One of his
research students was another refugee, Eugen Glueckauf, who worked
mainly on changes in the helium content of the atmosphere. He was to
move to Durham with Paneth and later became head of the physical chemistry section at the Atomic Energy Research Establishment at Harwell.[103]
An interesting question is why Paneth was not appointed professor of

physical chemistry at IC when Philip retired in 1939. Perhaps he was offered the position. His obituarist suggests that he missed Königsberg and was happy to find a chair in an old university town. As is discussed in Chapter Seven, Paneth had a further impact on the department when, in 1943, he was appointed to head the chemistry division of the British–Canadian atomic energy team in Montreal (see Chapter Seven).

6.4 Jocelyn Field Thorpe and Organic Chemistry

After the war Thorpe was determined to build a research school and carry on with the work he had left off in 1914.[104] As mentioned in Chapter Four, he was a student in the department (1892–1893) before moving to the University of Heidelberg for further study. The Heidelberg department had a distinguished faculty, Bunsen, in his eighties, was still working there, and the head of department was Victor Meyer. Thorpe studied with Karl Friedrich von Auwers, gaining his PhD in 1895.[105] He then moved to Owens College (Manchester University from 1904) as an assistant to William Perkin and was soon appointed a lecturer. Like Tilden and Armstrong, Perkin was working on terpene and camphor chemistry. At the height of his powers, he formed a close personal and working relationship with Thorpe. Together they confirmed Bredt's camphor formula, setting themselves the task of determining the structures of camphor and its derivatives.[106]

In 1909, on becoming the Royal Society's first Sorby Research Fellow, Thorpe left Manchester for Sheffield. During his four years there he is said to have worked hard for weeks on end, often preparing two new compounds a day.[107] At IC he built his research group by effectively instructing students in the techniques he had developed, possibly instilling in them something of his work ethic. For a few years after the war he spent many hours in the laboratory, and a steady stream of publications followed. But professional obligations were to draw him away. Already in 1919 he spent a few months in India in his capacity as chairman of the Indian Chemical Services Committee, a position he held until his death in 1939. He also served as Treasurer of the Chemical Society, and was on several professional and government committees. An excellent committee man, he was much in demand. Ingold was impressed by Thorpe and learned much from him. He stated that 'courtesy and humour were ... the key to [his] relations with colleagues and students,' but by the 1920s it was his juniors who 'ran his research.'[108]

Thorpe was elected President of the Chemical Society for 1928–1931. The reason for the three year term was that the Society did not want a change of leadership when in the middle of complicated negotiations to found what was to be named the 'Chemistry House.' The plan was for a new building to house all the chemistry-related professional and learned societies; in the end financial support was not forthcoming. In his 1929 presidential address, Thorpe spoke of the war and how, despite its horrors, it had been a 'stimulus to discovery and production.' He praised the new industrial mergers, holding up their promise for chemistry in the future. On the occasion of his 1931 address, he unveiled a portrait of the society's first president, Thomas Graham, and spoke of chemistry closer to home, namely the research he had carried out since his return to IC.[109]

Thorpe was an outstanding synthesist, and recognised as such. He was remembered as having used simple apparatus in much of his work. He liked to carry out small-scale trials in test tubes, rarely using a rack and propping up the tubes on shelves and in drawers around the laboratory. Students had to take care not to knock them over.[110] Elected to the Royal Society in 1908, he won the Chemical Society's Longstaff Medal in 1921, and the Royal Society's Davy Medal in 1922. He was knighted in 1939, shortly before his death. He often made jokes at his own expense. In an after-dinner speech he told of an occasion when he was on Brighton Pier and weighed himself on a public scale. A man standing nearby, seeing the scale showing a suspiciously low 10st. 6lb., cried out, 'Blimey Bill, he's holler.'[111] Despite his weight, Thorpe was a keen cricketer and golfer, and enjoyed both tennis and duck shooting. Well rounded in more ways than one, he was a lifelong and knowledgeable collector of English china, and he enjoyed cultivating roses. According to Patrick Linstead, he was also a 'grand judge of port,' but 'above all' — and this was surely true — he had 'great force of character.'[112]

When Thorpe arrived in the department in 1914, the only organic chemist left of the old guard was Martha Whiteley. In 1920 she was promoted to Assistant professor (the rank converted to Reader after the college joined the university in 1929). Whiteley had worked closely with

Thorpe during the war and continued to do so after. Together they published a student manual and, as mentioned in Chapter Four, they worked on T. E. Thorpe's *Dictionary*.[113] Whiteley carried on with her work on the amides and oximes, some of it with her student, Hilda Usherwood.[114] According to Hickman, Whiteley was a 'wizard' in the laboratory, 'a stern disciplinarian and a fiend for tidiness.' However, he thought her lectures 'dry as dust and utterly humourless.'[115] He saw her as a natural target for pranksters, but claimed that it was not he who spiked the butter she kept in the laboratory fridge with phenolphthalein. Unpleasant though this must have been, as a woman in authority she was probably the target of far worse. Overall, however, her colleagues respected her, as did the students. She played an important role in college and departmental affairs, and continued to take an interest in them after her retirement in 1934. She supported women students, including those in other departments. Notable was her founding of the Imperial College Women's Association (ICWA) in 1912, and her nurturing of the association in the years following the war.

Many students came to study with Thorpe, and after the war he gathered some talented members of staff, among them Christopher Ingold.[116] Ingold was born in London but, on account of his father's poor health, the family moved to Shanklin on the Isle of Wight. He was educated at the Sandown Higher Grade School and, in 1911, entered Hartley University College, Southampton, where he gained an external BSc from the University of London in 1913. Later he wrote,

> I enjoyed both physics and chemistry, but physics distinctly more. At college I studied both with equal emphasis ... [but] as I saw the matter physics was tidy but dead ... the mysteries that Planck and Einstein had already touched upon ... were never put before me.'[117]

So Ingold decided to focus on chemistry and move to London as a research student.[118] However, war intervened and he worked with Thorpe mainly on poison gases, at first in the department and, from 1915, also at Porton Down.[119] And, as mentioned in Chapter Five, later in the war he was seconded to the Cassel Cyanide Company. At first he agreed to stay with the company after the war, but then had a change of heart. With the intervention of Thorpe, Baker, and the college Rector, he returned to IC as a demonstrator in 1920 and was placed in charge of the Whiffen Laboratory.[120] While in Glasgow Ingold had carried out some of his own research. He continued with this on his return to London, working at a hectic pace, such that by 1921 he had published enough to gain a DSc. He was awarded the RIC's Meldola Medal in both 1922 and 1923 and, in 1924 at the age of 30, he was elected FRS.[121] In 1922 he accidentally inhaled some phosgene but fortunately he was rescued by Hilda Usherwood whom he married 1923.[122]

Thorpe and his students thought deeply about the structure of complex carbon ring structures and about tautomerism (mainly prototropy).[123] Already in the early years of the war, Thorpe and Ingold noted the ways in which highly substituted molecules behave differently from their unsubstituted analogues. They termed the phenomenon 'valency deflexion,' namely the deflection of carbon bonds from strictly tetrahedral angles.[124] Ingold, especially, continued this work after the war, studying steric hindrance and molecular conformation in cyclohexane compounds, as well as in benzene and its derivatives. In the period 1920–1924 he published over 60 papers.[125]

In looking back over his career, Ingold stated that the 'new work made it inescapably clear that the old order in organic chemistry was changing, the art of the subject diminishing, its science increasing'[126] This was true. Jocelyn Thorpe, having fully mastered the art of the subject, passed on many practical skills to his students, Ingold among them. But Ingold also had great mathematical ability and knew much physics. He was not only gifted, but perfectly suited and perfectly situated to advance what he called the 'science' of organic chemistry. Derek Barton was not alone in using the word 'genius' to describe him.[127]

As Mary-Jo Nye has shown, even before leaving the department Ingold had become a leader in bringing the resources of physical chemistry to bear on the problems of organic chemistry. In this connection there was competition with others, notably with Robert Robinson. A priority dispute arose that appears to date back to a note that Ingold added to a paper published by Beesley and Thorpe in 1920. In it he outlined his early ideas on how valency deflexion might work.[128] According to Nye, the note was cited by Nevil Sidgwick and Erich Hückel in the late 1920s as the principal source of their ideas on strain and ring formation. Nye also quotes from a letter that Thorpe wrote to Nevil Sidgwick complaining that it was he who initiated the research into valency deflexion after the war, and that Sidgwick was responsible for promoting the false impression that Ingold alone was responsible.[129]

Soon after the 1920 paper was published, Lapworth and Robinson began speculating on electronic theories of reaction mechanism. They claimed that Thorpe and Ingold's ideas were too simplistic. Ingold, in turn, thought theirs were too speculative. In 1926 Robinson must have complained to Thorpe that his electronic interpretation of mechanism had been used, without proper acknowledgment, in a paper that Thorpe had published with Shoppee and Ingold. Thorpe wrote to Robinson that he would do all he could to 'reverse that impression,' as he was sure would Ingold. But, he added, 'I think, my dear Robinson, that you are just a little oversensitive.' A few days later Thorpe wrote to Ingold saying that he thought Robinson had a point, and that perhaps they had made too 'little reference' to Robinson's ideas. Ingold responded that he was shocked by the suggestion that he had 'stolen' Robinson's ideas and claimed that the ideas expressed in the paper with Shoppee were new insofar as 'any theoretical views are ever new (probably including Lapworth and Robinson's view), being a development and reinterpretation of views partially expressed by many others before.' He then listed many names, including those of Gilbert N. Lewis, Linus Pauling and Lowry, stating that Robinson and Lapworth were part of a larger mix and that 'all ... have been partly or largely right and partly inadequate.[130] This view of things is generally true in science; new ideas usually spring from older ones, albeit often indirectly. Whatever the priority in this particular instance, it was Ingold, together with his wife Hilda Ingold and a number of his research students, who published the most experimental papers on steric hindrance, and on kinetic and polar influences on reaction velocities, during the 1920s. After the Ingolds moved to Leeds their experiments became even more complex. Without them Ingold, Robinson, Lapworth, Sidgwick, and others, would have been without the support needed for their theoretical ideas. In his 1924 speech to the RCS chemical society, Baker mentioned Ingold's chemical successes and jokingly suggested that much should be attributed to Hilda Ingold.[131] There was some truth to this. In many ways, after their marriage in 1923, the Ingolds had a joint career — with some later help from Edward D. Hughes at UCL — not that this in anyway takes away from Christopher Ingold's brilliance.

Ingold left for the chair at Leeds in 1924 and, in 1930, moved to the Chair at University College. Two IC students joined him in Leeds, John Baker and Charles Shoppee. Baker had interrupted his studies to serve in the war (see Chapter Five), returning as a research student with Thorpe. He then spent a brief period as a schoolteacher before joining the staff, leaving with Ingold in 1924 to make his career in Leeds. Shoppee, later FRS, entered IC as an undergraduate in 1922. He began research with Thorpe, but left to join Ingold and completed his doctoral work in Leeds.[132]

When Thorpe went to India in 1919 he assured Baker and the college administrators that George Kon could take over his duties.[133] Kon's route to IC is interesting. He was born in St. Petersburg in 1890, to a Polish father and French mother.[134] When he was ten his father's work with a Russian bank took the family to Tientsin and, when he was 14, to Vladivostok. Kon was educated privately at home, and in several languages. At the suggestion of the British Vice-Consul in Vladivostok, he was sent to Cambridge University. His parents wanted him to study medicine, which he did. He gained an MB but did not pursue clinical studies. After a period of indecision he decided to study chemistry at IC and, finding Thorpe's lectures highly stimulating, became an organic chemist. As with Ingold, war interrupted his postgraduate studies. For two years he worked with Frances Mickelthwait on drug production, later stating that under her care, 'I soon realized that my ideas of what work meant had to be overhauled.'[135] In 1916, he became a British citizen and joined the army. (His army work was mentioned in Chapter five.) After the war Kon became Thorpe's private assistant and gained a DSc. He was appointed a lecturer in 1925 and reader in 1934. He did not give many lectures because of a speech impediment, but was put in charge of the organic chemistry teaching laboratory.

Kon's research was outstanding and he was elected to the Royal Society in 1943. Some of his earlier papers with Thorpe are cited above. Notable among the others are some on the then neglected Guareschi reaction, and on the *spiro* compounds.[136] Another of Thorpe's students (and another Cambridge graduate) was Arnold Stevenson with whom Kon used the Guareschi reaction to arrive at products displaying ring-chain tautomerism.[137] It was in the field of tautomerism that Kon developed his own research, working especially on tautomeric systems of the 3-carbon type.[138] In this he was helped by his student Patrick Linstead (see following paragraph). Later Kon was to work on steroids, especially sapogenins.[139] Working with him in this area was Stanley Harper, another IC undergraduate. On gaining his PhD, Harper was briefly a demonstrator (1934–1936) before leaving for a lectureship at King's College where he became a reader in 1949.[140] He carried out research in East Africa on the chemistry of insecticidal plants and was appointed to the first chair of chemistry at the University College of Rhodesia and Nyasaland in 1955.

Kon was a man of the world. His childhood travels and education had enabled him to become fluent in five languages. He was a wine connoisseur, a good ballroom dancer, and he knew much about 18th-century English furniture. The *Evening Standard* described him as 'the best dressed scientist in London.' According to Roberts, he was 'a man of natural elegance and great personal charm'; but he could be strict, and 'his verbal castigation of any student who incurred his displeasure knew few bounds.' In his memoir Geoffrey Wilkinson wrote that Kon, demonstrating in the organic chemistry lab, said, 'that's a f------ constipated condenser you've got there Wilkinson.'[141] One way of annoying Kon was to whistle in his presence. Knowing this, a group of students put on a testing performance — one whistled the Red Flag, and the others followed by whistling the Tsarist national anthem. On that occasion Kon was more amused than annoyed and no rebuke followed.[142] Kon left the department in 1942 for a chair at the Chester Beatty Research Institute where he began important work on carcinogenesis.

Kon's close contemporary, Ernest Farmer, was educated at the Municipal School, Derby, and under Frederick Kipping at University College, Nottingham, where he gained a BSc.[143] He worked as a schoolteacher until volunteering for the army. In 1917, he was severely wounded at the Battle of Messines, with injuries to his right arm and head. He spent almost two years in hospital, was left deaf in one ear, and had limited use of his right arm and hand. Sadly he was no longer able to play the piano and organ which he had much enjoyed. He decided to return to chemistry despite his handicaps. Kipping advised him to join Thorpe as a research student and he arrived in the department in 1919 while still in uniform. His first research project, together with Thorpe and Ingold, was on intra-annular tautomerism. It was followed by work on the muconic acids.[144]

In 1924 Farmer was awarded a DSc and joined the staff. He ran the Whiffen Laboratory after Ingold's departure. Together with his first research student, John Ross, he worked on cyclic unsaturated ketones, and on the formation and stability of organic anhydrides. They also noticed that the addition of bromine to butadiene usually resulted in polymeric masses, not the monomers they were seeking.[145] Farmer kept samples of the polymers which, in retrospect, can be seen as anticipating his later career. He also engaged in a range of other projects: one on the physical properties of hydrocarbons, one on the isolation of unsaturated acids from natural oils, experiments on autooxidation, work on thermal polymerisation, and on catalytic and selective hydrogenation. He established the structure of licanic acid, demonstrating that licanic and *iso*licanic acid corresponded to the α- and β- forms of eleostearic acid.[146]

Farmer ran a lively and friendly research group. He and his students often worked long into the night. According to Frank Warren, he was always ready 'to say a cheery word at any time between midnight and dawn.'[147] He sometimes took his research group out to dinner, and occasionally to a show. In 1930 he married Marjorie Wilson-Smith, one of his students. She worked with him for the rest of his life. Farmer resigned in 1938 to join the Research Association of the British Rubber Producers as Senior Chemist. At first he did not physically move since the Association rented Henry Armstrong's old laboratory space. With a staff of four, he began his new line of work while awaiting completion of the Association's laboratory in Welwyn. Farmer's departure surprised his colleagues who thought that he was in line for a major chair, possibly as successor to Jocelyn Thorpe. Farmer probably resigned knowing that this was not to be. He was elected FRS in 1948.

One long-time member of the organic chemistry staff, the afore-mentioned Philip Bull, was said to have been the only person in the department unafraid of Martha Whiteley. Educated at Harrow School, he became an undergraduate in 1908. On gaining his ARCS he went to the University of Munich to study with Alfred Einhorn, the discoverer of novocaine. When war broke out he returned to Britain, joined the army, was commissioned as a major, and served in France. He was awarded the DSO and somehow managed to survive all four years of the war unscathed. Bull was a large man, and independently wealthy. As a chemist he was not ambitious but he was a good departmental and college citizen. He was made a lecturer after the war, taught some third year organic chemistry in the advanced analytical laboratory, and occasionally lectured on local anaesthetics. He took many photographs and made films of college events, notably sporting ones. He is said to have eased the way for the college in getting favourable terms in its 1926 agreement with the University of London. The Vice-Chancellor, Louis Napoleon George Filon, had long complained that IC did not support the Officers' Training Corps (OTC). He wanted the college to have an OTC unit were it to become part of the university. The Rector, Thomas Holland, agreed that if the various associateship examinations were accepted as BSc degree equivalent, and if IC students were exempt from university examinations, then the college would start an infantry company. Bull volunteered to organise one, and did so after the agreement was signed. During WW2 he was made a Lieutenant Colonel.[148] He remained in the department until 1954. For much of that time he lived with his mother and sister in a large flat on Queen's Gate.[149]After WW2, from an office in the student hostel, he managed the college food services for four years.

Patrick Linstead came to the college as an undergraduate in 1920. He was to have a long association with the college as student, lecturer, professor of organic chemistry, head of department, and Rector. In this chapter we discuss his time as a student, and as demonstrator and lecturer from 1929–1938.[150] In her memoir, Lady Thorpe wrote that her husband interviewed Linstead when he applied to the department and told her that he had just met a remarkable young man 'who would make his mark on the world.'[151] Linstead's father was a pharmaceutical chemist, later a manager, with Burroughs Wellcome. His mother was interested in literature and the arts. Linstead inherited the interests of both his parents. As a student he was active in the Musical and Dramatic Society and, in 1923, directed a performance of *Pygmalion* (probably the production that shocked Baker). He played the part of Henry Higgins. One year later he took the part of Napoleon in *Man of Destiny*.[152] His IC colleagues remarked on his extensive knowledge of English literature; those at Harvard were surprised by his knowledge of the American Civil War. Linstead was politically conservative and, like many students, supported the government during the 1926 General Strike. He and his close friend, the zoologist Humphrey Hewer, were given just two days training before being let loose as signalmen, first at Paddington Station and then on the Great Central line near Rugby.[153]

In his fourth year, Linstead was taught by the inventive Hickman, then experimenting with acid-base indicators. Hickman gave him a small but interesting project which resulted in his first paper.[154] Linstead gained his BSc in 1923 and joined Kon as a research student. He worked on tautomerism, gaining a PhD in 1926.[155] Then, after a year as Thorpe's private assistant, he took a break from IC to work for the Anglo–Persian Oil Co. He returned in 1929 as a demonstrator in the advanced organic laboratory. Soon promoted to lecturer, he gave a course on organic colouring matters and took over Whiteley's introductory course in organic chemistry. He continued research on tautomerism, publishing an important paper on the subject in 1929; and began some new work on olefinic acids that included the total synthesis of Δ^{10}-n-undecenoic acid.[156] With his student, Arthur Cook, he furthered his research on fused ring chemistry, and with William Bone and Dudley Newitt he carried out some high pressure reactions.[157]

Linstead was remarkably productive and published about 90 papers before leaving the department in 1938. 1934 was an outstanding year, with 15 papers appearing in the *Journal of the Chemical Society*, one of which marked the start of important, but unplanned, work on the phthalocyanines. It came about because Scottish Dyes (soon to be part of ICI) sent Thorpe a sample of what turned out to be iron phthalocyanine. It showed up as an intense blue impurity in the manufacture of phthalimide (used to synthesise indigo) whenever the enamel of the reaction vessels became chipped. Thorpe suggested that Linstead investigate. In doing so Linstead discovered a new group of colouring materials, published many papers, and took out 26 patents between 1933 and 1942. ICI marketed the materials under the name 'Monastral Pigments'[158] In 1938 Linstead left for the firth chair of organic chemistry at Sheffield. But soon after arriving there he suffered a personal tragedy (his wife died during childbirth) and he wanted to get away. One year later he moved to a professorship at Harvard University.

One of Linstead's IC students was Henry (Harry) Rydon who arrived as an undergraduate in 1929. Together, they worked on the olefinic acids, notably on caryophyllenic acid.[159] On gaining his PhD, Rydon became a demonstrator, but left in 1937 to work with Robert Robinson in Oxford. During WW2 he worked at Porton Down, returning to the department as a lecturer in 1947. A major peptide chemist, he became a Reader in 1949 but left for a chair at the Manchester College of Science and Technology in 1952.[160] Arthur Cook, an undergraduate from 1931 was another of Linstead's research students (1933–1935). After two years with Richard Kuhn in Heidelberg, he joined the staff in 1937. Cook, and his work with Ian Heilbron during and after WW2, is discussed in the Chapter Seven. Two other organic chemists from the interwar period deserve mention. Alexander Bernard Manning was a student who joined the staff in 1913. He left in 1924 to become Principal Scientific Officer at the Fuel Research Station in Greenwich. Ralph Winton West was an undergraduate who interrupted his studies in 1916 to serve in the army. On the staff from 1919 to 1927, he worked on the reaction of organic substrates with halides, and was later appointed Principal of the Battersea Polytechnic Institute.

A surprising number of students from this period became biochemical/biomedical scientists, among them Elsie May Widdowson FRS and Juda Hirsch Quastel FRS. Widdowson came to the department in 1925 and spent her third year (the fourth year of the course) working with Samuel Schryver, the professor of biochemistry.[161] She then moved to the botany department where she joined the plant physiologist V. H. Blackman FRS for her PhD, which she gained in 1931. One of her fellow students was Helen Kemp Porter (later FRS), the first woman to become a professor at IC. While working on her PhD Widdowson met Robert McCance (later FRS), a physician and physiologist at King's College who specialised in food chemistry and nutrition. She moved with him to Cambridge where they worked at the MRC Laboratory, and together published the influential *The Chemical Composition of Foods* (1940).[162] Quastel grew up in Sheffield and left school at 16 to work in a medical laboratory. He joined the army in 1916 and his laboratory experience led to his being sent to St. George's Hospital as assistant to Robert Donaldson, the professor of pathology, and not to the battlefield.[163] (The hospital, used by the army, was desperately short of laboratory staff). Quastel came to IC after the war and later wrote that he didn't think 'there was any place in the world where he could have received a more thorough and stimulating instruction in the basic sciences.'[164] He moved to McGill University as professor of biochemistry in 1947. That so many students moved toward the biomedical sciences may reflect the strength of the biochemistry department at that time. Most graduates, however, were to work as mainstream chemists in government laboratories, universities, schools, or industry. Many left to work in the Dominions and the empire — later in the Commonwealth.[165]

When Thorpe retired in 1938 he was succeeded in the chair by Ian Heilbron.[166] Philip retired soon after, but the chair of physical chemistry was filled only after WW2. Briscoe and Heilbron became Joint Heads of Department. Their activities during WW2, and in the years that followed, are discussed in the Chapters Seven and Eight.

End Notes

1. At the time IC was seeking independent university status and did not wish to become part of the University of London. Loyalty to the RCS was far stronger than loyalty to IC. Before the war student clubs were largely centred in the old colleges. Philip and Baker encouraged the formation of new college-wide clubs. For the quotation, and a report of the speech, ICL archives, *The Phoenix*, **9** (3) (1924), p. 75; emphasis in the original.

2. A bronze plaque, designed by Sir William Rothenstein, accompanied the clock.

3. Before the war sporting activities took place in Hyde Park/Kensington Gardens, at the Chelsea Football Club's ground at Stamford Bridge, and at the Duke of York's army barracks on the King's Road. In 1936 Wembley Council expropriated the sports ground; new grounds were then purchased in Harlington.

4. One gifted chemist who stated that he came to IC in 1921 because he could not afford to go to Oxford or Cambridge was Charles W. Shoppee FRS. He is discussed further see Note 132. Based on average earnings, £39 in 1920 is roughly equivalent to £3,000 today; most families had far less disposable income than is now the case. James Norton, a chemistry student, 1928–1930, kept an account book showing how he kept within his budget of £41 per term. ICL archives, B/J. W. H. Norton.

5. This arrangement was to accommodate students who came from schools where the sciences were not taught to HSC standards. (The HSC was later replaced by the GCE, O, and A levels.)

6. Data for that year do not show how many of the first year students were chemists. The C&G students required chemistry in their first year, but were taught separately.

7. As before, the 20 chemists would have been joined by students from the RSM. Lower first year enrolment reflected a socio-cultural trend. After the war children stayed in school longer, more schools offered instruction in the sciences, and more pupils were taking the HSC examinations. This trend led to the abandonment of the first year course after WW2. By 1930 enrolment in the second year was kept to around 50, with the expectation of enrolments of around 40 in the fourth year. For enrolment figures, ICL archives, *Annual Reports*.

8. From 1929, when IC joined the University of London, students who wished to gain an internal BSc had to meet a three year residency requirement. Hence students who entered in the second year needed to stay for the fourth year not only for the DIC, but also for the BSc. Given the agreement with the university, the ARCS examinations were seen as BSc equivalent and, from 1929, students no longer had to take a second set of examinations.

9. The University of London research PhD was introduced in 1920. It was offered as an external as well as an internal degree and it soon became more popular than the DSc.

10. Several of the demonstrators left to become school teachers, for example, George Hazlewood Locket became a science master at Harrow School in 1931. A former pupil at the school, Locket had a strong interest in natural history and became a well known arachnid specialist, but he also wrote some elementary chemistry textbooks. For example (Locket, with Bishop, 1939). True to its name, IC saw itself as a training ground for the servants of empire; several demonstrators of the 1920s left for academic positions in the empire; for example Robert Fergus Hunter was appointed professor of chemistry in the Aligarh Muslim University, India, in 1929.

11. For example, Brunner Mond, a company later to be absorbed within ICI, provided a steady stream of research grants during the 1920s. After the war there was a noticeable change in the type of organised student visits to industrial sites. Places of possible future employment were chosen. During the 1920s, among the businesses visited were Kodak, Parke Davis and Co., Williams Bros. (aniline dye manufacturers), Bryant and May, Morgan Crucibles, British Oxygen, Peak Frean and Co., Osram GEC lamp works,

Hovis, Oxo, The South Metropolitan Gas Co., H. M. Fuel Research Station in Greenwich, British Drug Houses, J. Lyons and Co., as well as old stand-bys such as the Royal Mint, the Gas, Light and Coke Co. in Beckton, and the Whitbread and Barclay, and Perkins breweries. For this information, *Journal of the Royal College of Science Chemical Society*, 1922–1930. (The Society suspended its activities for the period 1914–1922 and later changed its name to Imperial College Chemical Society.) Graduates were to find work in most of the above mentioned businesses.

12. As quoted in A. A. Eldridge, 'Diamond Jubilee Lecture' (IC *Chem. Soc.*, 21 February, 1956), p. 8, (ICL archives B\Eldridge). Since Balfour was a scientifically literate politician, we suspect that Eldridge may have misrepresented the speech to add colour to his own lecture. Financial details on Whiffen Laboratory, KC\Eldridge correspondence, C. K. Ingold to Eldridge, 25 March, 1958. The Whiffen Laboratory, renovated more than once, is still in place in RCS-1. Many chemists, later to be famous, have worked there.

13. ICL archives, KC\1 Eldridge correspondence; Ingold to Eldridge, 25 March, 1958.

14. Some huts were erected on the site to house a laboratory and other facilities. Before the acquisition of Hurworth, and before the formalisation of the MSc degrees, Pollard instructed some students in field work at the Chelsea Physic Garden, at his own Sussex smallholding, and at the Royal Horticultural Society's gardens at Wisley.

15. For example, Albert B. P. Page and Charles Potter worked under Pollard; and Octavius Francis Lubatti, who had taken the course in food and drugs, returned to join Eldridge after working briefly for the colonial medical services in Hong Kong. Later Lubatti and Page were given lectureships in zoology, and all three were to work at Silwood Park on chemical insecticides after WW2. Page became reader in applied entomology.

16. By the mid-1930s the department ran its own store and the cost of start-up apparatus was lower, about £4.

17. Eric F. Thurston, 'Life at the RCS in the Thirties,' *The Record* series V, no. 10 (1940), pp. 11–14. Copy in ICL archives.

18. Eldridge, *op. cit.* (12).

19. We recognise that even today, with high fees and living expenses, there are some students who cannot afford to buy lunches. But disposable income was far less then than it is now.

20. Miss Hornsby was the first official department secretary, but typists worked in the RCS building earlier. Supervised by the formidable Constance Sherwood, they were part of the IC administration, then located on the

lower ground floor of the RCS building. Baker could call on their help when needed. Thomas Holland (Rector, 1922–1929), arrived at the RCS each day in top hat and frock coat. The administration moved to premises in the Union building on Prince Consort Rd. in the 1930s; the freed-up space was then allocated to the inorganic and physical chemistry sections. Sherwood, known as Sherry, came to the college as a shorthand typist in 1919, and later become personal secretary to the Rector. She worked at the college for over 40 years. For Holland, (MacLeod, 2004c).

21. Francis Walter Leslie (Les) Croker worked in the department for 51 years. He came to the college in 1926 at the age of 15, beginning work in the analytical laboratory under technician Freddy Edwards, and ending his career as laboratory superintendent. Croker recorded a memoir, transcribed by Bernard Atkinson, ICL; Bernard Atkinson, 'Department of Chemistry: Recent History, 1960–1989' (typescript saved on CD in ICL archives). Croker was involved in setting up training schemes for laboratory technicians in London (see Chapter Eight) and was made an honorary associate of IC in 1978. Alexander King (see below) complained of having to walk 200 yards to a pay phone outside the RCS building to make a call. Like others, he had no access to incoming calls, (King, 2006), p. 97.

22. ICL archives KC\1, Eldridge correspondence; Riley to Eldridge, 1 April, 1958. For a short biography of Philip Cecil Bull (1889–1960), *The Record*, (June, 1938), p. 93; copy in ICL archives. See also Chapter Seven, and (Anon, 1960). According to Roberts, *op. cit.* (24), pp. 97–98, Bull taught third year organic chemistry students in a section of the advanced analytical lab, and he referred to his 'little domain' as 'Borstal.' In military fashion Bull 'subjected students to occasional kit inspections, exposing many deficiencies in apparatus.' For Riley see below.

23. The Russians, not only chemists, were responsible for the great success of the IC Fencing team in the 1920s.

24. ICL archives, E. R. Roberts, 'History of the Chemistry Department at Imperial College,' (typescript, 1963), p. 63.

25. ICL archives, B\Lowry; memoir 'Pearls before Swine,' p. 8. Geoffrey Lowry was the College Secretary.

26. One student, Charles Holt (1919–1921), did not like Baker. In a retrospective letter, he stated that Baker was 'as elevated in his self-esteem as he was short of inches.' Holt was resentful that Baker did not allow students to use the lift, something allowed on the physics side of the RCS building. Holt went so far as to learn some locksmithing skills and made a lift key for

himself. ICL archives; Rectors' correspondence, Holt to Flowers, 26 March, 1975.

27. Hickman was an undergraduate, 1913–1916, and joined the war effort under Thorpe and Whiteley (see ch. 5). He was a research student under Baker, 1920–1923 (see below). For his two memoirs, http://solarsaddle. wordpress.com/2012/01/06/classic-kit-kenneth-charles-devereux-hickmans-molecular-alembic/. In the second memoir Hickman writes that as an undergraduate he became one of Baker's favourites because, like Baker, during years of childhood illness, he read and digested a wide range of popular science books and could answer just about any question Baker posed to the class. Something of a child inventor, he took out his first patent as a teenager and held about 200 more over his lifetime. Among other things, he developed a silver recovery process used in the photographic industry, introduced some widely copied high vacuum pump technology, and invented a centrifugal molecular high vacuum process, still used in the commercial production of vitamins A and E. Hickman ended his career as director of research at Distillation Products Inc. in Rochester NY. See also Note 46.

28. In his memoir, Sidney Young, the first year lecture demonstrator, wrote that he found Baker's lectures very stimulating, and that Baker was the best teacher he had experienced while working in the department. ICL archives, KC\1\Eldridge correspondence; Young's memoir sent to Eldridge in 1958.

29. Some of Baker's students who joined the staff are discussed below. Others joined industry or government laboratories. For example, Ramsay Middleton Winter (1897–1963), a student from Auckland who joined the army, came to the college while awaiting demobilisation after being wounded in France. After completing his degree in Auckland, he returned to Britain with a Royal Commission of 1851 scholarship. He carried out research in the chemistry department and at the Rothamsted Experimental Station before joining the explosives department of the Royal Arsenal, Woolwich, in 1921. In 1928 he joined ICI (Billingham), and became Research Controller for ICI in 1946. Obituary of Winter, (Fleck, 1964).

30. (King, 2006), p. 63; Eméleus quotation, (Archer, 1997), p. 3.

31. Baker and his student, R. R. Le G. Worsley, were the first to prepare this oxide. (Worsley was later an agricultural chemist in East Africa.) Its existence had been suspected ever since the discovery of selenium in 1818. Selenic acid had been made about 40 years earlier and there had been several previous attempts to prepare the anhydride.

32. According to Roberts *op. cit.* (24),101, Eldridge continued with the intimidation technique he had used on Hickman, solemnly writing down the

names of miscreants in his small notebook. Eldridge lost his wife at about the time he retired. A few years later he and Flora de Courcy (1904–1997) hoped to marry, but sadly he died about a month before the planned ceremony. Miss de Courcy was Eldridge's secretary in his capacity as assistant director of the laboratories. She continued to work for John Welch when he took on that job.

33. For Sugden, (Ellingham, 1945). James Netherwood Sugden (1894–1944) was a student at the Huddersfield Technical College before entering the IC chemistry department as a student in 1913. He gained the ARCS in 1914 and became a research student under Baker. His war work is mentioned in Chapter Five. Sugden joined the staff in 1919 and gained his PhD in 1924. After that he carried out little research, in part due to poor health.

34. Ben Clode identified the students who persisted in stamping their feet during Sugden's lectures by concealing himself under the lecture theatre. Reaching through the ventilation holes, he marked the heels of the miscreants' shoes with aluminium paint. Clode was the technician in charge of the main laboratory during the interwar period. He helped several of the inorganic chemistry staff with their research projects. See Croker memoir, *op. cit.* (21).

35. Roberts, *op. cit.* (24), pp. 94–97. Roberts' account of Sugden's death may not be entirely correct. In his memoir (*op. cit.* 21), Croker claims that Sugden rarely came into the college during the summer holidays and that, on this occasion, he came to collect a bottle of milk saved for him by the tea lady, Mrs. Hay. Bernard Atkinson added a note to Croker's comments, stating that Sugden was 'the most sarcastic member of staff I met in my experience as a student.' Flying bombs, known also as doodlebugs and more officially as V1 rockets, were the first cruise missiles.

36. ICL archives, KC\1–3; letter from R. A. E. Galley to Eldridge, 8 April, 1958.

37. Quotations, Roberts, *op. cit.* (24), p. 89. G. Wilkinson annotated his copy of Roberts' history (his copy is in the ICL archives), noting that when Harwood retired in 1940 he moved to Deganwy near Llandudno, and donated his mineral collection to the National Museum of Wales. In 1987 the Museum contacted Wilkinson asking who Harwood was. The collection, containing over 11,000 specimens, was transferred to Manchester University where Harwood had been an undergraduate. During the war, Harwood, Eldridge, and the geologist Percy Boswell (see Chapter Five) published a short book on glass sands, (Boswell, Eldridge and Harwood, 1916). Harwood also worked with the well-known geologist, Arthur Holmes, pioneer of radioactive dating.

38. See, for example, (Pollard and Chibnall, 1934); also for an annual review of the biochemical literature (Pollard and Stewart, 1934). Pollard was coauthor of several other annual reviews in the 1920s, 1930s and 1940s. Chibnall moved to a chair in Cambridge at the end of WW2 and the biochemistry department was closed down (it reopened in 1965).

39. ICL archives, Joseph Kitchener, typed memoir (not yet catalogued).

40. See below for more on the expedition. For more on Pollard, Chapter Seven.

41. For Jacobs, (Jayne-Williams, 1963). Arthur W. Marsden was another undergraduate who took the MSc in agricultural chemistry. He joined Pollard on the staff in 1936, (for Marsden, Chapter Seven).

42. Roberts, *op. cit.* (24), p. 36.

43. (Baker, 1922, 1923). These experiments were shown at the Royal Society soirée, 17 May, 1922 when Carlton was acknowledged. Margaret (Maggie) Carlton (1895–1969) was given a lectureship in 1946 and worked in the department until her retirement in 1960. Earlier, Baker looked after her interests, sought salary raises for her, and acknowledged her help in the work that won him the Davy Medal from the Royal Society in 1924.

44. Ronald Herbert Purcell (1904–1968) was appointed a demonstrator in inorganic chemistry in 1928, but a year later he became a lecturer in physical chemistry. He remained in the department until the end of WW2. From 1939 he worked on naval defence research. He was much admired for his contribution to the war effort (see Chapter Seven), was appointed superintendent of Research at the Admiralty Materials Laboratory in 1946, and became Deputy Director of Physical Research for the Admiralty in 1951. From 1954–1962 he was Chief Scientific Advisor to the Home Office and, from 1962–1968, Chief of the Royal Navy Scientific Service; Obituary, (Anon., 1969). According to Kitchener, *op. cit.* (39), Purcell gave students some good glassblowing lessons.

45. Samuel Francis (Frank) Boys FRS (1911–1972). At Cambridge Boys worked first with Martin Lowry, but after Lowry's death, with John Lennard Jones and gained a PhD in 1939. During WW2 he worked on rocket propellants at Woolwich Arsenal, returning to IC as an ICI Research Fellow in Chemical Engineering in 1945. He returned to Cambridge in 1949, (Coulson, 1973). For an RSC award in his name, see Appendix Three. The department has an S. F. Boys undergraduate prize for excellence in computational chemistry.

46. ICL archives, KC\1–3; Hickman to Eldridge, 28 April, 1928. Hickman was later to design some major installations, including a large still for a seawater desalination plant in North Carolina.

47. Hickman memoir, *op. cit.* (27).
48. Quotation from Hickman memoir, *op. cit.* (27). Hickman and Spencer published five papers on 'the washing of photographic products' in the *Photog. Journ.* beginning in 1923. Both men published much in this period. Obituaries for Spencer and Hickman, (Anon., 1980).
49. Hickman, *op. cit.* (27).
50. Humphrey Desmond Murray (1899–1960) was an Oxford graduate who joined the staff as a lecturer in 1922 and left to work for the firm full time in 1929. In his memoir, Croker (*op. cit.* 21) rightly claimed that Spencer was 'extraordinarily able', he also claimed that since Bull was very wealthy he put up the money for the business, and that Spencer had the ideas. Later, after Spencer joined the London branch of Kodak, Murray, too, joined the firm and the Fulham Road business closed in 1953. See (Spencer and Murray, 1939).
51. Spencer joined a small experimental photographic company where he worked on the Dufay colour process, much admired and emulated in its time, and produced several fine art photographs. By that time Hickman was established at Kodak, and he recommended that the company appoint Spencer to their London branch. Spencer later became director of research, and then Managing Director, of Kodak Ltd. in Britain. He was President of the Royal Photographic Society, 1936–1938. During WW2, Spencer was in charge of R&D of aerial photography for the RAF. Tom Ellingham recalled that he, Spencer, and former student William Randerson, were in the bar of a London theatre when the latter two decided to write a novel, (Spencer and Randerson, 1934), it was reviewed in *Nature*. B\Ellingham; Ellingham to Pingree, no date, but possibly 1965. For a further obituary of D. A. Spencer, (Jeffreys, 1980).
52. For Pearson, (Emeléus, 1964). Pearson had been a student of H. V. A. Briscoe at Armstrong College, Newcastle. He gained a PhD from Durham University in 1931 and a DSc from the University of London in 1938. He was appointed demonstrator in 1933, after working for a year in Frankfurt with K. F. Bonhoeffer. He left the department just before WW2 to work for the British Aluminium Company in Warrington and later became director of research at the company's Gerrards Cross laboratory.
53. Roberts, *op. cit.* (24), p. 43.
54. (Gibbs, 1935), pp. 126,130. Eldridge was appointed warden in 1934 and lived in the hostel together with his wife.
55. Riley became a respected expert in coking problems and, in 1946, joined the new National Coal Board as Director of Carbonization Research. Later he became director of research for United Steel in Worksop.

56. For Theobald, (Herringshaw, 1980). On leaving Basingstoke Grammar School, Theobald joined the army and was taken prisoner early in 1918. He was repatriated later that year but had to spend time in hospital recuperating. He came to the department in 1919, graduating near the top of his class in 1922. After a short period working for the British Refractories Research Association, where his lifelong interest in the analysis of silicate rocks began, he returned to the college as a demonstrator in 1925. He was an associate editor of *The Analyst*. An anonymous donor funded an annual RSC lecture in analytical chemistry in Theobald's name.

57. Kitchener, *op. cit.* (39).

58. (Thompson, 1987), p. 135. Thompson's observation is backed up by one of us (WPG) who recalls working in the advanced analytical laboratory and having to repeat a gravimetric analysis for calcium six times. However, Theobald is remembered also as having been kind to his demonstrators, and taking them to watch Wimbledon tennis matches, and to dinner afterwards in a Kensington restaurant.

59. Among other things, they developed a naphthalene crystal filter for collecting silica dust in coal mines, (Briscoe, Holt, Matthews, and Sanderson, 1937). Holt and (Miss) Sanderson were research students. Earlier, Janet Matthews (formerly Brown) was a PhD student in the botany department, but she carried out much of her doctoral research in the analytical laboratory. For Pedler, after whom the fellowship was named, see Chapter Three.

60. For Emeléus, (Greenwood, 1993, 2004), quotations, 1993:126–128; see also (Sharp, 1994). Emeléus was a descendent of Huguenots who settled in Finland. His father, a Swedish-speaking Finn, was a pharmacist who moved to Battle, Sussex, with his English wife. Emeléus helped out in the pharmacy: 'I always remember the tremendous pride I had in getting the weighing exact ... and I think that possibly was the beginning of my interest in science.' He also claimed to have had an excellent science education at Hastings Grammar School. Quotation, (Archer, 1997). As to the 'toughest assignment,' the external University of London BSc was known as one of the most difficult degrees to obtain. Emeléus was awarded the RSC Harrison memorial prize in 1932 and the Liversidge award in 1964.

61. In his interview (Archer, 1997) Emeléus stated that Baker had kept the radium in his desk, in a dirty glass tube with open ends and wrapped in a lead tube. Baker had no idea how much radium he had. Emeléus returned a 'lovely clean tube in which was the residue.'

62. (Emeléus, 1926). On some of the early phosphorus work his coworker was William Eric Downey; later it was Purcell. Downey was killed on a college climbing expedition in the Alps organised by G. I. Finch (see Chapter Three).

63. Stock suffered from serious mercury poisoning dating from his time working in Dahlem (Berlin) where mercury spills were not properly cleaned up. He kept a record of the progress of his disease and asked Emeléus to help in analysing his urine. Emeléus recorded isolating a minute, but visible under a lens, droplet of the metal, extracted from one litre of urine, (Greenwood, 1993).

64. Sir Hugh Stott Taylor FRS (1890–1974), professor of physical chemistry at Princeton, was a graduate of the University of Liverpool. He had studied also with Svante Arrhenius in Stockholm and Max Bodenstein in Hanover. Together with Eric Rideal he was the author of the first major textbook on catalysis, (Taylor and Rideal, 1919). For Rideal see also Chapters Five and Eight.

65. (Greenwood, 1993), 131. Emeléus met his future wife at Princeton through a common interest in folk dancing.

66. For an example of some work conducted after his return from the United States, (Emeléus and Welch, 1939).

67. (Emeléus and Briscoe, 1937). Deuterium was discovered in 1931 by Harold Urey, and its utility was soon recognised.

68. (Greenwood, 1993), p. 133, (Emeléus and Anderson, 1938). In its time the book was not used so much as a textbook, but as a review of new work in inorganic chemistry. Later, in light of its influence on Wilkinson and others, it came to be viewed as a textbook classic. The 536 page book sold for 25 shillings. One undergraduate who wrote his final examinations in 1938 wrote a short memoir in which he stated that the inorganic questions were based almost entirely on the book. 'I backed the wrong horse! I crashed particularly heavily.' But he stayed on for postgraduate work on 'haloacetylenes ... [making] 18g of mercury monochloroacetylide.' It's a wonder he survived to tell the tale. Thurston, *op. cit.* (17).

69. We suspect the fact that Emeléus haing been offered the chair of physical chemistry was upsetting to Purcell, and was one reason for his leaving the department in 1946 to pursue a career in government science (see Note 44). We do not know whether the chair was first offered to Paneth, but think it likely.

70. The delay in his professorship was because John Lennard Jones held the title, professor of inorganic chemistry. It took a year for his title to be

changed to professor of theoretical chemistry. Emeléus had other offers of chairs at the time, including from the University of California (Berkeley) and the University of Sydney, (Archer, 1997).

71. For Anderson, (Hyde and Day, 1992), (Day *rev*, 2004), (Tilley and Thomas, 1992).

72. Quotation, (Hyde and Day, 1992), p. 4.

73. Hieber's Munich student, E. O. Fischer, was to win the 1973 Nobel Prize with Geoffrey Wilkinson.

74. (Anderson, 1932).

75. See also Chapter Three, Note 124 for Zeise's salt.

76. (Anderson and Brockway, 1937). Lawrence O. Brockway (1907–1979) came to the United Kingdom after gaining a PhD under Linus Pauling. He worked at the Royal Institution with Lawrence Bragg and, like Anderson, was a pioneer in electron diffraction methods.

77. (Hyde and Day, 1992), p. 22.

78. (James and Anderson, 1937). F. W. James was Anderson's first research student. Anderson coauthored a remarkably advanced paper with W. G. Penney, a future college rector and possibly the best physical chemist the department never had, (Penney and Anderson, 1937). For more on Penney see Chapter Seven.

79. (Anderson, Bradbrook, Cook and Linstead, 1938).

80. Anderson returned to the United Kingdom in 1947, to a position at Harwell where he worked on uranium oxides and hydrides. He also used the electron microscope to study reaction mechanisms in the solid state. He was elected FRS in 1953. While carrying out analyses on fall-out from Britain's nuclear tests, he became fearful of nuclear war. The offer of a Chair in Melbourne allowed him to take his family back to where he thought they would be safer. Five years later, with his children grown and settled, he returned to Britain when appointed Director of the National Chemical Laboratory at Teddington, 1959–1963. From 1963–1975 he occupied the chair of physical and inorganic chemistry at Oxford. Anderson returned to Australia in his retirement so as to be near his family. He received three CS awards: the Tilden (1952), Liversidge (1963), and Longstaff (1975). He carried out bench work (in Canberra) well into his seventies, and published papers into his eighties. For Anderson at Oxford, (Williams, Chapman, and Rowlinson, 2009) Chapter Seven.

81. Another outstanding research student, Dudley M. Newitt FRS (1894–1980), came to the college after WW1. On leaving school he worked at the Ardent factory of Nobel Explosives, attending evening classes at the Royal Technical College in Glasgow where he gained an external BSc from the

University of London. Newitt had an eventful war serving in Mesopotamia; he won the MC for his actions during the capture of Samaria. According to college lore he held the record for the largest fish ever caught in the Tigris (110 lb). Newitt began as Baker's research student, but then moved to work on high pressure reactions with professor Bone. He became a reader in the chemical technology and engineering department in 1936, and professor and head of department in 1952. He published an important monograph, (Newitt, 1940), and won the Royal Society's Rumford Medal in 1962. For Newitt, (Ubbelohde, 1981, 2004).

82. Croker, *op. cit.* (21), p. 5.

83. For his presidential addresses, (Baker, 1927 and 1928).

84. Philip succeeded Baker as director of the inorganic and physical chemistry laboratories. While in Newcastle, Briscoe had carried out some pioneering work on rhenium chemistry. He brought his samples to London and later gave them to Geoffrey Wilkinson who displayed them on a board outside his office.

85. For Philip, (Egerton, 1942), p. 56. (Egerton succeeded Bone as head of the department of chemical technology and chemical engineering.) Philip was an elder at St. Columba's (Church of Scotland), on Pont Street in Knightsbridge and led the Student Christian Union. He was on the governing body of the college from 1932–1938, and served also on the senate of the University of London. Philip's early biography is covered in Chapter Four, and his work during WW1 in Chapter Five. Philip lived in Bedford Park, the Victorian suburb where the architectural ideals of John Ruskin and William Morris were adopted. For a student memoir of visiting the Philips,' W. J. Gooderham, *Report of the RCSA* (Winter, 1983–1984). See also Roberts, *op. cit.* (24), pp. 86–88.

86. One student's notebooks from the physical chemistry laboratory, 1925–1926, are held in the ICL archives; see B\Frank L. Warren.

87. (Egerton, 1942), p. 56.

88. Harold Thomas Ellingham (1897–1975), always known as Tom, was something of a polyglot and taught himself Arabic. See a short biography of Ellingham published on his retirement as Secretary of the Royal Institute of Chemistry, (Anon., 1963); for an obituary, (Anon., 1976). The Anglo–Persian Oil Co., later British Petroleum (BP).

89. Ellingham kept the letter from Baker offering him the demonstratorship. His salary was to be £230 per year. Baker wrote that the job 'makes a very good jumping off place.' ICL archives B\ Ellingham, box 1; Baker to Ellingham, 24 September, 1919.

90. Roberts, (*op. cit.* 24), p. 42. Wilkinson's marginalia in his personal copy, now held in the ICL archives.
91. (Allmand and Ellingham, 1924). The first edition, by Allmand alone, was published in 1912. Hubert Thomas Stanley Britton (1892–1960) was an IC student, 1923–1926, later lecturer at King's College and then professor at Exeter, (Gregg, 1961).
92. (Ellingham, 1944). This paper represents a major piece of work in thermo-dynamics, plotting standard Gibbs free energies of formation of oxides and sulphides against temperature. From such diagrams (later named for Ellingham) it is possible to deduce the temperature and pressure conditions needed in extraction processes.
93. For Ellingham, (Anon., 1963), p. 31.
94. For King, (May, 2004). King has given an amusing account of his under-graduate years in his autobiography, (King, 2006). He won the Harrison Memorial Prize in 1938.
95. (King, 2006), p. 63.
96. (King and Anderson, 1933) went into several editions. (King and Fromherz, 1951). When King left the department Margaret Carlton took over the German course.
97. (King, 2006), p. 88. When King married, Briscoe sent him a book on birth control and the physiology of sex. King was at first indignant, but later thought the gift was simply another mark of Briscoe's modernity, as well as an expression of concern for his future happiness.
98. For King's account of the Jan Mayen expedition, (Jennings and King, 1939). Publications by other members of the expedition followed in a range of specialist journals.
99. Kitchener, *op. cit.* (39).
100. For F. A. Paneth (1887–1958), (Hevesey, *revised* Gross, 2004), (Spitler, 1974), (Emeléus, 1960), (Glueckauf, 1959). Paneth was elected FRS in 1947. In 1953, he returned to Germany as Director of the Max Planck Institute for Chemistry in Mainz. According to the historians of UCL, Ingold wanted Paneth to succeed F. G. Donnan as professor of physical chemistry at UCL. But this was one of the rare occasions when Ingold failed to get his way; former IC student, Samuel Sugden, was appointed to the chair in 1938, (Davies and Garratt, 2013), p. 102.
101. (Paneth, 1942). He was not alone in carrying out this type of work. Otto Hahn and others were doing so too.
102. Paneth published widely; among his publications were some in the history of science. A paper from his period in the department is (Paneth and

Thompson, 1935). George Paget Thompson was professor and head of the physics department at IC. See also, (Paneth and Glückhauf, 1938), (Edgar and Paneth, 1941). Paneth pioneered studies of helium, ozone and nitrogen dioxide concentrations in the atmosphere.

103. Glueckauf left Germany in 1933, and worked with Paneth at IC, moving with him to Durham in 1939. There, on a small stipend, he continued research; his wife became Paneth's secretary. In 1940 he was briefly interned on the Isle of Man but, after that, continued working on atmospheric chemistry. In 1944 he began work on gaseous chromatography for the Tube Alloys project. In 1947 he moved to Harwell and changed the spelling of his name from Glückauf to Glueckauf, (Everett, 1984).

104. For Jocelyn Thorpe, (Ingold, 1941), (Kon and Linstead, 1941), (Armstrong, 1940), (Whiteley and Kon, 1940), (Costa, 1976). Surprisingly there is no *ODNB* entry for Thorpe, something we hope to remedy.

105. Thorpe is said to have caused astonishment in Heidelberg when, on the night of 5 November 1892, he threw about a pound of sodium into a large body of water. When a student in London, he is said to have thrown lumps of sodium into the Serpentine on 5 November 1892; however, knowing about Guy Fawkes people in London will have been less surprised.

106. (Perkin Jr. and Thorpe, 1897).

107. (Ingold, 1941), p. 535. An assistant carried out the analyses.

108. Quotations, (Ingold, 1941). ICL archives, KC\1 Eldridge, correspondence file; Ingold to Eldridge, 25 March, 1958.

109. (Thorpe, 1929, 1931). The Graham portrait was by Herbert Budd.

110. (Ingold, 1941).

111. Roberts, *op. cit.*(24), pp. 82–84.

112. ICL archives; R. P. L. [Linstead] *The Record*, (June, 1938), pp. 101–103. Others remember Thorpe drinking port in his office in the evening, and that he was a cigar smoker.

113. The student manual, (Thorpe, Whiteley, ter Meulen, and Heslinga, 1926).

114. (Whiteley and Usherwood, 1923). Usherwood wrote her 1922 PhD thesis on two topics, 'the detection of equilibria in gaseous tautomeric substances' and the 'formation of heterocyclic rings involving reactions with nitroso and nitro groups in their various tautomeric modifications.' She submitted 23 papers to gain her DSc in 1934.

115. Hickman memoir, *op. cit.* (27).

116. For Ingold, (Leffek, 1996, 2004), (Shoppee, 1972), (Ridd, 1971). For Ingold at University College, (Roberts, 1996), (Davies and Garratt, 2013).

117. Ingold, quoted in (Leffek, 1996), p. 22. Ingold was five years old when his father died.
118. Another Hartley University College graduate, George Reeves, gained a first class, Ingold only a second class BSc. Ingold and Reeves entered the IC department at the same time, both to study with Thorpe. Reeves later became Works Chemist with British Celanese in Derby.
119. Thorpe and Baker early recognised Ingold's brilliance. In 1915 Baker supported him for a Beit fellowship, stating 'he is an exceptional man and I believe he will have a distinguished future.' Because of his war work, Ingold asked that the fellowship be held over until after the conflict, which it was. ICL archives, Board of Study Minutes, 7 July, 1915. The land at Porton Down was used for testing a range of chemical and other weapons already in 1915. It was purchased by the government in January 1916. Ingold began testing some of Cassel's lachrymators, and shells for their delivery, at both Porton Down and Shoeburyness, in 1916.
120. See heads of chemistry department correspondence, 1920. ICL archives, KC/9/7. Ingold was given his suspended Beit research fellowship grant in addition to his demonstrator's salary.
121. After awarding Ingold the Meldola Medal for a second time, the RIC changed the rules so that it could be awarded only once to any one person. As to his FRS, Ingold was nominated by Thorpe, seconded by Baker, and the certificate was signed by 18 others, including Robert Robinson (see following notes). Ingold also won the CS Longstaff award in 1951 and the Pedler award in 1956. Many thought he deserved to win the Nobel Prize.
122. ICL archives; KC/1 Eldridge correspondence; F. Dickens to Eldridge, 21 March, 1958; C. Ingold to Eldridge, 25 March, 1958. Edith Hilda Usherwood, known as Hilda, was a research student with Whiteley at the time. Her father, Thomas S. Usherwood, a science teacher at Christ's Hospital, promoted Armstrong's heuristic methods (see Chapter Four) and developed a teaching stream in engineering at the school. For Usherwood, (Rayner-Canham and Rayner Canham, 1999), (Leffek, 1996).
123. By our reckoning, papers by Thorpe and his students occupy close to one quarter of the space devoted to papers in *J. Chem. Soc. Trans.* and *J. Chem. Soc.* in the 1920s. Thorpe never allowed his name to go first on papers that were on work conducted mainly by his students. Among his students were several Indians whom he encouraged to come to IC during his visit to India in 1919. For papers from this period representing some of his interests see, for example: (Jordan and Thorpe, 1915). Louis A. Jordan CBE became the first Director of the Paint Research Association in 1923. Also, (Ingold and

Thorpe, 1921), (Pedige, Chandrasena, Ingold, and Thorpe, 1922), (Farmer, Das Laroia, Switz, and Thorpe, 1927).

124. Valency deflexion is also known as the Thorpe–Ingold effect (see following notes). For an early discussion, (Beesley, Ingold, and Thorpe, 1915). For a later summary, (Ingold and Thorpe, 1928). Today the term 'Thorpe–Ingold effect' is used in a more limited sense — for the effect of *gem*-dimethyl groups in hastening ring closure.

125. See Note 123. For a further example, (Ingold and Baker, 1923); in regard to this paper, it should be remembered that cyclohexane was then widely seen as a flat ring, (Ingold, 1921). For benzene structure, (Ingold, 1922). According to Mary Jo Nye, the work on benzene was in part inspired by a lecture given by Frederick Soddy, (Nye, 1993), p. 203. Ingold was looking at the possibility of tautomerism between the benzene structures given by Kekulé and Dewar. He was not yet using electron valence ideas — those ideas were adopted only later in the decade by which time the Dewar formula had been dropped. For Ingold's mature ideas, (Ingold, 1953).

126. Ingold, quoted in (Shoppee, 1972), p. 356.

127. (Barton, 1996). Barton suggested that Ingold was blocked from receiving the Nobel Prize by the machinations of Sir Robert Robinson, Waynflete professor of Chemistry at Oxford, and that Ingold was the greater chemist — a debatable claim. (Robinson won the Nobel Prize in 1947, during his tenure as President of the Royal Society, for his work on natural product chemistry.) In his paper, Barton discusses those he saw as the titans of organic chemistry in his time: Ingold, Robinson, Winstein, Woodward and himself. For Robinson's views, see his posthumously published autobiography, (Robinson, 1976). He appears to have held a grudge against Ingold even into older age — possibly because Ingold's later terminology, and his way of framing the discussion on electrons and reaction mechanism, was accepted. Despite its cheeky subtitle (compare it with the title of Robinson, 1976), (Leffek, 1996) includes a balanced discussion of the Ingold–Robinson dispute.

128. (Beesley and Thorpe, 1920). R. M. Beesley came to IC with Thorpe in 1914, but stayed only briefly. Thorpe then asked Ingold to take over his research. The paper cited includes a note (pp. 603–610) by Ingold on the mathematical forces at play in 'deflexion'; in it he was critical of Baeyer's strain theory of 1885.

129. (Nye, 1993), Chapter Eight, 201, for the letter from Thorpe to Sidgwick. Nye gives a comprehensive account of the early development of ideas on reaction mechanism.

130. (Ingold, Shoppee and Thorpe, 1926), (Leffek, 1996), p. 92. Royal Society archives, Robinson papers; D33; Thorpe to Robinson, 4 July, 1926; Thorpe to Ingold, 11 July, 1926; Ingold to Thorpe, 12 July, 1926. In their obituary (Todd and Cornforth, 1976) state that Robinson claimed to have learned all his organic chemistry from Thorpe in Manchester.

131. *op. cit.* Note 1.

132. John William Baker (1898–1967) became reader in the mechanism of organic reactions at Leeds. He was the author of several books including (Baker, 1958). When at IC he wrote the entry 'tautomerism' for Thorpe's *Dictionary*. For Shoppee, (Mander, 2003). Shoppee later held chairs in Swansea and the University of Sydney where he specialised in the chemistry of steroids.

133. ICL archives; Rector's correspondence, Thorpe to Acland (then acting rector), 8 September, 1919. In this letter, Thorpe requested leave from late October to early March, and urged also the appointment of Ingold.

134. For Kon, (Linstead, 1952).

135. Quoted in (Linstead, 1952), 170 or 4550.

136. (Kon and Thorpe, 1919). The Guareschi reaction, often called the Thorpe–Guareschi reaction is the synthesis of 2-pyridones from cyanoacetic esters with diketones and ammonia.

137. See, for example, (Kon, Stevenson, and Thorpe, 1922). What became known as the Wallach–Kon ketone ($C_9H_{14}O$) was, as shown by both men, a notable 3-carbon type displaying tautomerism. (Otto Wallach, Nobel Laureate, 1910).

138. (Kon and Linstead, 1925). There were many papers published in this series.

139. (Harper, Kon, and Ruzicka, 1934). Otto Diels mentioned this paper, and how he had synthesised the same compound, in his Nobel Prize speech.

140. One of Harper's research students at King's College was Leslie Crombie FRS who joined the organic chemistry staff at IC in 1951. One of the foremost natural product chemists of his generation, Crombie ended his career as professor of organic chemistry and head of department at Nottingham. He is discussed further in Chapter Eight.

141. ICL archives B\Wilkinson, handwritten memoir.

142. Roberts, *op. cit.* (24), quotations, including from the *Evening Standard*, 62, 93.

143. For Farmer, (Gee, 1952), (Warren, 1954). Farmer's student and obituarist, Frank Louis Warren was on the staff, 1928–1931. He left for a lectureship at the University of Cairo, and was later professor of chemistry at the University of Natal, (Goosen, 1981). Warren's student, André Goosen, worked with Barton in the 1960s on a postdoctoral fellowship.

144. For example, (Farmer, 1922), the first of four parts.
145. Butadiene was then a rare compound that Farmer obtained by isolating/ preparing it from 'railway hydrocarbon' (soot) collected from a depot in Slough.
146. For example, (Farmer and Ross, 1926).
147. For Farmer, (Warren, 1954), p. 1654.
148. There was much opposition in the college to the OTC unit. Former student H. G. Wells wrote, 'I cannot imagine what a good RCS student can do for his country or himself by joining the OTC.' The general mood in the college was that it was through their scientific work that students could contribute most to their country. Quotation, *The Phoenix*, 11 (1926), p. 154. An agreement to join the university was reached in 1926 but came into effect only in 1929.
149. According to Croker, *op. cit.* (21), when Bull lived on Queen's Gate the family had 23 servants. When Bull first came to the college he was accompanied by a male servant who carried all his materials. Croker also stated that the family fortune declined during the Great Depression and that they then moved to a flat in Westminster that Bull told him, 'only cost £1200 a year.' As Croker noted, this was roughly what professor Baker earned in a year. (The family fortune was made in Australia by Bull's grandparents). In 1949 Bull moved to Cobham, Surrey. His photographic equipment was always the best, purchased from his close friend Wallace Heaton. Bull was also a prominent Freemason and member of the IC lodge.
150. For Linstead, (Barton, Rydon, and Elvidge, 1968), (Barrett and Barton, 2004), (Rydon, 1967). Linstead was another student educated at the City of London School who came to the department — in the footsteps of William Perkin.
151. Roberts, *op. cit.* (24); ICL archives, B\Jocelyn Thorpe, Lady Thorpe's memoir.
152. ICL archives, Musical and Dramatic Society files. Eric Ashby (later Lord Ashby FRS) played the role of Alfred Doolittle in the same production of *Pygmalion*.
153. ICL archives, B\Linstead\A22.
154. (Hickman and Linstead, 1922). By modifying the methyl orange with a so-called 'screened indicator,' in this case xylene cyanole FF, the colour change can be made sharper and the indicator function improved.
155. For some of his PhD research, (Linstead, 1927).
156. (Gaubert, Linstead and Rydon, 1937) brought much attention.
157. For example, (Cook and Linstead, 1934), (Newitt, Linstead, Boorman, Bone, Sapiro, and Thorpe, 1937).

158. See, for example, (Linstead, 1934), (Barrett, Dent, and Linstead, 1936). The work continued until the outbreak of war. Complexes, named by Linstead phthalocyanines, were made with 19 different metal elements; those with copper proved especially useful. One of blue copper pigments has long been used as a dye for the British £5 note. A Monastral blue was also used as the dye for the cover of Pelican Books. For a short article about the Pelican covers, (Ball, 2014). Ball notes that ICI, which held the patent for the pigments, made a film about them featuring Linstead. He amusingly points out that it shows Linstead 'conduct[ing] a chemical analysis while stylishly smoking a pipe.' See illustration 28 in this book — a still from the film — showing the stylish smoker.

159. (Rydon, 1937).

160. (Rydon, 1962). Rydon obituary, (Ridge, 1992). According to Croker, *op. cit.* (21), Rydon was unhappy in the postwar period because of a difficult marriage and this may have prompted his move to Manchester. In 1957 Rydon moved to a chair at the University of Exeter. Croker wrote that, by then remarried, Rydon was happy in Exeter. Rydon was awarded the RIC Meldola Medal (1937) and the CS Harrison Memorial Prize (1939).

161. Samuel B. Schryver FRS died in 1929, and was succeeded in the chair of biochemistry by his former student, Albert C. Chibnall FRS.

162. (McCance and Widdowson, 1940). A seventh edition of this book was published in 2014. For Widdowson, (Ashwell, 2002), (Whitehead, 2004). Widdowson's younger sister studied mathematics at IC and became a renowned apiculture expert.

163. For Quastel, (Macintosh and Sourkes, 1990). Quastel, known as Harry or Q, moved to Cambridge for postgraduate work with former RCS student Frederick Gowland Hopkins. After a few years working at Cambridge, Quastel became director of research at Cardiff City Mental Hospital. During WW2 he carried out soil research at Rothamsted. On retiring from McGill in 1966, he was invited to set up the field of neurochemistry at the University of British Columbia. Others who had notable biochemical/medical careers include: Harold W. Buston, undergraduate and research student, 1918–1925, who became reader in biochemistry at IC; Charles E. Dent FRS, student from 1930–1934, professor of Human Metabolism at University College London; Frank Dickens FRS, student 1921–1923, professor of biochemistry at the Middlesex Hospital Medical School; Charles H. Gray, student from 1929–1931, professor of chemical pathology at King's College Medical School; Nicholas H. Martin, student from 1929–1931, professor of chemical pathology at St. George's Hospital Medical

School; Kenneth V. Thimann, undergraduate and research student, 1921–1929, an expert in plant hormones, who worked at Harvard before moving to a full professorship in plant physiology at the University of California (Santa Cruz). Lisa Wilkinson (a Danish plant physiologist and wife of Geoffrey Wilkinson) was to work for Thimann when the Wilkinsons were living in Cambridge MA in the early 1950s; and Leslie Young, student from 1930–1932, professor of biochemistry at St. Thomas' Medical School.

164. Quoted in (Macintosh and Sourkes, 1990), p. 385.

165. Among the students not already mentioned are Sir Charles Mills Cawley who gained his BSc in 1929, left to work at the Fuel research Station and, in 1959, was appointed Chief Scientist to the Minister of Power. Maxwell B. Donald, a student in 1914–1915 and 1919–1921, became professor of chemical engineering at UCL. Paul E. Gagnon, a student from 1929–1931, became head of the chemistry department at the University of Laval and was the Canadian delegate to the International Conference on the Peaceful Uses of Atomic Energy in Geneva, 1955. Robert F. Hunter became professor of chemistry at the University of Aligargh in 1930 where he built new laboratories modelled on those in South Kensington. He later returned to the United Kingdom and worked for Bakelite. Hubert Martin, a student in 1915–1917 and 1919–1921, became professor of chemistry at the University of Western Ontario. Kurversti G. Naik, a research student from 1919–1921, became professor of Chemistry at the University of Gujurat. On his 60th birthday Naik's friends donated enough money to found a department of biochemistry at the university in his honour. Arthur C. C. Newman, a student from 1929–1932, became Head of the Manufacturing Department of Burroughs Wellcome. Lewis C. Nicholls, a student from 1919–1922, became Director of the Metropolitan Police Laboratory at Scotland Yard. H. C. Russell, a student from 1918–1922, became science mistress at York College for Girls, one of several women students who became science teachers in this period. William Dallas Scott, BSc (1927) and PhD (1930) was a senior executive with Monsanto who then moved to the petroleum industry; William J. V. Ward, a student from 1919–1921, became chairman of ICI, Billingham. Many more than those mentioned here left to work in the Empire/Commonwealth.

166. A congratulatory volume from the students and staff of the organic chemistry section was presented to Thorpe on his retirement. It is held at the RSC, ID AR0393.

Chapter Seven

The Department During the Second World War

7.1 Introduction: Staff Members in 1939

When war broke out in 1939 Vincent Briscoe was head of inorganic and physical chemistry and Ian Heilbron was head of organic chemistry. There was no overall head of department. Briscoe was born in Hackney and educated at the City of London School. He came to the RCS with a scholarship in 1906, joined T. E. Thorpe as a research student in 1909, and in 1911 was appointed demonstrator.[1] In that year he also bought his first motorcycle, the start of a lifelong passion for driving and motor vehicles. It was said that his knowledge of London streets would not have disgraced a taxi driver. According to Geoffrey Wilkinson, Briscoe claimed to be 'a disciple of Theodore W. Richards.'[2] Indeed, in the period before and after World War 1 (WW1), Briscoe developed new methods for purifying some of the elements, and for handling volatile hydrolysable halides. He determined the atomic weights of bromine, boron, tin, vanadium and thallium; his measurement for tin (118.70) was very close to what is accepted today. He also developed a highly sensitive flotation procedure for comparing the densities of samples of boron trichloride, made with boron of different geological origins.[3]

When Briscoe returned to Imperial College (IC) as professor of inorganic chemistry in 1932 he took an interest in industrial dusts; his method for analysing mining dusts responsible for silicosis won him a medal from the Institution of Mining and Metallurgy. He also made some 'inert' dusts that were used with some success in controlling weevil infestations in grain stocks. In addition, he explored the natural abundance of deuterium in water from a wide range of sources, mineral and biological, carrying out kinetic studies of deuterium–hydrogen exchange. An excellent experimentalist, his precise methods of density determination allowed the measurement of deuterium in very small samples of water or gas. He obtained H_2O^{18}, HDO … etc. by fractional distillation for which he built a still that is still talked about. It was constructed in the stairwell at the eastern end of the department (the stairwell in RCS1) and the column reached from the lower ground floor to the building's upper ceiling.[4]

According to Harold Smith, Briscoe's lectures were highly entertaining. He had 'a wonderful collection of experiments that went "bang," and could juggle with test [tubes] in a most professional manner'.[5] Emeléus credited him with keeping inorganic chemistry alive during the interwar period, first as a professor in Newcastle and then at IC.[6] During this war, however, he gave few lectures since much of his time was taken up with other work. Many people remembered him fondly. He was described as small and puckish, as kind, having great charm, being an excellent committee man, and very good at keeping up morale during bombing raids. And, as will be discussed in the next chapter, he was an outstanding mentor to Derek Barton and Geoffrey Wilkinson.

Ian Morris Heilbron FRS (1886–1959) was born in Glasgow. At the age of 16 he left Glasgow High School for the Royal Technical College where he came under the influence of professor, George G. Henderson FRS.[7] Henderson suggested that he move to Leipzig to study further with A. R. Hantzsch, an expert in the use of physical methods in organic chemistry. After gaining his PhD Heilbron returned to a lectureship at the Royal Technical College in 1909. He also joined the Territorial Army and, when WW1 broke out, joined the Royal Army Service Corps. He was appointed assistant director of supplies at GHQ in Salonika, was made a Lieut. Colonel, and received the Distinguished Service Order (DSO). After the war he worked briefly for the British Dyestuffs Corporation where he met Hugh Mills Bunberry with whom he later published the *Dictionary of Organic Compounds*.[8] Heilbron returned to the Royal Technical College as professor in 1919, but within a year had moved to

Liverpool as Heath Harrison professor of organic chemistry. In 1933 he was appointed professor of organic chemistry in Manchester where, in 1935, he became the Sir Samuel Hall professor and head of department.

Before coming to London Heilbron had established himself as a major organic chemist. With Henderson he had worked on the formulae of pinene, bornylene and camphene. On his return from Leipzig, he began work on the semicarbazones and, in Liverpool, he pursued his interest in structural questions and studied the chemical reactivity of conjugated unsaturated ketones, notably distyrylketones.[9] In turning to natural products, he at first saw cholesterol as a possible candidate for vitamin D, and then as its progenitor. A pioneer in both vitamin and steroid chemistry, he developed reliable methods for assaying vitamins in fats and oils, and carried out work on the chemistry of vitamin A. He worked on its synthesis and was close to having worked out its detailed structure when narrowly beaten by Paul Karrer and his team in Zurich. Karrer and Norman Haworth won the Nobel Prize for chemistry in 1937.[10]

In 1938 Henry Tizard, the college Rector, invited Heilbron to become Jocelyn Thorpe's successor. Heilbron replied, 'there is a great opportunity of building up in London a flourishing school of organic chemistry'; but it would be impossible, he wrote, without modernising the laboratories which fail to

provide even the bare minimum of services.... The research students are crowded into a number of unsuitable rooms with restricted bench space and bad lighting. Modern amenities are conspicuous by their absence and the conditions are altogether deplorable.[11]

This overstated things and showed little respect for what Thorpe had accomplished, but clearly Heilbron was in bargaining mode. He wanted to bring new physical methods to the organic chemistry section — molecular distillation, microanalysis, chromatography, and spectroscopy — and sought the means to do so. He told Tizard that he would encourage a wide range of research, but that he favoured natural product chemistry.

Briscoe was keen for Heilbron to join the department and informed Tizard that, 'if needs be,' they could manage without replacing Philip. Tizard agreed to this, and to some modernisation. The Whiffen laboratory and some small neighbouring rooms were converted into a research laboratory for Heilbron, and some other laboratories were renovated.[12] A new post, senior laboratory steward, was created and filled by Frederick G. Consterdine who came with Heilbron from Manchester (his position was soon renamed, laboratory superintendent). Consterdine was excellent but, loyal to Heilbron, left with him in 1949.[13] Heilbron also brought in Bill Boston as a laboratory technician. Boston set up an organic microanalytical laboratory, but sadly he died of a heart attack during the war. Heilbron found work for his widow, Ivy Boston. She was Eric Waight's assistant for many years (for Waight, see Chapter Eight).

With the promise of a new research laboratory, Heilbron agreed to move to London. In addition to Consterdine and Boston, he brought two of his younger colleagues, Donald H. Hey and E. R. H. (Tim) Jones.[14] Both were appointed lecturers. Already in place were the organic chemists George Kon, Philip Bull, and Arthur H. Cook. Cook, Linstead's former student, had joined the staff in 1937 and was to work closely with Heilbron. Bull carried out little research. He was the commanding officer of the IC officer's training corps and, according to wartime student John Wilkinson, was 'a fine figure of a man … nobody took any liberties with him.'[15]

As to physical chemistry, Paneth left for Durham in 1939. Briscoe released Ronald Purcell from running the teaching laboratory and put Tom Ellingham in charge. Stuart Lawrence (see below) joined the staff as a lecturer in 1935, but he, Ellingham, and Purcell were soon pulled away from teaching duties by war-related work. So, too, was Alexander King. As a result much of the teaching fell on the shoulders of Joseph A. (Joe) Kitchener, a newly appointed demonstrator. In the inorganic chemistry section, the staff remained largely unchanged and included Arthur Eldridge, James Sugden, Henry Harwood, Harry Eméleus, Leslie Theobald, Margaret Carlton, Alfred Pollard, Leslie Cobb, and Arthur Marsden.[16] Marsden, a former student in the department, joined the staff in 1936. He worked with Pollard on agricultural chemistry and later took over the course on foods and drugs from Eldridge. Harwood packed up his house in 1939 and put it on the market, thinking the department would be evacuated to Edinburgh. This turned out not to be the case, but he decided to leave London regardless. Close to retirement age, he resigned in 1940 and moved to Wales. Theobald took over the analytical laboratory and is said to have run an excellent course. A former student, A. J. E. (John) Welch, was appointed to work under him.[17] Also appointed in 1940 was another former student, Eric R. Roberts. He is discussed in Chapter Eight.

7.2 War Preparations and Daily Life during the War

Tizard set up a War Emergency Committee at the time of the Munich crisis in 1938. All departments were asked to draw up plans for the safe storage of records and dangerous chemicals. Bomb shelters were constructed in or close to the major buildings, first aid centres were set up, and members of the technical and laboratory staff were assigned to maintenance parties. At the same time negotiations began for evacuating the college to different regional universities, and plans were soon in place for most departments, including chemistry, to be moved to Edinburgh. Early in 1939 Tizard asked for those plans to be enacted. The laboratory staff washed solvents and acids down the drain, and emptied gas cylinders outdoors, including those containing poisonous gases. Whether they acted on their own, or were given instructions by Briscoe and Heilbron is unclear. However, the evacuation plans were soon abandoned, resulting in a frantic effort to replace the scarce materials that had been wasted. The chemical technology and chemical engineering department did better, securing its chemicals, gas cylinders, and flammable liquids in outdoor sheds.[18]

Imperial was the only major college in London to remain largely in place during the war, and the administration soon began to issue all kinds of instructions, some of them contradictory. For example, the department was first asked to close and tape, and then to open, all the windows. No one seemed to know what would be best in the case of bomb blasts or gas attacks. The final instructions were to close and re-tape all the windows, and to install blackout curtains. A bomb shelter was built into the ground at the back of the Royal College of Science (RCS) building (on the physics side). It was large and supposedly gas proof, had a reinforced roof, and was equipped with emergency food rations, buckets of water, fire extinguishers, stirrup pumps, shovels, picks, crowbars, hurricane lamps, and blankets.[19] Three mobile blast and splinter-proof shelters were set up in the basement of the building for use by students and staff in case of daytime air raids. When the public sirens sounded, members of the maintenance party blew whistles inside the building, and it was then compulsory to enter one of the shelters (where smoking was forbidden). All citizens were issued with gas masks, and students and staff were told to bring theirs to work each day. Routine emergency drills revealed that these instructions were not always followed. Several members of staff joined the local Home Guard company, under the command of Major W. H. Bevan.[20] Bevan looked after the college and its environs well and the Rector put his name forward for a state honour at the end of the war. A few members of staff, those with heavy wartime duties, lived in the college hostel (closed to students during the war). Geoffrey Wilkinson left an account of his life as a wartime student and claimed, not entirely accurately, that there was little social life. He, for example, went cross country running with friends, joined others on weekend trips out of London, went on camping trips with Alfie Maddock (see below), joined the dramatic society (working on props, scenery etc.), and went to the cinema and the occasional concert — including the Promenade concerts which came to the Albert Hall after the BBC's Queen's Hall was destroyed during the Blitz. He also joined the Home Guard for a short period.

The RCS maintenance party was drawn from the technical and stores staff of both the chemistry and physics departments; those from chemistry were under the direction of Consterdine. Members of the party kept watch over the RCS building day and night, guarded the underground tunnels against possible saboteurs, and had to prevent unauthorised persons from entering the building. They were issued with whistles with which to raise the alarm. At least two members had to be present in the chemistry side of the building at any one time, one in a control room equipped with a phone. Both physics and chemistry members slept in a room on the chemistry side of the basement. It was fitted with bunks and showers. Ellingham described the maintenance party as 'very cheery'. Graham Martin wrote that it held parties 'better described as orgies,' and that luckily no air strikes occurred when they took place.[21]

Briscoe, too, spent many nights in the department. Collectively, he and the maintenance party were known as Snow White and the seven dwarves. Eleméus took charge of the firefighting arrangements, was responsible for keeping the firefighting equipment in proper order, and for ensuring that everyone knew the location of the hydrants and hoses. He was also in charge of a group of eight — four students and four of the laboratory staff and, whenever the air raid siren sounded, two of them had to staff a sandbagged post on the roof of the building. The post had a phone and those on duty had to be ready to spot any problems and report them immediately. Briscoe sometimes did roof-top duty and, like the others, dealt with the occasional small incendiary bomb that landed on or near the building. They did their job well and none of the incendiaries caused much damage.[22] Emeléus held a commission in the Home Guard as battalion gas officer and, because of his various duties, was given a room in the hostel and often slept there. He and Ewart (Tim) Jones were appointed senior gas advisors for London by the Gas Identification Service and ran courses on poison gases for people volunteering as gas officers, responsible for protecting the larger population. About 50 people arrived each Monday for the week-long course; between 1941 and 1944, about 2000 did so. Practice drills were carried out in the road outside the department, and on the roof, though Jones had first to convince the College Secretary that the drills would be of no risk or inconvenience to others.[23]

Tom Ellingham, who had served with the Royal Engineers in World War One (WW1), was the drill sergeant for the local Home Guard unit which included Ronald Purcell and some of the technical, stores, and clerical staff. Les Croker joined the unit and recalled that, together with staff from other departments, they drilled and practised throwing hand grenades in Kensington Gardens, learned shooting with hand and machine guns at Bisley, and were taught how to dig people out of bombed buildings. They also took turns standing on guard duty for Buckingham Palace, General de Gaulle, and Burlington House. Some helped members of the battalion operating the anti-aircraft guns in Hyde Park. Chemistry students took turns as firewatchers on the roof of Burlington House, then the location of the Royal Society as well as the Royal Academy and the Chemical Society.[24] Major bombing began only in 1940 and, as it turned out, most college buildings, including the RCS building, escaped being seriously hit. However, blasts from the 'doodlebug', V1 and V2, raids of 1943–44 destroyed many windows as well as some of the department's hard-to-replace glassware.[25] Some people were cut by flying glass but there were no fatalities on RCS premises.

Alfred Pollard and his students carried out research in the agricultural chemistry hut at Hurworth; luckily no one was there when it was destroyed by a bomb in 1940. All that was recovered from the wreckage were some platinum electrodes. Pollard then moved the work to the newly erected pavilion at the college sports grounds in Harlington. He was doing double duty since the college wanted to keep the army from occupying the pavilion. A large sign was placed outside the building declaring it to be the site of the Grasslands Research Association. Arthur Marsden was put in charge and, when asked, told people that those working there were examining different grasses to see how they absorbed the trace elements needed in animal feed — which perhaps they were. But the ruse failed and the pavilion was soon taken over by the army.[26] The college was without its sports fields and pavilion until the end of the war. Luckily the fields were used for sports by the Scots Guards and were not dug up 'for Victory'. However, the Harlington site was large enough for seven acres of undeveloped land to be loaned to the Middlesex committee for growing vegetables. One small area was dug up for air raid protection trenches, and another was left for the agricultural chemists. Agricultural chemistry was taken seriously by Briscoe who wrote to Tizard, 'our work in agricultural chemistry will make a material contribution to the national campaign for the increase in vegetable production by intensive allotment practice.'[27] One of the agricultural chemists, Albert Page, was seconded to the Ministry of Food and became an insect pest control officer. After the war, he joined the applied entomologists at Silwood Park.

Despite all the extra duties taken on by the staff, undergraduate instruction continued throughout the war, though the first-year course was suspended (and was abandoned after the war). Students, too, were expected to help in various ways, and the first task for those arriving in October 1939 was to fill sandbags in Imperial Institute (now Imperial College) Road.[28] The government saw a need for trained chemists so, unlike in WW1, no special effort was made to enlist students in the army.[29] However, as we will see, the government seconded some research students to chemical and pharmaceutical companies, and five were asked to work on the 'Tube Alloys' project in Canada (see below). The department took in some Jewish refugees at the start of the war, among them the students Franz Sondheimer and Heinz Peter Koch. On gaining their

BSc, both became research students with Heilbron. There were also some Polish airmen who wished to study chemistry, and a group of refugee Dutch chemists who worked on poison gases under Jan Hendrik de Boer. De Boer became a professor at the University of Amsterdam after the war.[30]

The government failed to recognise the need for support staff such as cleaners, laboratory assistants, tradespeople, caterers, stores staff, and secretaries at the college. Many such people were conscripted into the army, or for work deemed more essential than the support of chemical instruction and research.[31] In 1940, when Tizard was called away on war-related work, James Philip came out of retirement as Acting Rector. Philip also chaired a joint committee of the Royal Society and the Ministry of Labour and National Service. It gave advice to the government on the Central Register of Scientific Personnel, and on how the scientists listed should be used during the war. At the time Philip wrote,

> we are determined, each of us, to contribute in every possible way ... [but] let us recognise the limitations and frustrations of science and admit frankly that it is precisely the resources of chemistry and engineering which are being relentlessly and unscrupulously exploited by the enemy, and which we ourselves are driven to develop with the utmost efficiency if we are to prevail.[32]

Philip was also President of both the Chemical Society (elected in 1941) and the Society of Chemical Industry (elected in 1939). It is possible that overwork contributed to his sudden death in 1941.

7.3 Scientific Contributions to the War Effort

Because of their many duties, Briscoe and Heilbron were away from the department for much of the time. Both did their best to be there in the evenings when they gave instructions to the staff; often they slept in the department overnight. Heilbron fitted in some undergraduate teaching and was said to lecture with a strong Glaswegian accent.[33] Although gas warfare and defence were less central to the war effort than in WW1, research on poison gases was carried out. The department was again designated as the place where poison gases would be identified, were they to be used by Germany. Several students worked at Porton Down on the manufacture of liquid arsine with which experiments, offensive and defensive, were performed. Graham Martin recalled a semi-industrial scale operation set up under a tarpaulin in the middle of Salisbury Plain. During his first stay at Porton he and some other students crushed 3400 lbs of solid CO_2 and 2500 lbs of ice, and made fifty pounds of arsine.[34]

During WW1 Briscoe had worked for MI5 on the development of chemically sophisticated invisible inks. He picked up this work again in this war, helped by Derek Barton. Together they developed some invisible inks used to write messages on the human body.[35] Briscoe engaged also in a range of other covert activities that are difficult to pin down. According to Croker, much equipment was secreted into the department, allowing people (probably from MI5) to listen in on wireless messages and telephone calls made to and from the various foreign embassies in South Kensington. Embassy mail was also intercepted and Briscoe was responsible for opening (but not reading) it; later it was re-sealed in ways that could not easily be detected. Letters sealed with wax were opened with waxed cotton dental floss, a rare commodity which Croker had to 'run all over London' to find. Research students were taught how to open and reseal the letters. Further, Briscoe 'appointed' a fictitious woman to the laboratory staff and told Croker that if anyone made enquiries about her he was to immediately inform a certain colonel at the War Office.[36] Briscoe was peripherally involved with the Special Operations Executive (SOE) and its large operation in the basement of the Natural History Museum. Experiments in camouflage were carried out there, along with the making of personal items, such as culturally appropriate and aged clothing, toiletries, and cigarettes, for agents who were to be secreted into occupied Europe.[37]

Briscoe also arranged for work to be carried out on incendiary devices. William Gilpin remembered making pyrotechnic materials for decoy fires and testing the materials in a film studio. Of one explosion he later wrote, the flame and smoke were such that 'any aircrew seeing it might well be excused for thinking they had hit the Royal Arsenal.'[38] Pyrotechnical field work was largely carried out under Alexander King's supervision. He took on this task after Lord Rothschild, in charge of an

MI5 unit called Military Intelligence Research (MIR), asked Briscoe and Heilbron for technical help. King described Rothschild as 'a real cloak and dagger type' who held secret meetings at his headquarters in Wormwood Scrubs Prison.[39] As to pyrotechnics, the idea was to confuse German bomber pilots. The bombers were preceded by pathfinder planes dropping flares. If these landed near important targets, previously arranged bundles of wood which had been treated with a suitable mix of chemicals were set alight as decoys some distance from the intended targets. After the first bomber had flown over, milk bottles that had been previously rigged up were filled with liquid oxygen and made to slide down wires and empty on to the fire. After one spectacular blaze created somewhere in the Midlands, William Joyce (Lord Haw Haw) announced on German radio that a ferrous metal plant had been destroyed. But the Germans soon caught on to the decoys and they worked for only a short period of time.

King described the group of students who worked with him as being 'like a bunch of kids after their first chemistry lessons doing dramatic, if macabre, experiments.'[40] Gilpin worked with King also on methods of sabotaging chemical plants, deemed necessary were there to be a German invasion. One thing they did was to make tablets that looked like aspirins but which, when introduced into chemical vats, ate holes through the walls. A major concern was figuring out how Britain's petrol supplies could quickly be put out of use should the country be invaded. It was known that adding sugar to the petrol tanks of cars could stop the motors, but sugar was in short supply and was being stockpiled for food. Rothschild asked King to find something else and gave him a car on which to carry out experiments — which he did on the roads within Kensington Gardens and Hyde Park. At first nothing worked well, 'the car seemed to enjoy every foul mixture we fed it.'[41] King then decided to experiment with nickel carbonyl, $Ni(CO)_4$, speculating that a layer of nickel would deposit on the spark plug and bring the car to a halt. The carbonyl was difficult to handle so he asked the director of the Mond Nickel Co. in Swansea for advice. He was told that the company had developed a technique by which small quantities of the carbonyl could be stored safely in glass bubbles, and that it was worth seeing whether these would stop cars when dropped into petrol tanks.[42] King went to Swansea, was instructed in the bubble technology, and was given a Winchester quart bottle of

$Ni(CO)_4$ with which to experiment. He returned to London with the bottle packed in a box stuffed with active charcoal — to absorb the gas in case the bottle broke! His return trip was hair-raising. The train was halted just outside Cardiff because of a bombing raid at the docks. King feared that he and his fellow passengers would be killed — either by a direct hit or, were the bottle to break, by poison. The train windows shattered but the Winchester did not. A further bombing raid was in progress when the train reached Paddington, but King carried the bottle safely back to the laboratory with one further delay. While walking back he was stopped by an armed soldier and spent the rest of the night in a police cell because he refused to open up the box. As it turned out, nickel carbonyl worked in coating spark plugs, but was too dangerous to be of any practical use.

This crazy phase in King's life ended when Tizard returned from leading a secret mission to the United States (the British Scientific and Technical Mission, September 1940). The idea was for Britain to share some of its military secrets with the Americans in the hope that they would then cooperate in the scientific war effort. The secrets included the University of Birmingham's radar magnetron, and the memorandum written by Otto Frisch and Rudolf Peierls (both then in Birmingham) on the critical mass of fissile uranium needed for an atomic bomb.[43] Tizard's mission was successful and a small team of American scientists (James Conant, Warren Weaver and Larry Havsted) soon arrived in Britain to see what was going on. Tizard asked King to show them around the major defence and R&D centres and installations — all under the Ministry of Supply. King performed well and was drawn into further work for the Ministry. He resigned from the department in 1943 and, by the end of the war, had met many technical experts and learned much about military scientific research. It was the start of a major postwar career.[44]

Physical chemistry lost two other members of staff to the war effort, Ellingham and Purcell. Ellingham became acting college secretary in 1941 when the incumbent, Geoffrey Lowry, enlisted in the army.[45] Lowry was no longer young, but he had a military background and wanted to help in training army recruits. Ellingham also became assistant secretary to the scientific advisory committee of the Ministry of Supply. His work load was such that, he gave up departmental work and resigned from the Home Guard. After the war he was appointed Secretary of the Royal Institute of

Chemistry (RIC) and resigned from the department. Purcell began working for the Admiralty in 1944. Even before 1944, he spent much time on defence research, including operational research with Charles Goodeve at University College. With the loss of nearly all the physical chemistry staff, much of the teaching fell to Kitchener, and some to A. S. C. (Stuart) Lawrence. Lawrence also ran an important wartime research group working on lubricants, and on chemicals for de-icing planes and ships. He left the department in 1944, joined the navy, and taught people working on the Arctic convoy about de-icing. After the war he became a senior lecturer, then professor, at the University of Sheffield.[46] Gordon van Praagh, a member of Lawrence's wartime research group, was a chemistry teacher at Christ's Hospital who came to work in the department in 1943. He, too, advised the navy on de-icing.[47]

Inorganic chemistry retained more of its staff, though most were engaged in war-related activities and had little time for teaching. Among his many activities Briscoe supervised research that was a continuation of Baker's WW1 work on respirators. In this connection, Wilkinson, who became Briscoe's research student in 1941, was put to work on the vapour phase hydrolysis of phosgene — he found it does not hydrolyse except in the presence of liquid water. Later he was to say that Briscoe directed his research from a safe distance. Danger aside, Wilkinson was bored with the project and later wrote that he preferred examining bits of German incendiaries that he gathered in the neighbourhood. From the chemical traces, he identified the inflammable compounds used (mainly diethyl zinc (Et_2 Zn)). Some suspicious sticks containing antimony sulphide were brought into the laboratory, but they turned out to be West African cosmetics.[48]

Eméleus' students worked on a range of fluorine and interhalogen compounds, most of which 'had never been seen in the United Kingdom before.'[49] They were tested on a colony of rats so as to determine their toxicity. Some students (possibly zoology students) carried out dissections of the dead rats, sending the more interesting specimens to Porton Down for further study. Each morning Mrs. Hay, the tea lady, brought Briscoe a copy of the *Daily Mirror* with his tea and toast; she then fed the rats that were kept in a room next to his laboratory.[50] Wilkinson witnessed some of Eméleus' students wearing gas masks while sitting in a fume cupboard filled with S_2F_{10}.[51] Perhaps they were testing the efficacy of a new respirator. As to the novel sulphur fluorides and interhalogens, their properties were being investigated in part for chemical reasons, and in part because it was feared that Germany was preparing to use them in warfare.[52] Some were easily liquefied and were tested in shells, but shells containing liquids often yaw in flight. Eméleus was asked if members of his team could make some workable solids. They mixed potassium fluoride with bromine trifluoride which, he claimed, 'was excellent. It just blew the whole thing sky high.'[53] Several students gained their PhDs working on interhalogens and other war-related gases, leading to what were declared 'secret theses' under wartime regulations. Their work was published, if at all, only after the war. Fortunately poison gases were not used in this war — at least not for military purposes.

Working closely with Eméleus early in the war, was the future nuclear weapons specialist, Kenneth Stewart. Stewart had gained his BSc and PhD in the department, and was appointed as a demonstrator in 1937.[54] Joining the organic chemistry section in 1943 was Leonard (Len) Owen.[55] He worked on the nitrogen mustards, some of which were later used in cancer chemotherapy. He also synthesised the antiarsenical drug, BALINTRAV.[56] His line of work meant that unpleasant odours permeated much of the department. Owen is discussed further in subsequent chapters. Another person to join the staff was John T. Hannen. He arrived in 1944 and later took over Eldridge's course on the chemistry of food and drugs.

In January 1944 Eméleus was asked to go to the United States to work on a secret project. Since life at the college was not easy he was pleased by the opportunity to get away. However, the new college Rector, Richard Southwell, unaware of the work being done in North America, was reluctant to give permission. Later he tried, unsuccessfully, to limit Eméleus' time away.[57] Eméleus left in great secrecy, only finding out that he was bound for Oak Ridge, Tennessee, after his flying boat had left England. His family had no idea where he was until the war was over. He was not allowed to reveal his whereabouts, and all correspondence back and forth was checked and sent via Washington. On arriving in the United States he learned that he was to help with an unforeseen chemical problem associated with the electromagnetic separation of uranium isotopes — using the principle of mass spectrometry. Much of the UF_6 vapour escaped the beam and settled on the walls of the stainless steel containers. To recover it the containers had to be opened, exposing the UF_6 to moist air. The resulting

HF attacked the container welding, and exposed the UF_6 to heavy metal impurities. Eméleus joined some other chemists in a crash uranium purification programme. Later he downplayed his role, saying that one of his better contributions was in ensuring that his co-workers had a steady supply of whisky, something he purchased during his monthly visits to Washington — to report to James Chadwick on progress being made in uranium enrichment.[58] Eméleus returned to IC just before the first atomic bomb was dropped on Hiroshima; he left for Cambridge soon after. In 1963 he was made Fellow of Imperial College (FIC).

William (Bill) Penney worked for the Manhattan Project. Although not in the chemistry department, he was an outstanding theoretical chemist.[59] From 1936–1945 he was a reader in the mathematics department at IC and, when war broke out, became a member of the Ministry of Supply's physics of explosives committee chaired by Geoffrey Taylor. He carried out theoretical work on the outcome of explosions and, in 1944, was recruited to work under J. Robert Oppenheimer at Los Alamos. As was the case with Eméleus, the college was reluctant to let him go.[60] Penney, able to calculate the effects of blasts and shockwaves more quickly and accurately than anyone else at Los Alamos, became a legendary boffin. In his memoir General Groves, the head of the Manhattan Project, listed five men whom he regularly consulted over 'vital decisions', Penney was among them.[61]

As mentioned in Chapter Six, 1944 was the year in which Sugden was killed by a flying bomb, and, with Eméleus' departure in 1945, the inorganic chemistry staff was diminished. The organic chemists lost Kon in 1942 when he became professor of chemistry at the Chester Beatty Research Institute. But up to then he helped Heilbron with his various projects. Heilbron was a scientific advisor to the Ministry of Supply from 1939–1942, and to the Ministry of Production from 1942–1945. He was also an advisor to the cabinet office, and was on many committees. He put the day-to-day operation of the organic chemistry section in the hands of Ewart (Tim) Jones.[62] Despite all the difficulties, research in organic chemistry was carried out in surprisingly large number of areas, and included work that led to the industrial synthesis of vitamins B1 and A, the industrial production of acetylene, the purification of penicillin, the production of dichlorodiphenyltrichloroethane (DDT), and the identification of the chemical constituents, especially sterols, of seaweeds. These various projects required some gifted lieutenants and many subalterns — no wonder Heilbron had demanded a large research laboratory.

The vitamin A work was largely delegated to Jones.[63] He, and those working with him, were sidetracked into thinking about acetylene production because of the wartime need to find a better synthesis. This paved the way for work on polyene and carotenoid chemistry after the war. The work on penicillin was new and, from 1941 onwards, it came to dominate much of the research in the department. It was part of an Anglo–American effort that required many workers in many laboratories for the production of a usable antibiotic.[64] Among the problems addressed at IC were, establishing which of the various strains of penicillin was the most potent, and whether either a chemical synthesis, or a biosynthesis (or both), could then be made to work on a large scale. Much of the penicillin work was delegated to Arthur Cook who, with his students, purified enough of one strain to allow for some structural studies to be carried out.[65] They contributed to an understanding of the structure of *n*-amylpenicillin, and their work suggested some possible chemical syntheses. In turn, this led to much novel chemistry and to new work on thiazolidines, oxazolones, and imidazoles. They also carried out research that established the feasibility of obtaining penicillin through biosynthesis — though they were unable to achieve this themselves. Heilbron, as always, looked at the broader chemical picture which allowed him to see the possibility of synthesising yet more heterocyclic compounds, something he was to do after the war when he found some 'novel routes to certain amino acids, polypeptides, and purines.'[66] For all of this bio/chemical work, the microanalytical laboratory set up by Boston was essential, as were Heilbron's new spectroscopic facilities, and the chromatographic techniques that he brought to London. The latter were improved by Cook for use in the purification of penicillin.[67]

Work on DDT came to the department via the zoology department. James Munro, professor and head of the department of zoology and applied entomology, was seeking a substitute for pyrethrum. This widely used plant-sourced insecticide came mainly from Kenya, and supplies had largely dried up. A Geigy product, Gesarol, was being tested at the Rothamsted Experimental Station and looked promising. Munro persuaded Heilbron to determine its chemistry. Heilbron discovered that the active insecticide was one of the chemical isomers of Gesarol's main component, soon to be known as DDT. Heilbron, Alexander King and Alfred Egerton, head of the chemical technology and chemical engineering department and, like Heilbron, a scientific advisor to the cabinet office, persuaded the government to obtain a licence from Geigy for Gesarol's manufacture in the United Kingdom. Munro organised a team to test the new product on malaria mosquitos in British Guiana (now Guyana). The tests were remarkably successful and soon DDT was being manufactured on a large scale. Its first use was in protecting British troops in the tropics against malaria mosquitoes. DDT's many problems were recognised only later.[68] Further, several antimalarial drugs were synthesised in the department; the patents were assigned to ICI, sponsor of the research.

During the war it was shown that cortisone was an effective therapy for rheumatoid arthritis. Jones looked for a good synthetic route to this compound and, with his student Bernard Henbest, succeeded. In this connection Jones formed close ties with Glaxo.[69] In 1944 he made a splash with a compound that Robert Robinson was having great difficulty in making. Robinson was sceptical that Jones, or for that matter anyone else, could do better. He wrote to Jones, 'we shall be pleased to test the material you obtain, *if any*!.'[70] The compound, δ-hexenolactone, was a growth inhibitor. Jones won praise in the popular press for having made what was said to be a new anticancer drug. Like King, he also made use of the availability of $Ni(CO)_4$ and, after the war, together with his student Mark Whiting, carried out Reppe carbonylations.[71] Jones' group of wartime, and early postwar IC students was perhaps the best he ever had. In the year 1946–1947, 15 future professors of organic chemistry were working with Heilbron and Jones.[72] Jones returned to Manchester as professor of Chemistry in 1947 and, in the 1970s, led the move to bring the Chemical Society and the Royal Institute of Chemistry together.[73] He had been President of both bodies earlier, and was elected as the first President of the Royal Society of Chemistry, 1980–1982.

7.4 Some Notable Wartime Students

About 40 students gained their ARCS and BSc in each year of the war. About 12 stayed on as research students, joined by others from elsewhere.

We can mention only a few. Five inorganic chemists, Henry G. Heal, Alfred (Alfie) G. Maddock, Nicholas (Nick) Miller, Graham Martin and Geoffrey Wilkinson, were recruited by the Tube Alloys project to work in Canada. Heal came to the department in 1938, became a research student with Eméleus, and gained a PhD in 1942. After the war he stayed in Canada for some years, later moving to a chair at Queen's University, Belfast. Maddock (1917–2009) lived surprisingly long given that he had a justifiable reputation for being slapdash with radioactive materials — albeit a good radiochemist.[74] His family were close neighbours of professor Philip in Bedford Park which may account for why he chose to study at IC. He gained a BSc in 1938, stayed on as a research student under Eméleus, and gained a PhD in silicon hydride chemistry in 1942. However, like others working with Eméleus, he was sidelined into working on poisonous gases, notably arsine, sulphur fluorides, and interhalogens. When a scout from the Tube Alloys project came looking for expertise in fluorine chemistry, Maddock was recruited.[75] After the war he was appointed acting head of chemistry at Harwell for a short period — when the research centre was being built on the site of an old airfield. In 1947 Eméleus, by then at Cambridge, asked him to join him there. Maddock spent the rest of his career at Cambridge, retiring as reader in radiochemistry in 1984. He was the first recipient of the RSC Becquerel Medal in 1996. Martin (see above) and Miller completed their undergraduate studies at the start of the war. Miller took a fellowship in the United States and moved to Montreal from there. After the war he joined the University of Edinburgh as lecturer in radiation chemistry where he was the PhD supervisor of Wilkinson's younger brother, John.

Before coming to IC Geoffrey and John Wilkinson were pupils at Todmorden Secondary School, the same school that John Cockcroft, a future Nobel Laureate and head of Tube Alloys in Montreal and Chalk River, had attended earlier. Geoffrey came to the department in 1939 with a Royal scholarship. He took geology as his optional subject, recalling that 'I began to wish I'd taken geology instead of chemistry — on the whole it's as well I didn't'.[76] He was 'invited' to join Tube Alloys by Fritz Paneth.[77] Bored with his work at Imperial he was pleased to try something new, even though he had no idea what was in store for him. First, together with Heal and Maddock, he had to sign the Official Secrets Act. Then, after a briefing in Cambridge, all three sailed to Halifax from where they took the train to Montreal.[78] Wilkinson worked at the Université de Montréal, supervised by Jules Guéron, a professor from Strasbourg. His immediate co-workers were two recent McGill PhDs, William E. Grummitt and Leo Yaffé (later a professor at McGill).[79] He shared lodgings with Alan Nunn May of KCL. He also shared Nunn May's whisky, not knowing that Nunn May was a spy, nor that the whisky was provided by his Russian spymaster. Wilkinson also came to know Klaus Fuchs and Bruno Pontecorvo, until later he had no idea that they, too, were spies for the Soviet Union.

Wilkinson claimed to have been bored with the initial tasks he was given in Montreal, but livened up when asked to study the yields of the fission products of U^{235} and U^{233} irradiated in the Chicago pile. He wrote that at last his training in analytical chemistry under Harwood was paying off. With Grummitt he produced the famous double-humped curves in which the fission product yields of U^{235} were plotted as a function of mass number. His first papers, published in the *Canadian Journal of Research*, were on some of this work; written earlier, they were not released until 1946.[80] He was, however, allowed to use the work as part of his 1945 PhD thesis (kept secret until 1946). In 1945 he took a trip to the Rockies and British Columbia; he was in Calgary when he heard that the atomic bomb had been dropped on Hiroshima.

After his trip to Western Canada Wilkinson returned briefly to England to defend his thesis and see his family. Briscoe advised him to get out of nuclear chemistry, advice he repeated more than once, and which Wilkinson took a few years later. Before doing so he accepted a research fellowship with Glen Seaborg at the Lawrence Livermore Radiation Laboratory at Berkeley. There he produced new isotopes of the transition metals by bombardment in a cyclotron. He published 14 papers between 1947–1951 and, according to Seaborg, produced more artificial isotopes than anyone else.[81] Wilkinson jokingly claimed to have been the first successful alchemist since he achieved the transmutation of platinum into gold.

John Wilkinson, came to the college during the war and gained his BSc in 1947. He remembers Barton as a demonstrator, and that the students called him 'Special Agent' after the radio programme, *Dick Barton — Special*

Agent. He also remembers VE Day when, together with other students, including his friend R. W. (Bob) Hudson, he had a 'grand tour of the West End' on the top of a double decker bus.[82] He and two other wartime students, Douglas Payne (BSc 1944), and Grace Payne (BSc 1946) are among the few surviving students of their generation. All three have excellent memories of their time in the department. Douglas Payne knew Barton before coming to IC. Close neighbours in Gravesend, they commuted to the college together, and Barton gave Payne his old analytical chemistry notebooks. Nonetheless, the Paynes found Barton remote. They said that his large physical presence, his intellect, and his remarkable memory for everything he read, set him apart. Wilkinson's considerable intellect was less apparent to them, and they disliked his Yorkshire bluntness. The former Prime Minister, Harold Wilson, once held forth on the tough character of what he called 'Pennine Man'. According to John Wilkinson, his brother Geoffrey fitted the archetype: tough, blunt, a hill walker, a scree runner, and very hard working.

The Paynes and John Wilkinson remember Heilbron as a remote professorial figure, that Margaret Carlton gave German classes, and that Alexander King gave a weekly chemistry lecture in German. They also remember John O'Mara Bockris (see subsequent paragraph and Chapter Eight) as a 'departmental character' who worked in his lab late at night and that he was often joined by fellow research student John Bowler–Reed. Croker's memoir notes that Bockris was often discovered by members of the maintenance party asleep at his bench in the early morning, with a blanket over his head to keep warm. Another departmental character mentioned by the Paynes was Wally the porter, a former WW1 guardsman who, during the war, controlled entry to the front door of the RCS building. In 1945 Douglas Payne moved to Cambridge with Eméleus for his PhD. He returned to the department as a lecturer but stayed for only a brief period before moving to the University of Glasgow in 1949.[83]

One of Briscoe's students, Peter Alexander, gained his PhD in 1943. A colourful character, he worked on several war-related projects and was the coauthor of Derek Barton's first paper. At the end of the war he was made an acting lieutenant colonel with the task of inspecting the ruins of the IG Farben factories. Later, as a professor at the Chester Beatty Research Institute, he had a major career in radiobiology.[84]

Very little physical chemistry research was carried out during the war, but the above-mentioned John Bockris began some interesting work in electrochemistry. Bockris had gained an external London BSc at Brighton Technical College before coming to the department in 1943.[85] He joined the staff after the war, built up the field of electrochemistry, and was to make a major academic career in the United States. He is discussed further in Chapter Eight. Felix Sebba, a postdoctoral research fellow with Briscoe, was more of a physical than inorganic chemist. An expert in colloid and surfactant chemistry, he became a Professor, first at the University of the Witwatersrand and then at the Virginia Polytechnic Institute.[86] At the former he supervised Sir David King's doctoral thesis. Discussed briefly in Chapter Eight, King was a post-doctoral fellow at Imperial before moving to Cambridge.

As can be inferred from what has already been written, research in organic chemistry was the most active, and the organic section had the largest number of research students. We can mention only a few. The best known, Derek Barton, is discussed in later chapters. One of his later collaborators on natural product chemistry, Leonard John Haynes, came to the department as an undergraduate in 1941, gaining a PhD with Heilbron in 1946. He won an ICI research fellowship at Cambridge and was later (1956–1968) professor of organic chemistry at the University of the West Indies. David G. Jones came to the department in 1936 and gained a PhD with Cook in 1940. He became director of research and development at ICI, where he was later Deputy Chairman. Walter C. J. Ross, a student who left with Kon, made his career at the Chester Beatty Research Institute where he became a professor. Reginald J. Meakins came to the department with a BSc from the University of Sydney and gained a PhD in 1941. He returned to Australia after the war, and to a career with the Australian Council for Scientific and Industrial Research. Marc Julia, after whom the Julia olefination is named, gained his PhD with Heilbron and Jones in 1948, and was later a professor at the École Normale Supérieure in Paris. John Arthur (Jack) Elvidge was an undergraduate in the department, gaining his BSc in 1943 before joining Cook and the penicillin team. He gained a PhD in 1947 and after a brief period with Frank S. Spring FRS at the Royal Technical College in Glasgow, returned to the department as a lecturer.[87] Harold Bernard Henbest (known as Bernard), came to the department as an undergraduate in 1942, later carrying out research under Heilbron and Jones. He found a way to synthesise cortisone for which he gained a PhD in 1948. He left with Jones for a lectureship in Manchester. There he supervised the PhD research of the future Nobel Laureate, Michael Smith. Later Henbest was professor of organic chemistry at Queen's University, Belfast, 1958–1973. Remarkably he turned down an FRS believing that such awards adversely affected teaching.[88]

Alan W. Johnson came to the department in 1936 and was awarded a Royal Scholarship in 1937. He gained a BSc in 1938 and a PhD in 1942. He was a keen ballroom dancer, had an interest in music, and invited students from Bedford College and the Royal College of Music to dances at IC. He worked with Heilbron on vitamin A for his PhD, but was soon seconded to work on acetylene chemistry at ICI and, after the war, published two major works in this field. He returned to the college for a brief period but then went back to ICI before moving to Cambridge.[89] One of Johnson's close friends, Alfred Spinks, another Heilbron student, came to the department in 1938 with a BSc from University College, Nottingham. He joined the vitamin A group but on gaining his PhD he, too, was seconded to ICI — in his case to work on sulphanilamide drugs. After the war he studied pharmacology at Oxford, returning to ICI as director of its pharmaceuticals division. Later he was head of R&D at ICI.[90] Basil Weedon came to the department as an undergraduate in 1942, gained a BSc in 1944, and then joined Heilbron and Jones in the vitamin A group.[91] On gaining his PhD in 1946, he moved to ICI, returning a year later to a lectureship in the department. He is briefly discussed in the following chapter. Ralph Raphael entered the college as an undergraduate in 1939, gaining a BSc in 1941. He took the course for London gas officers and was the gas identification officer for Walthamstow. He won the Hofmann Prize for practical organic chemistry and came second to Wilkinson in the final BSc standings in 1941. Raphael met his wife, a violin student at the RCM, through Johnson's musical and dance activities. He worked under Heilbron and Jones for his PhD, focussing on acetylene chemistry. Later Jones was to write,

Ralph carried out ... the only individual [experiment] in my whole experience the result of which I can still visualize. We put away a colourless

solution one evening and the next morning it was bright yellow .... It was the discovery of a spectacular isomerisation which made possible the synthesis of vitamin A and the carotenoids by Otto Isler in Basel'.[92]

On gaining his PhD in 1943, Raphael was seconded by the government and sent to work for May and Baker on penicillin. He returned after the war having been awarded one of the new ICI research fellowships and rejoined the team working on acetylenic chemistry.

1945 marked not only the end of the war but also the 100th anniversary of the founding of the Royal College of Chemistry.[93] In October the college acknowledged both and there was a grand celebration in the Albert Hall attended by King George VI and Queen Elizabeth. The King made some glowing remarks about the college's wartime contributions, including those of the chemistry department. A two-day open house followed. As part of the celebrations, Ralph Raphael and Franz Sondheimer traversed the upper walls of the Whiffen laboratory and abseiled down the front of the RCS building.

End Notes

1. For Briscoe, (Emeléus, 1962), (Eldridge, 1961), (Wilkinson, 1961). Henry Vincent Aird Briscoe (1888–1961) used his second name, Vincent.
2. For comment on driving, ICL archives, KC; an anonymous typescript with biographical details on Briscoe. Also, B\Wilkinson; handwritten memoir; quotation, 13. Wilkinson only found out that Theodore Richards was a Harvard Professor and Nobel Laureate when he, himself, went to Harvard and was given Richards' desk to work at.
3. (Briscoe, 1915), (Briscoe, Robinson and Smith, 1927). Briscoe was one of two Britons then on the International Committee on Atomic Weights.
4. (Winter, Carlton and Briscoe, 1939). Ernest Roy Sealey Winter, who was instrumental in building the still, started work as a lab boy in a colliery at age 14. He was a student in the department, 1936–1940, and was on the staff, 1945–1949. He also constructed a mass spectrometer with his own hands and carried out further work on ^{18}O. A specialist in metal oxides, he was later managing director of J. and E. Sturge Ltd., Birmingham. (The firm's Quaker founders, Joseph and Edmund Sturge, were well known anti-slavery activists. Edmund's brother-in-law, Arthur Albright, joined the firm and later

separated the phosphorus and match part of the business, creating the new firm Albright and Wilson.)

5. ICL archives, KC/Eldridge correspondence; Smith to Eldridge, 25 March, 1958. Smith came to the department as a lab boy under the supervision of Les Croker. He became Briscoe's lecture assistant and laboratory technician. When the first year course was dropped and the three-year BSc introduced after the war (see Chapter Eight), lecture demonstrations became largely a thing of the past. Smith became Wilkinson's Assistant and was reputedly very good at preparing the compounds needed.

6. (Emeléus, 1962).

7. For Heilbron, (Cook, 1960), (Jones, 1962), (Cook, *revised* Watson, 2004). Heilbron won the CS Longstaff Award in 1939, and the Pedler Award in 1947. Throughout his life, Heilbron spoke of Henderson's mentorship; he delivered the RIC's first Henderson Memorial Lecture, (Heilbron, 1947). See also, (Irvine, *revised* Watson, 2004b). G. G. Henderson FRS was remembered also by others as an outstanding teacher and mentor. After Heilbron's time as his student, Henderson was appointed to the Regius chair at the University of Glasgow.

8. (Heilbron and Bunberry, 1934–1937). A fourth volume of the dictionary was published in 1953, coedited with A. H. Cook and E. R. H. Jones. A standard reference work, the dictionary came out in later editions, including a 9-volume 6th edition published by Chapman and Hall in 1998.

9. Heilbron also worked with Edward Charles Cyril Baly FRS (1871–1948), the senior professor in Liverpool, in applying physical chemical methods in organic chemistry. Baly started his career in Liverpool before moving to UCL where he worked with William Ramsay for many years. He returned to Liverpool as professor in 1910.

10. For Haworth see Chapter Four. Haworth won for his work on carbohydrates and vitamin C, and Karrer for his work on vitamin A and the carotenoids more generally.

11. ICL archives, KC/10/2, Heilbron to Tizard, 19 February, 1938. Interestingly, Tizard asked E. F. Armstrong to look at the organic chemistry research laboratories at Manchester and report on how they compared to the ones at IC. We were unable to find a written report from Armstrong in the college archives. The Rector, Sir Henry Thomas Tizard FRS (1885–1959), studied chemistry at Oxford and, on the advice of his tutor, N. V. Sidgwick, then spent a year in Berlin with H. W. Nernst. It was there that he first met Frederick Lindemann whose later WW2 career was to intertwine with his own. Tizard volunteered as a pilot in WW1, testing the performance of

service aircraft. He came to IC after a period as Secretary of the DSIR; (Piller, 2004).

12. ICL archives, KC10; Tizard to Heilbron, March 4, 1938. The governing body committed about £6000 to laboratory renovations and Tizard directed an additional £500 to the department's annual budget. External funding for the laboratories was also forthcoming. ICL archives, GB minutes, 11 February, 1938. Renovations to the advanced analytical laboratory had begun in 1937 and were close to completion in 1938. C. Bamber Ltd. dismantled the old Whiffen Laboratory, carried away the equipment free of charge, and paid the department £118 for the resaleable contents.

13. After Heilbron's death in 1959, Consterdine moved to Cambridge where he worked for another former Manchester chemist, Alexander Todd.

14. Hey did not stay in the department for long, returning to Manchester in 1941 as director of the British Schering Research Institute. Its wartime function was to look into German drug patents and to promote research into, and then manufacture, drugs that had previously been imported. While there Hey continued some work he had begun at IC on sulphanilamide drugs. After the war he became professor of organic chemistry at KCL. He received the CS Pedler Award in 1970.

15. John Wilkinson (personal communication). John Wilkinson, younger brother of Geoffrey, was a student in the department, 1944–1947. He then worked at Harwell for two years before studying for a PhD with Nicholas Miller in Edinburgh; (for Miller, a former IC student, see below). After gaining his PhD in 1953 Wilkinson had two postdoctoral fellowships, one with the NRC in Ottawa and another with Graham Martin in Durham; (for Martin see below). Wilkinson was senior lecturer at the Salford Technical College (later University of Salford). For Kon and Bull see also Chapter Six.

16. Leslie Hamilton Cobb was a student, 1935–1939, and then joined the staff for just one year before joining ICI Plastics in Welwyn in 1940. From there he published some patents on thermoplastics. He also published two wartime papers with J. S. Anderson and Briscoe. Arthur Whitcombe Marsden came to the department as a student in 1929. For the others see Chapter Six.

17. For Theobald, Chapter Six, Note 56. John Wilkinson (personal communication) wrote 'everyone was in awe of Theobald' and that on Fridays he made the students polish their benches. Archibald John Edmond Welch (known as John) came to the college as a student in 1934, studied with Eméleus for his PhD, and was on the staff from 1940–1982, as demonstrator for one year, then assistant lecturer (1940–1944), lecturer in physical chemistry (1945–1951), and senior lecturer in inorganic chemistry (1951–1982). He was

assistant director of the department, 1960–1982. As an exclusive Plymouth Brother he was not supposed to socialise with non-brethren. However, he was given special dispensation by the Elders to do so at the college and was therefore able to have a cup of tea with his colleagues and attend some other social functions. Welch displayed a traffic signal outside his door. If it showed red you were not allowed to knock, let alone enter. For more on Welch see subsequent chapters.

18. ICL archives, The Croker memoir is transcribed in Bernard Atkinson, 'Department of Chemistry: Recent History, 1960–1989' (typescript saved on CD). Atkinson was a student during the war. He entered the college in 1941, gained his BSc in 1944 while acting also as an air-raid warden. Late in the war and, for some years after, he worked on nerve gas antidotes at IC and at Porton Down. For more on Atkinson refer to the rest of the book.

19. The emergency food rations included large stocks of flour, cooking fat and margarine, large quantities of tinned food, 48 lbs. of Ryvita and a range of other crackers, 84 boxes of cheddar cheese, all kinds of jams, sauces and pickles, biscuits and coffee essence (no tea). None of this was to be touched except in an emergency.

20. The company belonged to the 2nd County of London Battalion.

21. ICL archives, B\Ellingham; Ellingham to Locket, 16 October, 1940; KC/ Eldridge correspondence file; G. Martin to Eldridge, 11 May, 1958. Graham Martin was a student who moved to work with Paneth after the war. He became a reader in radiochemistry at Durham, and was later the inaugural professor of Chemistry at the University of Kent. Wilkinson and Martin both worked in Montreal from 1943; for Martin, (Hudson and Wade, 1990).

22. ICL archives; Eric Roberts, 'History of the chemistry department' (to 1962), (typescript), 102.

23. ICL archives, GX, Jones to Lowry, 27 September, 1939.

24. ICL archives, Croker, op. cit. (18), and KC\Eldridge, D. H. Hey to Eldridge, 26 March, 1958. Hey remembered organising the students for firefighting duty. The Royal Academy paintings were largely stored outside London.

25. A doodlebug (V1 rocket) landed in Exhibition Road demolishing numbers 66, 68 and 70 (where the Mormon Church now stands), killing 20 people and injuring more. The old RCS/Huxley building (now the Henry Cole Wing of the V&A) was severely damaged. Other doodlebugs landed nearby, some in Hyde Park. Earlier, during the blitz, a bomb landed on the RSM building but caused only minor damage. A large bomb landed in the C&G building's boiler house but did not explode. Geoffrey Wilkinson lived at 4, Elvaston Place with 7–8 other students. They paid £2.10s. per week (breakfast and

dinner included). In his memoir (*op. cit.* 2), he recalls going into the basement when 'the bangs got close,' and that he had a narrow escape in 1941 when a nearby house fell down after a bomb exploded unexpectedly several hours after it had been dropped. Alan W. Johnson, who also lived just off Queen's Gate, mentioned listening to music on his gramophone, oblivious to the noise of bombing raids and air-raid sirens.

26. A mobile unit of the Scots Guards was housed there. The Harlington property was one of the largest flat areas without buildings near London, and the military chiefs thought it a possible site for an airborne parachute invasion.

27. After the Harlington site was taken over by the army, some allotment field work continued there; further research work was carried out at the ICI research centre at Jealot's Hill, and at the Royal Horticultural Society's gardens and laboratories at Wisley. The department made about £40–£50 a year selling experimental vegetables grown at Harlington. ICL archives, KCA.

28. Geoffrey Wilkinson records filling sandbags on his arrival in 1939. He also remembered sitting the 2-day practical examination, a requirement for the Royal scholarship that he won. The invigilator was the recently arrived Donald Hey. Ralph Raphael (see below) also won a Royal scholarship in 1939; Wilkinson memoir, *op. cit.* (2).

29. Conscription for single men aged 20–22 was introduced in April, 1939. When war broke out in September, men aged 18–41 were 'liable to conscription,' except for those in reserved occupations. By 1942 men between 18 and 51 and women between 20 and 30 were 'liable to conscription' — not necessarily to the armed services. By and large chemists and chemistry students were not conscripted. Geoffrey Wilkinson went before the recruiting board and 'was told to stay where I was'; Wilkinson memoir, *op. cit.* (2).

30. Briscoe was active in lobbying the Rector to allow Jewish refugees to work or become students in the department. Sondheimer later had a major career, (see Chapter Eight, Note 30). Koch became a senior lecturer at Manchester University, but sadly was killed in a mountaineering accident in 1951. De Boer was working for Philips in Eindhoven when he escaped. The Polish airmen joined with Poles from other departments (there were many refugee Poles at the college, especially in civil engineering) to found their own technical college, attached to the Battersea Polytechnical Institute (now University of Surrey).

31. The department had to apply for the retention of employees to the District Manpower Board; its bureaucrats were not always sympathetic.

32. For Philip, (Egerton, 1942), quotation, p. 60.

33. John Wilkinson, personal communication.

34. Martin to Eldridge, *op. cit.* (21).
35. Briscoe's work is briefly mentioned in (Andrew, 2009). Briscoe and Barton developed some waterfree inks that could not be developed with iodine. Barton experimented with them on the body of a woman of Chinese origin, work that he carried out in a government laboratory on Baker Street.
36. For dental floss and the fictitious woman, Croker memoir, *op. cit.* (18), p. 6.
37. (Mackenzie, 2000).
38. ICL archives, KC\Eldridge correspondence, W. C. Gilpin to Eldridge, 1 April, 1958. Gilpin, a research student with Briscoe, later worked for Steetley Magnesite in Hartlepool. Another student, J. R. Knowles, was killed during experiments with incendiaries.
39. (King, 2006), Chapter Eleven. N. M. V. (Victor) Rothschild (later FRS) was a Cambridge zoology graduate who shared a flat in London with Guy Burgess and Anthony Blunt. For Rothschild, (Rose *revised* 2004).
40. (King, 2006), p. 117. Information on pyrotechnical work in this book.
41. (King, 2006), p. 115. King also drove the car to Dover to pick up soldiers rescued from Dunkirk.
42. The carbonyl was manufactured in large quantities and used to separate nickel from other metal contaminants.
43. (Zimmerman, 1996). The Frisch–Peierls estimate turned out to be too low.
44. After the war King became Secretary to the Advisory Council on Scientific Policy. In 1950 he was appointed Chief Scientific Officer of the DSIR and, in 1957, Director of the European Productivity Agency for the Organization for European Economic Cooperation (OEEC) in Paris. In 1960 he became Deputy Director-General of the renamed and expanded Organization for Economic Co-operation and Development (OECD). Concerned about the Earth's limited resources and the environmental impact of population growth and industrialisation, he contacted Aurelio Peccei, President of Olivetti, who had expressed similar concerns. Together they founded the Club of Rome in 1968. They involved IC staff in its activities. King was made CMG in 1975, won the Erasmus Prize in 1987, and was awarded many honorary degrees, (May, 2004). For an obituary, *The Telegraph*, 26 March, 2007.
45. ICL archives B\Ellingham. Ellingham left several boxes of papers. They contain very neat notes and memoranda having to do with college affairs. For more on Ellingham see Chapter Six.
46. A. S. C. (Stuart) Lawrence (1902–1971) was educated at the Battersea Polytechnical Institute (now University of Surrey). At the age of 18 he became an assistant, first to James Dewar and then to William Bragg at the

RI. He later gained a PhD at Cambridge, working on colloid chemistry with Eric Rideal. He came to IC in 1935; (Anon., 1971).

47. (Brock, 2004d). Like Lawrence, van Praagh had a PhD from Cambridge where he, too, worked with Rideal. He joined the Admiralty in 1944 and returned to teaching at Christ's Hospital after the war. According to Brock, he was another exponent of Henry Armstrong's heuristic method, following in the footsteps of Charles Browne (Chapter Four, Note 93). The author of several school chemistry texts, van Praagh later joined the Nuffield Foundation where, in the 1960s, he developed new GCE syllabi for O and A level chemistry.

48. Wilkinson, *op. cit.* (2).

49. Emeléus quotation, (Archer, 1997), p. 11.

50. ICL archives, KC\Eldridge correspondence; Hay to Eldridge, undated, but probably 1958; also G. Martin to Eldridge, 11 May, 1958. Mrs. Hay worked in the department for 31 years. On one occasion she came across a fire in one of the labs and threw a bucket of water at it. Luckily it went out since what was on fire was dioxan being distilled over sodium. Roberts, *op. cit.* (22), p. 108.

51. One person is said to have died from poisoning by one of Emeléus' compounds but the records are unclear.

52. Wilkinson memoir, *op. cit.* (2).

53. Emeléus, quoted in (Archer, 1997), p. 11.

54. There is a brief obituary of Stewart in *Imperial Matters* (Winter issue, 2003), p. 36 (copy in ICL archives). Stewart decided to join the army in 1940 and served with the Royal Engineers in India. After the war he worked at Aldermaston and became a renowned expert on the potential hazards of nuclear weapons accidents. Another of Emeléus' wartime students, Cyril Reid, became a professor at the University of British Columbia.

55. Leonard Newton (Len) Owen (1914–1999) lost a lung as a result of his wartime work with mustard gas. He was the son of a Shropshire station master and retained a lifelong love of steam trains. He won a scholarship to study chemistry at Birmingham University where he stayed for a PhD under Norman Haworth, working on the methylation of cellulose. Before coming to IC in 1943 he was an assistant lecturer at the University College of North Wales (Bangor) where he collaborated with J. L. Simonsen. At IC he lived for many years in a room in the Beit hostel. Obituary, *The Times*, 10 November, 1999.

56. British Anti-Lewisite (BAL, 2, 3-disulphanylpropan-1-ol), developed in Oxford early in the war, was used to treat skin lesions caused by the

organo-arsenic vesicant, lewisite. Owen prepared a version that could be administered intravenously, hence BALINTRAV. The biological testing was carried out by J. F. Danielli and his associates at Cambridge University, (Danielli *et al.*, 1947).

57. See correspondence in ICL archives, GXE: Edward Appleton to Southwell, 26 January, 1944, and Richard Southwell to Sir John Anderson, Chancellor of the Exchequer, 15 August, 1944 (Tube Alloys was under the Treasury).

58. (Greenwood, 1993), (Archer, 1997). Archer's interview transcript with Emeléus gives UCl_6; it should be UF_6.

59. Penney entered the mathematics department as an undergraduate in 1927 and gained both a BSc and PhD. It was during his postdoctoral years with John H. van Vleck at the University of Wisconsin that he learned much theoretical chemistry. From there he won a Royal Exhibition Scholarship to Cambridge and gained a second PhD. In a classic paper Penney laid down what became the basis of ligand field theory which helped to revolutionise chemists' understanding of coordination chemistry, (Schlapp and Penney, 1932). He also wrote papers on the bonding and structures of a wide range of compounds, and a book on valence, (Penney, 1935). As noted in Chapter Six, Penney collaborated with J. S. Anderson. And he taught Geoffrey Wilkinson the technique of fire eating (i.e., how to extinguish an ignited petrol fire in the mouth).

60. The Chairman of the governing body, Lord Falmouth, wrote to Sir Edward Appleton that he did not see what Penney could possibly contribute to the war effort in the United States. ICL archives, GXE, Falmouth to Appleton, 8 May 1944. The Cambridge professor, Sir Geoffrey Taylor, had predicted the energy output of nuclear explosions. Penney witnessed the bombing of Nagasaki (from the air) and went to Hiroshima and Nagasaki after the atomic bombs had been dropped. Simply by examining the devastation, and studying many bent and destroyed objects picked up at different distances from the explosions (objects he took back to London), he was able to accurately estimate the yields of both bombs. His calculations were accepted and he later worked on the Bikini tests for the Americans.

61. Quotation from (Sherfield, 1994). See also (Cathcart, 2004). After the war Penney turned down chairs at Imperial and Oxford. He moved to Fort Halstead, then to Aldermaston, as 'father' of Britain's own atomic and hydrogen bombs. In 1964 he was appointed chairman of UKAEA, Harwell and, from 1967–1973, he was Rector of IC.

62. Ewart Ray Herbert (Tim) Jones FRS (1911–2002), later Sir Ewart, but known as Tim to all, took his first degree at the University College of North Wales (Bangor). He gained his PhD with Heilbron in Manchester and, in

1947, returned there as professor. He was appointed to the Waynflete Chair in Oxford in 1954. He played a major role in the formation of British science policy after the war. For Jones, (Jones, 2003), (Watson, 2004), (Cadogan, 2003). During the war, Jones published a paper in which he used what became the eponymous 'Jones reagent', a famous, though fearsome, solution of chromium trioxide in concentrated sulphuric acid, used in the oxidation of various substrates, notably primary alcohols to carboxylic acids or aldehydes, and secondary alcohols to ketones. For example, (Bowden, Heilbron, Jones and Weedon, 1946).

63. The first commercial production of vitamin A, by Hofmann-La Roche in Switzerland in 1946, followed some of the procedures mapped out by Jones, Heilbron, and their students; notable among them, Ralph Raphael (see Note 92).

64. This work was collected in what Tim Jones called a 'monumental treatise,' namely (Clarke, Johnson and Robinson, 1949). In Britain much penicillin work was done by Howard Florey and Ernst Chain at Oxford. Together with Sir Alexander Fleming, penicillin's discoverer at St. Mary's Hospital, they won the Nobel Prize for medicine in 1945.

65. (Elvidge, 1991). Cook was elected FRS in 1951.

66. (Jones, 1962), quotation, p. 244; also Heilbron's presidential address to the Chemical Society, (Heilbron, 1949).

67. A few examples of wartime papers: (Heilbron, Carter and Lythgoe, 1939), (Heilbron and Jones, 1940), (Heilbron, Catch and Cook, 1942), (Johnson, Jones and Raphael, 1943), (Heilbron, Jones, McCombie and Weedon, 1945). The last of these papers was part 20 in a 36 part series.

68. DDT (dichlorodiphenyl trichloroethane, now known to be $(p\text{-}ClC_6H_4)_2CCl_3)$, was first made by the Austrian chemist Othmar Zeidler in 1874. He was unaware of its insecticidal properties, later discovered by the Swiss chemist, P. H. Müller (1889–1965). Müller patented Gesarol in 1939, and won the Nobel Prize for medicine in 1948. DDT was also tested in Sheffield, on a group of conscientious objectors, as well as on some animals. Its toxicity (for mammals) was said to be low, (Mellanby, 1967). The spraying technology was developed at IC (at Hurworth), (Gay, 2012).

69. Glaxo has always had strong ties to organic chemistry at the college. Its earliest research laboratory was sited next to Perkin's factory in Greenford. One of Jones' wartime students, P. A. Wilkinson, joined Glaxo after the war and worked there on sterol chemistry.

70. Quotation in J. H. Jones' obituary memoir, (Jones, 2003), emphasis in original.

71. (Jones, Shen and Whiting, 1951). Later, when Whiting worked at Harvard, he was a thorn in the flesh of Geoffrey Wilkinson who claimed, possibly unfairly, that Whiting butted in on his research (memoir, *op. cit.* 2; see also Chapter Eight). Whiting later became professor of organic chemistry in Bristol (1965–1984). T. Y. Shen came to the department from China at the end of the war. He moved with Jones to Manchester where he gained his PhD and then had an illustrious career in medicinal chemistry in the United States.

72. (Jones, 2003). See also Chapter Eight.

73. Jones was awarded the Meldola medal in 1940 and the Tilden prize in 1947.

74. Wilkinson (*op. cit.* 2) gives an account of two of Maddock's mishaps in Montreal, one a spill of the precious heavy water (allegedly the first litre to be brought to Canada from Norway via France) which then had to be recovered from the floor and several mopping-up cloths; another with plutonium — a flask in which a solution was being heated, cracked and spilled. It had to be recovered from an asbestos covered table which was sawn up and the plutonium salt extracted from the sawdust with boiling water. Maddock managed both recoveries — with some help — remarkably well. Years later, after his retirement from Cambridge, his radioactive laboratory had to be professionally decontaminated, for a paper with Heal and others on plutonium chemistry carried out at Montreal, and later at Chalk River, Ontario, (Harvey, Heal, Maddock and Rowley, 1947).

75. The chief scout was Fritz Paneth. Tube Alloys was the code name for the secret Anglo–French atomic bomb research project. The French team focussed on radiochemistry and was at first headed by Frédéric Joliot. The English team, more focussed on nuclear physics, was centred at the Cavendish Laboratory before moving to North America. Hans von Halban, Jean Guéron and Leo Kowarski managed, secretly, to bring the precious supply of 169 kg of heavy water from Norway to Cambridge via Cherbourg. In 1942 they moved their precious cargo to Montreal and led the radiochemical team there, and at Chalk River. The first overall Head of the Canadian project was von Halban but the Americans objected to his German name, even though he was a Parisian. He was replaced by Sir John Cockcroft. Late in the war Maddock helped to build Canada's first uranium heavy water reactor, and was later a consultant in the design of facilities at CERN. For an obituary of Maddock, (Shakeshaft, 2009), pp. 14–16; also (Adloff and Kauffman, 2010).

76. Wilkinson memoir, *op. cit.* (2) p. 12. Wilkinson did better than the geology students in the final examination and was awarded the Murchison Medal (and £10 for books). In later years he often said that it was the medal of which he

was most proud — he had many, including the Nobel. More biographical detail for Wilkinson is given in Chapter Eight.

77. Wilkinson, (*op. cit.* 2), claimed that Briscoe told Paneth that he (Wilkinson) was 'the best man he had.'

78. They sailed on the RMS *Andes*, commandeered as a troop carrier. Wilkinson was told he would travel first class, but had to share a cabin marked 'for 1 seaman only,' with three other scientists. Also on board were Paneth and his son, two of Paneth's colleagues from Durham, Frank Morgan and William Arrol, also Jules Guéron and his family, Hans von Halban, and Alan Nunn May.

79. Wilkinson and Heal also had a side trip to the Canadian National Research Council (NRC) in Ottawa where they analysed samples of beryllium oxide and graphite to be used in reactors for absorbing neutrons. They made a further trip to Flushing, New York, to learn micro methods from the specialist, A. A. Benedetti-Pichler, at Queens' College.

80. Wilkinsons second paper, (Grummit, Yaffé, Guéron, and Wilkinson, 1946). His first paper in the same journal was on the growth of ^{140}La from ^{140}Ba. See also Wilkinson, *op. cit.* (2).

81. (Bennett, Danopoulos, Griffith, and Green, 1997). Wilkinson made 89 new radioisotopes.

82. John Wilkinson, personal communication. For Hudson, a future professor of organic chemistry and FRS at the University of Kent, see Chapter Eight, Note 40.

83. Bockris, Bowler-Reed, and Bernard Lewis Archer had earlier been fellow undergraduates at Brighton Technical College. For Archer see Chapter Eight. Payne was later professor of chemistry at the University of Hong Kong. Grace Payne, a President of ICWA, told us that chemistry students were placed alphabetically at the lab benches — except for the women who were classified under W and worked next to each other. (By the 1950s women were integrated with the men.) After graduating, Grace Payne taught high school chemistry at a number of schools including one in Hong Kong.

84. Obituary of Peter Alexander (1922–1993), *The Independent*, 22 December, 1993. For his work with Barton see Chapter Eight, Note 16.

85. B. P. J. (John) O'Mara Bockris (1923–2013) was born in South Africa but grew up in Brighton. Croker memoir, *op. cit.* (18) p. 6.

86. Felix Sebba (1912–1989) was born in Cape Town and gained both a BSc and PhD from the University of Cape Town. He came to Imperial in 1939 with an 1851 Exhibition scholarship and his chosen research project, supervised by Briscoe, was 'The permeability of monolayers deposited on

aqueous substrates.' Sebba spent time also at Cambridge where there was more expertise in surface and colloid chemistry. Later Sebba wrote to Eldridge (ICL archives, KC\1–3; 25 March, 1958) that the possibility of using monolayers to reduce evaporation from dams and reservoirs started at the college after a visit by Irving Langmuir. Listening to him, Briscoe became intrigued by the effects of monolayers on water, inspiration for his work on silica dusts in relation to silicosis. Sebba did not get involved with that project but wrote that, because of severe droughts in South Africa, he began to speculate on using thin films to prevent water evaporation from reservoirs, and that Briscoe was supportive of his project.

87. Elvidge is discussed also in Chapter Eight. In his obituary of Cook (Elvidge, 1991), Elvidge wrote about fire watching duties during the war. He also noted that he and the other postgraduate students working under Cook prepared and characterised about 50 new compounds per year.

88. (Davies, 2004).

89. Later Johnson was head of the department of chemistry at Nottingham and, in 1968, was appointed head of department at Sussex; for Johnson, (Jones and Bonnet, 1984), (Jones, 1983 and 2004). For a 2 volume book on acetylenic compounds, (Johnson, 1946 and 1950). Johnson is perhaps best known for his work on vitamin B12. He received the RIC Meldola Medal in 1946, the CS Tilden Award in 1952 and the Pedler Award in 1974.

90. For Spinks, (Johnson, Rose and Suckling, 1984), (Johnson, 1982).

91. For Weedon, (Pattenden, 2005).

92. For Raphael, (Crombie, 2000), (Sanders, 2004). Quotation from Crombie's memoir. Isler worked with Hofmann–La Roche. Raphael had considered studying to become a rabbi before entering the college. Raphael was to win the RIC Meldola Medal (1948), the CS Tilden Award (1960) and the Pedler Award (1972). In 1949, he moved to a lectureship in Glasgow. This was followed by a chair at Queen's University in Belfast, the Regius professorship in Glasgow, and his appointment as the 1702 professor at Cambridge in 1972. Willie Motherwell who gained his PhD with Raphael in Glasgow told us that, years later, when Raphael had been at Cambridge for many years, he told him that IC was his spiritual home. Motherwell told us that the same was true of him and that he admires what he sees as IC's 'can do' attitude.

93. The Rector, Richard Southwell, predicted that the war would end before the centenary of the RCC in October 1945. He planned the celebrations accordingly, and was lucky that the war finally ended in early September.

Chapter Eight

New Research and Departmental Reorganisation After the Second World War, 1945–1965

In 1957, in a speech given on the occasion of Imperial College's golden jubilee, Patrick Linstead, then Rector, looked back at the period since the war and stated that 'a highly technical war gave place to a highly competitive peace in which the standard of living and stability of the currency could only be maintained by greater technological efficiency.'[1] This view of things and, more generally, the ongoing Cold War, were important factors in shaping the ideological context for what happened at the college during the period covered in Chapters Eight and Nine. Investment in science grew, and the number of students began to increase. Plans for a major expansion, including an upgrade and enlargement of the chemistry department, were made after the government's 1953 decision to increase significantly the number of students at IC. However, as we will see in Section 8.4, the enlargement of departmental space and facilities occurred only slowly, and in stages — and not in the way originally intended.

8.1 Departmental Governance

After Baker retired in 1932, the professor of Inorganic Chemistry shared the Headship of the department with the professor of organic chemistry — that meant Vincent Briscoe and Jocelyn Thorpe became joint heads of department.

As director also of the physical chemistry laboratories, Briscoe was the nominal head of physical chemistry, even though physical chemistry had its own chair, occupied by James Philip until his retirement in 1939. Each of the administrative sections received its own materials vote from the college. In 1945 the joint heads were Briscoe and Ian Heilbron, and the physical chemistry chair was vacant. In 1948 Roderic Hill succeeded Richard Southwell as Rector and decided, in the name of efficiency, to have a single head of chemistry. He chose Briscoe, the obvious choice because of his long association with the department, as student, lecturer, and professor, and because it was known that Heilbron was planning to retire soon. Nonetheless Heilbron, the more renowned chemist, was understandably offended. Although having a single head may have been a good idea, Hill should have waited until Heilbron had officially resigned before making the change. Heilbron resigned sooner than intended — in protest — and, a few weeks later, he wrote an angry letter to Lilian Penson, Vice-Chancellor of the University of London. In it he stated that if the professor of organic chemistry had to work under a head of department it would reduce his status making him 'scarcely more than a reader or senior lecturer' and 'to my knowledge not one organic chemist of repute has applied for the appointment.'[2] Arthur Cook, reader in organic chemistry, also resigned and left with Heilbron.[3]

Heilbron was right about the difficulty in finding someone to succeed him. In the end, some members of the college's governing body persuaded Patrick Linstead to accept the chair.[4] He, too, disliked the new arrangement and began making plans for a departmental constitution to come into effect on Briscoe's retirement. Linstead's constitution was tripartite but it met Hill's requirement that there be an overall head. The three sections, inorganic, organic, and physical chemistry were each to have a professor, and the three sections were to have separate budgetary provisions for teaching and research, though the undergraduate laboratories came under a separate budget. Whoever was chosen as head of department would be responsible for broad policy and for coordinating undergraduate teaching by the three sections.[5] Briscoe retired in 1954, and Linstead became head of department. However Hill died soon after, and Linstead was appointed Rector in January 1955, after serving only one term as head of department. The organic chair was not re-advertised since it was feared that, as before, there would be no plausible applicant. Linstead appointed Ernest Braude, a promising young chemist in his research group who had earlier worked with Heilbron and Jones. Braude won the RIC's Meldola Medal in 1950, but had only recently been promoted to reader.[6]

The department replaced Philip only after Briscoe's retirement in 1954 when Richard M. Barrer moved from the Chair in Aberdeen to become professor of physical chemistry. A few months later he succeeded Linstead as head of department. Linstead had not been head for long enough to experience problems with his new constitution — if he had, he would probably have smoothed out the wrinkles. Barrer and Braude, both new to their roles, had some disagreements over how to interpret it. Sadly, Braude took his own life after just one year as Professor, a tragedy that meant the organic chemistry chair became vacant yet again.[7] Linstead wanted to appoint Derek Barton, but Barton had only just settled in to the Regius Chair in Glasgow after his appointment in 1955. Once again, it took the diplomacy of some of the college governors to bring him back to London in 1957.[8] Geoffrey Wilkinson was appointed to the chair of inorganic chemistry in 1955 but arrived in January 1956. So, by the late 1950s the department had in place the three heads of section who were to see it through a period which, despite much frustration over new buildings and funding, was one of growth and great academic success.

8.2 Vincent Briscoe as Mentor to Derek Barton and Geoffrey Wilkinson

Derek Barton and Geoffrey Wilkinson both came from trades families, Barton from a family of carpenters, though his father ran a small timber business. Wilkinson's father and paternal grandfather were master painters; his mother and others on her side of the family were weavers. Wilkinson was perhaps better prepared for university than Barton, and had developed an early interest in chemistry from tinkering in the laboratory of a small chemical company owned by his aunt and uncle. It made Epsom and Glauber's salts. He received an excellent education at Todmorden Secondary School, supplemented by evening classes in chemistry at Rochdale Technical College.[9] It is our impression, though hard to verify, that Wilkinson also had more family support than Barton, not just as a student but throughout his life. His family was proud of his school, college, and later professional, successes. Barton attended Tonbridge School until his father's sudden death in 1935 when he left at age 17 without the qualifications needed to attend university. He began working in the office of his father's timber business, possibly with a view to eventually taking it over. After two years, however, he 'felt that there must be something more interesting in life' and decided to pursue a university education.[10] He left the business for the Medway Technical College in Gillingham, took science classes and prepared for the higher school certificate examinations. After three years of work and study, he came to IC in 1938, at the age of 20. Wilkinson arrived one year later. As was typical of those with the higher school certificate in science and mathematics, they both entered the second year of the undergraduate programme.

Both men were excellent students, though Wilkinson had slightly higher marks overall. Wilkinson appears in all kinds of college records in addition to those of the Board of Studies, evidence that he had a college life beyond chemistry. As noted in the previous chapter, he lived near the college and took part in student activities.[11] For Barton we could find no evidence of extracurricular activity. However, in his memoir, he mentions that, for financial reasons, he lived at home in Gravesend and spent about two hours twice a day in commuting back and forth to the college. Since he was a serious student, he would not have had much time for anything else.[12]

As already noted, Barton joined Ian Heilbron for his PhD which he completed in 1942. It appears, however, that he and Heilbron did not get along. Heilbron did not help Barton seek work on graduation, though a few years later he signed his nomination papers for the Chemical Society's Harrison Memorial Award and, yet later, supported his election to the Royal Society.[13] Since Heilbron helped to promote the careers of many other young organic chemists with whom he was associated, Barton's case is surprising.[14] It is perhaps significant that, for his doctoral research, Barton was not assigned to any of the more exciting projects going on in the organic chemistry section, and was put to work on the synthesis of vinyl chloride.[15] In his memoir Barton mentions that his relations with Heilbron were strained, but he blames himself. He noted his tendency to challenge Heilbron over what he saw as errors in his formulae, and that he often asked Heilbron questions that he could not answer.[16] That, *per se*, seems an unlikely explanation; perhaps Barton's manner when challenging his professor was unacceptable, something that could have been due to feelings of insecurity.

On completing his PhD, Barton seems not to have known where to turn. However Briscoe appreciated Barton's ability, took him under his wing and, as discussed in the previous chapter, put him to work on a number of war-related activities. In the final year of the war, Barton was seconded to Albright and Wilson in Birmingham where he worked on organo-phosphorus compounds.[17] At the end of the war he was again at a loss. He wanted an academic career and turned to Briscoe for help. It is difficult to reconcile the letters that Barton wrote to Briscoe and Eldridge at this time with the memoir he wrote in his sixties. In the letters he comes across as a rather insecure young man, though by several accounts he had a tough exterior.[18] In his memoir he displays great self-confidence, along with an outstanding intellect. By the time he wrote that, however, his world had changed. He was in a second marriage that brought him much happiness, and had achieved much.[19] Not only had he won the Nobel Prize for his early work, he carried out outstanding work also later in his career.

Despite the fact that Barton's PhD was in organic chemistry, Briscoe came to his rescue and, in 1945, gave him an assistant lectureship in inorganic and physical chemistry. He was given the task of lecturing to engineering students. To make up for this unpopular assignment, Briscoe allowed, indeed encouraged, Barton to continue with his research in organic chemistry. At first Barton worked on a project suggested to him by Tim Jones. As Barton put it, Jones knew that 'I was an eccentric maverick, but he encouraged me all the same at critical moments in my life.'[20] Barton's return to Imperial College was one such moment and he made the most of it. Using optical data in a way recently introduced by R. B. Woodward, he elucidated some structural aspects of the triterpenoids and steroids.[21] He worked at a rapid pace, helped by the award of a two-year ICI research fellowship in 1946. In 1948 he was given a lectureship and gave physical chemistry lectures to chemistry students.[22] His organic research attracted attention, not only did he win the Harrison Memorial Award in 1948, he was offered a one-year visiting position at Harvard in 1949. Barton wrote to Briscoe that he did not know whether to accept. Although ambitious, he had much self-doubt and little idea how to achieve his goals. Briscoe encouraged him to take up the Harvard offer, promising to hold the lectureship for him on his return.[23]

The temporary position at Harvard opened up because Robert Woodward was on sabbatical leave and someone was needed to give his undergraduate lectures. Barton had met Woodward a year earlier, after a lecture that Woodward gave in the IC department on the structure of santonic acid. Barton was inspired. He later wrote that he 'had never heard anyone pose and then resolve a problem in such a clear and logical manner', and he appreciated Woodward's application of mechanistic thinking to problems in natural product chemistry.[24] Fortunately for Barton, Woodward continued his research at Harvard during his sabbatical. Barton was to learn much from him, not only about steroids and the synthesis of natural products, but also about work habits.[25] The two men became friends. Barton learned yet more about steroid chemistry from Louis Fieser with whom he had corresponded earlier, indeed Fieser's seminar led to a turning point in Barton's career (see Note 62). Despite getting along well at Harvard, the letters that Barton wrote to Eldridge and Briscoe show that he was not entirely happy in America. His chemical work was gaining recognition, he was invited to give talks at other universities and at industrial laboratories, and he received a DSc from the University of London. Further, he thought highly of Harvard's chemistry department and admired what he saw as American efficiency, but he was homesick. There was also much about American life that he disliked. Surprisingly for someone who had lived through wartime deprivation, he complained about American food, and he disliked the democracy of American university departments. He wanted to become a professor in Britain where, in his view, the position was respected and held in high esteem. Eldridge wrote to him that even in England professors were no longer as revered as they had once been, and encouraged him to make the most of what America had to offer.[26]

Barton impressed his Harvard colleagues and they offered him a tenure-track position but he was ambivalent and, once again, consulted Briscoe. Briscoe told him that he could do well at Harvard, but that if he really wished to return to Britain the lectureship was still there for him. However, Briscoe advised him to apply for the then vacant readership at Birkbeck College, and that he would do what he could to help him win the position. The letter that Briscoe sent to the University of London on Barton's behalf is full of praise. Barton was 'first rate in every way,' he wrote; 'his breadth of interest and scholarship in the chemical field is quite extraordinary, and he is indefatigably skilful, original and ingenious in scientific enquiry.' One could not wish for a better letter. Briscoe sent Barton a copy and Barton replied thanking him for 'a magnificent piece of English prose that made me feel quite enthusiastic about the candidate.'[27] But by then the candidate had done much to help himself, and had amassed an impressive list of publications. He was indeed appointed to the readership (he was informed of this by Briscoe before the official notification was sent[28]) and was finally set for academic success in Britain. That he later returned to Imperial, however, is the result of the historical accidents described above.

In his memoir Wilkinson wrote that when he came to London for the two-day practical examination set for the Royal Scholarships, and to attend the college entrance interview, Briscoe advised him to read the recently published *Modern Aspects of Inorganic Chemistry* by H. J. Eméleus and J. S. Anderson.[29] Wilkinson followed this advice. Indeed, he was a wide reader of the chemical literature, including historical material in areas that interested him. He had an excellent memory, something that served him well throughout his life. Barton, too, had an excellent memory for chemical detail, but knew less than Wilkinson about the history of chemistry, or about adjacent disciplines such as geology, botany and metallurgy. As mentioned in Chapter Seven, Wilkinson won the Murchison Medal, the highest undergraduate award in geology, and geology remained a lifelong enthusiasm. He also wrote a long paper on the anodizing of metals — something a little out of the ordinary for a chemistry under-graduate. It would appear, however, that Barton had the greater mathe-matical and logical skills, skills that served him well in his early work on optical activity, in his work on conformational analysis, and in his later work figuring out possible routes in complicated chemical syntheses.

Wilkinson wrote that he had intended to become an organic chemist, but was disappointed by his performance in the organic practical exam. As he later discovered, he received a higher mark than had Barton in the organic written exam. Barton won the Hofmann Prize for best overall performance in organic chemistry, the prize won by Ralph Raphael in

Wilkinson's year. Both Barton and Wilkinson came top of their IC class, and of the university's consolidated BSc chemistry list for 1940 and 1941 respectively. Two years later another brilliant chemist, Franz Sondheimer, did the same.[30] It was Briscoe who advised Wilkinson to become an inorganic chemist, and Wilkinson was the last of his PhD students. Although Briscoe later proved a good mentor, his war-related work meant that he had little time for Wilkinson. As noted in the previous chapter, Wilkinson was bored with his PhD work. He claimed, no doubt correctly, that he learned more from Harry Eméleus than from Briscoe in this period.[31] Among other things, Eméleus taught him how to blow glass and build a good vacuum line.

As we have seen, Fritz Paneth came seeking talent for the Tube Alloys project in 1942 and Wilkinson was among those recruited. After the war he joined Glen Seaborg at Berkeley where his first job was to make his own Geiger counter. The work at Berkeley was not altogether to Wilkinson's liking. Besides, he was sensitive about ownership of his research and, unlike Barton, had little self-doubt. He was not prepared to put up with senior people taking credit for his work, and claimed that some at the Lawrence Livermore Laboratory were doing just that.[32] He wrote to Briscoe for advice and was told, not for the first time, to leave nuclear chemistry where he would always play second fiddle to the physicists, and that he should find a position in a proper chemistry department. When Wilkinson returned to Britain in 1949 to attend the first postwar conference on nuclear and radiation chemistry, organised by the Royal Society and held in Oxford, he used the opportunity to visit his family, and to have a long chat with Briscoe about possible jobs in Britain. Briscoe repeated his earlier advice, namely that first he should become a proper inorganic chemist.[33] Wilkinson then moved to MIT on a fellowship and, a year later, to Harvard as an assistant professor. There he returned to more traditional chemistry and began work in the new area of organotransition metal chemistry that was to bring him fame.

Unlike Barton in this early period, Wilkinson enjoyed American life. However, when he was offered the assistant professorship at Harvard, he wrote to Briscoe asking for his advice on the advisability of accepting. According to Wilkinson, Briscoe replied 'in no uncertain terms that I should go to Harvard', and that sooner or later 'I would get back to

England.'[34] The Harvard department was full of distinguished chemists, including its Chairman, the spectroscopist E. Bright Wilson. However, like Barton earlier, Wilkinson was most influenced by Woodward and carried out some work with him. Indeed, in working out the sandwich structure of ferrocene with its new type of organometallic bonding, they caused a sensation.[35] It was, in fact, Wilkinson who envisaged the molecule's novel structure, an act of great imagination given that nothing like it was known to exist. He was lucky, however, to be in a department that possessed good spectroscopic instruments, allowing him to produce the evidence needed to support his ideas. He was soon engaged in making a series of analogous compounds using many of the Group 4–10 transition metals, and made also some cyclopentadienyl metal carbonyl derivatives.[36] Aside from ferrocene, perhaps his best known work from this period was his use of NMR to study metal-hydride linkages, such as in the unusual cyclopentadienyl hydrido complex, $Re(\eta-C_5H_5)_2H$.

Wilkinson's work in this new type of organometallic chemistry, begun at Harvard and continued at IC, was to win him the Nobel Prize in 1973 (see Chapter Nine). Whether he would have remained at Harvard, had he been given tenure is an open question, even though he later wrote, 'I would have returned to England even if they had offered me a gold-plated full professorship.'[37] It is clear that Briscoe wanted Wilkinson to be his successor at IC, and was perhaps not unhappy at how things turned out. Indeed, as soon as he heard that Wilkinson had not received tenure, he wrote saying that he was retiring and that the university was already advertising for his successor. He sent Wilkinson all the application forms and encouraged him to apply. Briscoe then lobbied on his behalf, coached him for the interview, and took him out to lunch before putting him in a taxi to Senate House where the interview took place. Wilkinson was informed of his appointment by Linstead who, by then, was Rector of Imperial College. In offering him the not very high salary of £2000, Linstead told Wilkinson, 'of course if you become an FRS or win the Nobel Prize, then you get a salary boost'. 'I got both', Wilkinson wrote, and 'I didn't in either case.' And, he added, 'I remember quoting this once in a Board of Governors meeting and it brought the house down. They were always a stingy lot at IC as far as I was concerned.'[38]

Barton and Wilkinson had very different personalities but their early history illustrates the importance of mentorship, even in the lives of outstandingly gifted people. The more self-confident Wilkinson would surely have made a good academic career no matter what, but the career that he *did* make was to a degree fashioned by his mentor, though he himself would probably not have acknowledged this openly. In 1964, however, he donated the funds for a prize in Briscoe's memory — for students excelling in inorganic chemistry. Barton, on the other hand, needed help to get started on the academic path, regardless of his considerable intellectual ability. One has the impression that without Briscoe his life could have been very different.

8.3 Research: (a) Organic Chemistry; (b) Inorganic Chemistry; (c) Physical Chemistry

(a) Organic Chemistry

In 1945 Heilbron was head of the organic chemistry section and his two lieutenants, Cook and Jones, were working alongside him.[39] By 1949, all three had left and Linstead was the professor of organic chemistry. His earlier ideas on the structure of phthalocyanine pigments had been confirmed in the late 1930s, by J. M. Robertson at the Royal Institution using X-ray crystallography. This prompted Dorothy Crowfoot Hodgkin to state that it 'provide[d] the first purely physical demonstration of the truth of organic chemistry.'[40] Linstead was elected FRS in 1940 and, in 1949, he brought research on phthalocyanines back to the department. Several students, including Margaret Whalley, later on the staff, gained doctorates working in this field.

Linstead set in place a number of other research programmes, including one on the kinetics, and mechanism of hydrogen transfer processes with Braude and Lloyd M. Jackman.[41] Some related research was carried out by B. C. L. (Jimmy) Weedon, appointed a lecturer in 1947. He worked with Linstead on the fatty acids, and carried out some electrochemical oxidations of the Kolbe type.[42] However, he was soon drawn back to the brightly coloured polyene pigments that he had worked on for his doctorate.[43] Jackman, an Australian, had come to the department as a postdoctoral fellow in 1951. On one occasion Prince Philip came to college and was shown a display of Linstead's phthalocyanine pigments. Spotting Jackman standing in a corner, the Prince asked him what he did. After listening to his reply, he said that he hadn't understood a word but, recognizing the Australian accent, asked 'what do you think your chances are in the test match?' Jackman replied, 'we'll lick the pants off you', an answer that pleased the Prince and led to an animated discussion about cricket rather than a *pro forma* one about chemistry.[44]

As mentioned in the previous chapter, Jack Elvidge worked on penicillin during the war, gaining his PhD under Cook. After a brief period in Glasgow he returned to the department in 1948 as a lecturer.[45] Together with Linstead he began work on iminoheterocycles and the structure of the muconic acids.[46] Elvidge also collaborated with Len Owen. Owen was a little unusual in that he was able to maintain his own research programme, largely independent of both Linstead and then Barton. He came to the college as a lecturer in 1943 and continued with his wartime work on the nitrogen mustards, focussing on their use as chemotherapeutic agents in the treatment of cancer. Later he returned to his earlier work on sugars, beginning some important work on the thio sugars.[47] A gentle and quiet man, Owen took on much undergraduate teaching and was admired as a lecturer. He was given a personal chair in 1961.[48]

After the war, the Rockefeller Foundation decided to fund biochemically related work in Britain. Linstead received a major grant for new research on photosynthesis, chlorophyll, and bacteriochlorophylls. Much of this work was carried out by postdoctoral fellows, though Braude was involved. Among other things they confirmed the earlier, but then still disputed, theory of the Nobel Laureate Hans Fischer on the structure of chlorophyll.[49] To facilitate work on these various projects, Linstead acquired funds for a laboratory to carry out work in radioactive tracing. In 1952 he appointed David W. Turner to run the laboratory under Braude's direction. Although initially appointed as a technician, Turner was encouraged to carry out research toward a PhD. He began some ^{14}C tracer research on anionotropic rearrangements, bringing a range of physical techniques to bear. Echoing back to H. B. Baker, he noted the importance of solvent dryness in carrying out studies in chlorobenzene and other aprotic media. Braude gave Turner a vacuum spectrograph to set up and, when an NMR spectrometer came to the inorganic chemistry section, Turner was allowed to work on it together with Jackman. He was stimulated also by W. R. S. (Reg) Garton who was working on vacuum spectroscopy in the physics department. Turner's work led to a range of new spectrographic techniques, including the development of photoelectron spectroscopy for which he became renowned.[50]

Linstead also invited Frances Hamer to come to the department as an honorary lecturer after her retirement from Kodak Ltd. in 1951. She was a specialist in photographic dyes and was to edit a volume on cyanine dyes.[51] She helped in the instruction of third year organic chemistry students, notably by showing them how to carry out small-scale preparations. Leslie Crombie, who came to the department as a lecturer after the war, was assigned much teaching, but nonetheless managed to keep up the research he had begun with Stanley Harper, his doctoral supervisor at King's College. He returned to King's College as a reader in 1958.[52]

During this period Linstead's closest collaborator was Braude. Indeed, it appears that Braude did little independent work and so would have been under great pressure when, unexpectedly, he inherited Linstead's chair. Linstead was a tough act to follow; a very distinguished chemist, he had a clear idea of how to advance certain areas of organic chemistry, and had set up some good research programmes. Further, he was able to secure the funds to support them. As we will see below, he also began a major reorganisation of the undergraduate curriculum.

When Barton arrived back in the department in 1957 he brought along Paul J. de Mayo and Alastair I. Scott.[53] They helped him to establish his own research interests; people already working in the organic chemistry section had either to adjust or to leave. For example, by 1957 Jackman was a lecturer. Many years later he wrote a brief memoir in which he recalled that Barton came into his office shortly after arriving as Professor. 'Have we ever thought of writing a book?,' he asked. Jackman replied that he was beginning to write one on the work he had carried out with Linstead and Braude on oxidation and reduction mechanisms. 'Ah,' said Barton, 'one only writes a book to make one's fame or fortune and a book on oxidation will do neither. Why don't we write one on NMR spectroscopy?' This was Barton's not so subtle way of persuading a young colleague that he should move into a new area of research. The use of the pronoun 'we' did not imply that he would be a coauthor. Barton was right about fame and fortune. Jackman's *Applications of nuclear magnetic resonance in organic chemistry* undoubtedly helped to make his name.[54] In the 1950s organic chemists were using IR and UV absorption spectroscopy in the elucidation of structure. Barton, interested in the structures of certain natural products, wanted access to the new tool of NMR, correctly believing that it would shed light on problems in conformational analysis and structural organic chemistry.[55] Jackman wrote that he learned a little about NMR from a lecture given in the department by John D. (Jack) Roberts of the California Institute of Technology, who had shown slides of a Varian HR-40 MHz machine. Like others Jackman was 'dazzled' by what he then saw as a massive electromagnet. He soon learned more about the subject and, when Wilkinson purchased the department's first NMR machine, was given access to it.[56] Weedon, too, explored the uses of NMR — in determining the structures of both natural and synthetic carotenoids.[57]

Another person who had his arm twisted by Barton was Eric Waight.[58] He, too, had worked with Braude, was already adept in spectroscopic methods, and knew something about NMR. Barton persuaded him to add mass spectrometry to his other skills, and the two obtained a grant to purchase an AEI MS9 machine. A Perkin Elmer 270 was added in 1965.[59] Waight became successful in this area, carried out work of his own, but also played a supportive role in carrying out measurements for other organic chemists and, later, also for people in biochemistry.[60] Barton was clearly intent on putting in place the kinds of physical instruments he needed, and in finding people to carry out measurements on the molecules he was interested in. It should, perhaps, be pointed out that the machines available in the 1950s had yet to cross paths with computer technology. Although the possibility was anticipated, attaching computers to NMR and other machines would have been far too costly before the 1970s. It is also interesting to speculate on whether the introduction of expensive new technology in the decades after the war, and the fact that the new instruments had increasingly to be shared within the department, spelled the beginning of the end of the tripartite departmental structure.

It is impossible to do justice to Barton's extraordinary range of research (he published well over 1000 papers on many different topics).[61] Here we will briefly summarise some of the work he carried out to about 1965. His later period as professor of organic chemistry is discussed in Chapter Nine. While still at Harvard, Barton wrote the short paper that helped win him the Nobel Prize in 1969, shared with the Norwegian chemist Odd Hassel.[62] Hassel's work informed the way in which Barton thought about conformational analysis — showing how conformation influences the course and rates of reactions in cyclic systems — work that engaged Barton while at Birkbeck. By the time he returned to IC from Glasgow, however, conformational analysis had become a routine tool. He continued to use it, for example in exploring whether conformational effects were transmitted through molecules and, if so, how far.[63] However, like Linstead before him, he was keen to start on something new and looked to discover new synthetic methods that would allow him to make interesting and complex molecules under stereochemical control.

Barton soon appointed three new members of staff, J. K. (Hamish) Sutherland in 1958, Gordon Kirby in 1960, and Benjamin Sklarz in 1961.[64] He also attracted several excellent doctoral students. As he moved further into synthesis, he followed in the footsteps of his idol Robert Woodward and brought in as many postdoctoral fellows as he could to work alongside the research students. One student who stands out from this period is Jack Baldwin.[65] Like Woodward, Barton was a workaholic and set an almost impossible standard. He is reported to have said that an 80 hours work week should be the norm.[66]

Barton's work in synthesis included that with Kirby on the amaryllidaceae alkaloids.[67] One of their papers was on the biosynthesis of galanthamine, a molecule that caused some excitement at the time as a possible treatment for Alzheimer's disease. Another paper was on the elucidation of the final stages in the biosynthesis of morphine.[68] With Sutherland, Barton worked on the cyclisation products of some sesquiterpenes. As Barton's principal lieutenants, Kirby and Sutherland had to make sure that everything ran smoothly whenever he was away on consulting and lecture trips.

Barton also began work on the photochemistry of linearly- and cross-conjugated dienones. For this he had the help of the German chemist, Gerhardt Quinkert, whom he described as 'a very gifted post-doctoral colleague'.[69] Another notable visitor was the Australian chemist, Athelstan Beckwith FRS (1930–2010), a specialist in free radical intermediates in organic reactions, who came on a Nuffield Foundation grant in 1965.[70] He later held a chair at the Australian National University (ANU) and, since he was a very frequent flyer, he became known as the QANTAS professor. Barton was connected also to an important new project in Cambridge MA, at the Research Institute for Medicine and Chemistry. (RIMAC, funded by the Schering–Plough Corporation, was partly under the aegis of Harvard University though located next to the MIT campus.) Its director, Maurice Pechet, invited Barton to accept responsibility for chemical synthesis of compounds that could have some application in medicine. Already in 1958 they identified aldosterone, a hormone that helps to control the electrolyte balance in the body, as needing a good synthesis. Barton directed this, and other work, from a distance — though he made many visits to the institute.[71]

Barton was keen to point out the good offers that he received from the United States and Linstead was worried about keeping him at IC.[72] It is not that Barton wanted to leave; but he did want to strengthen his position. He knew that a new building was planned (see below) and urged Linstead to speed things up. In this period he co-founded, and was on the board of, the new journal *Tetrahedron*. He was also joint chief editor of *Comprehensive natural products chemistry*. His later research is discussed in Chapter Nine.

(b) Inorganic Chemistry

Vincent Briscoe was professor of inorganic chemistry to 1954, but carried out little research in the postwar years.[73] Shortly after the war he appointed a few people to help with undergraduate teaching but none of them stayed for long.[74] Joseph Chatt had a brief stay in the department, though not as a teacher. He came on an ICI research fellowship in 1946, intending to work on Pt-olefin complexes, but he found the departmental facilities so run down after the war that he gave up the fellowship and went to work for ICI instead.[75] The British Iron and Steel Research Association provided some funds for bursaries and for upgrading facilities, as did the Permutit company and the Imperial Smelting Corporation.

When Wilkinson arrived in January 1956, working in the inorganic section were Leslie Theobald, John Welch, Eric Roberts, Margaret Carlton, Arthur Eldridge, and five younger lecturers, none of whom stayed long: Jimmy Dalziel, Albert Stoessl, David Sharp, Raymond Peacock and Alexander Cross.[76] Eldridge, as assistant director of research, was the departmental Administrator. Theobald carried out work in gravimetric analysis, but his retirement in 1963 saw an end to this as a research field, and the beginning of the end of its central role in undergraduate teaching. The appointment of T. S. (Tom) West to succeed Theobald is discussed in Chapter Nine. Welch used X-ray diffraction in his work on the structures of the rare earth oxides; he also studied the properties of some solid metal sulphides, and had an interest in dense refractory materials. However, this work was largely given up when he succeeded Eldridge as assistant director in 1960. For Carlton see Chapter Six. Roberts was senior tutor. He carried out research on the enzymes that contribute to nitrogen fixation by legumes. In this connection he built his own mass spectrometer and used it for some tracer work with ^{15}N.[77]

The agricultural chemistry section remained small, but the bombed-out Hurworth laboratory was rebuilt at Harlington and work resumed there. Arthur Marsden (see Chapter Seven) left in 1946 to become director of the Commonwealth Bureau of Dairy Sciences in Reading, John Hannen retired in 1960 and the head of the sub-section, Alfred Pollard, retired one year later. Archibald Cornfield, a former student who had been appointed to replace Marsden, kept the MSc course going until the late 1970s. Research in this sub-section was mostly related to market garden crops and insecticides, and there was collaboration with IC's entomologists.

Before Wilkinson returned to London his Harvard doctoral student, F. Albert (Al) Cotton, suggested that he write up his undergraduate lecture notes as a textbook. Wilkinson agreed, provided that Cotton join him as coauthor. So, in the summer of 1956, Cotton joined the Wilkinson family in Denmark and the two men spent time thinking about how to structure their book.[78] Wilkinson's Harvard lectures were gradually transformed into chapters which were then tested on Cotton's students at MIT and Wilkinson's at IC. The book, revised in the light of student comments, was published in 1962 as *Advanced Inorganic Chemistry: A comprehensive text*. It was indeed both advanced and comprehensive (pp. 925), and was one of the first textbooks to treat transition metal chemistry seriously. It included also a good section on ligand field theory written by Cotton — much reduced by the sixth edition. In his memoir Wilkinson noted that he told the publisher, Interscience (Wiley), that they would be lucky to sell 3000 copies — in total. As it turned out the book was a runaway success and sold well over 3000 copies in its first year. By 1999, and into its sixth edition (pp. 1325), more than half a million copies had been sold. It was translated into many languages and the royalties allowed the Wilkinsons to leave their small Bayswater flat for a house nearby. Later, they purchased some land with a cottage in the Sussex countryside, and the family often spent their weekends there. Wilkinson was proud of having planted over 2000 trees on the property.

When he arrived back in the department as professor of inorganic chemistry, Wilkinson was 34 years old. Raring to go, he soon revived the inorganic section. Indeed, his obituarists wrote that in his early years as professor,

> *The spirit in his research group was more akin to that of an urgent gold rush in the Wild West than the scholarly and disciplined calm expected of academics. If anything this understates the truth: he expected his students to work as hard as he did — seven days a week or at least six, from early morning to late evening. He was, however, remarkably tolerant of eccentric behaviour, and when thwarted he made creative and ingenious use of expletives and always had a ready sense of fun.*[79]

As this suggests, Wilkinson put much pressure on his students. He wanted them to come up with ways of making new and interesting compounds, and spent time in the laboratory urging them along. He would visit them almost every day, always starting the conversation by asking, 'what's new?' (actually, 'what's noo?'). But before anything new could happen the laboratory had to be set up, something that took close to two years. Wilkinson was given space in a new wing that was added to the back of the RCS building, and completed only shortly after he arrived.[80] He was fortunate that Sir Alexander (later Lord) Todd, chairman of the SRC, was looking to spend some serious money on chemical rather than physical research, and agreed to make a case for the Varian–40 NMR machine mentioned above. The IC department was the first in the country to have such a machine. David E. H. Jones, a research student at the time, remembers that it was installed in the basement next to the men's lavatory so as to exploit the water supply needed to cool the magnet. However, flushing toilets led to variation in the water pressure which affected the temperature of the magnet. As a result the 'NMR spectrum [often] went haywire' and it became necessary to have a separate cooling system plumbed in. The machine was also sensitive to the mains frequency and the operator had to phone the Central Electricity Generating Board to ask what the frequency was. While the front office always replied 50Hz, the engineers on duty could be relied on to give a more accurate figure.[81]

Wilkinson's new laboratory space was sufficiently organised by the autumn of 1956 for him to be able to welcome his first doctoral student, Malcolm Green, and his first postdoctoral fellow, Eddie Abel.[82] More students arrived in the following year. Wilkinson adopted the informal behavioural style he had enjoyed in the United States and addressed his research students by their first names. His open door policy allowed them and members of staff to talk with him when needed. All were soon calling him Geoff — close to revolutionary at the time. His casual and friendly manner contributed to his popularity also with the cleaning and secretarial staff. All of this, together with his informal clothing, set Wilkinson apart from other professors of the period.

In addition to research, Abel helped Wilkinson with the first in what became the multivolume *Comprehensive Organometallic Chemistry*.[83] However, Abel is best remembered in the department for causing an explosion that blew out some windows as well as the door to Wilkinson's office. It also damaged some apparatus. Ken Packer, then an undergraduate carrying out his third year research project with Abel, witnessed first-hand, the glass windows in Wilkinson's laboratory bulging outwards before collapsing (for Packer see Chapter Ten, Note 12). At the same time, Michael Sammes, then a first year undergraduate, remembers Wilkinson being 'ten minutes into his lecture when the double doors of the lecture theatre bowed inwards'. The building shook, people outside the doors were running around shouting, and some were unravelling fire hoses. Wilkinson, however, carried on lecturing until someone came and grabbed him saying 'professor Wilkinson, please come!' But he soon returned 'grinning,' picked up his chalk, and resumed the lecture. The students then stamped their feet causing him to pause, 'Oh, you want to know what is going on … well my lab's on fire from floor to ceiling but there is nothing I can do about it.' Fortunately Abel was not seriously injured, but a number of documents, including part of the Cotton and

Wilkinson book manuscript, were blown out of the lab along with the windows.[84] It was raining at the time and, only later realizing the loss, Wilkinson recovered the sodden pages from the glass and other debris in the courtyard below. The explosion had one positive result. It was reported in the press (including on the front page of the Evening Standard), and because of the publicity the London Fire Brigade gave IC second priority — after Heathrow Airport.

In 1956 Wilkinson appointed Dennis Evans and Jack Lewis to lectureships. He consulted Rex Richards at Oxford on whom to appoint and was told that Evans, just returned from a postdoctoral position in Chicago, was an excellent chemist. Further, he knew about NMR even though it was not strictly his field. Jack Lewis, already teaching at Sheffield, very much wanted to join Wilkinson and did so for just one year.[85] He was interested in the magnetic susceptibilities of transition metal complexes, and metal-ligand bonds; and he introduced Wilkinson to metal nitrosyls — a topic on which they published several joint papers. According to Wilkinson, as soon as Lewis arrived he 'started acting as my right-hand man without even asking'. He also gave a well-remembered third year undergraduate course.[86] One year later Les Pratt, another of Richards' doctoral students, someone who *had* focussed on NMR, was appointed. He was given the task of commissioning the new NMR machine. Both Pratt and Evans spent their entire careers in the department.[87] Good friends, they worked together on the NMR spectrometer and improved its performance. Pratt became the machine's guardian, and published a number of papers together with Wilkinson. Evans developed both a method for using NMR for measuring the magnetic susceptibilities of paramagnetic compounds in solution, and an ingenious adaptation of the Gouy method for magnetic measurements on solids. Both methods are in use to this day.[88]

Like Wilkinson, Evans was a chain smoker. Wilkinson relied on him for his own supply of cigarettes since that way he didn't have to waste time buying them for himself. Besides, Evans had a cheap supplier. Smoking during lectures and in laboratories was still permitted in the early 1960s and Evans would sometimes show students how ether (instead of water or stamping under foot) could extinguish a cigarette.[89] He used to pace while lecturing and, on one occasion, 'fell off the dais in full flight.'[90] Wilkinson relied on Evans for much more than cigarettes: for help in reviving the inorganic section, building new research activities, and for his sound chemical advice. Evans read the chemical literature carefully and appears to have had a photographic memory. He was a store house of chemical information, from the arcane to the very practical. Students and colleagues soon learned that if they mentioned what they were working on, Evans was able to direct them to papers they should read. In the late 1950s he built a cell for studying the electronic spectra of hydrocarbons mixed with oxygen under high pressure. Molecular oxygen is paramagnetic and his idea was to see how it perturbed the singlet-triplet energy levels in compounds such as benzene and acetylene.[91] On one occasion, with oxygen and acetylene under 140 atmospheres' pressure, the cell exploded. It had been held together by three metal bolts at each end. One of the bolted ends blew off, flew across the laboratory almost destroying a new spectrometer borrowed from Barton, ending up plugged into the side of a gas cylinder. Evans was lucky to have escaped with only minor lacerations and a few glass fragments embedded in his body — they were surgically removed. It was fortunate that the cylinder was not penetrated. Evans kept the empty cylinder in his laboratory for a few years, and the triple indentation was a constant reminder to his students that chemistry can be a dangerous occupation.[92] According to his obituarists, when Evans lectured on this work outside the department he passed around a cell filled with a yellow benzene–oxygen mixture — yellow because of the electron shift. The cell was under a relatively tame 50 atmospheres, but only brave members of the audience took the opportunity to peer through it. In this period Evans began working with Grignard reagents and other metal alkyls.[93]

Not only was Evans a daring experimentalist, he was renowned for his party tricks. Some of them appeared reckless but, like his research, they were well thought through. For example, he would chew pieces of glass or old vinyl records and pretend to swallow them, while actually storing the ground up bits in his cheek for later disposal. Not so sensible was telling his audience that one could swallow glass without harm, provided it was well ground up. Another trick was inhaling pure oxygen and then exhaling it through a lighted cigarette which would burn out in a flaming flash. Evans was also interested in hallucinogenic chemicals. He grew the peyote cactus in his laboratory, and studied the chemical as well as physiological properties of mescalin. His attempt at growing magic mushrooms was less successful, but he experimented with psilocybin. He also ordered lysergic acid diethylamide (LSD) from a chemical company's catalogue (easy and legal to do at the time), studied its chemistry, and synthesised some derivatives. The stories of his drug-taking experiments were fascinating but, knowing the dangers, he never encouraged others to emulate his behaviour.[94] Evans was much loved, in part for his eccentricity but more because his brilliance was combined with an engaging and modest demeanour. Further, he was very generous with his time, willing to help anyone who asked. There were, however, two things for which he could not be relied on: the taking on of administrative tasks, and giving morning lectures. His working day began only after midday and went on far into the night.

Wilkinson had learned much about the chemistry of the transition metals, the lanthanides and actinides, while working at the Lawrence Livermore Laboratory where he devised procedures for separating their isotopes. This knowledge served him well in the chemistry carried out at Harvard and IC. His inaugural lecture at IC was appropriately titled 'Some aspects of the renaissance in inorganic chemistry.'[95] As he stated in the lecture, his research focus was organometallic complexes, and coordination chemistry involving transition metals — though he worked occasionally with other metals. Highly ambitious, he worried about his publication rate given his new administrative duties. During his first two years as professor most of his papers were of work carried out with his former Harvard students.[96] However, papers from IC soon followed. Indeed, given the fecundity of the new organometallic chemistry, they flowed not only from Wilkinson's laboratory but from many others. Competition, however, only spurred him on. In addition to Green, among those lucky enough to be his PhD students during this exciting period were, Martin Bennett, Ray Colton, Laxmi Dave, Alan Davison, James (Jimmy) Down, Robert (Bob) Gillard, William (Bill) Griffith, Nigel P. Johnson, Colin Lock, William McFarlane, Jon McCleverty, Brian Moore, and John Osborn.[97]

Shortly after he arrived at IC Wilkinson almost took another turn. After reading in N. V. Sidgwick's 1950 book, *The chemical elements and their compounds*, that potassium reacts with cyclopentadiene in benzene, he considered embarking on research that could have led to the synthesis of crown ethers, something for which Charles Pedersen, working at

DuPont, was to receive the Nobel Prize in 1987. Wilkinson received a tip on how to make polyethers, and had some ideas of his own on how this might be achieved, but, like others at the time, he did not fully believe that Na^+ or K^+ formed organic solvates. However, he set his doctoral students Jimmy Down and Brian Moore the dangerous task of determining the solubility of K and Na and their alloys in ethers, and of carrying out a spectral investigation of the blue solution of the sodium-potassium alloy.[98] But this work went no further.

Early on Wilkinson made sodium cyclopentadienide which, when dissolved in tetrahydrofuran, became a standard precursor in the preparation of a range of metallocenes. Work on metallocenes continued at IC, but only for a few years. Having discovered that metals in the sandwiches could be protonated, Wilkinson also made a number of hydrides.[99] Other metal complexes were made, including ones with nitric oxide, oxygen, acetylene, and some with unsaturated fluorocarbons as ligands.[100] Wilkinson's later work in coordination chemistry is discussed in Chapter Nine which includes also a short discussion of work relating to his Nobel Prize in 1973.

Among the new staff in the inorganic section were A. J. (Tony) Poë and Anne Dunne, both appointed just prior to Wilkinson's arrival. Poë was an Oxford graduate, who had spent a few years working at Harwell, and Dunne was an IC graduate. Neither had a doctorate and they were appointed to help with undergraduate teaching in the analytical laboratory. Dunne acted also as women's tutor but she soon married a flying dentist and left to join him in Australia. Telling Poë that a PhD was his 'way to get a union card,' Wilkinson took him on as a PhD student — only in name since he did not actually supervise Poë's work.[101] Poë left for a professorship at the University of Toronto in 1970. Naida Gill (1923–1993) joined the staff in 1959 after gaining her PhD with Ron Nyholm at UCL. She worked on transition metal complexes before returning to her native Australia, and a position at the ANU in 1961. Also in 1961, Wilkinson appointed David Goodgame and, one year later, Margaret Goodgame. The Goodgames, both Oxford graduates, had spent a brief period as postdoctoral fellows with F. A. (Al) Cotton at Manachusetts Institute of Technology (MIT). They were experienced in electronic and IR spectroscopy, and soon added Mössbauer spectroscopy to their areas of expertise. They are discussed further in the following chapters. Ronald (Ron) Mason, a crystallographer, was on the staff for just two years. He told us that Wilkinson was 'incredibly supportive' with equipment and money, and that he worked with him on the structures of some transition metal complexes.[102]

When Bill Griffith returned to join the staff in 1962, the department acquired a Raman spectrometer under a University of London intercollegiate research scheme and he became an expert in that field. His work as a staff member is discussed in subsequent chapters. John F. Gibson arrived in 1965. He, too, is discussed in Chapter Nine but is mentioned here because in bringing expertise in electron spin resonance (ESR) to the study of inorganic complexes, he completed what was a period of great expansion in the use of instrumental methods. A technological addition of a different kind, the department's first Xerox photocopying machine, arrived in 1963 and was fiercely guarded by its operator.

Both Barton and Wilkinson, brought people with expertise in new instrumental methods to their sections. However, the staff that Wilkinson appointed had more freedom to pursue independent research than did their counterparts in organic chemistry. This was a continuation of a pattern set by earlier professors. Thorpe, Heilbron, and Linstead all had a firm grip on what went on in the organic section and, by and large, only supported research in which they themselves were interested. Barton followed in their footsteps. Baker, Briscoe and Philip were less controlling. People who worked in the inorganic and physical sections were encouraged to carry out their own research, whether or not it was of direct interest to the professor. This did not preclude cooperation with the professor and was a pattern that continued under Wilkinson.[103]

(c) Physical Chemistry

When Richard Barrer was appointed professor of physical chemistry in 1954, little could he have imagined that he would become head of department one year later. Indeed, he probably accepted the headship out of a sense of duty and would have preferred to have pursued his research without the extra administrative responsibilities. Barrer was a New Zealander, born in Wellington and brought up on a farm near Masterton, a small town about 115 km north of the capital. He and his siblings received their elementary schooling at home with their mother, a former school teacher. From 1923 Barrer attended the Wairarapa secondary school which opened in the same year. The headmaster had a DSc and although Barrer received an all-round education, it was unusually strong in the sciences. He won a scholarship to Canterbury University College in 1928 where he gained both a BSc and MSc in chemistry. In 1932 he won the 1851 Exhibition scholarship — only one was allocated to New Zealand at any one time — allowing him to move to the University of Cambridge for a PhD. While at Canterbury, Barrer read Eric Rideal's book, *An Introduction to Surface Chemistry*, and wrote to Rideal to ask whether he could join his colloid laboratory in Cambridge. It was Rideal who pointed Barrer toward zeolites, the compounds that became the subject of his life's work. After gaining his PhD in 1935, Barrer was appointed to a research fellowship at Clare College and published a paper on gas sorption by zeolites that drew some attention.[104] In 1939 he was appointed head of the chemistry department at Bradford Technical College, in 1946 he became reader at Bedford College, London, and, in 1948, professor of chemistry at Aberdeen. He was elected FRS in 1956.

Barrer was a good athlete as well as a good scholar and represented Cambridge in long distance running events. He won the Oxford and Cambridge cross country race in 1934, was an excellent 10,000 m runner, narrowly missing selection for the 1936 British Olympic team. He was also good at tennis, and played regularly until shortly before his death in 1996. People in the IC department remembered him as an excellent table tennis player. Beyond sports, he was an accomplished amateur artist. As head of department, however, he was a remote figure.[105]

Like Wilkinson, Barrer came to his major research area at just the right time. A founder of modern zeolite chemistry, he was among the first to work out the structures and properties of natural zeolites and, by careful study, was soon able to modify them and to synthesise artificial ones. His 1948 pioneering synthesis of a modified mordenite (carried out under high pressure and temperature) helped to pave the way for a major new industry in the synthesis of designer zeolites.[106] He showed that zeolites have large internal pore and channel volumes, that the channels are of molecular size, and that the internal frameworks can be modified in various ways, notably by ion exchange. He recognised that zeolites could be used not simply as absorbents, but as highly active and selective catalysts, and as ion exchangers. And, because of their channelled structure, he saw they could be used as molecular sieves capable of separating molecular mixtures on the basis of size and shape.[107]

When Barrer came to IC he brought some members of his Aberdeen research team with him. Included were J. A. (Jim) Barrie and Lovat V. C. Rees, both with Aberdeen PhDs, appointed as lecturers.[108] George L. Kington, also from Aberdeen but not part of Barrer's research group, was appointed a reader in 1956. Kington was a thermodynamicist who specialised in cryogenics and carried out some detailed studies both on the zeolite, chabazite, and on Wilkinson's ferrocene.[109] Barrie worked on diffusion in polymers, including the diffusion of water in zeolites. Later he was to commission a new laboratory for polymer characterisation which was equipped with instrumentation for spin echo NMR. The laboratory was used by Manfred Gordon, appointed a reader in 1960, who began work on the thermodynamics of polymers.[110] The technician assigned to the new laboratory, R. N. Sheppard, worked with Barrie on spin echo NMR and was later to apply his electronics expertise to high field NMR spectrometers.[111] Rees, discussed further in Chapter Nine, carried out Mössbauer spectroscopy and some radioactive tracer work for Barrer's group, but soon formed a zeolite research group of his own.[112] Ian S. Kerr and Richard Ash were appointed lecturer–research assistants in 1956.[113] Kerr carried out X-ray structure analyses and produced electron micrographs for Barrer's group. Already in the late 1930s Barrer had an interest in polymer membranes and contributed significantly to both theory and experiment in that field. Ash, a specialist in the diffusion of gases through membranes, worked closely with him.[114] Brian Fender, who gained his BSc in 1953, was one of Barrer's first PhD students. He was to have a distinguished career, including as director of the Institut Laue–Langevin in Grenoble, Vice-Chancellor of Keele University and, in 1995, Chief Executive of the Higher Education Funding Council for England (HEFCE).

Barrer saw that altered zeolites had industrial potential well before coming to IC, though he was far from recognizing their full potential. In light of his growing understanding, by the late 1950s research students were kept busy studying the properties of zeolites, and examining ones tailored for specific purposes.[115] A rare naturally occurring tectoaluminosilicate was named Barrerite in his honour in 1975. RMB, as he was known, is said to have been a good supervisor, coming to the lab almost every day and immersing himself in discussions with his students. He was also an industrial consultant and, in 1959, started a zeolite synthesis programme supported by both Union Carbide and the Mobil Corporation — he turned to the American companies after having been unsuccessful in interesting some British ones. The use of zeolites mushroomed in the second-half of the 20th century as industrial needs for selective catalysts, absorbents, and ion exchangers were increasingly met — with some help from Barrer and his research team. Acid zeolites used as cracking catalysts revolutionised the petroleum refining industry, leading to the production of high octane fuels and, indirectly, to lead free petroleum and greater energy efficiency overall.[116] Barrer's team grew into the 1970s and he continued his research after retiring from the chair in 1977.

Barrer's research may have been less exciting on a day-to-day basis than that carried out by Barton and Wilkinson, but it was important nonetheless. According to Lovat Rees, Barrer was nominated for the Nobel Prize several times, including in the year of his death.[117] As department head, however, he was less stellar. A shy man who withdrew from social exchange, he did what was expected of him under the new constitution, but no more. He kept departmental meetings, and communication with Barton and Wilkinson, to a bare minimum. It cannot have been easy working in the same department as those two outsized personalities, but a more confident head would have been better at keeping lines of communication open. The department owed much to Bernard Atkinson (see below) who was an intermediary between the department and the college administration during those 'frozen' years. Barrer's life was made yet more complicated by the reader in physical chemistry, Frederick C. Tompkins, who had expected to be appointed to the chair. Perhaps resentful, Tompkins shut himself off from Barrer and refused to participate in departmental committees. As a result the two principal research teams in surface chemistry, which could have profited greatly from cooperation, remained apart — though there was some communication among their young research students.

Barrer made use of crystallographic measurements and was helped in this not only by members of his own research group but also by John

Welch. After Welch became assistant director of the laboratories in 1960, Barrer brought in Donald (Don) Rogers from University College, Cardiff, as reader in chemical crystallography. Rogers was given a personal chair in 1965 (see Chapter Nine). Barrer also invited his former PhD supervisor at Cambridge, Sir Eric Rideal, to join the department as a senior research fellow on his retirement from the chair at King's College in 1955. Rideal had worked in many different areas, including heterogeneous catalysis, high pressure/temperature syntheses, colloid chemistry, and electro-chemistry. He was a helpful presence in the section until 1967.[118] Another person invited to be a senior research fellow, following his term as President of the Royal Society, was Sir Cyril Hinshelwood.[119]

As mentioned, the reader in physical chemistry was Frederick Tompkins.[120] His earlier work at the University of Natal was in the kinetics of the decomposition of solids, but he became best known for his work on chemisorption on metal surfaces.[121] He trained a number of students and postdoctoral fellows in this area who furthered the work worldwide. One of his postdocs was David King who came from South Africa in 1960. In a 2009 interview, King reflected on his time at IC and claimed that he was the only member of Tompkins' research group allowed to use his first name, and the only one to be invited to dinner at his home. Tompkins, he noted, was a well-rounded intellectual, and though 'very shy' was one of the 'leaders in his field [and] taught me an awful lot.'[122] Tompkins had an acid wit and students regarded him with some awe. He was editor and secretary of the Faraday Division of the Chemical Society, 1950–1977, was elected FRS in 1955 (one year before Barrer), and was given a personal chair in 1959.

Patrick W. M. Jacobs was an MSc research student under Tompkins in South Africa. After service in the army, he followed Tompkins to IC for his PhD which he gained in 1951.[123] Jacobs continued with the work in solid state chemical kinetics begun at the University of Natal. Appointed assistant lecturer in 1951, he, too, is remembered as being sharp and witty. He led a small research group on the composition and properties of disordered and unstable solids. In the early 1960s one of his students, Anthony Russell-Jones, was asked to study the thermal decomposition of hydrazine perchlorate and was lucky to escape unharmed. He began by stirring hydrazine hydrate and perchloric acid in a beaker, in 5–10 g quantities. Jacobs soon had second thoughts and asked for the perchlorate to be made at Aldermaston. It arrived in large steel ammunition boxes, each containing 10 small pill boxes. Inside each pill box was a 50 mg pellet of the perchlorate, and the pill boxes were surrounded by large quantities of padding.[124] Jacobs left in 1965 for a professorship at the University of Western Ontario.

Physical chemists already in place when Barrer arrived were Joseph (Joe) Kitchener, Bernard Atkinson, Charles F. Cullis, and three electrochemists: John F. Herringshaw and John O'Mara Bockris appointed in 1945, and Graham J. Hills appointed in 1950.[125] Kitchener, whose work was supported by the British Iron and Steel Research Association, continued his research on molten silicates and liquid metals at high temperatures. He also introduced some new work on ion exchange resins. However, he moved to the metallurgy department when appointed reader in the science of mineral processing in 1961.[126] Atkinson was a student in the department during the war, gaining his BSc in 1941 and PhD in 1943. After a year at Porton Down, he returned to the department as a lecturer in 1944 and carried out research in gas phase kinetics, notably on the thermal reactions of unsaturated fluorocarbons and perfluorocyclobutanes. He is discussed further in Chapter Nine. Cullis joined the chemical engineering department in 1958 and later became reader in chemical combustion. He moved to a chair at City University in 1967. His research in the chemistry department concerned the kinetics and mechanism of oxidative combustion, and base-catalysed liquid-phase oxidative halogenation reactions. He is still remembered in the department for having almost run over his former DPhil supervisor, Cyril Hinshelwood, in his car.[127]

Bockris came to IC in 1943 to study for a PhD with Tom Ellingham, but because of wartime duties Ellingham was rarely in the department and Bockris saw little of him.[128] According to his own testimony, Bockris spent much time at the Chemical Society reading Russian journals and papers, notably those of A. N. Frumkin.[129] The Russians were leaders in the field of electrochemistry and Bockris was inspired to study the kinetics of electrode processes, a field that was to remain important in the department for many years. He gained his PhD in 1945 and was appointed a lecturer. According to Roger Parsons, John Wilkinson, and David

Waddington, he was an impressive lecturer who did not need notes. He attracted a sizeable group of research students, Parsons and Brian Conway among them.[130] In 1947 Bockris and his students attended one of the Faraday Society's discussions at which many of the world's leading electrochemists were present.[131] It was an important moment for the young group, all in their early twenties. Welcomed into the wider community of electrochemists, they left the discussion invigorated.[132] In 1954 Bockris moved to the University of Pennsylvania and was to have a major career in the United States.

In 1947 Herringshaw reluctantly agreed to take Martin Fleischmann on as a PhD student since Bockris had 10 students and could not accommodate any more. However, to all intents and purposes, Fleischmann, now remembered more for his ideas on cold fusion than for his outstanding work in electrochemistry, was a member of the Bockris group. With others, he re-examined some of the electrode potential data given by W. M. Latimer.[133] He also joined the group on weekend social/picnic trips into the country.[134] In 1967 Fleischmann was appointed to the Faraday chair of chemistry at the University of Southampton, where another former IC electrochemist, Graham Hills (see above), was professor of physical chemistry.

Barrer expanded the physical chemistry section yet further and, by 1960, had appointed Tristan Findlay, John Walkley, John L. Wood, Manfred Gordon, Neville Parsonage, and Michael Spiro. In 1960, after just three years in the department, Findlay returned to his native Australia, and a position at the University of New South Wales. Walkley, a thermody- namicist, came to the department as a lecturer in 1960 from a postdoctoral fellowship with Joel Hildebrand at the University of California (Berkeley). He left for Canada and a position at Simon Fraser University in 1966. Wood, a spectroscopist and Cambridge graduate, was appointed a lecturer in 1959. Interested in low frequency molecular transitions, he developed the sections resources for work in far infrared spectroscopy. His left-wing views were well known and, at one seminar, he was introduced as 'being a bit too far into the infrared.' In the early 1970s he worked also with a He/ Ne laser Raman spectrometer and, in 1977 after a sabbatical leave at the University of Victoria (British Columbia), he decided to take early retirement and live in Victoria. Manfred Gordon wanted the department to move in the direction of materials science, something that happened years later. He left for a chair at the University of Strathclyde in 1964 and, in 1967, set up the Polymer Research Consortium at the University of Essex.[135] Parsonage and Spiro worked in the department for much longer and are discussed in Chapter Nine, Spiro also in Chapter Ten.

8.4 Departmental Reorganisation and Undergraduate Teaching

After the war Briscoe decided to help laboratory technicians upgrade their skills and, in 1948, he allowed a meeting to be held in the department to which technicians from universities around the country were invited. About 100 showed up and decided to set up the Science Technicians Association with the idea of promoting suitable courses. Les Croker, for many years the departmental superintendent, became an important figure in the Association. He helped it to link up with the City and Guilds of London Institute which set up a good examination system and courses given around the country were designed to meet the C&G exams.[136] Briscoe became chairman of a University of London committee on technician training, and worked to raise standards for technicians within the university, and to improve their career prospects.

Briscoe also planned and oversaw the construction of new laboratories and workshops that opened in 1951, and put in place plans for the new inorganic chemistry wing mentioned above. The 1951 renovations entailed redevelopment of the enormous first-year laboratory on the ground floor. The original space was bisected at half its height, thus creating two floors. On the lower floor, the western half was retained for analytical chemistry and refurbished roughly on the original island bench plan. The eastern end was converted into stores for inorganic and physical chemistry, new workshops for glass blowing and metalwork, a small lecture theatre, and two small teaching laboratories for the MSc course in food and drugs.[137] On the upper floor three new teaching laboratories were created, the Crookes Laboratory for inorganic chemistry, the Frankland Laboratory for organic chemistry, and the Philip Laboratory for physical chemistry. Each had adjacent small offices for the demonstrators and small balance rooms. The justification given by Briscoe for creating the new teaching laboratories was that they met needs resulting from major changes in the curriculum. These came about for two reasons. First, demand for the first year course dropped off after the war since more schools were teaching chemistry, and most people applying to the department had gained their higher school certificate (soon to be replaced by the GCE A-level examinations). Second, the University of London's new rules for the internal BSc required a minimum of three years instruction at a college of the university. The old rules under which students could enter in the second year and leave with a degree after the third year no longer applied. The department responded by eliminating its first year course. The old second year became the new first year, and the fourth year, which previously had been used as an entry to research became the new third year. The BSc became a three-year degree and the curriculum was redesigned accordingly. However, one thing marked IC as being different from other institutions. The BSc examinations were taken at the end of the second year. In their third year, students could specialise without having to worry about being examined on the material they had been exposed to earlier. They could focus on inorganic, organic, physical, or analytical chemistry and take short courses in their chosen field. For the first half of the year laboratory instruction was given in advanced techniques and in the use of physical instruments; in the second half students engaged in short research projects. This encouraged many to stay on for a PhD.

The departmental staff had to think how best to reorganise the teaching and to create short courses suited to the new third year programme. In the organic section Linstead asked Henry Rydon, the newly created reader, to oversee the curriculum for third year students.[138] The idea was that staff in the section would propose suitable experiments for the first part of the year, as well as short courses to be given throughout the year. Rydon had to decide which experiments would be set up, and which courses would be given in any year. As to the experiments, they helped to introduce students to techniques such as chromatography in its various forms, spectroscopic methods, fractional distillation under controlled pressure, vacuum line procedures, and so on. In the second part of the year students had to find a member of staff willing to supervise them on a short project of mutual interest.[139] Elvidge was placed in charge of the Frankland Laboratory and the early students in the new programme were guinea pigs. However, after a couple of years testing various experimental procedures, Elvidge and Whalley prepared a manual, *A course in modern techniques of organic chemistry*, which, after further consideration by Linstead, was published in 1955. The instructions were professionally illustrated — Butterworths, the publisher, sent an artist to the laboratory for that purpose.[140] The second-year organic laboratory had been modernised by Heilbron immediately after the war, but the experiments were not new. The instruction manual for the second-year course had been written by Linstead in 1930. When Linstead returned as professor he asked Basil Weedon to revise the manual and bring the experiments up to date.[141]

Linstead also introduced a tutorial system, at the suggestion of Eric Roberts who became senior tutor in 1962. The system was developed in the later 1950s and, with some changes, continues to this day. At first students had a single tutor who acted as a personal/pastoral tutor as well as a chemistry tutor. These roles were later separated and, by the 1960s, students had tutors in each of inorganic, organic and physical chemistry, one of whom acted also as personal tutor. Students had three tutorials a week in groups of about seven. There was also a women's tutor who, in the late 1950s, was Anne Dunne.

The inorganic and physical sections were a little slower in modernizing their undergraduate curricula, something that occurred seriously only after Barrer and Wilkinson were appointed; but roughly the same principles applied.[142] On becoming head of department, Linstead added a third year course that had to be taken by all undergraduate students. It was a course in the writing of English, given one afternoon a week at Birkbeck College. He also had a modern telephone system installed. As mentioned in Chapter Six, before WW2 there was only one telephone in the department. By the early 1950s there were telephones in all academic staff offices, as well as in the main laboratories, stores, and workshops.

This early phase of refurbishment was followed by what was known as the Jubilee expansion. Planning for this began in 1953 with the idea that construction would begin in 1957, the year in which IC reached the age of 50. The expansion came about as a result of two government committee reports on the framing of higher education, both of which favoured giving priority to science and engineering.[143] A Ministry of Education committee report of 1945 stated 'the position of Great Britain as a leading industrial nation is being endangered by a failure to secure the fullest possible application of science to industry and … this failure is partly due to deficiencies in education'. The second committee was asked to report on the 'use and development of our scientific manpower … and the training of technical personnel'. Both reports led to much debate in government and university circles. IC fitted the Labour government's utilitarian ideals, ideals the later Conservative government shared, and received much support. The Rector, Roderic Hill, began planning the expansion in 1953, immediately after the government announced that IC would receive funding to increase its number of students from 1650 to 3000 by 1962.[144] However, because of Hill's death one year later, the task of seeing this through fell to Linstead. The department was affected in a major way in that physics was to be given a new building, and chemistry was asked to plan for how it would occupy the entire RCS building.

When physics moved into its new building in 1960, the department suddenly had more space — a total of about 20,000 square feet.[145] Beginning in 1956, Barrer began planning for the extra space and an architect drew up some plans, however they were not approved by the UGC which stated that it would be cheaper to tear the RCS building down and redevelop the site. Barrer and Linstead should, perhaps, have put up a fight, as Wilkinson did. He was bitterly opposed to the demolition, but to no avail.

In the original plan part of the RCS building was reserved for the return of the biochemistry department, something Linstead very much wanted. He began looking for a professor of biochemistry in 1955 and his first choice was Norman W. Pirie FRS. When Pirie turned him down he turned to Ernst Chain FRS. Chain was interested, but made extravagant demands. He wanted a major new laboratory, a fermentation plant of the type that existed at his institute in Rome, and nearby accommodation of a rather luxurious nature.[146] Linstead should probably have looked further for a Professor, but the idea of luring a Nobel Laureate to the college seems to have clouded his vision.[147] He decided that the RCS site would be redeveloped, beginning with the demolition of the west end of the building, so that Chain's demands for new buildings could be met. However, funding way above what the UGC was prepared to offer was needed. Linstead found a donor in the Wolfson Foundation which had supported him earlier. The Foundation agreed to finance the fermentation plant, and to equip the new biochemistry laboratories once they were built. This marked the end of the chemistry department's original plans.

In 1961 the department began planning yet again, this time for two new buildings. Len Owen was chairman of the Planning Committee and Bernard Atkinson was the committee secretary, it was Atkinson who liaised with the architect.[148] Two buildings were necessary because the RCS building could not be totally demolished in one go. There was nowhere that chemistry could move to on a temporary basis. Problems arose because spending on biochemistry soon exceeded the original budget. The UGC had set a limit to what could be spent on the Jubilee expansion and, in 1962, decided that it would only fund the first of the chemistry buildings (CI), and that the second of the chemistry buildings (C2) would have to wait. Even C1 was not straightforward and there were arguments with the UGC over the size of lecture theatres and under-graduate teaching laboratories.[149] Since the inorganic research laboratories were almost entirely within the area designated for demolition it was given special consideration in C1, but the plan was to establish a good research base in all three sections in the new building. Demolition began in 1967 and construction in 1968. Needless to say there was tremendous pressure on space in this period, but undergraduate numbers were allowed to grow in anticipation of larger laboratories and lecture rooms. Occupation of C1 began in 1971, but because of a major recession it was a long time before the construction of C2 was approved. As will be seen in Chapter Nine, despite many problems the department performed remarkably well in the period 1965–1985.

End Notes

1. Quotation from Linstead's speech, as recorded in *The Phoenix* (Summer, 1957); copy in ICL archives. The Russian Sputnik had recently been launched, a symbolic and also very real reminder that a race was on.
2. ICL archives, ULP/chemistry/org/2; Heilbron to Penson, 8 December, 1948.
3. Heilbron and Cook set up a laboratory for the Brewing Research Foundation in Nutfield, Surrey; Heilbron was director, and Cook, assistant director. Cook succeeded Heilbron as director in 1958.

4. For more on Linstead's earlier period in the department see Chapter Six; obituaries and *ODNB* entry for Linstead are cited in Chapter Six, note 149. At the start of the war Linstead was a full professor at Harvard. In 1942 he took a leave of absence, returned to Britain, and was appointed deputy director of Scientific Research at the Ministry of Supply. He resigned his Harvard chair in 1945 and was appointed director of the Chemical Research Laboratory in Teddington. He returned to the department in 1949 and was knighted in 1959.

5. The relevant part of the Linstead memorandum (21 May, 1954) reads: 'There should be a head of the chemistry department who would be responsible for broad policy and co-ordination of the work of the divisions (at present two, later three) of the Department. The three Professors of Inorganic, Organic, and Physical Chemistry (of whom the Head of the Department will be one) will be responsible for the teaching and research in his own division. Each professor will receive a definite budgetary provision for the research in his division. There will be a separate provision to the Chemistry Department as a whole for the undergraduate laboratories and facilities, which will be administered by the head of department. … The head of department will be assisted by an assistant director of the Laboratories (who will be responsible to one man instead of two as at present)…'. Quoted in B. Atkinson, 'Department of Chemistry, Recent History' (1989), typescript on disc; copy in ICL archives. Until 1971 staff salaries were paid by the college and were not part of the departmental vote. The UGC introduced the annual vote for research apparatus only in 1968; so, in the period covered in this chapter, equipment was mostly paid for either from the college reserve or with grants from the UGC, the DSIR, industry, or charitable foundations. The Linstead constitution was revoked by the department in 1976, urged to do so by the Rector, Brian Flowers.

6. Ernest Alexander Rudolph Braude (1922–1956) came to England as a refugee from Germany in 1937. He studied chemistry first at Birkbeck College and then at Imperial College where he gained his BSc in 1942, and his PhD under Heilbron in 1945. He was appointed an assistant lecturer in 1945, lecturer in 1947, and reader in 1952. For a short but perceptive obituary, (Linstead, 1957).

7. According to the *Evening Standard*, 25 July, 1956, Braude died at his home in Kew from cyanide poisoning. Whether his disagreements with Barrer, or the burden of the organic chemistry chair, were in any way connected to his death is unknown.

8. It was not that Barton did not wish to return, but he felt obligated to the University of Glasgow. The Glasgow department had wanted him to take up the chair earlier but he asked for a delay since he had applied to succeed Robert Robinson in Oxford when a decision on that appointment was still a year away. The Glasgow department complied with his request, hence his hesitation in leaving so soon. As it happened Linstead was also a candidate for the Oxford chair but he was rejected as being too removed from the laboratory bench. Barton was rejected as being too young and without sufficient administrative experience. The position went to E. R. H. (Tim) Jones. For the Oxford appointment, (J. H. Jones, 2003).

9. Todmorden Secondary School was a small school with about 300 pupils. It had an excellent record for pupils gaining university scholarships. An earlier pupil was the Nobel Laureate, John D. Cockcroft. Another future scientist was John Nuttall of the Geiger–Nuttall Rule. Among Wilkinson's classmates were three other professors and a Canadian High Court judge. Wilkinson was proud to have been taught physics by the same teacher who, a few years earlier, had taught Cockcroft.

10. (Barton, 1991), p. 3. Douglas Payne (see Chapter Seven) grew up in Gravesend and knew the Barton family. He told us that Barton's father made coffins for soldiers killed in WW1. This was profitable and was the start of his timber business.

11. Wilkinson wrote a memoir which includes details of his life as a student; ICL archives, B\Wilkinson. Also in the archives is a handwritten memoir (now available in typescript), and a CD with an oral memoir, both by Wilkinson's brother John. The former is titled, 'Geoffrey Wilkinson, 1921–1976; Some reflections on his early years.' For John Wilkinson, Chapter Seven.

12. (Barton, 1991). For Sir Derek Harold Richard Barton (1918–1998), (Ley and Myers, 2002), (Coley, 2004b), (Rees, 1998).

13. Briscoe was Barton's principal nominator for the Harrison award. He rounded up all the living IC chemistry professors, past and present, and asked them to sign the papers. Barton won the award in 1948.

14. For example, Heilbron helped E. R. H. (Tim) Ewart Jones and Donald Hey, as well as Barton's close contemporaries Ralph Raphael and Franz Sondheimer to major careers. Tony Barrett told us that Barton's manipulative skills were not especially strong. He speculates that Heilbron, who was an excellent experimentalist, may have detected this weakness and decided that Barton would not go far despite his intellectual brilliance.

15. Barton's doctoral work was supported by the Distillers Company with which Heilbron was associated. It was a wartime project aimed at aiding the industrial production of vinyl chloride. Barton's coworker on this project was an older man, Dr. M. Mugdan, with whom he shared a laboratory. Mugdan, a German–Jewish refugee, had worked in the chemical industry and Barton recalled learning much from him about industrial processes, and about homogeneous and heterogeneous catalysis, (Barton, 1991). Barton's first publication, with Peter Alexander (see Chapter Seven), was sent to the *Biochemical Journal* and the editor at first thought it a hoax. The topic was a curious one that had nothing to do with Barton's main PhD topic. Alexander, a PhD student with Briscoe, had noted that the flour beetle (*Tribolium castaneum*) left a dark halo in flour when it died. He may well have learned this from someone in the zoology and applied entomology department, where food security and flour pests were a major topic during the war. Barton's role was to determine the chemistry of the halo — which he did, in his spare time. In his memoir Barton claims to have grown 5000 beetles, but perhaps he received them from the applied entomologists who grew masses of these insects. He demonstrated that the beetles gave off ethylquinone that reacted with gluten in the flour turning it pink and then darkening, (Barton, 1991), (Barton and Alexander, 1943). Alexander, later a professor at the Chester Beatty Institute, returned to the department as an honorary lecturer in the 1950s.

16. (Barton, 1991), p. 11.

17. The evidence is not entirely clear, and Barton was not very forthcoming in his memoirs, but it would appear that Heilbron suggested he be seconded to Albright and Wilson and that he should spend a few years there. Barton had other ideas and Heilbron was not welcoming when he returned to the department so soon after the war.

18. Tony Barrett who knew Barton only later, described him as 'basically a shy man who hid this fact with a gruff exterior', (personal communication).

19. Barton married Christiane Cognet (his second wife) in 1969. She was his French teacher at the Institut Français in South Kensington. Cognet died in 1992 and, in 1993, Barton married his Texas neighbour, Judith Cobb.

20. (Barton, 1991), p. 13.

21. (Barton, 1944, 1946 and 1946b). The method used in these papers was useful in the correlation of double bond positions with molecular rotation. Barton claimed that his earlier lecturing to engineers had made him think about mathematical modelling, notably how to model the three-dimensional shapes of organic molecules.

22. His lectureship was in inorganic and physical chemistry. As an assistant lecturer his salary had been £350 per year; as a lecturer it was £700. He was granted a leave of absence to take the position at Harvard.

23. Barton's correspondence is in the ICL archives, B\Barton. It reveals that Barton had some marital problems already in the late 1940s, and that he found the new responsibility of fatherhood difficult. His son was born in 1947. His wife and baby son did not join him in the United States. While Barton was at Harvard, Briscoe remained in touch with both Barton and his wife and, in a few matters, appears to have acted as an intermediary.

24. (Barton, 1991).

25. Before working on steroids, Woodward was known for his synthesis of quinine, carried out in the early 1940s.

26. Barton also wrote to Briscoe that he felt uncomfortable being on first-name terms with the students and professors. In his reply, Briscoe wrote that he liked American informality, 'I do rather like it and like still more the genuine friendliness [it] connotes'. ICL archives, B\Barton, Eldridge to Barton, 8 December, 1949; Briscoe to Barton, 21 November, 1949.

27. In his letter Briscoe also noted Barton's mathematical ability and his interest in 'the theories and methods of physical chemistry'; and that he found Barton to be 'a most congenial colleague … I have kept in close touch with him.' Briscoe's letter to the University of London, 18 January, 1950. Barton's reply to Briscoe's copy, 25 January, 1950; copies in ICL archives B\Barton.

28. ICL archives, B\Barton, Briscoe to Barton, 2 February, 1950.

29. G. Wilkinson, *op. cit.* (11). Wilkinson's brother remembers him the night before travelling to London, 'marching about his bedroom shouting, "I'll show the buggers"', (J. Wilkinson, *op. cit.* 11). The Royal Scholarships were generous, were awarded by the Ministry of Education, and were tenable only at IC. Both Wilkinson and Ralph Raphael, who also entered the college in 1939, won scholarships.

30. For Sondheimer see also Chapter Seven. Unlike Barton, Sondheimer appears to have been one of Heilbron's favourites and was taken into the vitamin A group for his PhD. He made a major contribution to the knowledge of acetylenic linkages before moving to Harvard on a postdoctoral fellowship to work with R. B. Woodward at the beginning of the great period of steroid synthesis. He was awarded the CS Corday–Morgan Prize in 1961. Sondheimer played a significant role in the synthesis of testosterone, cortisone and cholesterol before moving to succeed Carl Djerassi at Syntex in Mexico. He was later head of the chemistry department at the

Weizmann Institute and, later still, held a Royal Society research chair, first at Cambridge, and then at UCL where he returned to the chemistry of the acetylenes. Sadly he suffered periods of depression and took his own life while on a visit to Stanford in 1981. (Jones and Garratt, 1982), (Raphael, 1982). Robert Robinson synthesised cholesterol independently.

31. Wilkinson, *op. cit.* (11). For security reasons, the fact that Wilkinson was studying phosgene was concealed behind the title of his 1945 thesis, 'Some physico-chemical observations on hydrolysis in the homogeneous vapour phase.' Also for security reasons there was no mention of the other half of his doctoral work which included two papers that were not allowed to be published until 1946. These were joint publications with Leo Yaffé, William Grummitt, and Jules Guéron on work carried out in Montreal, one on the growth of La^{140} from Ba^{140}, and the other on yields of Ba^{140} in fast and thermal neutron fission of U^{235} and U^{238}. For this work they used a Ra/Be neutron source embedded in a big paraffin block. The papers, published in the *Canadian Journal of Research* in 1946, were Wilkinson's first (see Chapter Seven, Note 80). Looking back he later wrote, 'if I had anybody who I could call a research mentor it would be Jules Guéron.' ICL archives; B\Wilkinson, Wilkinson to Booth, 7 December, 1992. Harold Booth was a chemist at the University of Nottingham.

32. In his memoir, *op. cit.* (11), Wilkinson mentions this and wrote that he had been a rebel against authority ever since he was first exposed to it at the Castle Hill Infants' School in Todmorden. However, he was on good terms with Glen Seaborg and the two became close friends.

33. Wilkinson, *op. cit.* (11).

34. Wilkinson, *op. cit.* (11).

35. This story has been told many times, including by Wilkinson, (Wilkinson, 1974). A compound with the empirical formula $C_{10}H_{10}Fe$ was first made in 1951, (Kealy and Pauson, 1951). The authors recognised that they had made a compound of iron and two cyclopentadiene rings and explained its thermal stability in terms of ionic covalent resonance. But, when Wilkinson and Woodward read their letter in *Nature*, unbeknownst to each other they immediately realised that the structure given was incorrect and that the extreme thermal stability of the new compound was unusual. When one of Woodward's doctoral students, M. Rosenblum, came asking to borrow some ruthenium, Wilkinson immediately guessed that Woodward had read the letter and was thinking along the same lines as he. He discussed the matter with Woodward and the two men agreed to work together to figure out the structure. They also agreed that Wilkinson would be the one to carry

out further work with iron and some other transition metals, and that Woodward would ask his postdoctoral fellow, Mark Whiting, to work on the organic chemistry of cyclopentadiene rings, thus preventing any competition. Whiting, who later coined the name 'ferrocene,' was a co-author on the paper giving the new structure; for Whiting, Chapter Seven, and the ferrocene paper, (Wilkinson, Rosenblum, Whiting, and Woodward, 1952). Pauson and Kealy were at Deuqesne University at the time of their letter. Peter Pauson came to work with Wilkinson at Harvard for a brief period before returning to England. Later he was professor of chemistry at the University of Strathclyde. There was much competition in the exciting new field that Pauson, Wilkinson, and others opened up. A notable competitor, E. O. Fischer, shared the 1973 Nobel Prize with Wilkinson. In his memoir Wilkinson wrote that someone from Union Carbide later told him that, in 1935, they had made some 'orange stuff when cracking dicyclopentadiene through an iron tube' and had thrown it out as 'gunk.' As William Perkin, and Patrick Linstead both knew, examining 'gunk' can sometimes be worthwhile.

36. At Harvard he created sandwich compounds containing ruthenium, cobalt and nickel.

37. Wilkinson, *op. cit.* (11), 99, wrote that it was his Harvard lectures that drew Al Cotton to become his PhD student. They worked well together in those early days, in part because Cotton was interested in making all kinds of physical measurements on Wilkinson's compounds. In his memoirs Cotton wrote that the senior faculty at Harvard were, 'almost to a man, intellectual snobs' and he speculated that Wilkinson was not given tenure because they saw him as lacking the mathematical and physical grounding they believed essential to chemical success, and that they failed to appreciate how far one could travel with ambition, great chemical knowledge, fine intuition, and extraordinary bench skills. Cotton mentions learning not only much inorganic chemistry from Wilkinson, but also all kinds of bawdy Yorkshire pub songs, (Cotton, 2014). Shortly before leaving Harvard, Wilkinson met Mino Green, a postdoctoral fellow with Charles Coryell at MIT. (Wilkinson first met Coryell through his association with the Manhattan Project and held his fellowship with him at MIT.) It was through Wilkinson's connection to Coryell that Cotton was later given a job at MIT. In 1955 Green was given a lectureship in physical chemistry at IC, working with F. C. Tompkins. This did not work out well, and he soon left. However, he was to join the electrical engineering department at IC where he became a professor. The Wilkinson and

Green families were close friends. For Green's personal tribute to Wilkinson, see *IC Reporter*, 21 October, 1996.

38. Wilkinson memoir, *op. cit.* (11), p. 99. When Wilkinson won the Nobel Prize he received a case of Krug champagne from the Harvard department, the traditional gift to one of their own awarded the prize.

39. Also on the staff was Robert Francis (Bob) Hudson (1922–2012), who left in 1947 after just two years as an assistant lecturer. A former student in the department, he was appointed professor of organic chemistry at the University of Kent in 1967 and was elected FRS in 1982. Another short term staff member (1946–1950) was Bernard Lewis Archer, also a former student. He joined the Rubber Producers' Association in Welwyn Garden City.

40. Hodgkin, quoted in (Elvidge, 1999).

41. In this work they used hydrogen abstractors, mainly quinones, and hydrogen donors such as hydroaromatic compounds, everything helped along by a range of precious-metal catalysts. See, for example, (Braude, Hannah, and Linstead, 1960). This paper was published after Braude's death. For Jackman see below.

42. For example, (Linstead, Lunt, and Weedon, 1951). (The first anodic synthesis, of a dimeric hydrocarbon, was carried out by A. W. H. Kolbe in 1849.)

43. For Weedon as a student see Chapter Seven. Later he synthesised astaxanthin, responsible for the brightly coloured feathers of flamingos. Basil Charles Leicester (Jimmy) Weedon FRS (1923–2003) was appointed reader in 1955 and moved to the Chair of Organic Chemistry at Queen Mary College in 1960. He was awarded the RIC's Meldola Medal and Prize (1952), Tilden Prize (1966), and was elected FRS in 1971. Later in his career he moved into administration and was appointed Vice-Chancellor of the University of Nottingham in 1975. In his love of the countryside, of colour and of natural colour pigments, he reminds us a little of Henry Armstrong — a milder version perhaps.

44. Michael Sammes, personal communication. Sammes was an undergraduate 1958–1961, stayed for a PhD and then worked for ICI in their plant protection division in Bracknell. Later he moved to the University of Hong Kong as a lecturer, becoming professor and head of department.

45. For Elvidge Chapter Seven. Elvidge was promoted to reader and left the department in 1965 to become professor of organic chemistry at Battersea Technical College (later the University of Surrey). He had caught the NMR bug and, at Surrey, pioneered tritium magnetic resonance spectroscopy. For a number of years after he left in 1965, Elvidge made financial

contributions to the department. For a brief obituary, see http://www. nmrdg.org.uk/History_of_the_NMR-DG/Obituaries_files/Elvidge.pdf.

46. For example, (Linstead, Elvidge, Sims and Orkin, 1950).
47. For example, (Adley and Owen, 1966).
48. For Owen's biographical details, Chapter Seven, note 55.
49. For example, (Eisner and Linstead, 1955). Ulli Eisner was a postdoctoral fellow who carried out much work with Linstead. She later worked at Howard University in the USA. However, it was R. B. Woodward, together with 17 postdoctoral fellows working over several years, who first synthesised chlorophyll-a in 1960.
50. Several others developed photoelectron spectroscopy at roughly the same time. David Warren Turner FRS was educated at the University College of the South West (later University of Exeter) where he gained his external (University of London) BSc. While working as a water analyst for the London County Council (LCC), he carried out research at Birkbeck College in the evenings. He did not complete a PhD at that time, but the head of department, recognizing his technical skills, suggested he apply for the job at IC. Turner's many innovations in physical analytical methods were remarkable. They included a method for spin decoupling (of C–H) which was widely used, notably by Barton and his group in their work on steroids and other complex molecules. Turner was appointed reader but, in 1967, moved to Balliol College and the physical chemistry department at Oxford taking three research students and all of his equipment with him. At Oxford Turner was appointed professor of electron spectroscopy in 1985. We are indebted to him for sending us a copy of notes on his career, made after retiring from Oxford in 1995 (with additions made in 2011). In them he states, 'the IC years [were] the happiest of my career by far.'
51. (Hamer, 1964). Frances Mary Hamer (1894–1980) was an undergraduate at Girton College, Cambridge before joining William Pope's research group (for Pope, see Chapter Four). She then worked at the Ilford photographic firm, later joining Kodak where she became Head of Organic Chemistry Research. (Jeffreys and Gauntlett, 1981), (Rayner Canham and Rayner Canham, 2008).
52. For Leslie Crombie FRS (1923–1999), (Pattenden, 2001), (Whiting, 2000). As noted in Chapter Six, Harper was a former doctoral student with G. A. Kon at IC. When Crombie returned to King's College, Donald Hey, formerly at IC, was head of department. Also there were Charles Rees and John Cadogan who were to come to IC in the future. Later Crombie was to leave King's for a chair at University College, Cardiff, followed by a chair

at Nottingham. He received the CS Tilden award in 1970 and the RSC Pedler award in 1982.

53. Paul Jose de Mayo FRS (1924–1994) gained his BSc and PhD from Birkbeck College under Barton. He moved with Barton to Glasgow and was given a lectureship. He moved again with Barton to IC. After one year in the department he went to work with R. B. Woodward at Harvard before accepting a full professorship at the University of Western Ontario. Alastair (Ian) Scott FRS (1928–2007) gained his PhD in Glasgow with Ralph Raphael and James Cook and, after military service, joined Barton on a postdoctoral fellowship at Birkbeck. He then moved with Barton, first back to Glasgow and then to IC — though he, too, did not stay long. Scott held chairs in several universities before moving to Texas A&M. It was he who invited Barton to move to Texas at the end of his career. In his memoir, Barton noted that the work ethic at Texas was 'above reproach ... they appreciate my own habits of beginning the working day at 3 to 4 in the morning and finishing about 7 in the evening', (Barton, 1991), p. 125.

54. Quotations from (Jackman, 2007). Lloyd M. Jackman came to the department in 1953 with a PhD from the University of Adelaide. He became a reader but left in 1962 to take a chair in organic chemistry at the University of Melbourne. He ended his career at Pennsylvania State University. In the list of acknowledgements in his book (Jackman, 1964), Jackman mentions L. H. Pratt and D. F. Evans, inorganic chemists who taught him much about NMR (see below). One of Jackman's IC students in NMR was James William Lown, an assistant lecturer in the department, 1962–1963, and later a professor at the University of Alberta.

55. Pioneering work in organic NMR was carried out by H. S. Gutowsky at the University of Illinois (Urbana) in the early 1950s. For a discussion of the role of physical instruments in structural organic chemistry (Morris and Travis, 2014).

56. It, too, was a Varian HR-40 machine, later upgraded to 60 MHz, allowing investigation of the fluorine nucleus as well as the proton.

57. For example, (Barber, Davis, Jackman, and Weedon, 1961).

58. Eric Stanmore Waight (1927–2003) came to IC as an undergraduate and gained his BSc in 1947 and PhD in 1950. He stayed on in the department, ending his career as reader. He is remembered by many as being a little dour, always very smartly dressed, an excellent cricketer, and a good spectroscopist and laboratory demonstrator. Together with Len Owen, he carried out much of the undergraduate teaching in organic chemistry. In his will Waight left money to the department and to the college.

59. Earlier, under Linstead, Waight was asked to manage a ^{60}Co radiation source installed in a concrete bunker near the main entrance to the department. But this facility turned out not to be useful and was later removed.

60. For example, (Baldwin, Blythin, and Waight, 1969), (Barrow, Barton, Chain, Conlay, Smale, Thomas, and Waight, 1971).

61. One of Barton's oft-repeated sayings was that if you cannot remember all the published papers in a field then it is time to move on.

62. The letter to *Nature* that set Barton running was (Bastianson and Hassel, 1946). Barton later wrote that their proposed two-chair *cis*-decalin conformation was not what was expected and that he was stimulated to carry out the first force field calculations on the conformations of cyclohexane rings (using logarithm tables and a slide rule). His results confirmed those of Hassel. Barton then began applying conformational arguments to steroids and came to some conclusions that contradicted those that Louis Fieser presented in a Harvard seminar that he was attending. Fieser encouraged Barton to publish, which he did, (Barton, 1950). The journal *Experientia* no longer exists but Barton's paper can be read online at the publisher's (Springer) website. Barton gave a more developed version of his ideas in the Tilden Lecture of 1953, (Barton, 1953). Chapter Nine includes further discussion of this, and of later work that led to Barton's Nobel Prize, awarded in 1969.

63. For example, (Barton, McCapra, de Mayo, and Thudium, 1960).

64. Gordon William Kirby (1934–2011) gained a BSc, PhD, and DSc at Cambridge. He left the IC department in 1967 for a chair at Loughborough and, from 1972–1997 was Regius professor of chemistry at the University of Glasgow. Kirby was awarded the CS Tilden Prize in 1974, and Sutherland in 1978. James Kenneth (Hamish) Sutherland (1932–2001) had a PhD from Manchester and returned there when appointed to a chair in 1970, (Joule, 2001). Benjamin Sklarz left for a position in Liverpool in 1965, and was later a professor at Bar-Ilan University.

65. Sir Jack Baldwin FRS was an undergraduate at IC and gained his PhD under Barton in 1964 for work on the structure of some fungal metabolites. Barton inherited the metabolites from Harold Raistrick at the London School of Hygiene and Tropical Medicine. Baldwin used chemical methods in his PhD work on the metabolites while others used physical methods. The metabolites included compounds with nine-membered rings and work on C_9 units took off. See for example, (Baldwin, Barton and Sutherland, 1965). In 1965 Baldwin was appointed an assistant lecturer at IC, but soon moved to the United States where he held positions at Pennsylvania State

University and MIT. He came back to the United Kingdom for a brief stint as professor at KCL before returning to MIT. He was elected FRS in 1978 and, in the same year, was appointed Waynflete professor of Chemistry at Oxford, (Hall, 1985). Working closely with Baldwin at Oxford was Robert M. Adlington, an IC student who gained his PhD with A. G. M. (Tony) Barrett. In his memoir Barton wrote that when 'Jack was an undergraduate … I recognized at once that he was someone unique. His capacity to wreck cars seemed to be matched only by his brilliance as a chemist', (Barton, 1991), p. 120. Barton was interested in cars and drove a Jensen sports car at the time. He also claimed that Baldwin had to leave KCL so soon because, having threatened to resign if his demands were not met, the Principal called his bluff. At Oxford the authorities were wiser; Baldwin retired from the Waynflete Chair in 2005. He received many awards, including the CS Corday–Morgan (1976), Tilden (1979), the RSC Pedler Award (1990) and, in 2008, both the RSC Barton Gold Medal and the Longstaff Medal.

66. Atkinson, *op. cit.* (5).
67. Barton entertained working on alkaloid biosynthesis because the accepted structure of Pummerer's ketone did not correspond to his ideas on the coupling of phenolate radicals.
68. As to Alzheimer's it was known to be one form of dementia, but did not have the publicity it has today. For the biosynthesis of morphine, (Barton, Kirby, Taylor and Thomas, 1963), (Barton, Kirby, Steglich, Thomas, Battersby, Dobson, and Ramuz, 1965). Sir Alan Battersby FRS was then at Liverpool. He and Barton, along with their students, collaborated on this work. In 1969 Battersby became professor of organic chemistry at Cambridge, later the 1702 Professor.
69. (Barton and Quinkert, 1960) Quinkert was to work out the photochemical mechanism in detail. Quotation from (Barton, 1991).
70. (Barton, Beckwith and Goosen, 1965). André Goosen was a visitor from South African, and later professor of organic chemistry and head of department at the University of Port Elizabeth. Another South African visitor in this period, Adriaan Wiechers, became professor of organic chemistry at the University of Pretoria.
71. (Barton, Beaton, Geller, and Pechet, 1960). What became known as the Barton nitrite photolysis was an important and innovative reaction. It allowed Barton and his colleagues to synthesise 60 grams of aldosterone at a time when the world supply was just a few milligrams. Their work was followed up by CIBA. Maurice Pechet (1918–2012) was a remarkable

scientist with a Harvard MD and a PhD in chemistry (Louis Fieser was his supervisor). He carried out important work in steroid chemistry and in areas of medically-related organic chemistry.

72. After Barton became the first recipient of the ACS Roger Adams Award in organic chemistry in 1959, Linstead wrote to Sir Keith Murray, Chairman of the UGC, attaching a letter from Barton describing some of the glittering offers he had received. Linstead wrote that Barton was one of the four best organic chemists in the country (he named the others as Jones, Ingold and Todd), and that Barton had 'a vigorous research school attracting people from around the world' and that he needed larger accommodation. Linstead knew that a new building was planned but, he wrote, 'something should be done about this now'. ICL archives KC/12/3; Linstead to Murray, 27 November, 1960.

73. This, despite Briscoe holding what was then still the only established chair of inorganic chemistry in the country. However, he was much occupied with other matters, see Section 8.4.

74. They included Eric Roy Sealey Winter, a wartime student (see Chapter Seven) who was on the staff from 1945–1949 and Bernard L. Archer (see note 39). Mary Estelle Dalziel was on the staff, 1947–1952, and worked in analytical chemistry, as did her brother, J. A. W. Dalziel (see Note 76). Ieuan David was on the staff 1947–1956 and worked with Welch. Douglas Sutherland Payne was on the staff 1947–1949, later a lecturer in Glasgow and then professor in Hong Kong.

75. Joseph (Joe) Chatt FRS (1914–1994). For him the final two straws were that his fume cupboard time was rationed, and a potentiometer he was assured had been ordered, had not been, (Shaw, 1994), (Eaborn and Leigh, 1996). Chatt became an eminent inorganic chemist, later working at the Unit for Nitrogen Fixation at the University of Sussex. He was awarded the CS Tilden (1961) and Liversidge (1971) Awards, and the RSC has a Joseph Chatt Award named for him. Nominated for the Nobel Prize several times, he won the Wolf Prize for his 'pioneering and fundamental contributions to synthetic transition metal chemistry, particularly transition metal hydrides and dinitrogen complexes'. Wilkinson regarded him as a great rival.

76. James (Jimmy) A. W. Dalziel was an undergraduate in the department who gained a PhD under Welch. He was appointed a lecturer in analytical chemistry in 1953 but left for a position at Chelsea College in 1961. At IC he was personal tutor to one of us (WPG) from 1954–1956, and we remained friends until he died. A person of wide interests and knowledge, he was

warm, popular, and brightened our undergraduate days. He received the RSC Theobald Lecture Award in 1991 for his contributions to analytical chemistry. His sister, Mary (Dalziel) Williams, has fond memories of her time at IC, 1947–1952 (personal communication). Albert Stoessl was an assistant lecturer in analytical chemistry, 1957–1960, before leaving for work in Canada. Raymond Peacock (1927–2012) was on the staff from 1953–1958; a fluorine chemist, he was later professor of inorganic chemistry at the University of Leicester. David William Arthur Sharp (1931–2013), another fluorine chemist, was a Cambridge PhD, on the staff from 1957–1961. He moved to what became the University of Strathclyde and was later the Ramsay professor at the University of Glasgow. He was also author of *The Penguin Dictionary of Chemistry*. For some joint work see, for example, (Peacock and Sharp, 1959). Alexander Dennis Cross joined the staff, 1958–1960, with a BSc and PhD from the University of Nottingham. He moved to the United States where he had a highly successful career in the pharmaceutical industry, including a period as President of Syntex International Pharmaceuticals.

77. Eric R. Roberts (1916–1975) was the editor of a departmental history completed in 1962. A copy is in the ICL archive. We are indebted to him for compiling this earlier work which has been of much value in writing this book. Roberts wore a fresh carnation in his lapel every day. Behind his old-fashioned patrician exterior, however, was a kind perceptive person much liked by the students and active in student affairs. For many years he was in charge of student admissions and devised a huge abacus type of machine to help in keeping records for that purpose — computers then existed only on the horizon.

78. While in California, Wilkinson met his Danish wife Lise Schou, daughter of the Rector of the University of Copenhagen's pharmaceutical college. She was studying for a PhD with Melvin Calvin (her first degree was in pharmacology). When he left Harvard in 1955, Wilkinson had a sabbatical break of nine months working in the Copenhagen laboratory of professor Jannik Bjerrum (son of Niels Bjerrum) as a Guggenheim Fellow. Wilkinson recalled that the fume cupboards in Bjerrum's lab had huge burners on top to create an upwards draught, and were totally unsuitable for his organometallic work which involved flammable solvents. Lise Wilkinson later inherited her family's country home at Tisvilde, about 50 km north of Copenhagen. The Wilkinson family were to spend time there each summer. Wilkinson's annual break from the lab was spent reading and writing papers and, later, revising his textbook for its later editions; (John Avery,

personal communication). The Wilkinsons had an arrangement with Avery who, after leaving IC for the University of Copenhagen in 1973, looked after the property in exchange for his own family being allowed to use it when the Wilkinsons were not there.

79. For Wilkinson, (Green and Griffith, 2000), (Griffith, 1997, 2004, 2008), (Abel, 1996), (Bennett, Danopoulos, Griffith, and Green, 1997), and (Cotton, 1997). In his obituary Cotton writes that Wilkinson was a great enthusiast of the French Revolution and was proud that his birthday was on Bastille Day, July 14. Wilkinson was elected FRS in 1965. His later honours are mentioned in Chapter Nine.

80. Rumour has it that the wing was designed by Welch who, hoping to be Briscoe's successor, had himself in mind as occupant.

81. We are grateful to David E. H. Jones for this, and for the many other stories he remembers from his time at IC as undergraduate, doctoral student, and postdoctoral fellow. Jones' inventive mind and his considerable literary talents are well displayed in his *Daedalus* pieces for the *New Scientist* that began in 1964. In 1988 the column moved to *Nature* with a more accessible version in *The Guardian*. The latter ended in 1996 but his column in *Nature* continued until 2002. In a 1966 piece in the *New Scientist*, Jones/*Daedalus* envisaged hollow carbon molecules, roughly anticipating in an amusing way the work published in 1985 by Harry Kroto *et al.*, on the 'buckminsterfullerine' molecule for which Kroto was later to win the Nobel Prize. Jones has published three books of his *Daedalus* columns.

82. Abel published several papers on metal complexes with Wilkinson and others in the group. See for example, (Wilkinson, Abel, Bennett and Burton, 1958). Edward W. (Eddie) Abel was appointed reader at Bristol University and was later the foundation professor of inorganic chemistry at the University of Exeter. He was awarded the RSC Tilden Prize in 1980 and was President of the RSC, 1996–1998. On gaining his PhD, Ray Burton left for a position in industry in the United States but sadly he and his wife were killed soon after in an automobile accident. For Bennett see Note 97. For Green see Note (97).

83. The editors of the first two volumes were Wilkinson, Abel and F. G. A. Stone. Volume one was published by Pergamon Press in 1982. The second volume, published in 1994, was a review, by Abel, of the literature from 1982–1994. Some of Wilkinson's students edited later volumes. Francis Gordon Albert Stone FRS (1925–2011) was then a research student of Eméleus' at Cambridge. After a period in the United States he was appointed professor of chemistry at Bristol University.

84. Michael Sammes, personal communication (see also Note 44). One of us (HG) was also present in the lecture room and is puzzled why she and her fellow students didn't all run out. Also puzzling is the absence of a fire alarm. It was the most memorable explosion that occurred during Wilkinson's early days in the department. Abel was making trimethylsilyl-chromate (about 15 cm^3) for the first time. His reaction vessel exploded and some solvent bottles caught fire (probably the rapid combustion led to the windows bulging before being blown out). Abel was told by professor Barrer that on no account was the synthesis to be attempted again in any of the departmental laboratories. Undeterred, Abel continued his work for a few more weeks. He came to the department very early on Saturday mornings and prepared the compound, needed for his characterisations, on the spacious fire escape outside the lab. He wore three lab coats and a big towel around his head for protection. There were some more flashes and bangs. With them came huge clouds of grey-green smoke (colloidal SiO_2 and Cr_2O_3). Some construction workers, working overtime on the new wing of the Science Museum, were amused witnesses and after each bang shouted 'do it again prof.' All signs of this work were cleared away before Wilkinson's arrival at 9.30, (Abel, personal communication). Another explosion, a year earlier, was caused by Malcolm Green who was making some sodium sand (a fine suspension of metallic sodium in an inert solvent). Pressure built up in his apparatus which came apart; some water spilled on the sand setting it alight. The fire burned through the approved plastic piping in the fume cupboard causing damage to the laboratory above. No one was hurt, but black scorch marks were visible for years on the concrete outside the new wing. (The wing was later demolished with much of the old RCS building). In those days there were few safety regulations; the HSE's COSHH regulations were introduced only in 1988, though people mostly acted with due caution, when working with chemicals viewed as hazardous. The toxicity of most chemicals was unknown. Rhodium, however, should have been tested before being so commonly used since cobalt was a known carcinogen (rhodium was later shown to be relatively safe). Perhaps the most serious accident of this period occurred in 1964, caused by a postdoctoral fellow in physical chemistry preparing a low temperature bath in a Dewar flask. By mistake, he added liquid oxygen rather than nitrogen to an organic solvent. The resulting explosion damaged all the apparatus in the lab and blew out the skylights. Three people were injured but fortunately none of them seriously. One was David King, not the person who made the mistake. He later became the head of department

at Cambridge and future Chief Scientific Advisor to the government. For King, see below.

85. Wilkinson memoir, *op. cit.* (11). Lord Jack Lewis FRS (1928–2014). It is remarkable that, while only at IC for 10 months, Lewis' name appears on 11 papers with Wilkinson in the period 1958–1961, six of these also with WPG. In 1961 Lewis was appointed to a Chair in Manchester; later he occupied chairs at UCL and Cambridge. For obituaries (Anon., 2014) and *The Times*, 18 October, 2014. Wilkinson later claimed, 'I was offered the [Cambridge] job on a plate by Alex Todd who sent Alfie Maddock down to try and twist my arm — I declined of course and recommended JL'. ICL archives; B\Wilkinson; Wilkinson to Booth, 7 December, 1992. (Wilkinson also refused the Oxford Chair.) For Lewis, (Johnson, Griffith, Clark, Evans, Robinson and Raithby, 2015).

86. Wilkinson memoir, *op. cit.* (11). Ray Colton (see Note 97) attended Lewis' course in 1956 and recalled 'not understanding a word he said to us'. Lewis recognised the more general lack of comprehension and, after talking with the students and reading their notes on previous inorganic lectures, discovered that they had not learned any modern inorganic chemistry in the second year course. He then gave them an extra 12 lectures on crystal field theory which for most was an eye-opening experience. Soon after, Wilkinson brought in a more modern curriculum.

87. For Evans, (Green and Griffith, 2000b). As an undergraduate at Oxford, Evans won the Gibbs Prize, and impressed Linus Pauling who was visiting the university where he gave some undergraduate lectures. Evans had already read Pauling's work, remembered all the formulae correctly, and was able to help Pauling out with his own formulae during the lectures. After gaining his DPhil Evans spent the year, 1953–54, as a postdoctoral fellow in Chicago with the Nobel Laureate, R. S. Mulliken. Evans was given a readership in 1964. Leslie (Les) Pratt (1929–1991) was on the staff from 1957 to 1988. He was much loved by the students (who once gave him a large tumbler full of a yellow liquid which he thought was beer but was in fact sherry — he drank it all before giving one of his lectures). He was Senior Tutor for a number of years. Mildly eccentric but popular, he was the best man at WPG's wedding in 1972. Prior to that he, WPG, and Dennis Evans would make a once-weekly tour of pubs in a specified area, and though no notes were kept Pratt remembered every detail of these establishments. Pratt was a great collector of books and had a noted collection on plagues and pestilences.

88. The first of these, subsequently known as the Evans Method, was used to measure the weak magnetic properties of molecules in solution; (Evans, 1959). For his highly ingenious adaptation of the Gouy method (the magnet is weighed rather than the sample), (Evans, 1974).

89. For cigarettes, Atkinson, *op. cit.* (5). Barton, too, was a smoker though he later gave it up. Like Jocelyn Thorpe before him, he smoked cigars and their smell forewarned students of his arrival in the lab.

90. Ray Colton, personal communication.

91. For example, (Evans, 1960 and 1961).

92. Hannah Gay was a PhD student with Ronald Mason, but was unable to move with him when he left for a chair in Sheffield. Dennis Evans agreed to be a joint supervisor and she worked with him on singlet-triplet shifts, and on the effect of oxygen in reducing phosphorescence lifetime and intensity in aromatic hydrocarbons — a couple of years after the famous explosion. Some of her samples were embedded in glass and, in those, some triplet-triplet transfer was also noted. Gay remembers having much help from John Avery when writing her thesis. Ray Colton (see below) remembers Evans avoiding the use of a high pressure cell when looking at an excited state of acetylene. He set up a long copper pipe running all the way down the corridor to an IR machine owned by the physical chemistry section — using it 'without permission of course'.

93. (Evans and Maher, 1962). John (Johnny) Maher gained his PhD with Evans in 1963 and was later a lecturer at the University of Bristol. See also (Maher and Evans, 1965) for a paper on thallium–proton spin–spin coupling constants. Thallium served a double purpose. The lab was located at the west end of the RCS building, in an area vacated by the physics department. It was next to a part of the building being demolished to make way for biochemistry. Displaced rats invaded the lab but did not last long after Evans sprinkled thallium salts around the skirting boards.

94. Like others, Hannah Gay was fascinated by Evans' use of drugs. Evans thought carefully about what he was doing and appears to have remained largely unharmed by the self-experimentation. In one experiment he overdosed on cocaine and brought himself back to normal by ingesting opium — recording his pulse rate throughout. Gay was once asked to help a friend of his, the author William S. Burroughs, who was a cocaine addict. Burroughs, an occasional visitor to the lab, came in one day with about a two-week supply of cocaine in a paper bag. Gay weighed it out into 'safe' individual doses. Earlier Evans had rescued Burroughs from Tangier, after

he became seriously ill from ingesting drugs and alcohol, and taken him to a private addiction clinic. Evans moved in a circle associated with the Chelsea Arts Club. Burroughs was just one of many literary friends. The painters Bridget Reilly (she gave him one of her paintings) and Francis Bacon were also friends. After the Profumo scandal broke in 1963, Christine Keeler stayed in Evans' flat so as to hide from the press. Also sharing his flat were a number of other exotics — animal pets such as snakes, lizards, and scorpions — all well cared for. When Evans first came to London he briefly shared a flat on Thurloe Street with Malcolm Green and a Caiman alligator named Augustus and, because they had nowhere else to put him, Augustus occupied the bath tub.

95. Wilkinson, *op. cit.* (11), records being offended when Ron Nyholm, who was present at the lecture, 'stole' his title in (Nyholm, 1957). Wilkinson could well have remembered things poorly. Nyholm gave his inaugural lecture at UCL, with close to the same title, in March 1956; Wilkinson gave his in June 1956. He saw Nyholm as a major competitor.

96. This work included papers on cyclopentadienyl compounds, including ones with mercury and copper, as well as the *tris* (cyclopentadienyl) compounds of scandium, yttrium, the rare earth elements, and the actinides thorium and uranium. Also published was work on cyclopentadienyl carbonyl compounds of vanadium, manganese, iron and cobalt.

97. Many did well. On leaving IC, Malcolm L. H. Green FRS moved first to Cambridge and then to Oxford where he was later appointed professor of inorganic chemistry and head of department. He was awarded the CS Corday–Morgan (1972), RSC Tilden (1980) and Frankland (1988) awards, and was the first winner of the Sir Geoffrey Wilkinson Award in 2000. Elected FRS in 1985 he was awarded the Davy medal in 1995. Martin A. Bennett FRS was to work with Nyholm at UCL before moving to a chair at the ANU in Canberra; William P (Bill) Griffith was awarded a postdoctoral fellowship and given an assistant lectureship at Chicago with Henry Taube, moving with him to Stanford before returning to join the staff at IC in 1962. Ray Colton moved from IC to the AERE Harwell and, in 1963, to the University of Melbourne. Aside from chemistry, he was deeply interested in astronomy and published on Stonehenge and astronomy in *Nature*. Robert D. Gillard (1936–2013) gained his PhD in 1961 and joined the staff for three years. He worked on rhodium catalysed reactions, and was later professor of chemistry at Cardiff. He won the RIC Meldola Medal and Prize in 1965, and the mineral Gillardite, $Cu_3NiCl_2(OH)_6$, is named after him. Alan Davison FRS (1936–2015) was appointed a professor at MIT

where, together with a Harvard professor of cardiology, he developed a perfusible technetium complex used worldwide in cardiac imaging — bringing a fortune to MIT from the patents, and perhaps a fortune also to the two developers. Davison is still remembered for having 'stolen' the C&G mascot, a large spanner forged in the Bessemer Laboratory. He managed this during a formal C&G event and, with the help of others, placed it in the middle of the Round Pond, Kensington Gardens. It was later retrieved by the C&G student President who had to wade in to find it. Colin Lock (1933–1996) was later a professor at McMaster University. William McFarlane became professor of inorganic chemistry at Newcastle, Jon A. McCleverty moved to Sheffield and later held chairs at Birmingham and Bristol. John A. Osborn (1939–2000) came to IC with a Cambridge BSc and gained his PhD in 1965. After further work with Wilkinson on a post-doctoral fellowship, he moved to Harvard in 1967 as an assistant professor and extended the work on homogeneous catalysis begun at IC. He found a way to catalyse the hydrogenation of prochiral alkenes to chiral products, the most important of which, L-DOPA, was used in the treatment of Parkinson's disease in the late 20th century. In 1975 Osborn moved to the chair of inorganic chemistry at the Université Louis Pasteur in Strasbourg and led some research also at CNRS. Osborn won the CS Corday–Morgan Award in 1975, the RSC Liversidge Award in 1995, and the Grand Prix le bel of the French Chemical Society. He had a distinguished career, sadly cut short by his premature death in 2000. For an obituary, (Schrock, 2001). Richard (Dick) Schrock, one of Osborn's Harvard doctoral students, won the Nobel Prize for chemistry in 2005 for his contribution to metathesis; work that was inspired in part by Wilkinson's (see Chapter Nine). Steven Ley called metathesis '*the* discovery in chemistry of the past thirty years'; quoted in *Nature News* (online, 5 October, 2005). The discovery has indeed aided synthesis worldwide.

98. (Wilkinson, Down, Lewis and Moore, 1959). Wilkinson's research students, among them, Griffith, Down and Moore, had great fun destroying some of the Na/K alloy by throwing it from the top of the new wing and waiting for the bang as it reached the ground. They usually checked that nobody was around but on one occasion failed to notice a car in the line of fire. Its paintwork suffered from the resulting deliquescing mixture of NaOH and KOH. The car belonged to George L. Kington, reader in physical chemistry, and Wilkinson had to pay for it to be repainted.

99. The model for these was a rhodium hydride that Wilkinson made with J. Birmingham, one of his Harvard students. For an example of work at IC,

(Wilkinson, Green, and Pratt, 1958). Later, Ray Colton remembers that Wilkinson asked him and Bill Griffith to take a reduced rhenium solution to Pratt. He found a hydride signal, 'none of us expected the species would turn out to be $[ReH_8]^-$'.

100. For example, (Griffith, Lewis, and Wilkinson, 1958), (Colton, Levitus and Wilkinson, 1960), (Davison, McCleverty, and Wilkinson, 1963), (Gillard and Wilkinson, 1963). For Wilkinson's catalyst see Chapter Nine.

101. Tony Poë, personal communication. Wilkinson agreed to supervise him, possibly because Poë, too, had worked in nuclear chemistry (Poë, when at Harwell, had isolated and characterised several radioactive isotopes). Poë gained his PhD in 1961 and, in a recent email, wrote that Wilkinson did not read his thesis which was on the kinetics of some inorganic reactions, including ligand displacement and the stereoisomerisation of complexes, until it was submitted for the oral examination. Poë's subsequent work was on Pt(IV), metal–metal bonded carbonyls, their mechanisms, and the 'kinetic strengths' of metal–metal bonds and metal–carbonyl clusters. Sadly, since hearing from Tony we heard of his death in Ottawa on 23 August, 2015. (Anthony John Poë, 1929–2015).

102. Sir Ronald Mason FRS was educated at the University College of Wales (Cardiff) where he heard Kathleen Lonsdale give a lecture on crystallography. It drew him to UCL for his PhD. Although only in the IC department for two years, he said (personal communication) that he had several good students during that time. Among them were Malcolm Gerloch, Neil Bailey, and Michael Bennett. Mason left for a chair in Sheffield in 1963 and was awarded the CS Corday–Morgan Prize in 1964. In 1971 he was appointed professor of inorganic chemistry at the University of Sussex. He was seconded to the Ministry of Defence on becoming chief scientific advisor, 1977–1988 (period of the Falklands War). In 1988 he left Sussex for work in the defence industry and, in 1993, became the first chairman of the UCLH NHS Trust. HG remembers Ron as always buzzing with ideas. One idea for which he had John Avery's help (for the Hückel calculations) was to distinguish which of the polycyclic aromatic hydrocarbons were likely to be carcinogens. For his crystallographic work Mason and his students used the University's Mercury computer (the size of a small house). This was before IC acquired its IBM machine (see Chapter Nine). Gerloch joined the staff at UCL, leaving later with Jack Lewis to work at Cambridge.

103. This pattern was noted earlier by Eric Roberts in his 1962 history of the department.

104. (Barrer, 1938).

105. For Barrer, (Rees, 1997, 1998). Barrer's mother, Nina Greensill Barrer, who taught him as a child, was a university-educated teacher — unusual at that time and place — and received the MBE for services to education. According to Rees, Barrer engaged with people in his home community and was a good family man.

106. For a later IC paper on this topic, (Barrer and Peterson, 1964).

107. Much of Barrer's research on molecular sieves was supported by a major grant from the Wolfson Foundation. For a later account of this work, (Barrer, 1978).

108. James Alexander (Jim) Barrie became a Senior lecturer in 1976. Lovat Victor Charles Rees became a Senior lecturer in 1977, and professor in 1991.

109. George Leslie Kington (1922–2013) left the department in 1959 and was later Research director at the British Aluminium Co.

110. One of Gordon's students from this period, Ian Hillier, gained his PhD in 1964. Hillier, a theoretical chemist, held a two-year postdoctoral fellowship with Stuart Rice at the University of Chicago, returning to a lectureship at the University of Manchester, where he was appointed professor of Theoretical Chemistry in 1983. For Gordon, see Note (135).

111. Sheppard told us that Wilkinson 'pulled me out of a physical chemistry position … to look after the Bruker 250 MHz machine which was about to arrive … got my previous … rather uncertain status regularised, and disposed very effectively of objections from the physical section.'

112. Rees had witnessed one of Britain's H-bomb tests during his national service and kept some neptunium in the first floor mezzanine (RCS 1) which he used for Np–Mössbauer measurements.

113. From the IC calendars it appears that Kerr and Ash were unique in the department in being lecturer–research assistants. Ash, a good mathematician who never completed his PhD in physical chemistry, escaped this strait-jacket to become a 'proper' lecturer in 1978, but Kerr, it appears, did not. Ash invigilated examinations into the 1980s, wearing his Oxford gown.

114. See, for example, (Ash, Baker, and Barrer, 1967).

115. For an example of molecular sieve work, (Barrer and Baynham, 1956). This paper was part of a long series with at least 21 parts.

116. Zeolite catalysts are used also in the petrochemical industry for the production of plastics and fibres. They are important also in air-conditioning units, air-brakes, laundry detergents, in cleaning up hazardous (including radioactive) wastes, and as desiccants in refrigerators that meet the 1989 Montreal Protocol's requirement that they be free of chlorofluorocarbons.

117. (Rees, 1997, 1998).
118. For Rideal, see also Chapter Five, (Eley, 1976 and 2004), and (Barrer, 1978b). After a career at Cambridge, Rideal was appointed director of the Davy–Faraday Laboratory at the Royal Institution, 1946–1949. He then became professor of chemistry at KCL, 1950–1955. While at IC he wrote *Concepts in Catalysis* (1968). Rideal received many awards, including the CS Liversidge (1945) and Longstaff (1960) prizes. There is also an RSC Sir Eric Rideal Award and Lecture.
119. For Hinshelwood, (Thompson, 1973), (Laidler, 2004). For an obituary by Hinshelwood's Oxford colleague, Edward J. Bowen FRS, (Bowen, 1967). Hinshelwood worked at Oxford throughout his career. A kineticist, he was President of the Chemical Society, 1946–1948, was awarded the Nobel Prize for chemistry in 1956 (with Nicolai Semenov), and was President of the Royal Society, 1955–1960, winning also the Royal and Davy Medals. His RS memoirist states that he was made a senior research fellow in the IC Chemistry Department in 1964. But he came to the department already in 1960 at the end of his term as PRS — although perhaps still formally at Oxford. He was given a small wooden office, more like a hutch, close to the main entrance of the old RCS building. For much of his life Hinshelwood lived with his mother in Chelsea. On her death he inherited her house, continued to live there, and was a frequent visitor to the college even before 1960. He possessed a remarkable intellect and his knowledge stretched well beyond chemistry. Among other things he was an excellent linguist, spoke several modern languages, and knew both ancient Greek and Latin. He was President of the Classical Association in 1959, but was a leading voice in getting universities to remove the (O-level) classical language requirement for matriculation in the sciences, something IC had never required. He was awarded the Order of Merit and was a much revered presence in the department until his death in 1967.
120. For Tompkins, (King and Enderby, 2004). This obituary of Frederick Clifford Tompkins FRS (1910–1995) appeared earlier in *The Independent*, 16 November, 1995. See also (Jacobs, 1996). Tompkins attended Yeovil Grammar School, followed by the University of Bristol where he gained both a BSc and PhD. Bristol was then a good place for surface and solid state science and he learned much both from his doctoral supervisor, William Garner FRS, and from John Lennard-Jones FRS. After a few years as an assistant lecturer at King's College, London, Tompkins moved to South Africa and spent nine years at the University of Natal. After the war he returned to King's College on a research fellowship and came to IC as

reader in physical chemistry in 1947. In Natal he carried out work in solid state kinetics and, with E. R. Prout (later professor of physical chemistry at the University of Cape Town), came up with the Prout–Tompkins equation that is still used, (Prout and Tompkins, 1946). Tompkins was elected FRS in 1955 and given a personal chair in 1959.

121. For example, (Gundry and Tompkins, 1956). P. M. Gundry was on the staff, 1957–1960, before moving to join the electrical engineering department.

122. David King, interviewed by Alan MacFarlane (www.alanmacfarlane.com), 27 November, 2009. In South Africa, King was the doctoral student of Felix Sebba (see ch. 7). King mentions that Tompkins drew many talented students and postdocs from commonwealth universities. One was Ian D. Gay, a PhD student (and husband of HG) who came from Dalhousie University on a Shell Scholarship in 1961. He worked with Tompkins on catalysis and was later a professor at Simon Fraser University. Gay (personal communication) said that he would never have called Tompkins by his first name but, like others, called him Fred behind his back. He also said that Tompkins would arrive in his (Gay's) lab about every two weeks wearing a three-piece suit and, in a friendly manner, interrogate him as to what he had done since the previous visit, (Gay and Tompkins, 1966). King was later head of the chemistry department at Cambridge, and Chief Scientific Advisor to the United Kingdom government. Another of Tompkins' postdocs, Meirion Wyn Roberts, was later the foundation professor of physical chemistry at the University of Bradford and then head of department at Cardiff. Others have testified to Tompkins' wide interests, and that he was an excellent pianist.

123. Patrick William McCarthy Jacobs (1923–2013). For a short obituary: http://www.uwo.ca/chem/news/2013-2014.

124. Ian Gay, personal communication. Although not an explosive, hydrazine perchlorate is a dangerous deflagrator. Jacobs was eminent in his field and shortly after his death a symposium was held at UCL in his honour. 'Advances in chemistry of disordered solids: A symposium honouring the contributions of professor Patrick Jacobs', 13 September, 2013.

125. G. J. (Sir Graham) Hills (1926–2014) left school at 16 to work as a lab assistant at May and Baker. He took evening classes so as to matriculate at Birkbeck College where he studied for his BSc, gained in 1946. His PhD supervisor was David J. G. Ives, a reader at Birkbeck who had earlier gained both his BSc and PhD at IC, the latter with Ellingham in 1932. (Ives returned to the department as a Special lecturer in 1943.) Hills gained his PhD in 1950, the year he came to IC. He was an excellent electrochemist

but, after moving to a chair in Southampton in 1962, he became interested in university affairs and was appointed deputy Vice-Chancellor. In 1980 he moved to become Principal and Vice-Chancellor of the University of Strathclyde where, by all accounts, he was an outstanding success. At IC he was remembered as being genial and having a quick mind. He enjoyed courting controversy, was an inveterate writer of letters to *The Times* and, in *Who's Who*, he gave his hobby as 'rocking the boat.'

126. Joseph (Joe) Kitchener gained his BSc and PhD from UCL before coming to the department as a demonstrator in 1938. He was the author of a book on ion exchange resins (Kitchener, 1961). Kitchener left a typescript, 'Some recollections of the chemistry department at IC, half a century ago'; it is in the ICL archives. In it he mentions running the physical chemistry laboratory after the war, and that students were still carrying out experiments described in the sixth (1934) edition of Alexander Findlay's *Practical Physical Chemistry*. Kitchener found the book 'old fashioned,' which it was, and embarked on bringing out a new edition. After a few years of trying out experiments he brought out a seventh edition in 1954, and an eighth in 1962. A ninth edition was brought out by Bryan Levitt in 1973. Kitchener recounts how difficult it was to find apparatus with which to carry out physical chemistry research when he arrived in 1938, and that he turned to the kinetics of decomposition because of what he could find. He received the CS Sir Eric Rideal Award in 1979. For an obituary of Kitchener, (Pugh, 2009).

127. Charles Fowler Cullis, now an Emeritus professor at City University, was head of the chemistry department, (1973–1984), Pro-Vice-Chancellor, 1980–1984, Saddler's Research Professor, 1984–1987, and Leverhulme Emeritus Research Fellow, 1987–1989.

128. Bernhardt Patrick (John) O'Mara Bockris (1923–2013), was born in South Africa but, after his parents' divorce, his mother took him to England where he grew up. He took an external University of London BSc at Brighton Technical College. A leading electrochemist, Bockris was a founder of the series, *Modern aspects of electrochemistry*.

129. Bockris interview; (Macy, 2013).

130. (Parsons, 2009). Parsons writes that Bockris gave lectures at Acton Technical College when a PhD student, and that one of his Acton students, Harold Egan (later Chief Government Chemist), came to IC with a Beit Fellowship and worked with him for a PhD. Roger Parsons FRS gained his PhD in 1948 and was appointed an assistant lecturer. He stayed at IC until 1951 before going to what soon became the University of Dundee. Later he

was director of the Laboratoire d'Electrochemie Interfaciale at CNRS, and ended his career as professor of chemistry at the University of Southampton. Brian Conway FRS (1925–2005) gained his PhD in 1949 and then moved to work with J. A. V. Butler, an electrochemist working at the Chester Beatty Research Institute. In 1955 Conway joined Bockris at the University of Pennsylvania. Two years later he moved to the University of Ottawa where he was to have a major career with over 100 PhD students. For Conway, (Bockris, 2007). Also members of Bockris' IC group were John Tomlinson, later a professor at the University of Wellington and Edmund C. Potter who had a major career at the Commonwealth Scientific and Industrial Research Organization in NSW, Australia.

131. (Bockris, Herringshaw, Conway, Fleischmann, Parsons, *et al.*, 1947). John Francis Herringshaw was a PhD student in the department, 1941–1944. He drifted toward the inorganic chemistry section, taught some analytical chemistry, and left for the food industry in 1963 where he had a successful career.

132. According to Parsons, the Faraday discussions prompted Bockris to keep his laboratory cleaner so as to get more accurate results. It clearly needed it. Parsons relates putting a Tesla coil down on the woodblock floor and that the discharge caused the cracks in the floor to light up due to mercury spills left there by the previous occupants. 'I think that the reason none of us suffered from mercury poisoning was that the windows did not fit well … also the floor was not very clean and the evaporation of mercury was slow,' (Parsons, 2009). Allegedly a pool of mercury was later found below the parquet flooring of the lab.

133. (Latimer, 1938).

134. According to Bockris some of their trips were 'salted with girls' collected from the local nurses' residence; (Bockris, 2013). Martin Fleischmann FRS (1927–2012) was born in Czechoslovakia and came to Britain with his family as a refugee. After the war he gained a BSc, and a PhD (1950) in the department. A postdoctoral fellowship with Reginald Thirsk at the University of Newcastle followed; he stayed on as a lecturer until appointed to the Faraday chair of chemistry at the University of Southampton in 1967. There he built a large and successful school of electrochemistry, developed the use of micro and ultramicro electrodes, and was one of the discoverers of Surface Enhanced Raman Spectroscopy (SERS) in 1974. He took early retirement in 1983, was elected FRS in 1985, and began a new life as peripatetic chemist, working around the world. Despite much excellent research, he is best remembered for work carried out in Utah with Stanley

Pons on 'cold fusion.' This took him back to his PhD at IC and his research on the palladium/hydrogen system. (Reginald Thirsk (1915–1995), an eminent electrochemist, was a former IC student who gained his PhD with George I. Finch in the chemical technology and chemical engineering department.)

135. (Allen, Dusek, Kennedy and Koningsveld, 1977). This was a tribute on the occasion of Manfred Gordon's 60th birthday.
136. For details see Croker's memoir, attached to Atkinson's history, *op. cit.* (5).
137. The chief glassblower was Arthur Madell and the chief instrument maker, Bert Cobley. Cobley's wife was head of the cleaning staff. A college central stores was situated on the lower-ground floor of the RCS building, supervised by Albert Moore. This was phased out gradually. By 1988 smaller stores units were in place. For later developments in the stores, see Chapter Ten.
138. H. E. Rydon left for a chair at the Manchester College of Science and Technology in 1952. For Rydon see also Chapter Six.
139. Some members of staff advertised in advance when they had short projects that they were willing to supervise.
140. (Linstead, Elvidge, and Whalley, 1955). For a later edition (Linstead, Elvidge and Sammes, 1966). Elvidge and Whalley were married in 1956. For Sammes, Chapter Nine.
141. (Linstead and Weedon, 1956).
142. In 1959 Barrer tried to persuade Linstead to allow the department to discontinue its practical examinations, but Linstead would not hear of it. ICL archives, KC/12/3; Barrer to Linstead, 12 November, 1959; Linstead to Barrer, 27 April, 1960.
143. Ministry of Education, Special Committee Report (Chaired by Lord Eustace Percy, Rector of the Newcastle division of the University of Durham) (HMSO, 1945). IC's Rector, Sir Richard Southwell was a member of this committee. The Scientific Manpower Report was commissioned by Herbert Morrison, Deputy PM in the Attlee government; its chairman, Sir Alan Barlow, recommended a major expansion of higher education.
144. The Robbins Report of 1963 led to yet further expansion plans, something to be discussed in Chapter Nine. Plans for the demolition of the Imperial Institute were made earlier, in connection with the Jubilee expansion. The acquisition of much of Princes Gardens for the development of new student residences and an indoor sports centre were also part of the Jubilee expansion plans.

145. John Avery, who came to the department in 1962, remembers standing in the long upper corridor 'seeing people disappear into the indoor fog [smog] as they walked down' (personal communication). Things slowly changed after air quality legislation came in with the Clean Air Acts of 1956 and 1968. The old RCS building was, however, atmospheric, and was much used by the film industry. *The Ipcress File* was filmed there with a memorable sequence shot in the Science Museum Library, then housed in the RCS building. *Charlie Bubbles* was filmed in the gents toilet in the basement (said to have been one of the finest Edwardian toilets in London), and much of the building was used for the BBC TV series *The Quatermass File*.

146. Chain asked for a neighbourhood house to be rented; one with 7 bedrooms, 3 bathrooms, 3 reception rooms, a music room, dining room, study, and large kitchen. The college did not agree to this but the Wolfson Foundation later provided funds for a large penthouse flat to be built on the top of the biochemistry building. It has since been converted to laboratories. ICL archives, Lloyd Davies, 'Memorandum on the history of the Biochemistry Department', 14 December, 1972.

147. Perhaps if Chain had produced a viral antibiotic to match penicillin's effectiveness with bacteria, something he attempted to do, we would look back on this history differently. As Rector, Linstead appears to have favoured biochemistry, as well as all aspects of nuclear science and nuclear energy engineering, over chemistry. An early postwar student, John H. C. Naylor (BSc, 1948) went to work for Beechams where he developed some of the second generation of penicillin drugs such as methicillin and ampicillin, (Doyle, 1993).

148. Anthony Cox, of Architects Co-Partnership, designed the biochemistry building; and later C1 and C2.

149. A letter to the department from the University of London stated, 'the [UGC] committee ... wonders whether your proposals are not rather lavish since the provision of 492 laboratory working places, 510 lecture theatre places, 80 seminar places and 6 tutorial rooms to cater for 290 full-time students and 160 students from other departments suggests that [only] one half of the teaching accommodation will be in use at any one time'. Quoted in Atkinson, *op. cit.* (5). The college reduced the number of working places to 484 and the lecture places to 400. C1 also included space for a new Central Stores. Similar arguments came up later with C2.

Chapter Nine

Modernisation in a Changing Political, Economic, and Technological Climate: 1965–1985

9.1 Some Political and Economic Problems of the 1970s

During the postwar years a broad consensus emerged that many more people than in the past should have access to higher education. This led to the growth of some existing institutions including, as we have seen, Imperial College (IC).[1] After the government accepted the Robbins Report of 1963, growth in higher education accelerated yet further.[2] Linstead, who was a member of the Robbins committee, was asked to envisage the future of the college and, for advice, he set up a committee consisting of prominent members of the academic staff, all under the age of 50; Derek Barton was among them. Linstead then decided that nuclear science and engineering, and computer technology, would be the major growth areas for the 1970s. Plans for the new chemistry buildings were already in place, and he wanted to see a significant rise in the number of chemistry under-graduates.[3] Linstead died suddenly in 1966 and the new Rector, William Penney, accepted his plans.[4] He also brought in a five-year (renewable) term for department heads. The old 'baronial' style headships slowly came to an end, and decision making at the departmental level became more democratic. However, department heads became more beholden to the Rector and to a growing central administration.

Because of a serious economic recession, Robbins' noble vision soon ran into trouble. In retrospect 1973 can be seen as a pivotal year, and not just for Britain. It was the year in which Britain became a member of the European Economic Community (EEC), saw the collapse of some of its major industries, and experienced several industrial strikes including a major one by the National Union of Mineworkers. At the same time, the Yom Kippur War triggered a huge increase in the price of oil worldwide — a price set by the Organization of Petroleum Exporting Countries (OPEC).[5] The college fuel bills more than doubled in the years 1973–1975. When the Labour Party returned to power in 1974, it faced job losses, social unrest, and inflation that came close to 30 percent in 1975. The recession did not bottom out until the early 1980s when Britain's investment in North Sea oil and gas was slowly beginning to pay off. For the department, however, 1973 had an upside. It was the year that Geoffrey Wilkinson won the Nobel Prize.

The events of the 1970s account for the hiatus in the planned expansion of departmental facilities. Funding for C2 was delayed, but there were further complications. By the early 1970s it was clear that the demand for university places in the sciences would not meet the projections envisaged in the Robbins Report — though in 1969 the number of BSc applicants to the department remained high at 424, with 71 being admitted. A 1972 Government Green Paper, 'A framework for Government research and development,' proposed that there be a decrease of 25 percent in funding for the research councils and that the money withheld be used by the government for contract research. There was much wrangling over this, and though 25 percent was not withheld there was increased oversight of research funding which, by then, was spread among more universities.

The collective problems led to a decade-long employment freeze at IC (and elsewhere) when there was already a brain drain of young staff to North America, and when student numbers were allowed to rise despite the cuts.[6] There was some relief in the mid-1980s when what was known as 'new blood' money became available for the appointment of young lecturers, and as research council budgets slowly began to recover. However, with new money came more oversight; 'efficiency' and 'doing more with less' became watchwords. The transition that began in this period is not over. A social contract is still being worked on, one in which the public pays for university research and instruction in exchange for the good that they bring. But how much should the public pay, how much the student, and how much industry? How many should receive higher education, and what exactly is the good expected in return? Further, how should young people be taught in the age of computers and the internet? Wilkinson joined in the larger debate. In 1984 he wrote to Sir Keith Joseph, Secretary of State for Education and Science, stating that the money spent on high energy physics over the previous 30 years had benefited only a few and was 'a gross misallocation of public funds.' The money, he wrote, would have been far better spent on 'provincial theatres and orchestras' and, of course, on 'chemistry' which, he wrote, 'is of far greater importance to the national economy (than high energy physics) and fares far less well.'[7]

IC was lucky to have Brian Flowers (appointed in 1973) as Rector in this difficult period.[8] He came to the college having served as chairman of the Science Research Council (SRC) and his understanding of the political and economic situation was good. Although he had some serious disagreements with the department, he nudged it in the direction of much needed reform.

9.2 Departmental Administration, Reorganisation, and Planning for the Future

Following the Robbins Report, the department set a target of expanding the number of undergraduates from 180 to 300, and postgraduates from 125 to 180 by the mid 1980s. This entailed a projected increase in the academic staff from 48 to 66, as well as an increase in technical, library, and secretarial staff. The planned expansion was seen to be manageable given that the department began occupying the new C1 building in 1971, and was expecting C2 to be built soon after. But, when the 1960s gave way to the more stringent 1970s, C2 was postponed and instead of staff numbers increasing they declined. By 1985, the number of academic staff had dropped to 34 and the technical staff from 49 to 33. Nonetheless, undergraduate numbers crept up to 221.[9] Barrer wanted to increase the number of postdoctoral fellows, believing that this would help to maintain stability in the research areas of the department; by 1985 their number had risen to about 45.[10] Most came from abroad, notably from Commonwealth countries. As to overseas research students, their number declined in the 1980s after the Thatcher government decided to greatly increase overseas student fees.[11] John Welch was the assistant director from 1960 to his retirement in 1982. Although not very approachable, he appears to have managed things as well as could be expected. He was greatly helped by Bernard Atkinson, appointed deputy assistant director in 1977; Atkinson succeeded Welch as assistant director in 1982.[12]

The period covered in this chapter saw the start of departmental reorganisation which, as discussed in the next chapter, continued into the 1990s. Changes to the financing of departments were introduced in 1971 when, for the first time, staff costs were included in the departmental vote. This allowed for increasing the expenditure on materials by reducing staff costs, and *vice versa*. The total vote was based largely on per capita considerations, so any reduction in student numbers usually meant a cut in materials since there was no easy or quick way to reduce staff numbers. By allowing student numbers to grow, the department avoided yet further cuts to its budget. By 1985, however, numbers could grow no further. Space was limited, the C2 building was yet to be finally approved, and few new staff appointments were permitted.

In Flowers' view a more rational way of administering the department and distributing its limited financial resources had to be found. He asked Barrer to step down as head of department a year before his retirement date in 1977.[13] With a new head in place, he believed, there could be a serious discussion on the department's future. In 1976, after consulting members of staff, he appointed Wilkinson as Barrer's successor. He then asked the department to abandon the Linstead constitution. This met with some opposition, including from Barton who wrote a long and well-reasoned memo on its merits.[14] However the department went along with Flowers, thus allowing change to come more easily in the future. A further sign of the times: in 1978 Wilkinson appointed the first woman to become a departmental Superintendent at the college. Christine Wright came from biochemistry to succeed Les Croker in the position.

Wilkinson did his best to boost the department. He even lobbied for a reduction in the number of chemistry departments in the country, and for increased funding for those that, like his own, were capable of turning out at least thirty PhD graduates per year. In his view the chemistry departments at the following University of London colleges were no longer viable: Bedford, Birkbeck, Queen Elizabeth, Westfield, and Royal Holloway.[15] This has to be seen in context. Unbelievable as it may seem today, the research funds coming to the department from government sources in 1984 totalled only £220,000, clearly insufficient for it to remain globally competitive. Even with funding from charitable foundations and industry, the department piled up deficits (with the college) during the 1980s, amounting to a collective debt of about £3 million by the time Wilkinson retired in 1988.[16] Needless to say the rest of the college was unhappy at having to support chemistry's overruns and, as discussed in Chapter Ten, the department was forced to change its ways.

In the 1960s Barrer placed chemical crystallography under physical chemistry but, when Don Rogers (see below) retired in 1980, the section came under the joint management of the inorganic and organic chemistry sections.[17] Organic chemistry paid also for biological chemistry, but the number of staff involved was small. Analytical chemistry had an academic staff of about six and was a sub-section of inorganic chemistry. Financing these groups working under separate professors was a source of tension. This was especially the case for analytical chemistry which Wilkinson was increasingly reluctant to fund from inorganic chemistry's shrinking budget. When Tom West (see below) resigned in 1975, probably tired of fighting with Wilkinson over funding, Barrer wanted to retain the field and asked Flowers for his opinion. Flowers replied,

> there is no doubt that under Professor West it achieved great distinction as one of the few university groups trying to develop analytical techniques seriously. It has strong ties with industry and commerce, it has been attractive to students for many years, and its graduates have been well received by industry. ... In spite of present economic difficulties it should remain a recognizably viable activity and when circumstances permit it should be led by a professor. I recommend ... it be accorded sectional status forthwith, in which guise its budget will be seen to be a charge on the department as a whole rather than on any one section. ...
>
> [And] in due course I hope it may prove feasible to develop theoretical chemistry.[18]

When Wilkinson became head of department, he sent Flowers a long memo on the recent history of the department, and on where he thought it should be heading. He stated, yet again, that it was losing ground to other departments because of underfunding. And, with some justification, he wrote that the 'UGC Chemistry Building grant was cannibalised by Rector Linstead to cover the deficit on the biochemistry building.' Further, he thought it a mistake for the college to have tried to force the UGC's hand by demolishing the central section of the RCS building.

> *The result of this exercise is a large hole. ... For what should be the premier chemistry department in the country, we are now worse housed than any comparable chemistry department in the Western Hemisphere. ... It is indeed a national scandal.*[19]

Wilkinson also noted that of the seven professors in the department, West had recently resigned and four others were due to leave or retire within the next two years. He wanted to use the opportunity to reorient the department, and he anticipated what came later. He suggested supporting research in broad areas such as materials, industrial processes, pharmaceutical and agricultural chemicals, environmental chemistry, energy problems (including the development of solar energy panels), synthesis, and the mechanistic study of complex molecules. As to new professors, he wanted expertise in catalysis (possibly for heavy industrial processes), synthesis, reaction mechanisms, and some bio-aspects of chemistry. Even though he had earlier supported Flowers' idea for a chair in theoretical chemistry, he was now of the opinion that this should not be a priority unless it was occupied by someone with close links to experimental chemistry.[20] He also stressed that it was important for the future well-being of the department that the number of chairs be increased. He did not agree with Flowers on the matter of analytical chemistry and was not enthusiastic about the almost physical research the analytical chemists were carrying out. He also thought it far too applied. However, the weakened sub-section hung on for a few more years until Gordon Kirkbright (see below) left to join the new department of instrumentation and analytical science at UMIST in 1980.[21] Allowing the demise of analytical chemistry was, perhaps, a mistake, for the reasons Flowers outlined. Besides, Barrer's successor as professor of physical chemistry, W. J. (John) Albery, was carrying out research of importance to the field. However, in Wilkinson's view it was not his opposition to analytical chemistry, but the department's opposition to a chair in theoretical chemistry, that was behind what he saw as Flowers' relative neglect of the department. Wilkinson was probably wrong about this: both in assuming that Flowers held a grudge, and in believing that the department was neglected. Flowers had a difficult time dealing with demands coming from all the departments during the recession and does not appear to have played favourites.

The fact that less money was coming to the college from the UGC, coupled with the government's view that universities needed to get more research funds from industry, led Flowers to devise a new vote formula. There is little doubt that this caused the department some difficulty because it favoured those departments with good industrial contracts, and forced others to seek more industrial funding — which was the point of the exercise.[22] Although chemistry had some good contracts, it could not easily compete with the engineering departments that had many more. Most chemistry PhD students were funded by the SRC and, unlike engineering students, had no agreements with industry. Wilkinson made the reasonable argument that his department had many more PhD students than did any of the engineering departments, and that it should be rewarded for bringing in SRC and MRC funding.[23] He stated, that what the industry expected of his department was that it train people to the doctoral level in pure chemistry. Further, he correctly noted that such research often leads to discoveries of industrial importance. Flowers' response was that if that was indeed the case, then it should be in industry's interest to finance 'blue sky' research, and the department should make a greater effort in bringing its work to the attention of industry.[24] At the same time Flowers wanted to 'tax' those who took on contract and consulting work. He suggested a levy of 25 percent on all outside earnings. Wilkinson opposed this, stating that in his own case he could not carry out research without the loan of platinum metal salts from Johnson Matthey, and that he carried out contract work in exchange. Further, he argued, those in the department who took on outside work were 'diligent in their teaching duties', and should not have to face a 'prohibitive' tax of 25 percent and that, besides, outside work could be defended on intellectual grounds.[25] The debate over how to finance the department continued into the rectorships of Eric Ash and Ronald Oxburgh. Wilkinson urged Ash to counter the UGC's 'outdated ideas' on the norms for research space, and on what should be the size of lecture theatres and seminar rooms for C2.[26] These and other issues were not resolved entirely satisfactorily; but slowly the department faced the inevitable and sought more industrial support to stay afloat.

When Wilkinson became head of department, one of his first tasks was to find good successors for Barton and Barrer, both of whom caused a few problems at the time they left. In 1976 Barton was 58 years old. He had not wished to become head of department and had long stated that he would leave at the age of 60. In the summer of 1976, looking to find somewhere he could work beyond the official retirement age of 65, he began some research at the *CNRS Institut de Chimie des Substances Naturelles at Gif-sur-Yvette* (near Paris).[27] In 1977, without informing the authorities at IC, he accepted the position of Director at the institute, and left the department taking some postdoctoral fellows with him.[28] Flowers first heard of his appointment through the grapevine, and from an announcement in *Chemical and Engineering News*. However, since Barton had said that he was resigning his chair in 1978, Flowers decided to do nothing about this apparent case of double dipping. Flowers also believed that the previous rector, swayed by Barton's Nobel Prize, had made a mistake in naming him the Hofmann professor of organic chemistry in 1970. Flowers disliked named chairs and asked Wilkinson to remove the name. However, Barton's successor, Charles Rees, wanted to keep it, and suggested to Wilkinson that the inorganic chemistry chair be named after Sir Edward Frankland. Wilkinson liked that idea and, on this matter, Flowers gave way.[29] Barrer, planning to stay on as a research fellow after his retirement in 1977, caused a problem by refusing to give up research space for his successor. Wilkinson also faced problems with undergraduates who complained, among other things, that the laboratory courses were open-ended and that they were assigned a minimum amount of work, but no maximum. Quantity, they claimed, was rewarded over quality. Chemistry was the only department in the college with open-ended laboratory courses and Flowers asked that they end. However, he was happy to see members of the department collaborating on new interdisciplinary research projects. Links were cultivated with chemical engineers, with those working in the fields of materials and biochemistry and, beyond the college, with those in biomedicine.[30]

Flowers insisted that Wilkinson hold regular staff meetings — something Barrer had avoided — and that there be a broadly based management committee in addition to the already existing professorial committee. The departmental management committee came into being in 1977 and two of its early decisions reflect the end of the old era. First, it oversaw the updating and rationalisation of the various student prizes. In 1979 the formerly much coveted Hatton Prize was worth only £30, and the Hofmann Prize a ridiculous £2.50. Second, since classical gravimetric analysis was no longer taught, the committee decided to sell off the departmental collection of platinum dishes and crucibles, as well as a valuable platinum gold-parting apparatus. However, as Atkinson noted, 'the relief was short lived' and money remained extremely tight for several more years.[31]

On a different note, in 1979 Wilkinson lobbied for a pedestrian crossing with traffic lights for Exhibition Road after a visiting professor, Jacek (Jack) Lubinkowski, was knocked down by a car and seriously injured when crossing near the junction with Imperial College Road. Wilkinson found an ally in the College Secretary, John Smith, and the much-used crossing was installed.[32] Also worth mentioning is that Wilkinson supported young artists and commissioned a number of paintings from students at the Royal College of Arts (RCA). These included the painting of the Yorkshire Dales that hung over his office desk. He also much cared for the plants in his office.

This period saw a major rise in the use of computers. Flowers, an early computer user, was chairman of the SRC's Academic Committee on Computing in the 1960s and played a role in the University of London's acquisition of a Ferranti Atlas computer (to replace its older Mercury machine). When, in 1963, IBM gave IC one of its 7090 computers, his committee wanted the SRC to purchase another computer and make the college the South–East regional centre for academic computing. However, the university blocked that idea and the CD 6600 machine joined the Atlas machine in Malet Street. As we will see, members of the department used both the university and the college facilities; and, as computers became cheaper, more powerful, and smaller, new possibilities in chemical research arose.

9.3 Two Nobel Prizes

Despite the many problems of the 1970s, the chemistry department received an enormous boost with the award of the Nobel Prize to Derek Barton in 1969 and to Geoffrey Wilkinson in 1973. Some of their Nobel Prize work was mentioned in the Chapter Eight; in this section we add a little to the earlier material and refer also to their Nobel lectures.

Barton and Odd Hassel were awarded the Nobel Prize for 'their contributions to the development of the concept of conformation and its application in chemistry.'[33] Barton began his Nobel lecture with a short historical account of conformational ideas. He noted that J. H. van't Hoff won the very first Nobel Prize for chemistry in 1901 for his work on osmosis and chemical kinetics, but that earlier he had worked with Kekulé on stereochemistry. In that connection he had speculated on restricted rotation around double bonds and free rotation around single bonds though, as was shown later, rotation around single bonds can also be restricted. It was Herman Sachse who introduced the idea of conformation in the late 19th century, giving a mathematical argument for the existence of cyclohexane in two different non-planar forms. The terms 'boat' and 'chair' were introduced later, and the term 'conformation,' used for non-superimposable arrangements of molecules with the same constitution and configuration, was used first by another Nobel Laureate, and former staff member, Norman Haworth (see Chapter Four).

Barton's co-winner, Odd Hassel, used electron diffraction to show that the chair conformation was preferred in cyclohexane and argued that this was because the hydrogen atoms were kept as far apart as possible (before this it was not known for sure that the barrier to free rotation around bonds in the cyclohexane ring was important, and whether attractive or repulsive forces came into play). Chemists, including Barton, appear to have thought about stereochemistry in ways similar to Ingold and Thorpe in their discussion of 'valency deflexion' (see Chapter Six). Barton clearly had an extraordinary ability to visualise in three-dimensions, and to think about conformations in new and interesting ways, including consideration of axes of symmetry, angle strain, bond compression, bond extension, and so on. One might think that such factors would lead to an infinite number of conformations but, by carrying out force field calculations, Barton accounted for what was empirically recognised; namely that some conformations are preferred. Further, he was able to visualise the interactions between non-bonded groups, and to predict the consequences of adding substituents.

In 1954 Barton came to an agreement with other leaders in this new field (Hassel, V. Prelog, and K. S. Pitzer) on the standard nomenclature for equatorial and axial bonds.[34] Much of his work in the later 1950s and 1960s was devoted to the synthesis and structure of triterpenoids and steroids with skeletons composed of fused cyclohexane rings. How to think of these three dimensionally, how to prepare new compounds given the geometrical requirements of the intermediates, how to predict configuration by postulating preferred conformation, and how to work out the long-range effects of conformation on the structure and chemistry of such compounds, were the problems that he addressed. Because Barton extended his earlier work in such fecund ways, he was a deserving winner of the Nobel Prize.[35] Much of Barton's Nobel work was carried out just before the revolution in physical methods. As a result some of it became redundant, notably due to improved X-ray crystallography. Further, the tedious semi-empirical calculations of the kind that he carried out in the 1950s, using logarithm tables and a slide rule, became far easier once cheap electronic computation became available.

Wilkinson and E. O. Fischer won the Nobel Prize in 1973 for 'their pioneering work, performed independently, on the chemistry of the organometallic, so-called sandwich compounds.'[36] Like Barton, Wilkinson carried out important work after his initial breakthrough, including further work on the metallocenes. Interestingly both Wilkinson and Fischer looked forward rather than back in their Nobel lectures. Both men spoke more about their current research than about their Nobel discoveries, perhaps with some reason. Wilkinson may well have believed that his later work was more important, that it influenced the Nobel committee in their decision, and that he should therefore talk about it. His lecture contains little on ferrocene and far more on what interested him in 1973, namely homogeneous catalysis and his work on metal alkyls (discussed in section 9.4 below).

However, in his brief mention of ferrocene, he did recount how he arrived at its structure. As discussed in the previous chapter both he and Woodward believed that, given the stability of the new compound, the structure proposed by Pauson and Kealy, entailing two Fe–C σ bonds, was incorrect. In his lecture Wilkinson stated that, in thinking about this, he remembered reading about the binding of ethylene in Zeise's Salt, and of butadiene in Reihlen's compound, $(C_4H_6)Fe(CO)_3$.[37] The latter was a species he had read about in Eméleus and Anderson's 1938 textbook (see Chapter Six). Further, he had learned about resonance from reading Linus Pauling's *The Nature of the Chemical Bond* (1939) and speculated that, if all the aryl carbon atoms in ferrocene were equivalent, then the cyclopentadienide anion could behave in a way similar to benzene.[38] He then showed that ferrocene was diamagnetic and, by using IR and NMR spectroscopy (the latter not reported in his original paper), that its H atoms were equivalent. This gave grounds for his idea that the carbon atoms were equivalent and possibly π–bonded to the metal. Given these various considerations he intuited the sandwich structure for *bis*-cyclopentadienyl iron (ferrocene). Although π–bonding accounted for the compound's stability, whether or not π–bonded ligands actually existed was debated for a while longer, not only for ferrocene but also for Zeise's salt. (See Chapter Eight, Note 36 for further details, and for the role of others in Wilkinson's discovery.)

9.4 Research: (a) Inorganic Chemistry, (b) Organic Chemistry, (c) Physical Chemistry

In 1965 the three departmental sections were still headed by Barrer, Barton, and Wilkinson. In 1978 John Albery succeeded Barrer as professor of physical chemistry, and Charles Rees succeeded Barton as professor of organic chemistry. Also in 1978, Alan Fersht was appointed the Wolfson Research Professor of the Royal Society. He headed a small sub-section in biological chemistry. Wilkinson remained head of department until 1988. Although the Linstead constitution was given up in 1976, the three main sections continued much as before but without the old financing formula. Major reorganisation, including the dissolution of the old sections, came later under the headship of David Phillips (see Chapter Ten).[39]

By 1976 it was clear that much in chemistry had changed. There was a new emphasis on synthesis and on the theoretical understanding of reaction mechanisms. This was in part due to the increasing importance of materials science and biomedical research. Further, new physical methods had swept away traditional analytical procedures, gravimetric and degradational;[40] and the integration of computer technology in spectroscopic and crystallographic instrumentation allowed the determination of molecular structures at speeds previously unthinkable. In 1976 a departmental instrument committee was set up, responsible for the operation of all large research instruments and for the smaller ones used in teaching. Physical instruments and services became centralised and were no longer operated by the separate sections. In the 1980s some services were further centralised under the University of London Inter-Collegiate Research Service (ULIRS). Two of these services were run from IC, a Raman service (administered by WPG) and an X-ray powder service.

(a) Inorganic Chemistry

For Wilkinson this was a productive period. He and his co-workers published roughly 40 papers on homogeneous catalysis, 50 on metal alkyls, and 170 on novel or unusual compounds, often with X-ray structures. Most significant was his work on homogeneous catalysis and metal alkyl chemistry. With respect to the former, he focussed almost exclusively on the six platinum metals, particularly rhodium and ruthenium (he called Rh, Ru and Re 'the three R's', treating rhenium as an honorary platinum metal).[41] His most innovative use of these metals was in the homogeneous hydrogenation of alkenes to alkanes, and in hydroformylation.[42] In 1965 he published some preliminary notes showing that $RhCl(PPh_3)_3$ would catalyse the hydrogenation of alkenes and alkynes, and that *mer*-$RhCl_3(PPh_3)_3$ and other rhodium complexes would, with $CO + H_2$, hydroformylate alkenes to aldehydes. A year later he published a comprehensive, now classic, paper (with for Wilkinson an uncharacteristically long unpunctuated title) on $RhCl(PPh_3)_3$, now universally known as Wilkinson's catalyst, the first effective homogeneous hydrogenation catalyst.[43] This remarkable discovery led to further work on a plethora of related reactions (e.g., oxidative addition of substrates). Although too air-sensitive for extensive commercial use, the catalyst is used in the fine chemicals industry for deuteriation and tritiation reactions. Wilkinson is even more celebrated for his work on RhH(CO)(PPh$_3$)$_3$, often incorrectly also called Wilkinson's catalyst. Although not the first to make this species, he was the first to realise its remarkable potential as a hydroformylation catalyst. It is used mainly for the relatively low-temperature hydroformylation of propene to n-and iso-butyraldehydes, and for similar conversions of industrial importance.[44]

As mentioned, metal alkyls feature in Wilkinson's Nobel Prize lecture of 1973. Between 1965 and 1985 he made about 80 new alkyl complexes of 11 transition metals, many of them homoleptic (i.e., the alkyl groups are the only ligands). He was well aware of the historical ties of this work to that of his predecessors at IC: Frankland, of course, who made the first alkyls of zinc, mercury and tin (Chapter Three), and William Pope (Chapter Four) who, in 1907, made alkyls of gold and platinum. Wilkinson's first alkyl complex, Cr^{IV}(CH$_2$SiMe$_3$)$_4$ with the bulky trimethysilylmethyl ligand, was made in 1970. However, the most extraordinary of his new discoveries were the methyl complexes, since they defied the accepted wisdom that transition-metal alkyl complexes were inherently unstable and that alkyls could not coordinate to metal centres in high oxidation states — the latter normally requiring electronegative ligands such as fluoride. Wilkinson proved the doubters wrong. His first success was the synthesis, in 1972, of the complex hexamethyltungsten, W(CH$_3$)$_6$, from methyllithium, and WCl$_6$ in ether. He published this result in a short 25 line note.[45] To characterise the many new alkyls that followed, Wilkinson typically used a range of physical techniques such as multinuclear NMR, photo-electron, ESR, and vibrational spectroscopies, as well as X-ray crystallography.

Among those working with Wilkinson in this period were Richard A. Andersen, Manfred Bochmann, John Bradley, Bruno Chaudret, George Christou, Ernesto Carmona Guzmán, David Cole-Hamilton, Richard Jones, Konstantinos (Kostas) Mertis and, a little later, Andrew Barron. Andersen, a postdoctoral fellow, is now professor of chemistry at the University of California (Berkeley). He told us, that the two years he spent with Wilkinson, 1974–1976, 'were the most enjoyable of my life because all I had to do was chemistry. ... I evolved from being a kid from Wyoming into an organometallic chemist in the London town.' He told us of the help he received from 'Geoff,' and that he made many lifelong friends while working in the lab.[46] Bochmann, a Marburg BSc, gained his PhD with Wilkinson in 1979. He was a coauthor of the final, 1996, edition of Cotton and Wilkinson's *Advanced Inorganic Chemistry*, and today is head of the school of chemistry at the University of East Anglia. Chaudret was a doctoral student and is now Director of Research at the CNRS in Toulouse. Christou, who gained his PhD with Abel in Exeter, was appointed a temporary lecturer (1982–83). He worked on thiolate complexes and is now Distinguished professor of chemistry at Florida State University. Guzmán, a postdoctoral fellow from 1974–1977, is now head of the chemistry department at the Universidad de Sevilla. He and Chaudret were winners of the RSC Sir Geoffrey Wilkinson Award in 2007 and 2009 respectively. David Cole-Hamilton came for an interview just after Wilkinson returned from the Nobel ceremony in Stockholm. He recounted that on first entering Wilkinson's office, Wilkinson 'threw the Nobel Medal at me. I caught it and got the job' — namely a postdoctoral fellowship, 1974–1975, followed by a temporary lectureship, 1975–1978.[47] Cole-Hamilton, who said he found Wilkinson inspirational, was awarded the RSC Corday–Morgan Prize in 1983 and was the first to be given the Sir Edward Frankland fellowship in 1984. Jones and Barron were undergraduate and PhD students in the department. Jones won the RSC Meldola Medal in 1983 and is now a professor at the University of Texas (Austin). Barron, a winner of both the RSC Meldola (1990) and Corday–Morgan (1995) medals, left the department for eight years at Harvard.[48] For Bradley and Mertis see Note 45.

Wilkinson won many awards in addition to the Nobel Prize and was offered several honorary degrees; he responded positively to only a few. Similarly, he gave only a small number of the named lectures he was invited to present.[49] He was elected FRS in 1965, won the Lavoisier Medal of the French Chemical Society in 1968, was knighted in 1976, gave the first Mond lecture in 1980, and was the first to win the RSC Frankland award in 1983. In 1983 he won the University of Pisa's Galileo Medal, in 1981 the Royal Society's Royal Medal and, in 1987, the RSC Longstaff prize. He was awarded the Royal Society's Davy Medal shortly before his death in 1996.[50]

Still working in the inorganic section during this period were Eric Roberts and John Welch, by the 1970s the longest serving members of the department. Roberts retired in 1975 and Welch in 1982. Also in the section were Wilkinson's early appointees, Dennis Evans, Les Pratt, David Goodgame, and Margaret Goodgame. Sadly illness led to Pratt's early retirement in 1988.[51] Evans continued with his innovative research until his premature death in 1990. He was elected FRS in 1981 and given a personal chair in the same year. Using a range of spectroscopic techniques, he studied hydrogen bonding in some complex cyanic acids, main-group fluoro and oxygen-donor complexes, and the structures of Grignard reagents and metal alkyl complexes in solution, showing also that divalent lanthanides could form Grignard-like compounds.[52] He also investigated the chemistry of beryllium; this latter work resulted in a posthumous paper published in 1992. It begins with the sentence 'Beryllium is the most toxic non-radioactive element in the Periodic Table.'[53] It appears that Evans pushed the limits of safety to the very end of his life.[54]

Using a wide range of physical techniques, David Goodgame worked in the area of synthetic coordination chemistry and its application in the fields of medicine, environmental chemistry, and new materials. He was made a reader in 1976 (a rare promotion in this period), was Senior Tutor from 1988–1996, and received a personal chair in 1996.[55] Margaret Goodgame specialised in the synthesis and characterisation of metal ion complexes with ligands of biological importance; and in the applications of spectroscopy to inorganic chemistry.[56] In 1962, John Avery came to the department as an assistant lecturer while still working on his PhD. He was appointed at the suggestion of Ron Mason (see Chapter Eight) who wanted help in applying quantum theory to some biological problems.[57] On gaining his PhD Avery was given a lectureship and began a collaboration with Janos Ladik, of the Hungarian Academy of Sciences, to determine the electronic structure of a number of polypeptides and polynucleotides. An early computer user, Avery was given time (in the middle of the night) on the unreliable University of London's Ferranti Mercury machine. Things improved after IBM gave IC a 7090 computer (programmes written on punched cards). Avery was the founding editor of *The Journal of Bioenergetics and Biomembranes*, serving from 1969–1980. Atkinson wrote that he was 'greatly appreciated but very little understood.'[58] This was true, and the department was sorry to see him leave for a position at the University of Copenhagen in 1973.

Two of Wilkinson's 1960s appointees, William P. (Bill) Griffith and John F. Gibson were mentioned in Chapter Eight. Since returning to the department in 1962, Griffith has published on all the transition metals, and on most of the lanthanides. In the period of this chapter he synthesised a range of coordination complexes, examining their structures in both the solid state and solution with the use of physical methods, notably Raman and NMR spectroscopy. He was interested also in the application of some complexes as catalysts for organic oxidations, notably complexes of the six platinum-group metals, and shared two students with Steve Ley for aspects of this work.[59] Gibson was appointed as a lecturer in 1965 and worked on the spectroscopy (particularly ESR) of transition metal complexes and metal-containing proteins and their relevance to biological and clinical problems.[60]

Joining the section a little later were Brent Young and Derek Woollins. Young arrived in 1977 as a Hercules Research Fellow and temporary lecturer. He collaborated with Wilkinson before leaving for a lectureship at Goldsmith's College in 1980, returning a year later to a lectureship. Young's research was on reaction mechanisms involving (or mediated by) organometallic derivatives of d-block elements. With mechanism in view, he carried out the synthesis and characterisation of several new compounds, and studied the chemical kinetics of some thermolytic, photolytic and electrolytic reactions.[61] He was a popular lecturer but took early retirement in 2001. Woollins came to the department as a 'new blood' lecturer in 1983. A synthesist, he worked on main group chemistry, metalla–sulphur–nitrogen compounds and phosphorus-selenium chemistry.[62]

In the 1960s and 1970s, analytical chemistry was a thriving subsection of inorganic chemistry, soon to be transformed by new physical methods and computer technology. Thomas (Tom) West came to the department from the University of Birmingham in 1963 and two years later was appointed professor of analytical chemistry.[63] He created an excellent research group that included staff members Roy Dagnall, Bernard Fleet, Barry Sharp, and Gordon Kirkbright. Kirkbright, Dagnall, and Fleet were students of West in Birmingham.[64] The group worked, though not exclusively, on atomic absorption and atomic fluorescence spectroscopy, applying atomic spectroscopy to flame media and radio frequency plasmas, and carrying out sub-micro analyses down to 10^{-13}–10^{-14} g. Innovations included microwave excited atomic line devices, rapid scan photon counting, and ruby-laser sampling. Their work attracted many MSc and PhD students who were supported by the SRC and ARC (later AFRC). In the early 1970s analytical chemistry attracted more industrial funding than any other group in the department.

Kirkbright came to the department with West but, as mentioned, he left for a professorship in Manchester in 1980.[65] Fleet was appointed in 1965 and supervised some MSc and PhD students working on the application of computers to the control and recording of analytical measurements — but he left in 1970 and set up a company in Toronto. Sharp, a PhD student at IC, worked with West on some of the techniques mentioned above. He joined the staff as a lecturer in 1972 but moved to Aberdeen with West in 1975.[66] Fred Alder, appointed a lecturer in 1976, left in 1980 and was replaced by Richard (Dick) D. Snook, another of West's IC PhD students.[67] West resigned in 1975, but remained a visiting professor until 1978. However, with no further support the sub-section withered away.[68]

(b) Organic Chemistry

I consider that originality is the most important quality in academic research. Thus the invention of new reactions has been a major activity in my life from about 1960 onwards. Before that time, my new reactions were discovered by accident.

If you know, in the academic world, how to do a reaction, you should not do it. You should only work on reactions that are potentially important and that you do not know how to do! (Barton[69])

In this period Barton continued his research into reaction mechanisms, but moved from the direct study of natural product molecules to the development of synthetic methods for making, or structurally modifying, biologically active molecules. Despite difficult economic circumstances he managed an active laboratory with many doctoral students and postdoctoral fellows. Indeed he found room and funding for almost anyone he thought capable of research, filling his laboratory at the college and placing others at the Research Institute for Medicine and Chemistry (RIMAC) in Cambridge MA, where he worked with the Director, Maurice Pechet, on corticosteroids (see Chapter Eight). He also ran a laboratory at Chelsea College where his lieutenant was Robin Boar. The Whiffen Laboratory, designed for 24 after its reconstruction under Heilbron, could hold up to about 30 people.[70] Jim Hanson, who worked there as a postdoctoral fellow in 1963–1964, wrote that it 'ran like a machine' in part due to its excellent technician, Dennis Aldrich. Nonetheless it was showing signs of age and one can understand why Barton was impatient for the new building. According to Hanson, dust and rust showered down from the overhead steam pipes when the steam baths were turned on each morning; there were open drains in the floor, and open waste bins by each working place. Once, after someone had dumped some sodium sulfate used to dry an ether extract into a bin, Barton flicked his cigar ash in the same direction. Watching the inevitable, he remarked 'we won't do that again will we.' The lab had a glass roof and was very hot in summer and cold in winter. The summer heat led some students to sit in the cold room for short periods; others simply abandoned their clothes and wore just lab coats.[71] Barton arranged for a tea/coffee trolley to arrive three times a day at 10:00, 15:00, and 17:30 so as to discourage anyone from taking breaks away from the lab. Instead they were encouraged to join in serious discussion, and a blackboard was placed near the tea urns for writing out reaction mechanisms. More than one person has recorded that they were afraid, or in awe, of Barton, and that they hesitated to join in discussions when he was present. However, being shot down in flames during a tea-break discussion did not necessarily lower one's reputation with the Professor. Barton genuinely enjoyed chemical debate.

During the early 1970s the synthesis of tetracyclines was an active research project, one that made use of photochemical reactions of the type Barton had pioneered earlier. Also active was the biosynthesis of sterols, notably of ergosterol.[72] Several Australian postdocs worked in the Whiffen Lab at the time. One of them, Robert Stick, joined the staff for two years. He stated that, although he was assured that Barton had mellowed since winning the Nobel Prize, he 'still ruled the roost with an iron fist' and, in the weekly meetings, 'any weakness was seized upon immediately.' All was not work, however. Stick recalled the regular Friday night poker games — not confined to Fridays since they often resumed when 'word was spread that the "old man" had left for one of his many consulting trips to the USA.' On Sundays there was a laboratory walk around some part of London 'with a stop for lunch and a pint or two.' Stick noted that David Widdowson was a good friend to the Australians and helped them repair their 'heaps'.[73] Widdowson was appointed assistant lecturer in 1967 and lecturer in 1968. During the 1970s he worked with Barton on the biosynthesis of alkaloids and began some work on synthetic model systems incorporating features of natural processes, notably biologically interesting enzymic redox reactions. Widdowson said that he found Barton remote and always called him 'Professor Barton.'[74]

Stick recalls having learned much while at IC, not only from Barton and Widdowson but also from Tony Barrett, Stuart McCombie, Philip Magnus and, later, Steve Ley. The eponymous Barton–McCombie deoxygenation reaction for alcohol deoxygenation to alkyls came about in connection with work being carried out by chemists at RIMAC and Schering–Plough. They were seeking a way of removing hydroxyl groups from aminoglycoside antibiotics so as to increase resistance to bacterial degradation.[75] Free radicals were invoked in a theory called phenolic oxidative coupling used to explain how complex structures such as morphine were made within plants and how, perhaps, they could be made in the laboratory.

Over his career Barton received much recognition; not all his awards can be mentioned here. In addition to the Nobel Prize, he was elected FRS in 1954 and received the Royal Society's Davy Medal in 1961. He gave the Bakerian lecture in 1970, won the Royal Medal in 1972, and the Copley Medal in 1980. He was knighted in 1972, made Chevalier de la Légion d'Honneur in 1974, served as President of the Chemical Society, 1973–1974, received eight honorary degrees, and was especially pleased to be recognised on a postage stamp when the Post Office issued its series on British Nobel Laureates in Chemistry in 1977. Appropriately there is a Barton Prize awarded to the undergraduate who performs best in the third year organic lecture course. Barton enjoyed the recognition that came his way and would travel far for his honorary degrees, to give named lectures, or to receive other awards. Wilkinson and Barton jokingly called each other the 'absent professor,' Barton because of his many travels. Wilkinson cared less for honours and travel, and enjoyed spending time with his family.[76] He was named 'absent' because he usually arrived in the department at least two hours after Barton. However, he often worked late and returned to his Bayswater home by walking across Kensington Gardens. On one occasion, after the gates to the park had closed, he climbed over the railings and was apprehended by a policeman. Asked for his name he uncharacteristically pulled rank and replied 'Professor Sir Geoffrey Wilkinson'. According to Wilkinson, the policeman replied, 'yes, and I'm the Queen of Sheba'. Wilkinson was not charged.

We can mention only a few of the many other people who worked with Barton in this period. Phil Magnus FRS, already mentioned, was a former prize-winning undergraduate who gained his PhD with Barton in 1968. He did not tie himself to the lab bench in true Bartonian fashion, however, and spent a fair bit of time on the Richmond Park golf course. Nonetheless he was soon made a member of staff and continued his PhD work on the synthesis of tetracyclines and on new synthetic routes to the terpenoids. Although Magnus appears to have been a Barton favourite, he later stated that he was disenchanted with the Barton regime and, seeing little prospect of promotion, left for Indiana University in 1975.[77] Tony Barrett, another outstanding undergraduate, joined Barton for his PhD in 1973, working on toxisterols.[78] He remembers Barton differently, not only as a brilliant chemist but as a kind friend, and mentor. In 1975 W. B. (Willie) Motherwell joined Barton on a postdoctoral fellowship. He had a PhD from the University of Glasgow where his supervisor was Ralph Raphael (for Raphael, Chapter Seven). As mentioned, Motherwell moved with Barton to the CNRS laboratory in 1977 where he was soon appointed *Chargé de Recherches*.[79] Barton changed the direction of his research at that time and the two worked together closely on some organo-bismuth chemistry and what became known as the Gif system of oxidation (of hydrocarbons). They published many joint papers into the 1990s.[80] Motherwell returned to the department as a lecturer in 1983, and is discussed further in Chapter Ten.

Also joining the staff in this period were Gerald (Gerry) Moss, Peter Sammes, Laurie Phillips, Brian Challis, Steve Ley, and Tony Barrett. Moss, a former undergraduate in the department, gained his PhD at Cambridge. He was appointed an assistant lecturer in 1964 but left after two years for a position at Queen Mary College. Sammes, Phillips and

Barrett gained both their BSc and PhD degrees in the department. Sammes worked closely with Barton on photochemical routes to the tetracyclines, routes to novel alkaloids, and on the chemistry of penicillin.[81] He joined the staff in 1964 leaving for a chair at City University in 1975.[82] Phillips was an NMR specialist who studied organic fluorine compounds using ^{19}F and ^{13}C, the latter then newly available. According to Atkinson, he 'presided over an increasingly sophisticated array of instrumentation' before leaving in 1979 to work for Shell.[83] When David Turner left for Oxford in 1967, Challis was appointed as his replacement to carry out radiochemical work.[84] Challis' interests were fairly broad and included reaction mechanics, stereochemical studies on sterols and terpenes, and theoretical modelling of biological systems, notably with regard to the mechanism of tumour induction. The latter related to his work on nitrosamines as possible carcinogens. Steve Ley came to the department as a postdoctoral fellow in 1974 having gained his BSc and PhD from Loughborough University of Technology, and having spent two years at Ohio State University as a postdoctoral fellow with Leo Paquette. With interests similar to Barton's, he was to move natural product research forward in novel ways. He much impressed Barton, no easy feat, and was given a lectureship at a time (1976) when few were given. In 1983, Flowers agreed to Wilkinson's request that Ley be made a professor — skipping the readership stage — so as to keep him from accepting an offer in the United States as Tony Barrett had just done.[85] Barrett was another exceptional case, one of very few people to be appointed at IC in the mid 1970s. Younger than Ley, he left in 1983 to take up a full professorship at Northwestern University. He did so on Barton's advice, so as to move his career forward at a time when promotion was very difficult.[86] He returned as a Professor in 1993 and is discussed further in Chapter Ten. Ley and Barrett collaborated on a number of projects and, in 1982, shortly before Barrett left, they won a large grant of £200,000 from the Wolfson Foundation to work on the newly discovered avermectins and milbemycins, natural products that showed unprecedented biological activity as antifeedants (slimming pills for insects, as Ley put it) while being relatively non-toxic to mammals.[87]

Charles Rees, who succeeded Barton as Hofmann Professor in 1978, was a synthetic chemist known for his work on heterocyclic systems.[88]

During the 1980s he used nitrene intermediates in the synthesis of a range of natural products, and continued also his work on sulphur–nitrogen ring systems.[89] Less driven than Barton, Rees is remembered as a convivial colleague and as being, perhaps, overly deferential to his predecessor. For example, Barton retained some students in the department after his move to Gif-sur-Yvette and occasionally returned to see how they were getting along. Until their research wound down, Rees vacated his office for Barton whenever he appeared.[90] Rees attended many departmental seminars, not only those in organic chemistry. He often asked questions, always politely, but with the occasional bite. At one inorganic chemistry seminar, after looking to be asleep, he joined the discussion with 'I'm only a plain old organic chemist, but I have the feeling that five slides back you showed us a pentavalent carbon.'[91] He had a good eye for formulae and structures, and could write out complicated ones from memory. In 1979 one of his former doctoral students, Christopher (Chris) Moody, joined the department as lecturer. He, too, was interested in heterocyclic compounds and the synthesis of biologically active molecules.[92] Also in 1979 Rees invited his friend and former King's College colleague, Sir John Cadogan, to be a visiting professor in the department, a position Cadogan held until 2002.[93] Rees is remembered for his good, if sometimes blue, after-dinner speeches. A dapper dresser, he always wore a bow tie — on formal occasions related to chemistry it was dyed in Perkin's mauve. He was awarded the CS Tilden prize in 1974, the Pedler lectureship in 1984, and was the recipient of the first RSC award in heterocyclic chemistry in 1980 — this award was named for him after his death. He was elected FRS in 1974, and was president of the RSC, 1992–1994.

Henry Rzepa and Edward (Ed) Smith, joined the organic section in the late 1970s.[94] Rzepa, an undergraduate in the department, worked with Brian Challis for his PhD. After a postdoctoral fellowship in the United States, he returned to the department on a North Atlantic Treaty Organization (NATO) fellowship in 1977. Appointed a lecturer in 1980, he became the department's expert in applying computational methods to chemistry.[95] Smith was a prizewinning undergraduate. He gained his BSc in 1968 before moving to Exeter for his PhD. After a postdoctoral fellowship at the ETH, a period working at the University of Karlsruhe, and then at Shell, he returned to the department in 1978 on an SRC advanced fellowship.

Appointed a lecturer in 1982, his research concerned the use of mechanistic knowledge to develop new methods in organic synthesis. In 2009 he joined the department of biophysics as a senior research fellow.[96]

As mentioned, Alan Fersht came to the department as the Royal Society Wolfson Research Professor in 1978. He headed a small sub-section in biological chemistry and studied enzyme reactions together with David Blow,[97] professor of biophysics, and Brian Hartley, professor of biochemistry.[98] Fersht at first focussed on the effects of physico–chemical forces on DNA, and the ways in which enzymes are able to overcome them. Later he moved to study the structure, activity, and folding of proteins. In 1986 he won a special equipment grant of £450,000, a huge sum at the time. Much of it went towards the purchase of a 500 MHz NMR spectrometer and on computers that allowed the display of protein structures and behaviours.[99] For more on Fersht see Chapter Ten.

(c) Physical Chemistry

This section saw little change until Barrer and Tompkins retired in 1977. Lovat Rees continued his zeolite research into the 1980s and was appointed to a personal chair in 1987. By then he appears to have moved increasingly toward theoretical work and, among other things, wrote a major computer programme to predict the kinetics of ion exchange in zeolites. In 1987 he was joined for three years by John Meurig Thomas FRS, the newly appointed Director of the Royal Institution, who came to the department as a visiting professor. Rees retired in 1993.[100] As noted above, Bernard Atkinson took on a heavy administrative load in this period; but he also carried out some photochemical studies of quinones in excited states.

Although there were several physical chemists on the staff, few were young, something that became a problem with the employment freeze of the 1970s. Those still under 40 in 1965 were David Hayward, David Bassett, David Nicholson, Martin Sutcliffe, Neville Parsonage, Michael Spiro, and Bryan Levitt. They were joined in 1966 by Maurice George. As mentioned in Chapter Eight, Hayward worked closely with Tompkins, but his own interest was in the application of molecular beam scattering to the study of surfaces.[101] Bassett came to the department from the National Chemical Laboratory where he had set up Britain's first field ion microscope. An outstanding experimentalist, he was appointed a lecturer in 1965 and used field ion microscopy to study molecular and atomic diffusion on transition metal surfaces.[102] When John Albery succeeded Barrer as professor of physical chemistry, he won a Science and Engineering Research Council (SERC) grant for an Electron Spectroscopy for Chemical Analysis (ESCA) instrument (photoelectron spectroscopy) that Bassett set up. Joining him in this work was the department's first 'new blood' lecturer, Russell (Russ) G. Egdell.[103] In these various ways surface chemistry remained an active field in the department. Maurice George was appointed a lecturer in 1966; a specialist in polymer kinetics, he built a research group working on the synthesis of ionic and grafted polyurethanes and their properties. He was also to collaborate with Albery on membranes for ion-selective electrodes.[104] Sutcliffe began some work on molecular transitions, but had a largely teaching career before leaving in 1987.

Parsonage, Nicholson, Levitt, and Spiro worked in the department for many years. Parsonage, a thermodynamicist and theoretician, was appointed a lecturer in 1960, took up the cryogenic work started by Kington (see Chapter Eight), and carried out calorimetric studies on various materials down to $1°K$.[105] When, in the late 1960s the University of London acquired a Ferranti mercury computer, he and Nicholson decided to make use of it. Nicholson had come to the department as a British Petroleum (BP) postdoctoral fellow in 1960 to work with Barrer; he joined the staff in 1963.[106] Together they designed Grand Canonical Ensemble Monte Carlo (GCEMC) simulations in the study of physisorption — previously only chemisorption simulations had been tried. With Les Rowley, a postdoctoral fellow, they designed a method suited to non-uniform three-dimensional systems and applied it first to the Lennard-Jones model for argon absorbed on a graphite surface. They successfully predicted some thermodynamic properties previously found by experimentalists.[107]

Levitt came to the department from Cambridge in 1962; his interests were in gas phase kinetics. He constructed and used shock tubes for the observation of very fast high temperature reactions, notably the dissociation of small molecules. His work on combustion kinetics was of interest in a number of areas, including in the modelling of rocket propulsion and heat release.[108] But he soon moved into departmental administration where he made a considerable and long-lasting contribution. He introduced an open day for schoolchildren, starting in 1970, and was especially active in developing computer skills in the department (see subsequent paragraphs). Spiro joined the department in 1960 as a lecturer and shared a large office with Parsonage in the recently vacated physics end of the RCS building.[109] His research was in the area of electrode reactions, transference numbers (the Spiro equation is still used for these), and in the kinetics of heterogeneous and homogeneous catalysis in solution. In this connection he discovered the catalytic properties of Pt electrodes in some solutions.[110]

Electrochemistry received a boost with the appointment of John Albery as professor of physical chemistry in 1978.[111] Albery was a colourful new broom after Barrer's long reign. A fine chemist, noted for his earlier studies of the kinetics of electrode surfaces using spinning platinum ring-disc electrodes, he redirected some of this work toward photovoltaic effects that he thought could be used to harness solar energy. As Wilkinson had foreseen, this was a fashionable topic that drew much support both from the research councils and from industry. Albery's outgoing personality, his energy and enthusiasm, drew many students to his research group, and led to collaboration with others in the department, not only electrochemists but those working in the fields of polymers and surfaces. Electrodes developed by Albery depended for their use on new computer technology, and on rapidly responding sensors.[112] In that connection, and together with Levitt, he founded a microprocessor laboratory which helped in advancing the computer control of many departmental instruments. The laboratory was supported by the Laboratory of the Government Chemist, and several of its staff came to IC to take a short post-experience course on the application of microprocessors to chemical measurement. Albery also invited Sir George (later Lord) Porter, a specialist in fast reactions who had extended his techniques into the nanosecond region, to join the department as a visiting professor.[113]

As mentioned in the Eight Chapter, Barrer appointed Donald (Don) Rogers to a new readership in chemical crystallography in 1961. He was given Welch's former teaching duties.[114] Rogers, known mainly for X-ray powder crystallography, and for the Rogers–Flack parameter, was given a personal chair in 1965. He inherited a Siemens automatic single-crystal diffractometer that was handed over to chemistry when the physics department moved into its new building. The machine was controlled by punched paper tape, and its output was fed into an offsite computer. It was slow and yielded data for the analysis of about one crystal per month. In 1975, before resigning from the headship, Barrer created a new sub-section in chemical crystallography and Rogers was appointed to an offi-cial departmental chair in that field. His main interest was in the structure of natural products, and in synthetics of biological significance. In the mid-1970s he was working on molecules such as cephalosporin and strep-tomycin and, in 1965, was joined by Welch's former PhD student, Andrzej C. Skapski. By 1975, however, Skapski was working on organometallic and coordination complexes mainly of interest to the inorganic chemists.

David J. Williams came to the department as a technician in 1960 and joined Rogers' group in 1962. In 1964 he took leave to take a physics BSc, returning in 1968 as Rogers' research assistant. He soon began work on alkaloids and terpenes, molecules of interest to the organic chemists, gain-ing a PhD under Rogers in 1978. When Rogers took early retirement in 1980, work in crystallography was reorganised. The section was no longer financed by the physical chemistry section, instead, Skapski's work was supported by inorganic chemistry, and Williams' by organic chemistry — though he solved many structures for the inorganic chemists. By then, however, Williams was studying the structures of fifteen-membered organic rings and the geometries of crown ethers.[115] He was appointed a lecturer in 1982, promoted to a readership in 1991, and made professor of structural chemistry in 1996. Skapski and Williams shared equipment which, by the 1980s, included a modern X-ray diffractometer controlled by up-to-date on-line computer technology. The pace and accuracy of struc-ture determination improved considerably. The X-ray lab is remembered also for its Christmas parties. Williams would prepare a turkey with all the trimmings for about a dozen guests. On one occasion there was insufficient cutlery and Derek Woollins went to borrow some from the Senior Common Room. Observed removing a suspiciously large number of items, he was chased back to the department by a member of the catering staff; but he eluded his pursuer and made it safely back to the lab.

9.5 Undergraduate Teaching and MSc Courses

By 1965 most of the laboratory teaching, lectures, and examination ques-tions reflected the developments discussed in Chapter Eight. However, because each section was taught independently there was some duplication. For example, each section had similar polarimetry experiments in their undergraduate laboratories. This prompted Barrer to ask Spiro to chair a committee (the course committee, still in existence) to look at avoiding such duplication in both lecture and lab courses. By the early 1970s the problem was being addressed, and the undergraduate courses modernised. The first year laboratory was the last to change. Indeed, students still spent many hours carrying out traditional volumetric, qualitative, and gravimetric analyses. The balances used had pan scales that had to be calibrated. The new foundation course, introduced in 1974, eliminated much of this. It also provided more basic instruction since many incoming students were not well prepared for the undergraduate degree.

As mentioned in Chapter Eight, in the early 1950s the second year organic laboratory course was modernised by Weedon, the third year laboratory course by Elvidge and Rydon, and the third year lecture courses by Rydon. These various courses were further modernised when Barton returned to the department. The second and third year inorganic laboratory courses were modernised after Wilkinson had a few new lecturers in place. David Goodgame, for example, was given the task of updating the second year laboratory — phasing out advanced qualitative and quantitative analysis, and replacing it with instruction in new synthetic methods. The analysis that remained was microanalysis (this also became a departmental service). The reasons for the turn to microanalysis were various: cheaper, safer, and more environmentally friendly. The scientific instrument trade responded to this more general trend and many instruments for microanalysis came on the market. On average about 12 students per year chose the analytical chemistry option in their third year. Les Ebdon, a student in the late 1960s, stated 'I have a strong strategic sense and I realised that analytical chemistry was going to come up very quickly. And so it has proved'. Ebden stayed for a PhD in analytical chemistry and, after a varied and successful academic career, was appointed to head the Office for Fair Access (OFFA) in 2011.[116] The third year laboratories for both inorganic and physical chemistry introduced students to new physical methods including electroanalytical chemistry taught by Bernard Fleet. When the C1 building opened in 1971, the laboratory courses in the second and third years were updated yet further. In part this came about because the new building prompted the staff to rethink what they were doing, and in part because the building came with some equipment money which was spent on spectroscopic and other instruments that the staff needed for their own research.

Safety rules were more lax in the 1960s and 1970s than they were by the 1990s. Lab coats and safety glasses were, however, required. Students had free use of many chemicals that are now restricted (benzene, for example), and carried out reactions that had to be dropped when new government safety rules came into effect after 1988. In the 1960s Bunsen burners were routinely used, open flames not yet being seen as especially hazardous; by the 1980s heating mantles had almost entirely replaced them. If students still wanted to use a Bunsen burner they had to sign for it. Quickfit glassware was new in the 1960s and undergraduates used it only occasionally. Most of the time they used rubber bungs or corks through which holes had to be bored for glass tubing. They sealed off glass capillaries for melting point determinations, and heated the chemicals indirectly, by suspending the capillaries in larger tubes containing Nujol (a viscous liquid paraffin). This procedure was overtaken by various automated melting point devices which came with ready made capillary tubes. The new devices were computerised in the 1980s and 1990s. Today's students can watch the melt digitally; those of the 1960s watched it first hand, sometimes with the aid of a magnifying glass. More generally, greater manual dexterity was needed for undergraduate work than it is today — though for experimental research it is of course needed as much as ever. The department continued to place great emphasis on practical skills including, by this period, computer skills.

As for the lectures, they, too, changed; those on descriptive chemistry gave way, though not entirely, to lectures on chemical bonding and mechanism in both organic and inorganic chemistry. New physical methods were also stressed. The descriptive material that remained related more to recent, rather than historical, discoveries. If faced with an examination question on the properties of rhenium, for example, students would be expected to write something about Professor Wilkinson's recent work. Similarly they needed to take note of Barton's research. Jeremy Sanders remembers that, in his second year lecture course, Barton handed out 'copies of his famous 1956 *Quarterly Reviews* article as the course notes and bible.'[117] Organic chemistry lectures and examinations included also new material on natural products and interesting syntheses. Kinetics, thermodynamics, and quantum theory remained the mainstay of physical chemistry lectures, with polymers, electrochemistry and spectroscopy having walk-on roles. John Avery gave a course on quantum theory which not only introduced students to the mathematical and computational tools needed, it included biographical details of the scientists who had contributed to the theory. News of the course reached the publisher McGraw Hill and Avery was asked to write a book based on his lectures, namely *The quantum theory of atoms, molecules, and photons* (1972).

In addition, students took two compulsory courses in the first year, one in mathematics and one in physics. In the second year they took an additional course in physics, mathematics or geology. There were also optional courses in scientific French and German; not optional, however, were the two translation tests that had to be taken before graduation — Russian could be substituted for one of the languages. The foreign language requirement was dropped in the mid-1970s. Linstead's compulsory, but not examined, course in the writing of English for third year students was dropped in 1964. In 1977 two joint BSc courses were introduced, chemistry and biochemistry, and chemistry and management science. A joint chemistry and biotechnology degree was offered later.

Computer programming was a much sought after skill and the first departmental course in FORTRAN, given by Bryan Levitt in 1971, became part of the second year programme. Henry Rzepa, a computer enthusiast already at school, took the course and recalled that some of his fellow students used 'four-letter words' as variables. In those days programmes were still key punched by female operatives, some of whom refused to key in the questionable words. As a result the programmes failed, and the guilty ones failed the course.[118] Levitt helped to bring computing skills to the department more generally. In 1977, he installed the first graphics terminal and, one year later, attached it and an IBM printer to a nascent departmental network.[119] He also wrote computer programmes to help with admission records and the processing of examination results, and he published a number of computer aids for chemists. In the 1980s Atkinson extended computer record keeping to the booking of lecture theatres and to the departmental inventory. Rzepa followed in

Levitt's footsteps and, in the 1980s, introduced a new undergraduate programming course on NMR simulations. By the 1980s, students were word processing and learning BASIC, and by the 1990s they were coming to terms with microcomputers, and acquiring computer simulation and data acquisition skills.[120]

In the late 1970s and early 1980s MSc courses were seen as useful not only from the viewpoint of vocational training, but as a way of bringing income to the college in a difficult time. Indeed, when the department went into deficit, it was criticised for having too few students enrolled in such courses. The earlier MSc course in food and drugs was no longer offered, and the MSc in agricultural chemistry ended in the late 1970s. There had been a few other short lived courses. Manfred Gordon, for example, set up a joint MSc course in materials with the metallurgy department, but it folded when he left in 1964. Don Rogers set up a chemical crystallography MSc in 1968, and Tom West together with Bernard Fleet set one up in analytical chemistry in 1966. Offered jointly with Chelsea College, it focussed on trace analysis using polarography and atomic spectroscopy, including radiofrequency and microwave-excited emission spectroscopy. It was heavily oversubscribed but enrolment was kept low. Overseas students were not allowed to outnumber the SRC-supported United Kingdom students, and only five such grants were given each year. By 1986, when Michael Spiro set up an MSc in chemical research, all the older MSc courses had been dropped.

End Notes

1. Eight new universities opened during the 1960s, including the Open University. In addition, 14 university colleges were given full university status.

2. IC was promised funding for a major expansion. Lionel Charles (Lord) Robbins, head of the economics department at the London School of Economics, was the Chair of the 1961 Committee of Enquiry into Higher Education (*Report of the Committee on Higher Education* (Cmnd 2154, 1963)). Before the new universities of the 1960s opened, about 4% of school leavers went to university and about 8% received other types of further education. The committee was asked to consider the ethical question of access, and the bureaucratic problem of delivery. Stating that justice

requires that there be places for all those able to benefit from higher education, it recommended increasing the number of university places from 216,000 to about 560,000 in three phases by the early 1980s. To achieve this it suggested elevating some technical and teacher-training colleges to universities, and that there be a total of about 60 universities. As to disciplines, it was deemed necessary to recognise 'the needs of the nation' and to open up places accordingly. The committee, with only one representative from Oxbridge, was set up by the Macmillan government but its report was dealt with by the Wilson government. Wilson had a clear view on what 'the needs of the nation' were. He wanted to see expansion in science and engineering, and believed that most state-funded research should benefit industry. Subsequent Prime Ministers, Callaghan, Heath, and Thatcher, believed much the same.

3. Linstead also wanted to see increased numbers in physics and mathematics. The new Robbins-related funding led to the demolition of the Imperial Institute, the construction of the central library, the Sherfield building, and several other buildings, mostly for the engineering departments. It also allowed for the development of Prince's Gardens and the construction of new student residences. Both the island block and Prince's Gardens were granted to IC in the 1950s with future expansion in mind. The first of the new residences, Weeks Hall, was built before the new funding.

4. Owen Saunders was Acting Rector until Penney took over in 1967.

5. An underlying reason for the sudden price rise was that President Nixon had earlier severed the link between the US dollar and the price of gold. The nominal price soared in this period, as oil producers claimed they were being paid in devalued dollars. One could argue that the OPEC crisis of 1973 was the tipping point for major changes in the funding and governance of universities worldwide. The price of oil rose even further after the Iranian revolution of 1979.

6. Already in 1967 the UGC set a senior to junior staff ratio of 35 percent. The college argued that this was unrealistic, but managed to reach 36.9 percent by October, 1969. The emphasis on 35 percent tied the college's hands on promotions and further fed the brain drain. As head of department, Wilkinson was unhappy that younger staff were, as he put it, 'defecting'. 'Why should IC be treated the same way as minor league universities?' he asked. ICL archives, B\Wilkinson; Wilkinson to Flowers, 5 May, 1978. In 1985 he wrote to Sir David Phillips FRS who was on the advisory board of the research councils, stating that more should be done to keep young chemists in the United Kingdom and that the university system needed

reform. He believed that young lecturers had too much routine teaching of the type carried out by postgraduate teaching assistants in the United States, that tenure was given too easily, and that those with tenure had too little prospect of promotion. The department, he wrote, had lost eight junior staff members and promising PhD graduates to the United States in the past year.

7. ICL archives, B\Wilkinson; Wilkinson to Joseph (draft), 24 May, 1984. In this period Wilkinson wrote a number of letters to politicians, including several to Margaret Thatcher. In one, congratulating her on her FRS, he wrote that he wanted to see more democracy at the Royal Society, a postal vote for the election of fellows, and an end to the 'self-perpetuating oligarchy'; Wilkinson to Thatcher, 12 July, 1983. The Thatcher government took note of his view that British universities adopt the United State system of tenure, but ignored his opinion that people in the financial world were earning 'ridiculous amounts.' He also named a top civil servant, Sir David Hancock, as someone who earned 'a vast amount more' than 'the combined salaries of Professors Albery, Fersht, and Ley.' Wilkinson to Thatcher, 31 July, 1985. (This was in the context of the government's Top Salaries Review Board set up at the time.) Earlier he had written to Thatcher with a plea for maintaining selectivity, and for privileging universities where major research is carried out. He thought it not a bad idea to assign undergraduate science teaching to the polytechnics and allow a select few universities to carry out postgraduate teaching and research; Wilkinson to Thatcher, 21 June, 1979. He was also opposed to increasing the number of Caribbean and Asian immigrants to the United Kingdom. Letters on this topic began during Harold Wilson's premiership and continued into Margaret Thatcher's. More amusing and less reactionary were letters to officials in the Soviet Embassy in London complaining about pirated copies of his textbook. He claimed, not unhappily, to have embarrassed the Foreign Office by sending copies of those letters to the press, and to the heads of chemistry departments at other universities. For reasons unclear, the Soviet ambassador insisted that his letters to the embassy be addressed to the Agricultural Councillor who turned out to be one of the close to 100 spies expelled by the British government in 1971. Wilkinson refused to accept a 1971 invitation from the USSR's Academy of Sciences unless they paid all his expenses and those of his entire family: first class tickets to Moscow, a stay in a first-class hotel, and spending money in lieu of lost royalties. Amazingly this was eventually agreed, but the Wilkinsons could find little to spend the money on. As a last resort Lise Wilkinson purchased

a fur coat, and Wilkinson a traditional fur hat which he proudly wore on his return. A later topic of correspondence was his opposition to the release of radioactive waste from Windscale into the sea; Wilkinson to Thatcher, 10 July, 1981. Wilkinson wrote many more letters to the prime ministers of the day, including to James Callaghan who he called 'Calorgas,' though presumably not in his correspondence. He also wrote several letters to his local MP about IC. For the correspondence, ICL archives; B\Wilkinson, sections F45–52.

8. For Flowers, (Smith, 2004). Lord Flowers was Rector of Imperial College, 1973–1985.

9. Of these, 16 were taking the joint chemistry/biochemistry BSc and 20 were taking the BSc in chemistry and management. ICL archives; B\Wilkinson, information notes sent to the Rector, February, 1985. The number of PhD students in 1985 was 116.

10. One problem of attracting good postdoctoral fellows was the high cost of London housing. Wilkinson wrote to Flowers, asking for housing support. ICL archives, B\Wilkinson: Wilkinson to Flowers, 1 February, 1980.

11. The numbers recovered in the 1990s when increased scholarship money was provided, and more funding came from the students' home countries.

12. Bernard Atkinson (1923–2009) was promoted to a senior lectureship in 1962, and made Senior Tutor in 1975. He was also appointed to the new position of Director of Undergraduate Studies in 1982. When he succeeded Welch as departmental administrator, Bryan Levitt succeeded him as director of undergraduate studies. Atkinson was later responsible for overseeing the construction of the C2 building. Many, including Wilkinson, saw him as an outstanding and accessible administrator. For Atkinson see also Chapter Eight.

13. Barrer held his chair until 1977 and then stayed on in the department as a Senior Research Fellow.

14. ICL archives B\Barton; 'The Constitution of the Chemistry Department,' typescript dated 17 March, 1975. Barton credited the success of the department both to wise appointments and to the Linstead constitution. He believed the IC department was the best in the country insofar as research was concerned. He noted that of the department's seven professors, four were FRS and two had won the Nobel Prize. By comparison, he noted, the department at UCL had nine professors, none of whom was FRS. He blamed that state of affairs on Sir Christopher Ingold who, earlier, had dissolved the departmental sections at UCL with the declaration 'chemistry is one.' And, while that was true in an intellectual sense, it was a bad decision.

Ingold, he wrote, dominated all aspects of chemistry for a decade but was one of the rare scientists capable of doing so; his successors were not. Barton also wanted a return to the pre-1970 system in which there was a head technician for each section and not a centralised technician service.

15. Wilkinson told WPG (already in the 1960s) that the country could only sustain about 20 research departments, and that some rationalisation was needed. In his personal tribute (Chapter Eight, Note 38), Mino Green wrote that not only did Wilkinson see chemistry as the central science, he 'cared very deeply indeed for the department of chemistry and the college, in that order. He fought wherever and with whomever he could for the cause of good chemistry at IC.'

16. Under the old UGC (UFC from 1988 to 1992 when HEFCE was introduced) there were eleven different bands for the funding of disciplines. This was reduced to four during the period of cutbacks. Although chemistry remained in the top band, the differential was not what it had been earlier, and a deficit was almost inevitable. As Wilkinson had anticipated (and wished), several chemistry departments around the country were closed.

17. Rogers was then one of only two members of staff (the other was Archibald H. Cornfield) interested in the college's premature retirement compensation scheme, introduced in the late 1970s to encourage senior people to take early retirement. Welch wrote to the College Secretary, John Smith, that the department wanted to run down the crystallography section. ICL archives, B\Wilkinson; copy of letter from Welch to Smith, 31 October, 1979.

18. ICL archives; B\Wilkinson; Flowers, typed document (dated, 2 December 1975) outlining the future of the chemistry department as he saw it, and announcing that Wilkinson would succeed Barrer as head of department on 30 September 1976. (West was a vocal proponent of IC becoming an independent university).

19. ICL archives; B\Wilkinson; Wilkinson, typescript memo to Flowers, 12 November, 1976. Wilkinson tended to hyperbole in his memos to the Rector, probably a mistake. He also pointed out what he saw as a 'disturbing age spectrum,' stating that the last permanent appointment in inorganic chemistry was made 10 years ago, in physical chemistry 11 years ago, and in organic chemistry 8 years ago. He also thought that the organic and inorganic staff were at the absolute minimum consistent with teaching needs, and that physical chemistry was overstaffed.

20. A proposal for a new chair in this field was made earlier, in the submission for the 1962–1967 quinquennium, but was given low priority. When Flowers was chairman of the SRC, he suggested that it fund such a chair.

At that time Wilkinson supported the idea, but it was rejected by Barton and Barrer. Later he was less certain; he might well have supported Flowers if he had had the support of the three professors appointed in 1978.

21. Wilkinson's memory of these events was poor. In a 1988 letter to the Rector, Eric Ash, he wrote that the MSc course in analytical chemistry was 'effectively destroyed by Rector Flowers who confiscated the established chair of analytical chemistry (in addition to the chair of X-ray crystallography) to provide for Sociology, when Professor West left. ... The consequence was that the reader, Dr. G. F. Kirkbright, left for greener pastures.' He also noted, correctly, that the department had reduced its staff by about 25 percent during his tenure as head. He blamed departmental underfunding on the Flowers vote formula — with some justification, but with little understanding of the overall situation. ICL archives, B\Wilkinson; Wilkinson to Ash, 28 September, 1988. His letter was prompted by criticism of the department for not introducing more income-generating MSc courses. His mention of sociology refers back to the recommendation, following the Robbins Report, that undergraduate science students needed a broader education, and that future leaders of industry be exposed to ideas in the history, philosophy and sociology of science. IC moved in that direction in the late 1960s but Wilkinson was opposed. For West and Kirkbright see below.

22. Flowers was a fierce critic of the Thatcher government and its policies affecting universities, but he was a realist.

23. The SRC, together with other research councils, was created in 1965 to replace the DSIR. In 1981, it was renamed SERC. In 1994 SERC was split into separate, more specialised, research councils, including the EPSRC.

24. There was much anger among academics about the decline in government funding of research, and at the idea of increasing industrial sponsorship. Even engineers objected. Bruce Sayers, Dean of the C&G in the early 1980s, envisaged the college turning into a company, 'Imperial Enterprises.' See 'City and Guilds at Imperial College,' *The Times*, 27 February, 1985. In 1984 Wilkinson wrote to Flowers that the inorganic section had lost about one-third of its research workers over the past decade and that he had kept things going with a donation of £47,000 from his personal trust; 'if I did not have my own funding I would be completely out of business.' ICL archives, B\Wilkinson; Wilkinson to Flowers, 17 September, 1984. Later Wilkinson wrote to the Pro-Rector (Alan Swanson); 'in the years [Flowers] has been here he has made not the slightest attempt to help the department — on the contrary. On C2 he has always been a defeatist and unwilling to

light fires under the UGC,' (B\Wilkinson; Wilkinson to Swanson, draft, 4 July, 1985). This was not entirely fair; both Flowers and Swanson, the Pro-Rector who stepped in when Flowers was unwell, had written to Sir Peter Swinnerton Dyer, chairman of the UGC, about C2 and, when the UCG failed to move, Flowers asked that IC be allowed to bring in extra funding from other sources so as 'to ensure better than normal facilities,' ICL archives' B\Wilkinson, Flowers to Swinnerton Dyer, 14 June, 1985. Wilkinson wrote that the department was 'dismayed' both by Flowers' letter to Swinnerton Dyer, and that construction of C2 was likely to begin only in 1988. Further, he stated that the space allowance was 'deficient by at least 1700 m^2.' Exasperated, Flowers wrote to Wilkinson that 'what chemistry now needs to do if it wants to help is to get its head out of the sand and work out a strategy for raising private funds. If the department is valued by everyone except the UGC that should not be difficult'; Flowers to Wilkinson, 28 June, 1985.

25. ICL archives, B\Wilkinson; Wilkinson to Flowers, 26 June, 1985.
26. On the matter of C2, the UGC reconsidered its funding in 1985. Also being considered was the possibility of the department expanding into the Queen Elizabeth College laboratories after that college closed. Flowers was in favour, but a decision, perhaps short-sighted, was taken against a split site by the department. Queen Elizabeth College and Chelsea College united with King's College in this period of rationalisation. Given their location, having the science departments join IC might have been a better decision.
27. Le Centre National de la Recherche Scientifique (CNRS). Barton is said to have been persuaded to move there by his French wife who wanted to return to the Paris area. On arrival he insisted that the working language be French even though many of his students and coworkers were anglophones.
28. Among them Willie Motherwell and Robyn Motherwell. Barton's years in France were creative and productive but, at the age of 68, and once again facing compulsory retirement, he accepted an invitation from his former colleague A. I. (Ian) Scott (see Chapter Eight) to join him at Texas A&M University. Barton accepted and was appointed Distinguished Professor of Chemistry. He remained active there until his death, working at the bench and travelling to many international gatherings. Steve Ley told us that he attended a memorial service for Barton in Texas. Barton's widow (his third wife, Judy), who did not drink, told Ley and others to throw a party in her house and drink whatever was in Barton's wine cellar. Ley said that the cellar held some very good wines and the party lasted well into the night.

29. After the chair was renamed, Wilkinson received a few letters addressed to Sir Edward Frankland and sometimes sent amusing replies, signing them appropriately. For example, P. M. Crosby wrote about some 'helium neon lasers' that his company (Coherent United Kingdom) was selling. 'Frankland' replied that, of the three terms, the only one with which he was familiar was 'helium' and that 'the prices are well beyond my means.' ICL archives, B\Wilkinson; Crosby to Frankland (Wilkinson) 26 May, 1982; Frankland (Wilkinson) to Crosby, 7 June 1882. Wilkinson also received a letter from Jeremy Knowles, chair of the chemistry department at Harvard, asking whether he wished to apply for an assistant professorship. Clearly this was either a joke or a mistake. Wilkinson replied that since Harvard possessed the chemicals in which he was interested only in microgram quantities, and since he needed quantities of 10^{10} grams or more, 'I feel that we are many orders of magnitude too far apart for me to consider applying.' Knowles to Wilkinson, 14 January, 1981; Wilkinson to Knowles, 21 January, 1981. In 1985, Wilkinson tried to persuade Knowles to apply for the vacant chair in biochemistry at IC, but Knowles was not interested.

30. There had always been a degree of interdisciplinarity, but it increased during the 1970s and 80s as chemists collaborated with people engaged in materials and biomedical research — the latter especially after St. Mary's medical school joined the college.

31. B. Atkinson, 'Department of Chemistry, Recent History' (1989), typescript on disc; copy in ICL archives; section on administration and finance, p. 8.

32. ICL archives, B\Wilkinson, Wilkinson to Smith, 26 September, 1979. With the redesign of Exhibition Road as a 'pedestrian-friendly precinct' in the early 21st century, the crossing was removed.

33. For citation and Barton's Nobel Prize lecture 'The principles of conformational analysis,' see website at Nobelprize.org. Barton invited Phil Magnus, Peter Sammes and Dave Widdowson see Notes 77, 82 and 74 respectively to the ceremony.

34. Vladimir Prelog won the Nobel Prize in 1975. He showed Hassel's findings to be correct for large alicyclic rings.

35. At Birkbeck, Barton extended his work on structural chemistry, notably his work on the pentacyclic terpenoids and sesquiterpenoids, but also on some steroidal alkaloids. He used conformational analysis in his work and wrote that he gained much satisfaction from discovering the relation between conformation and reactivity in steroids; (Barton, 1991, 1996). See (Barton,

1996) pp. 45–46, for his comments on his early work in conformational analysis.

36. Nobelprize.org for the citation and Wilkinson's Nobel lecture, reprinted in (Wilkinson, 1974). According to Willie Motherwell, when Wilkinson told Barton about winning the Nobel, Barton responded, 'well, I didn't nominate you.' Motherwell said that there was rivalry between the two men and that they were not the best of friends. As Barton did earlier, Wilkinson received many congratulatory letters. One from J. S. (Stuart) Anderson, then head of the chemistry department at Oxford, stated, 'if you are not careful they will make an establishment figure of you yet.' Neither Anderson nor Wilkinson ever became true establishment figures. For letters, ICL archives, B\Wilkinson, section A. After winning the Nobel Prize, Wilkinson set up a trust fund, using income from it to support research students. Later, money earned from consulting work in homogeneous catalysis see Notes (43) and (44) was added to the trust.

37. For Zeise's salt, Chapter Three, Note 122.

38. F. A. Cotton, Wilkinson's PhD student at the time, carried out some heat of combustion experiments and determined that the combination of resonance within the rings and the iron to carbon bonding was consistent with the molecule's stability.

39. WPG remembers a meeting of the department held at 170 Queen's Gate. The Rector, Brian Flowers, stated that in his field, physics, disciplinary sections were labelled 'heat, light, and sound' in the 19th and early 20th century, and that the labels for chemistry, 'organic, physical, and inorganic,' were similarly archaic. Wilkinson appears to have agreed with Flowers on this point, recognising that by continuing to use the labels the department was failing to indicate to the larger world the areas in which it was making advances. ICL archives; B\Wilkinson; memo to Flowers, 'The chemistry department,' 12 November, 1976.

40. Degradational chemistry was itself degraded. Carbon, hydrogen, oxygen etc., analysis continued to be important for determining empirical formulae, but was done by machines (the automation of old-fashioned chemistry) operated by technicians in microanalytical laboratories. Further, gas chromatography and high pressure liquid chromatography allowed for the efficient separation of complex mixtures.

41. (Green and Griffith, 1998).

42. The conversion of an alkene $RHC=CH_2$ by a gaseous CO/H_2 mixture under pressure to an aldehyde $RH_2C–CH_2CHO$ — in effect the addition of

formaldehyde HCHO across the double bond of the alkene — is often called the oxo process.

43. (Osborn, Jardine, Young, and Wilkinson, 1966). Jardine was the first to make $RhCl(PPh_3)_3$; the chemistry and mechanism of the reactions are described in detail in the paper. Twenty years later Wilkinson received a letter asking him which of his discoveries he thought the most important. In a marginal note, he wrote that it was the rhodium catalyst discussed in the paper cited here; ICL archives B\Wilkinson, U. Jacobs to Wilkinson, 23 January, 1986, Marburg. A bronze ACS Citation for Chemical Breakthroughs plaque to commemorate the paper was presented to the department in 2008. J. Francis Young was a New Zealander who came to IC on an 1851 Exhibition scholarship and worked with Wilkinson for his PhD. On the day that Wilkinson won the Nobel Prize those working in the lab bought two bottles of champagne which 'with suitable ceremony' they delivered to Wilkinson's office at lunchtime. In return Wilkinson took them all to the pub for further celebration. (The Harvard chemistry department sent Wilkinson a case of Krug champagne; see Chapter Eight, Note 38.) Young left the pub early to finish some work in the lab. While there he had an accident and burned his hand. Although not unsympathetic, Wilkinson said, 'served him right, he should have stayed in the pub.' (Fred Jardine, personal communication). Young's experience before coming to IC was in cement chemistry. He was later a professor of building science at the University of Cincinnati.

44. (Evans, Osborn, and Wilkinson, 1968). At first it was thought that $RhCl(PPh_3)_3$ effected this reaction, but it was shown that the first step is its hydrocarbonylation to give $RhH(CO)(PPh_3)_3$, which then reacts catalytically. After some complicated legal proceedings having to do with the illegal use of some hydroformylation patents, Wilkinson won a large settlement, in the order of £1 million. Ironically, neither catalyst made much money for Wilkinson directly, though he was paid well as a consultant. For two excellent reviews covering the literature up to 1981, (Jardine, 1981, 1982).

45. (Shortland and Wilkinson, 1972); see also (Galyer and Wilkinson, 1976). Wilkinson's strategy in this work was to avoid the possibility of β-elimination of hydrogen (whereby a H atom migrates from the β-carbon atom of the alkyl to the metal, giving a metal hydride) since this could not occur with methyl groups or some bulky alkyls. Despite frenzied attempts, which included at least one major explosion, his students could not make the compound again until it was shown that some adventitious

oxygen is necessary. Improved procedures were devised, still based on the WCl_6–$(CH_3)Li$ reaction. The compound is coordinatively unsaturated and so can give, for example, salts of $[W(CH_3)_8]^{2-}$. Subsequently Wilkinson made species such as $M(CH_3)_4$ (M=Cr, Mn), $Re(CH_3)_6$, $[Re_2(CH_3)_8]^{2-}$, $[M(CH_3)_6]^{3-}$ (M = Ru, Rh, Ir: the three platinum group metals he had so successfully used in 1953 to make ferrocene analogues). A final surprise came in the year of Wilkinson's death (1996) when X-ray studies carried out in Germany showed that $W(CH_3)_6$ and $Re(CH_3)_6$ were not octahedral as expected, but trigonal prismatic. John S. Bradley, a Leeds and Oxford graduate who came to IC after postdoctoral work with John Osborn at Harvard was a postdoc with Wilkinson in 1973–1975. He moved from IC to work at Exxon Corporate Research in New Jersey, and after 20 years moved first to the Max Planck Institut fur Kohlenforschung in Muelheim an der Ruhr, and then to the University of Hull. He wrote to us about one of the above-mentioned explosions — the detonation of 50g of hexamethyl tungsten in an untaped Dewar. It resulted in a serious injury to the hand of Konstantinos (Kostas) Mertis, another postdoc (1972–1980) who later became head of the chemistry department at the University of Athens. Wilkinson was lucky to get away with just a cut to his ear lobe. Bradley also wrote that Wilkinson asked him to make trifluoromethyl uranium, and that he was given a 'lump of uranium, a gas bottle of fluorine, and a hacksaw, and told to "read the book."'

46. Andersen, personal communication.
47. When Wilkinson's knighthood was announced, Cole-Hamilton greeted him, 'Morning Sir Geoff,' only to get a reply, that in language and attitude was not atypical, 'if anyone gives me any more of that kind of crap, I'll kick him in the balls.' On the same day Cole-Hamilton recalled hearing Wilkinson on the phone saying 'I've been trying to break the system from the inside for many years and all they can do is go and give me a knight-hood.' One could argue that without that kind of inclusion (people moving up the class ladder, being given knighthoods, etc.) the British class system could not survive. David Cole-Hamilton left for a lectureship at Liverpool and later became professor of chemistry at St. Andrews. We are grateful to him for sending his reminiscences of time spent working with Wilkinson.
48. Andrew Ross Barron left the department in 1986 for a postdoctoral fellow-ship with Alan Cowley at the University of Texas (Austin). That was fol-lowed by eight years as an assistant, then associate, professor of chemistry at Harvard. In 1995 he moved to Rice University where he holds the Charles W. Duncan Jr.–Welch Chair of Chemistry. Since 2014 he has held

a joint position as the Ser Cymru Chair of Low Carbon Energy and Environment at Swansea University, where he is Director of the Energy Safety Research Institute.

49. These claims are supported by his correspondence. See ICL archives, B\ Wilkinson. See Chapter Eight for more on Wilkinson and for obituary references.

50. A 1986 portrait of Geoffrey Wilkinson by Keith Grant was exhibited at the Royal Academy. Iconographic, it portrays a model of ferrocene and, on a blackboard behind Wilkinson, a drawing of the structure of Wilkinson's catalyst.

51. Pratt was appointed senior tutor 1977–1984. The senior tutor takes an overall view of the students. Individual tutors refer students to the senior tutor if there are serious problems of a non-chemical nature. For Pratt see also Chapter Eight.

52. Two often cited papers: (Evans and Fazakerley, 1971), (Evans, Fazakerley, and Phillips, 1971).

53. (Evans and Wong, 1992). We should note that Evans' death was not related to this work, but to melanoma.

54. For Evans, see (Green and Griffith, 2000b). Further obituaries in *The Times*, 5 December, 1990, *The Independent*, 10 November, 1990, and *The Guardian*, 10 November, 1990. The Evans silver medal is awarded for the best final year undergraduate research project in inorganic chemistry.

55. For examples of Goodgame's work, (Goodgame, Jeeves, Phillips, and Skapski, 1975), (Goodgame, Grachvogel, and Williams, 1999). One of Goodgame's students in the 1980s was Richard Winpenny who obtained both his BSc and PhD in the department. Winpenny's research was on metal-organic frameworks (before they were called that). Winner of the RSC Tilden Prize in 2011, he is professor of inorganic chemistry at the University of Manchester.

56. (Goodgame and Piggot, 1971), (Goodgame and Johns, 1980). Margaret Goodgame recounted a story of a student who rushed to the front of the lab when she was demonstrating, crying out 'cyanide, cyanide.' He thought that he had inhaled some HCN. She dissolved some ferrous sulphate in distilled water and made him drink it; his face then turned green. An ambulance took the student to St. George's Hospital and, shortly after, the chemistry department received a phone call from the hospital asking how they should treat cyanide poisoning! The student soon recovered since he had not, in fact, inhaled HCN. Wilkinson summoned Goodgame into his office. She thought she was going to be reprimanded, but he said 'sit down, I think you need a stiff brandy.'

57. John Scales Avery came to IC with a BSc from MIT and an MSc from Chicago. Before joining the department he had begun work on a PhD, applying quantum theory to biological problems, with the Nobel Laureate Albert Szent-Györgyi at the Marine Biological Laboratory in Woods Hole, MA; but he gained his PhD from IC in 1965. Avery is prominent in the international peace movement. He was chairman of the Danish National Group of Pugwash Conferences in Science and World Affairs, and has been a technical advisor to the WHO.

58. Quotation, Atkinson, *op. cit.* (31). Avery used the journal to help spread the chemiosmotic ideas of Peter Mitchell, and those of Jens Christian Skou on the mechanism of active transport. Both were to become Nobel Laureates in chemistry — in 1978 and 1997 respectively. For Avery see also Section 9.5.

59. For the platinum metals, (Griffith, 1967). This book was written just before the crest of the wave in the study of these elements, and became an important resource. For the work with Ley see Chapter Ten.

60. (Gibson, Hall, Thornley, and Whatley, 1966), (Beardwood and Gibson, 1992). John Frederick Gibson gained his BSc and PhD at the University of Southampton (1955, 1958). Before coming to IC he worked for two years at ICI, at The Frythe, Welwyn, in Joseph Chatt's group. He is fondly remembered in the department as is his postdoc, Peter Beardwood, described as a 'really helpful chap,' who provided a free ESR service for the department.

61. George Brent Young, known as Brent, gained his BSc and PhD at the University of Glasgow (1972, 1975) and won a NATO research fellowship to work with George M. Whitesides at MIT. For examples of his research at IC, (Himmel and Young, 1988), (Ankianiec, Christou, Hardy, Thomson, and Young, 1994).

62. (Kelly, Slawin, Williams, and Woollins, 1992). John Derek Woollins, known as Derek, gained his BSc and PhD at the University of East Anglia (1976, 1979). He came to IC after postdoctoral positions at the University of British Columbia, Michigan State University, and the University of Leeds. He recalls that his first IC pay slip wasn't wide enough to carry the word 'new' and simply stated he was being paid 'blood money.' He received the RSC Sir Edward Frankland award in 1990. 'Celebrated' in the department for fires, explosions and malodorous smells (no serious injuries reported, but see Chapter Ten), Woollins left for a chair at Loughborough in 1994. He later became head of the chemistry department at the University of St. Andrews. Research on the eponymous Woollins reagent for the selenation of carbonyls was begun at IC, (Woollins, 2012). In this paper, not

only does Woollins describe the development of his reagent, he also has something to say about life in the IC department.

63. Thomas Summers West CBE FRS FRSE (1927–2010) was a Scot who gained his BSc from the University of Aberdeen and PhD from the University of Birmingham where he subsequently held a lectureship. A RIC Meldola Medal winner in 1956, he won the Gold Medal of the Society of Analytical Chemistry in 1977 and was elected FRS in 1989. Before coming to IC he carried out important work in analytical chelate chemistry and designed quartz fibre torsion ultramicrobalances. While at IC he published *Analytical Chemistry* (1973). He was Hon. Sec. of the Chemical Society 1972–1975, and a RSC fellowship in analytical chemistry was set up in his name in 2012.

64. Roy Dagnall soon left for a position in industry. He was appointed an honorary lecturer in 1963–1975.

65. Gordon F. Kirkbright was known at IC for his rumbustious approach to life, and was a popular and creative member of staff. After his premature death, the University of Manchester created a bursary in his memory which helps students and non-tenured young scientists to attend recognised scientific meetings, or to visit places of learning, (West, 1985).

66. Barry Leonard Sharp became head of the analytical division of the Macaulay Land Use Research Institute in Aberdeen, and later professor of analytical chemistry at Loughborough University.

67. John Frederick (Fred) Alder worked for the Ministry of Defence before coming to IC. In 1980 he moved to UMIST, joining Kirkbright in the department of instrumentation and analytical science, and was later a professor in that department. He is remembered for his good humour and for having a still in his lab used to distill mead so as to make mead brandy. Richard (Dick) D. Snook moved to the UMIST department in 1985 where he, too, was later appointed professor.

68. West returned to his *alma mater*, the University of Aberdeen, to become Director of the Macaulay Land Use Research Institute.

69. Two separate quotations, (Barton, 1996 and 1991). The 1996 volume includes reprints of Barton's favourite papers. In the 1991 book he uses the term 'gap jumping' for intuitive thinking in chemistry. He believed that one cannot rely solely on the kind of deductive logic that Woodward taught his students at Harvard, especially when thinking about how to synthesise complex molecules. Some of what Barton termed 'accidental' work, for example some work he carried out before 1960 on clerodin and limonin, is impressive. Historians of science might think this work neither accidental

nor solely intuitive, but rather the result of tacit knowledge gained through the learning and practice of organic chemistry.

70.   There was also an outdoor laboratory on the roof for dangerous preparations, such as of nitrosyl chloride (NOCl). The lab was known as The Nook, and WPG remembers using liquid HCN stored there in a cylinder which had to be upturned to release the liquid.

71.   We thank Jim Hanson for his recollections of the Whiffen Lab. He told us that he may have paraphrased the Barton quote, but that it is close to the original. (We note that it includes Barton's typical use of the royal 'we.') James R. Hanson, a specialist in natural product chemistry, moved to the University of Sussex in 1964 where he is now Professor Emeritus. Smoking was still permitted in laboratories in the 1960s and 1970s (see Chapter Eight, Note 84 for the COSHH regulations of 1988).

72.   For example, (Barton, Gunatilaka, Jarman, Widdowson, Bard, and Woods, 1975). Bard and Woods worked in the genetics department of the University of Sheffield. Biosynthesis of sterols present in yeast preceded that of ergosterol.

73.   By 'heaps' he meant old second/third-hand vehicles. For Stick, (Williams, 2009). Stick went on to a major research career at the University of Western Australia. Among the other Australians working with Barton at the time were Richard K. Haynes, appointed a visiting lecturer, 1972–1975. He returned to Australia where he held several positions, the last at the University of Sydney, before moving to the University of Hong Kong. Richard Russell, a postdoctoral fellow with a PhD from the ANU, joined Barton in 1972 and was appointed a visiting lecturer, 1973–1974, before returning to the ANU, and then to a position at the University of New South Wales. William Arthur (Bill) Bubb, a postdoc in 1975–1976, was directed by Barton to use S_4N_4 as a sulfurising agent. When he pointed out that the compound was explosive, Barton replied that that was good since the reaction should proceed faster, (Steve Ley, personal communication). Haynes and Russell were not the only ones appointed as visiting lecturers. Such appointments were a way for Barton to fund people carrying out research in his laboratory.

74.   David Arthur (Dave) Widdowson came to the department in 1961 with a BSc from the University of Nottingham. He carried out research on peptide synthesis under Hamish Sutherland (see Chapter Eight) for his PhD. After a postdoctoral fellowship with Alex Nickon at Johns Hopkins University, where he learned more about physical organic chemistry, he returned to work with Barton in 1965. Widdowson was the departmental safety officer, 1975–1982. See also Chapter Ten.

75. Stuart W. McCombie was to work for the Schering-Plough Corporation (a drugs manufacturing company later purchased by Merck), (Barton and McCombie, 1975). (The McCombie Prize for undergraduates is named for another McCombie, John McCombie; see Chapter Seven Note 91.) For Barrett, Magnus, Motherwell and Ley see below. After leaving the department, Barton followed the deoxygenation with work on radical decarboxylation and the chemistry of the Barton esters.

76. In 1983 Wilkinson was invited to be the first Robert Burns Woodward visiting Professor at Harvard. In a draft response, Wilkinson turned down the invitation stating 'I wouldn't stay in anybody's department for three months — or even three weeks ... a few hours is the absolute maximum I can stand.' He wrote of the lure of the three Yorkshire peaks, and of the dales, and that he would rather spend time there than at Harvard. We do not know whether the draft letter was sent, but Wilkinson did not accept the invitation. ICL archives, B\Wilkinson, A43. Wilkinson was less interested in worldly success, in honorary degrees, and in playing important roles in scientific societies, than some of his well-known contemporaries — Barton, Cotton, Nyholm, and Lewis, for example. He was also less politically astute, though scientifically he was highly competitive and, of course, very successful. Occasionally a little resentful of the more worldly success of others, he could be bluntly, sometimes unfairly, critical. For Wilkinson, however, his family, the Yorkshire countryside, and the lab bench trumped all.

77. See, for example, (Barton and Magnus, 1971). In an email, Magnus stated that he might have stayed at IC had he known that Barton would soon be leaving; however he has had a highly successful career in the United States, moving from Indiana to the University of Texas at Austin. He won the CS Corday–Morgan Prize in 1978 and the RSC Robert Robinson award in 1996.

78. (Barrett, Barton, and Johnson, 1978). This work was in connection to the synthesis of vitamin D_3. Barrett remembers Barton with great affection, stating that, aside from teaching him much chemistry, he helped him financially and taught him 'much about life.' He said that Barton allowed his good students a certain freedom, so long as they did not stray far from his main research agenda, (Barrett, personal communication). For more on Barrett, Chapter Ten.

79. Motherwell told us that he arrived at IC just after the appointment of Steve Ley and Tony Barrett as lecturers. Since there were no further openings he decided to move to France with Barton. He said he has no regrets in having

spent several years working with Barton before getting a lectureship and that he learned much.

80. Willie Motherwell's wife, Robyn Motherwell, gained a second PhD while working with Barton at Gif. It was the only way she could get research funding as a non EEC citizen. Her BSc and first PhD were from the University of Queensland. She held a postdoctoral fellowship at UCL in 1976–1977, working with Alwyn Davies, after returning from Gif she held a further postdoctoral position with Davies. In 1988 she moved to IC as a postdoctoral fellow and personal assistant to Geoffrey Wilkinson. She published 13 papers with Wilkinson between 1989 and 1997. See also Chapter Ten.

81. (Allen, Barton, Girijavallabhan, Sammes and Taylor, 1973). Penicillin was a continuing interest of Barton's long after he left the department. With respect to the photochemical work, Sammes was interested in trapping active intermediates such as enols.

82. Sammes was awarded the CS Corday–Morgan Prize in 1972. He was one of several entrepreneurs of this period and founded a microanalytical service called Medac Ltd., which still exists. When the department at City University closed, Sammes became head of the chemistry laboratory of SmithKline and French at the Frythe, Welwyn. He was later a professor at Brunel University. One of Sammes' PhD students, and a former undergraduate in the department, is Stephen Matlin. Matlin moved first to an academic career with professorships at Cardiff and City Universities, but later made a bigger splash in the world of governmental and non-governmental agencies. He was the Executive Director of the Global Forum for Health Research and, today, is an adjunct professor at the Institute of Global Health Innovation at ICL.

83. Atkinson, *op. cit.* (31).

84. Challis told us that Barton was generous in buying equipment such as liquid scintillation counters, paying for an elemental analysis, and so on. Challis gained his BSc and PhD at UCL, the latter with John Ridd. He came to IC in 1967 after a postdoctoral fellowship at Cornell with Frank Long and three years as a lecturer at St. Andrews. He left for a chair at the Open University in 1986.

85. ICL archives; B\Wilkinson, Wilkinson to Flowers, 27 January, 1983. Ley appears to have been something of a chemical prodigy. He told us that he kept a diary from the age of seven and that before the age of ten he had drawn many chemical structures in it. Like many future chemists he also had a chemistry set and was encouraged to experiment by his mother. For Ley see also Chapter Ten.

86. See Note 6. Anthony Gerald Martin (Tony) Barrett FRS FMedSci first came to IC as an undergraduate in 1970. He is remembered in this period not only for his organic chemistry but also for his, not unrelated, skill in making a fine 'home-brew' of Grand Marnier and/or Cointreau.

87. This project involved the Pfizer animal health division in Sandwich. Both Ley and Barrett published on the avermectins and milbemycins, but separately. The Pfizer in-house programme resulted in a successful product, Doramectin, used globally for animal health. Nigel Walshe, a former PhD student with Peter Sammes, worked at Pfizer on Doramectin. Avermectins are also used against the helminth parasite that causes River Blindness (*Onchocerciasis*). (William Campbell and Satoshi Omura won half of the 2015 Nobel Prize for medicine for their discovery of the avermectins.)

88. Charles Wayne Rees CBE FRS (1927–2006) left school to become a laboratory technician at the Royal Aircraft Establishment, Farnborough, where he worked for two years before attending University College, Southampton, gaining his BSc in 1950, and PhD in 1953. He spent two years as a postdoctoral fellow at the Australian National University working with Adrien Albert, before returning to an assistant lectureship in organic chemistry at Birkbeck College. In 1957 he moved to King's College as lecturer, then reader, 1957–1965. He was professor of chemistry at the University of Leicester, 1965–1969, and professor of organic chemistry, then Heath-Harrison Professor, at the University of Liverpool, 1969–1978. While at KCL he worked with D. H. Hey (see Chapter Seven) on heterocyclic chemistry, an interest that continued throughout his career. See obituary by Christopher J. Moody, *The Independent* (12 December, 2006); also (Russell, 2004e), (Moody, 2015), and Chapter Ten.

89. Rees' method of producing high yields of indoles was widely copied. His 1983 synthesis of the bacterial coenzyme PQQ (methoxatin) used this method and was followed by the synthesis of the potent antitumour agent CC-1065. (MacKenzie, Moody, and Rees, 1986), (Bolton, Moody, Pass, Rees, and Tojo, 1988).

90. The Hofmann professor's office was home to Jocelyn Thorpe's old desk. The desk is now in Tony Barrett's office. Barrett avers that neither he nor Rees ever used the desk, and that it was originally found full of empty (potable) alcohol bottles.

91. WPG remembers this occasion but the quote is paraphrased.

92. Christopher Moody gained his BSc at KCL, and his PhD at the University of Liverpool. After holding a postdoctoral fellowship at the ETH in Zurich,

he worked briefly with Roche before coming to IC in 1979. In 1990 he moved to a chair at Loughborough University and is now the Sir Jesse Boot professor of organic chemistry at the University of Nottingham. He was awarded the RSC's Corday–Morgan Medal in 1986, the Tilden medal in 2000, and, in 2012, the Charles Rees Award for outstanding contributions to heterocyclic chemistry. For two copublications with Rees see Note 89. See also (Halton, 2015).

93. Sir John Ivan George Cadogan FRS, is a Welshman. He was a prize winning student at KCL where he gained both his BSc and PhD. After national service working at the Chemical Defence Establishment at Porton Down, he returned to King's College as a lecturer where he and Rees became close friends. President of the Chemical Society, 1951–1952, he became Purdie professor of chemistry at St. Andrews in 1963 and, in 1969, Forbes professor of organic chemistry at the University of Edinburgh. In 1979, he joined BP as its chief United Kingdom scientist, becoming worldwide director of research in 1981. He held that post until 1992 and saw the research budget grow from £60m to £400 m. At BP he was a proponent of 'green' issues and of research related to them. He was chairman of the SRC's Chemistry Committee, Director General of the Research Councils, and a member of HEFCE. He served as President of the RSC, 1982–1984, and is a recipient of the RSC's Corday–Morgan and Meldola medals, and of the Lord Lewis Prize.

94. WPG was Rzepa's inorganic chemistry tutor when Rzepa was an undergraduate, 1968–1971.

95. Rzepa's postdoctoral fellowship was at the University of Texas (Austin) with Michael Dewar working on minimum energy paths for organic reactions. On his return Charles Rees gave him a small room with a computer terminal which he moved into Laurie Phillips' lab. Phillips had a grant to buy a Bruker NMR machine and asked Rzepa to go to Switzerland to negotiate the specifications. It came with a fluorine probe and a 10 MB hard drive that was the size of a small fridge. Phillips left in 1979 and Rzepa was the first to operate the Bruker machine, working on its teething problems together with R. N. (Dick) Sheppard (see Chapter Eight). As an organic chemist with NMR and computer skills, Rzepa interpreted some NMR spectra of Wilkinson's rhodium complexes. It was this, he believes, that persuaded Wilkinson to make his lectureship permanent when his probationary period ended in 1983. A further bonus was that Wilkinson included Rzepa as coauthor on three papers published in *Polyhedron*. (Rzepa, personal communication). Rzepa's work is at the forefront of the application

of the internet to chemical problems, (Rzepa, Whitaker, and Winter, 1994), (Camilleri, Eggleston, Rzepa, and Webb, 1994).

96. (Davies, Hall, and Smith, 1991), (Khan, Morris, Smith, and Walsh, 1991). Smith continues to work at the bench in biophysics, currently on the receptor sites for the anaesthetics propofol, etomidate and isoflurane. There is a brief entry on the IC Centenary Memories website by Mark Chapman, a former PhD student of Smith's. Chapman, who had been an undergraduate in the department, had a cycling accident during his first year as a PhD student (1992). It resulted in serious head injuries and he spent over two years in hospital and rehabilitation. He wrote of the support he received from Smith who visited him in hospital, encouraged him, and welcomed him back to the department as he slowly recovered.

97. In 1987 David M. Blow FRS won the Wolf Prize in chemistry, together with the Oxford chemist, David C. Phillips FRS.

98. Sir Alan Roy Fersht FRS, FMedSci came to the department from the MRC molecular biology laboratory at Cambridge where he gained his PhD, on intramolecular catalysis of ester hydrolysis, with Anthony Kirby FRS in 1968. He came to IC at roughly the same time as his former MRC colleagues, Brian Hartley, professor of biochemistry, and David Blow, professor of biophysics, and continued to work with them on the mechanism, energetics and specificity of enzyme catalysis.

99. Money toward this NMR machine came also from another large grant won by Steve Ley. See Chapter Ten.

100. Lovat Rees (1927–2006) returned to his native Scotland where he led an active research group as an honorary research fellow in the condensed matter and materials chemistry department at the University of Edinburgh. For an obituary, visit http://www.scotsman.com/news/obituaries/ professor-lovat-rees-1-1126286.

101. David O. Hayward (1930–2015) was a Cambridge graduate who spent some time at the University of Chicago before coming to IC. He wrote two books directed at students, (Hayward and Trabnell, 1964), and (Hayward, 2002).

102. The field ion microscope was invented by E. W. Müller in 1951. J. Stuart Anderson (see Chapters Six and Seven) was head of the NCL when Bassett was there and encouraged his work. David Bassett (1934–2015) had earlier gained a PhD from KCL and held a postdoctoral fellowship in Canada. He left the department in 1994 to pursue his other love, the cultivation of delphiniums. It was he who provided delphiniums for the annual examiners' meeting for the BSc and MSci finals.

103. Russell G. (Russ) Egdell gained his PhD at Oxford in the area of gas phase photoelectron spectroscopy, and worked there until coming to IC in 1983. He was the first lecturer to be appointed in physical chemistry since Sutcliffe in 1967 and studied the electronic structures of solids and the surface chemistry of oxides, using photoemission and other physical techniques, though always regarding himself as an inorganic rather than physical chemist. He returned to Oxford in 1990.

104. Maurice Hilary George (1928–2009), who gained his PhD at the University of Birmingham, came to the department after two years as a lecturer at the University of Queensland. Albery called George, Jim Barrie and Lovat Rees 'The Three Musketeers'.

105. A special cryogenic laboratory was set up in the new C1 building. Liquid helium was the cryogenic fluid and the gas was recovered for future use. One of us (HG) remembers attending a thermodynamics lecture given by Neville Parsonage when none of the other students showed up (HG cannot remember why). Nonetheless Parsonage insisted on giving his lecture, so HG felt obliged to sit and listen to it.

106. David Nicholson retired from ICL in 2002, but not from chemistry. He moved to Australia, became an honorary professor at the University of Queensland, and collaborated on several papers with theoretical chemists there. We are grateful to him for his reminiscences of the physical chemistry staff in this period.

107. (Nicholson and Parsonage, 1982), (Parsonage, 2001).

108. Bryan Philip Levitt was Director of Undergraduate Studies 1981–1996. For his teaching see Section 9.5. Levitt was also a local Conservative politician who served both as a councillor and as Mayor of the Royal Borough of Kensington and Chelsea.

109. Spiro and his parents were German Jewish refugees who fled to New Zealand when Spiro was nine years old. He gained a BSc (1949) and MSc (1950) from the University College of Canterbury and, like Barrer, won New Zealand's 1851 Exhibition Scholarship. This allowed him to move to Oxford (Balliol College) where he worked with Ronnie Bell FRS. His DPhil work was on reaction kinetics but, on completing it, he returned to electrochemistry, the field he had worked on for his MSc under Hugh Parton. Before coming to IC Spiro held a postdoctoral fellowship at the University of Toronto with Andrew Gordon and, in 1955–1959, was a lecturer at the University of Melbourne when J. S. Anderson was head of department.

110. (Spiro and Sidebottom, 1973). Later Spiro became interested in energy storage. One of his PhD students was Mary Archer who came to IC from

Oxford in 1966. She was later a lecturer in Cambridge where she developed an interest in solar energy. Although better known for her eventful marriage to Lord Jeffrey Archer, she had a successful career of her own, both in chemistry and working for various public bodies. WPG and Spiro shared two students for collaborative work on peroxide bleaching catalysis by transition metals. For Spiro see also Chapter Ten.

111. Wyndham John Albery FRS (1936–2013), known as John, had many chemical interests. The following kinetics paper was one of his favourites and is still often cited, (Albery, 1980). Albery was a member of a well-known theatrical family and possessed theatrical as well as chemical talent. He would sometimes take the physical chemistry staff to the Garrick Club where, it is said, a drink was always waiting for him. As a young man he contributed sketches to the 1960s satirical BBC TV show, *That was the week that was.* He was a student at Oxford, gaining his DPhil with Ronald (Ronnie) Bell. Together they developed rotating disk electrodes, using them to study the kinetics of fast reactions in solution. Perhaps Albery was also drawn to Bell for his theatrical leanings. In an obituary of Bell (*The Independent*, 18 January, 1996), Albery noted that as a young man, Bell worked in Copenhagen with J. N. Brønsted and, while there, is said to have 'fallen in with a troupe of disreputable actors,' and disappeared from the lab for three months. Albery told the physical chemists that he expected each of them to publish at least two papers a year and, a little dated, that they should not apply for promotion without a DSc. Several people have said that Albery was very much an 'Oxford man,' who did not fully understand the ways of IC. Nonetheless he was a lively presence in the department. What his obituarist wrote is as true for his colleagues at IC as for those at Oxford, namely that memories of him as 'rumbustious ... full of irreverence, laughter and alcohol ... live on joyfully and somewhat embarrassingly in the memory' (*The Telegraph*, 13 December, 2013).

112. Sensors on silicon chips were being developed in this period and were already used for many purposes. Work on selective electrodes brought in a major grant from the Wolfson Foundation, with further funding from Unilever; the company was interested in Albery's work on the link between charged surfaces and colloids. One of Unilever's scientists, Anthony (Tony) L. Smith, joined the department as a visiting professor.

113. Lord George Porter OM FRS (1920–2002) gained his BSc at Leeds University and then served in the Royal Navy Volunteer Reserve as a naval officer during WW2. After the war he went to Cambridge where he studied under R. G. W. Norrish for his PhD. Together they developed flash

photolysis and won a half-share of the 1967 Nobel Prize for chemistry, for their studies of 'extremely fast chemical reactions' (the other half was won by Manfred Eigen). In 1955 Porter was appointed as professor of physical chemistry at Sheffield, and was later Firth professor and head of department. In 1966 he succeeded Sir W. Lawrence Bragg as Fullerian professor of chemistry at the RI. On retiring from that position in 1986 he gave up his visiting professorship in the department and later moved to the department of pure and applied biology as a senior research fellow. There he worked with James Barber in the newly created Centre for Photomolecular Science. Porter won the RSC Longstaff prize in 1981 and was elected President of the Royal Society, 1985–1990, (Archer, 2004).

114. Donald Rogers (1921–1999) was educated at KCL and before coming to IC was a lecturer at the University of Wales (Cardiff). One of his interests was using new computer technology, not only to manage chemical information, but also to translate the Bible into Braille.

115. During the 1980s and 1990s Williams collaborated in this area with Sir James Fraser Stoddart; (Colquhoun, Stoddart and Williams, 1986), (Amabilino *et al.*, 1998).

116. Ebdon, quoted in the 2014 summer issue of *Imperial Matters*. OFFA was created so as to ensure that universities and colleges charging higher tuition fees work also to attract students from disadvantaged backgrounds. Among other chemistry students from this period are Trevor Phillips, Ian Gillett and Peter Machin. Phillips is remembered in the department in part because of a benzene fire he accidentally caused. (The first official safety officer was appointed only in the 1980s). He was President of the IC Union, 1975–1977, and was elected the first black president of the National Union of Students in 1978. He became editor and presenter of the London Programme at London Weekend TV, and Head of Current Affairs in 1992. Active in the Labour Party, he became a member (and chairman) of the Greater London Authority in 2000. In 2003, he was appointed as chairman of the Commission for Racial Equality. Ian Gillett gained his BSc in 1974 before moving to the department of materials. As an undergraduate he was on IC's safety council. Safety became his area of expertise. He worked for the Health and Safety Executive as a specialist inspector in occupational hygiene, returning to IC as Assistant Safety Director. In 1990 he was appointed Director of Safety and, by 2000, led a team of about 14, including experts in radiation and biological security. Peter Machin came to IC in the 1960s and stayed on for a PhD in organic chemistry which he gained in the early 1970s. He was to make a major career in the

pharmaceutical industry working with Roche and then GlaxoSmithKline. Machin was also a trustee of the RSC and its Hon. Treasurer for four years.

117. For the famous article, (Barton and Cookson, 1956). Jeremy Sanders CBE FRS was an undergraduate in the department (1966–1969). He remembers Barton as an important and self-important figure, one who showed off in front of visiting speakers. However, Barton had the connections to 'fix' things for Sanders who wanted to go to Cambridge and study with Dudley Williams for his PhD; 'not my idea of chemistry' said Barton, but 'I have just spent the weekend with Lord Todd. It's all arranged ... don't change your mind'; (Sanders, personal communication). Sanders gained his PhD with Williams and, after a postdoctoral period at Stanford, made a fine career at Cambridge including as head of department, 2000–2006.

118. Rzepa, personal communication.

119. See the department website for Rzepa's 'The Imperial College (London) chemistry department online: 1968–2014.' The year 1980–1981 appears to have been an outstanding year with a fast line printer station and the first hard-disk drive connected to the Bruker 250 MHz NMR spectrometer. Further, a teletypewriter was installed to provide access to (Scientific and Technical Network) STN-International, giving the department access to *Chemical Abstracts* on-line and, via a convoluted route, to the then emerging internet. For more on this see Chapter Ten.

120. Early word processing in the late 1970s made use of an IBM golf printer attached to the network. In the 1980s Levitt, Rzepa and the few other enthusiasts had to cajole fellow members of staff into using email. (WPG was one of the last to succumb).

Chapter Ten

A Period of Change, 1985–2000

10.1 Introduction

In 1985, Geoffrey Wilkinson had three years left as head of department. During that time he continued to push for the construction of C2 and argued with both the college administrators and the UGC over the space and equipment needed.[1] In 1987 he wrote to the Rector, Eric Ash, on the future of departmental research stating that he wished to see an increase in interdisciplinary work, greater interaction with industry, new research in synthetic methods, biological and medicinal chemistry, catalysis, materials, electrochemistry, and solar energy capture. In this he anticipated the directions in which the department would soon move. He also urged Ash to 'wipe out' the department's accumulated debt so that the new Head would not be placed 'in a virtually impossible management position.'[2] Ash did not do so, but he did allow the department to continue carrying an annual deficit, provided it sought ways of bringing in new funding, both to support research and to slowly reduce the debt. In 1993, shortly after David Phillips became head of department, there was a new Rector, Ronald Oxburgh, and a new Pro-Rector, William (Bill) Wakeham. They were less forgiving. Earlier the deficit had been seen as money taken from one college pot and placed in another that needed it more (chemistry's), and therefore acceptable. Wakeham saw things differently, and believed he had a duty to protect the financial interests of all departments by not allowing any one of them to accumulate debt.[3] Not only did chemistry's deficit spending have to end, the debt had slowly to be repaid. Making matters worse, the college brought in 'space charging' without taking into account that some departments, including chemistry, needed more space than others. However, despite its many problems, the department retained its five-star rating in the 1992 Research Assessment Exercise (RAE), one of seven chemistry departments in the country so ranked.[4] One year later the department's teaching was assessed 'excellent' by a six-person inspection team of external academics from Higher Education Funding Council for England (HEFCE), the first department at Imperial College (IC) to achieve this rating. How the department faced its financial problems is discussed in Section 10.6.

In retrospect one can see that Wilkinson's retirement marks the end of an era,[5] and that the headships of John Albery and Steve Ley were periods of relative stasis before the changes that occurred during David Phillips' term. Already in the 1980s it was clear that computer technology would bring change to both teaching and research. But further change came with new staff members replacing the many who resigned or retired in this period, and with those filling positions that opened up as the national economy recovered in the later 1990s. With a younger staff there was more turnover, since some people soon left to pursue careers elsewhere. Further, a major organisational change occurred in 1997 with the end of the old tripartite division of the department and the introduction of new research sections. There had been discussion of such a change earlier, but the precipitating cause was the department's poor financial situation early in the decade. More generally, however, this change should be viewed as a response to developments in chemical science, to an increasing democratic ethos in universities, and to the needs of a modernising economy.

10.2 Heads of Department and Section Heads, 1985–1993

When Wilkinson retired in 1988 he was succeeded in the Sir Edward Frankland chair, and as head of the inorganic chemistry section, by Alan Cowley. Cowley, a University of Manchester trained chemist, came to IC from the University of Texas (Austin), but made only a brief stopover before returning to Austin six months later.[6] Dennis Evans was then appointed acting head of the section. After Evans' premature death in

1990, David Goodgame stepped in until Michael Mingos was appointed to the Frankland chair in 1992.[7] In 1985 Charles Rees was still the Hofmann professor and head of the organic chemistry section; he remained in that position until his retirement in 1993 and was succeeded by Tony Barrett. John Albery, professor of physical chemistry, succeeded Wilkinson as head of department; but he stayed in the position for only one year before returning to Oxford when appointed Master of University College in 1989.[8] His successor, Steve Ley, moved to Cambridge in 1992 as the BP 1702 chair.[9] Succeeding Albery as professor of physical chemistry was David Phillips and, when Ley left, he became head of department.[10] Phillips held the position until 2002, and by the end of his term had brought some stability to the department — by overseeing the many changes mentioned above. They are discussed further in Section 10.6. The section heads remained in place until new research groupings were introduced in 1997.

10.3 Some Staff Changes, 1985–2000

Staff numbers were down by 1985 because of the recession. The inorganic section had 10 members of the academic staff, the organic section had 12, and the physical section had 15. The bias toward the physical section in part reflects Barrer's long reign as head of department and was a legacy carried forward, with some adjustment, in later appointments. There were two visiting professors, Lord George Porter and Sir John Cadogan, soon to be joined by Alexander Smith and Sir John Meurig Thomas and, in the 1990s, by Kenneth Packer, Colin Poole, Terrance Wright, Patrick Camilleri, Richard Catlow, and Anthony Jones.[11] A few others are mentioned below. Howard Colquhoun was a visiting lecturer in 1992.[12]

By 1995 Evans and Pratt had died, and Lovat Rees, Spiro, Atkinson, Barrie, Waight, Parsonage, Bassett, Ash, and George had retired. Fersht had resigned his chair and returned to Cambridge and Challis, Gibson, Moody, Motherwell, and Woollins had resigned their readerships. Gibson left in 1993 to devote time to winemaking.[13] The other four left for chairs: Challis to the Open University in 1986, Moody and Woollins to Loughborough in 1990 and 1994 respectively, and Motherwell in 1993 to become the first holder of the Alexander Williamson chair at UCL. Egdell had resigned his lectureship and returned to Oxford, and Levitt was to retire in 1996.[14]

As to appointments, the department went beyond simply replacing those who had left. Between 1985 and 2000 there were 40 new lecturers, two new readers and eight new professors (see also Section 10.5; these numbers include some who also resigned within this period). Further, thanks to Steve Ley, the department appointed John Emsley as science writer-in-residence. A Manchester trained chemist, Emsley had worked at KCL before joining the department in 1990. He is the author of some well-received books in popular science and, during his time in the department, he wrote items for the press, including 'Molecule of the Month' for *The Independent*, and articles for the *New Scientist*. He also edited, and largely wrote, the *Chemistry Department News* (*CDN*), and helped to publicise the department.[15] The *CDN*, which ran as 38 monthly issues from January 1990 to November, 1993 was much appreciated by staff and students, though a few described it as a 'scurrilous rag.' Emsley left for Cambridge in 1997.

We cannot begin to do justice to the 50 new members of staff coming and going in this 15 year period.[16] In the following sections we briefly outline what we see as the more important research developments and, in section 10.5 include a little information on the newcomers.

10.4 Research into the 1990s: (a) Organic Chemistry; (b) Inorganic Chemistry; (c) Physical Chemistry

(a) *Organic Chemistry*

In the organic section Charles Rees continued his research on heterocyclic compounds — new ring systems, and ways to synthesise biologically active, and interesting, molecules. He was also Co-Editor-in-Chief of three major monograph series, and was elected President of the RSC (1992–94).[17] Vernon Gibson related a story which captures well Rees' offbeat sense of humour. Gibson had to introduce the eminent French organometallic chemist, Pierre Dixneuf, who came to give a lecture in the department. Dixneuf spoke about stringing together cumulene units and said that he hoped to make a 19-chain polymer because of his name. At the end of the lecture Rees asked, 'wouldn't it be simpler just to change your name?' (Wilkinson, who was a good friend of Pierre Dixneuf, always called him Pierre Dixhuit.)

David Widdowson continued his work in the organic section, furthering his work in organic synthesis.[18] He was also director of undergraduate studies from 1996 to 2003, and collaborated with Vic Pike of the MRC Cyclotron unit at Hammersmith Hospital, in seeking ^{18}F compounds suitable for use in positron emission tomography. In 1983 Willie Motherwell (see Chapter Nine) returned to the section from Gif-sur-Yvette. Appointed a lecturer, later reader, he built up a team dedicated to inventing new reactions for organic synthesis, using organometallic reagents, transition metal catalysis, free radical reactions, and fluorination. The reactions discovered at IC, and his philosophy of 'curiosity-driven research,' were summarised in an *Aldrichimica Acta* review in connection with his Alfred Bader Award from the RSC. There he refers to IC students as 'a very special breed.'[19] When he moved to UCL in 1993, the *CDN* ran the racy headline 'UC grabs Willie'; but Willie became a visiting professor at IC and is still seen in the department. His wife, Robyn Motherwell, became Wilkinson's personal assistant when he retired, and she set up the new Johnson Matthey laboratory.[20]

By 1985 Steve Ley was a professor running a lively research group.[21] He was materially aided by one of the so-called 'stars of the future' grants handed out by the Thatcher government to encourage innovation; only two were given in chemistry. The award, £400,000, was used by Ley to buy some modern analytical instruments, including an expensive NMR spectrometer.[22] With new tools he was able to tackle molecules as complex as any being studied elsewhere. Work on the avermectins and milbemycins (mentioned in Chapter Nine) continued and, by the late 1980s, Ley was directing the syntheses of these and other complex molecules with multiple stereogenic centres.[23] The work entailed the invention of new synthetic methods for which he became well known.[24] He had a number of outstanding students working with him, among them Alan Armstrong, today head of department, and Don Craig, now a professor. Among those of Ley's students working elsewhere are Annette Doherty, a senior administrator with GlaxoSmithKline, Steve Marsden, a former lecturer in the department, now head of chemistry at Leeds, Barry Lygo, professor at

Nottingham, and James C. (Jim) Anderson who succeeded Motherwell in the Alexander Williamson chair at UCL in 2013. Ley and his team worked hard and they had the occasional party. In 1987, after what Ley termed 'a joyous celebration' at an Indian restaurant, they headed back to the lab but found the building locked. Spotting a skip full of leaves, they decided that it would be a good place to rest; so they climbed in, ended their evening's conversation, and 'slumbered there contentedly until the early hours.'[25]

When Ley announced that he was leaving for Cambridge in 1992, Charles Rees, who was to retire one year later, wanted Tony Barrett to return as Head of section. Together with Eric Ash, Rees sought the means to make him an attractive offer. The Wolfson Foundation agreed to fund a new research centre and IC's future Rector, Sir Richard Sykes, arranged for Glaxo to fund a chair.[26] As a consequence, Barrett returned in 1993 as head of the organic section, and as Glaxo chair of organic chemistry at the Wolfson centre for organic chemistry and medical science. In 1999, as head of the new synthesis section, he was given the Sir Derek Barton chair of synthesis and the Hofmann chair lost its exclusive connection to organic chemistry.[27]

Barrett is yet another stellar organic chemist to have studied and/or worked in the department. He returned after 10 years as a professor in the United States. He said that he was pleased to be back, and that he would not have returned for a chair anywhere else in the United Kingdom. The Wolfson Centre soon became a lively place, with the synthesis of complex compounds having medical potential as its main focus. Not all the money that Ash had promised was forthcoming and Barrett came to an agreement, downwardly revised, with the next Rector, Ronald Oxburgh.[28] However, he received substantial research funding from other 'Big Pharma' sources. Indeed, during this period the pharmaceutical industry supported research in organic synthesis at universities in Britain and around the world. Like others of his generation, though with greater drive and determination than most, Barrett continues to work successfully on the synthesis of a range of interesting bioactive products.[29]

Many of today's academic scientists are entrepreneurial, and Barrett is no exception. In 1997, in collaboration with some people at the University of Cambridge, and with financial support from Rhône-Poulenc Rorer, he started the TeknoMed project, an IC based research programme in drug design (see also Section 10.7). Among other things he and his team developed techniques in parallel synthesis that were of use in the early stages of drug discovery since they allowed the rapid exploration of potentially useful medicinal molecules. Several chemists at Rhône-Poulenc Rorer (later Sanofi-Aventis) raised money to set up a pharmaceutical contract research organisation which then merged with an IC supported spin-out company, ChemMedICa, in which Barrett played a leading role. The new company, Argenta Discovery, raised £7,200,000 in private investment by 2000. Several of Barrett's students joined Argenta and, in 2007, the company signed a pre-clinical deal with AstraZeneca for the co-development of therapeutic agents for respiratory diseases. Much research leading to these developments was carried out in the department.[30]

The work that Alan Fersht (see Chapter Nine) brought from Cambridge in 1978 was cutting edge and his innovative work on protein folding has by now become part of mainstream science. It is no criticism of him to state that the department took a risk in appointing a professor in a field that had little connection to what others on the staff were then doing, and at a time when there were no funds for any supporting junior appointments. But Wilkinson was keen to bring biological chemistry to the department and, fortunately, things turned out well. Today chemical biology is a thriving departmental section. That it became so, was in large part because Robin Leatherbarrow was attracted to the department by Fersht's outstanding research and transferred his RS Pickering research fellowship from Oxford in 1984. Also fortunate was that he was appointed as one of the last 'new blood' lecturers in 1985. Fersht was to move his work back to Cambridge in 1988 when offered the Herchel Smith chair, though he remained a visiting professor at IC for five years.[31] Leatherbarrow, whose interests were in protein molecular recognition and enzyme–ligand interactions with application to new therapies, stayed on. By 2002, as professor and head of chemical biology, he had seen the section grow with the appointment of a number of younger people.[32] Interest in the field makes it likely that it will remain integral to the department over the longer term.

Don Craig returned as a lecturer in 1987. Today a professor, he heads a group in the synthesis section, with special emphasis on non-aromatic heterocycles containing oxygen and nitrogen. He has received several honours, including a Glaxo Wellcome award for innovative chemistry in 1996, and the RSC Corday–Morgan Medal in 1998.[33] He is also known for his rock band which, in the 1990s, provided entertainment at various venues, including the departmental summer barbecues, appearing sometimes with another musician, Brent Young. Andrew Miller, appointed in 1990, became known for work on molecular recognition and the development of new methods in drug discovery research. He joined the chemical biology section and set up the Genetics Therapy Centre in 1998 with the support of the Mitsubishi Chemical Corporation.[34] Sue Thomas (Gibson) came to the department in 1993 from a lectureship at the University of Warwick. She won the RSC's Meldola Medal in 1989, the first woman to do so.[35] She says that she found the atmosphere among the organic chemists working on the seventh floor very stimulating, and remembers Charles Rees coming into her lab on Saturday mornings for friendly and wide-ranging chats. She is another of the sophisticated synthesists then working in the department in areas of interest to the pharmaceutical industry.[36] On returning to the department in 1994, Ley's former student, Stephen (Steve) Marsden, formed a research group in the field of organo-main group chemistry, looking especially at silicon, boron and phosphorus compounds.[37] David Gollins was a lecturer in the organic section from 1992–1995. He came from Jack Baldwin's Oxford group and worked with Tony Barrett on α-lactams. Christopher Parkinson joined the section in 1995.[38]

(b) *Inorganic Chemistry*

Working in the inorganic section in 1985 were David Goodgame, Margaret Goodgame, Bill Griffith, Andrzej Skapski, Derek Woollins and Brent Young. Skapski retired in 1998. Griffith and Young continued with their respective research, discussed in Chapter Nine, before retiring in 2002. By 1990 both Margaret Goodgame and David Goodgame had taking on heavy administrative roles, not only in the department but also in the college. They retired in 1998 and 2000 respectively.[39] Woollins continued with the research described briefly in Chapter Nine. As mentioned he left for a chair in Loughborough in 1994 and, with some justification, is remembered in the department affectionately as 'flash bang Woollins'.[40]

Ten new inorganic chemists joined the department during the 1990s. One already mentioned was Michael Mingos, appointed to the Sir Edward Frankland BP chair and head of the inorganic section in 1992.[41] (The Frankland Chair received a generous endowment from BP shortly before Mingos arrived, hence its new name.[42]) Mingos continued the research he had begun in Oxford on precious metal coordination chemistry (particularly that of gold and palladium). At IC this resulted in a range of interesting compounds, including the first gold catenane, and further developments in the supramolecular chemistry of coordination complexes. In the 1980s people began applying microwave heating to chemical reactions. Mingos extended this technique to work on metal catalysis and reactivity and was assisted in this by David Baghurst who came with him from Oxford and was appointed a lecturer in 1993. Baghurst explored the basic science of solid state reactions in mixtures in which one reactant, such as a powdered metal, undergoes rapid heating.[43] Anthony Hill, another 1992 appointee, worked in organometallic and coordination chemistry. He left for Canberra and a Chair at the ANU in 2000.[44] Paul Lickiss, who joined the section in 1994, is now professor of organometallic chemistry.[45]

Vernon Gibson was appointed professor of polymer synthesis and catalysis in 1995 and, in 1998, became the first holder of the Sir Geoffrey Wilkinson chair in chemistry as head of the new catalysis and advanced materials section.[46] Gibson was seeking metal catalysts for the production of industrially-relevant polymers such as polyolefins and polyesters. Most widely recognised are his discoveries of exceptionally active ethylene polymerisation catalysts based on iron and cobalt.[47] In 2001 he was given the Sir Edward Frankland BP chair which he held until 2008 when he left to join BP as its chief chemist.[48]

In 1998, together with Edward (Ed) Marshall, he founded a biodegradable plastics company, Plaxica, a spin-out supported by Imperial Innovations. The company made use of some novel synthetic methods, to manufacture a range of high performance recyclable polylactic acid polymers. Marshall, a PhD student with Gibson in Durham, came to IC in 1999 as a postdoctoral fellow. He was given a lectureship in 2005 but soon left to head research at Plaxica.

Gibson, like Barrett, was far from alone in his entrepreneurial activities. By the 1990s entrepreneurship was much admired not only at IC but in the wider culture. By the early 21st century, both staff and students were actively encouraged to create spin-out companies by the new Rector, Sir Richard Sykes.[49] University and industrial research boundaries, never totally distinct, became more blurred than they were earlier in the 20th century.

Paul O'Brien came to the department in 1995 as professor of inorganic chemistry.[50] In the mid- 1990s IC invested in a research park in Newport, Gwent. It was run by the City of Newport with the support of the Welsh Development Agency. Attracted to the site was Sumitomo/STS, a subsidiary of Sumitomo Precision Products of Japan. The company funded a new chair, one of the few returns on IC's Welsh investment, and O'Brien was made Sumitomo/STS professor of materials chemistry in 1997. During his four years in the department he was associated with the interdisciplinary research centre for semiconductor materials set up by Bruce Joyce, a professor in the physics department. Among other things, he worked on thin films, and on quantum dots of chalcogenides deposited on silicon substrates.[51] In 1999 he left for a chair at the University of Manchester where, in 2002, he became head of the chemistry department.

Also in 1995, Nicholas (Nick) Long was appointed a Governors' lecturer.[52] Since 2011 he has held the Sir Edward Frankland BP Chair and is head of the catalysis, sustainability and applied inorganic section. Working on synthetic inorganic/organometallic chemistry, he is yet another to cross the old boundary between inorganic and organic chemistry.[53] Tom Welton came as a research fellow in 1993 and joined the staff in 1995. He said that when he came for an interview he was shown the lab that was to be his, and that it looked fine. By the time he actually arrived, however, it had been stripped bare. Blaming austerity, he said that when the previous occupant left, 'hungry vultures' descended and took away anything useful. A touch hyperbolic, Welton used the term 'spirit of the Blitz' to describe what he saw as the department's 'make do' attitude.[54] He soon found his feet, receiving his first grant jointly with Brent Young who taught him kinetics.[55] Welton became professor of sustainable chemistry in 2004 and head of department in 2007.

(c) *Physical Chemistry*

Michael Spiro continued in the physical chemistry section. Departing from his principal electrochemical and kinetics research, he made a splash with an article he wrote with his student, Deogratius Jaganyi, on the question 'what is tea scum?'. Using microanalytical techniques they found that the scum requires a base of calcium carbonate, that polyphenolic constituents of tea become oxidised in air and then deposit on the carbonate. The paper caused a surprising amount of debate in the scientific literature, and much interest in the media.[56] When Spiro retired in 1994 most of the few remaining physical chemists were close to retirement.[57]

As noted, David Phillips was appointed professor of physical chemistry in 1989. A photochemist with a good understanding of photophysics, he turned to the study of fluorescence in biological molecules using time-resolved Raman and infrared spectroscopy. The idea was to find some chromophores for use in photodynamic cancer therapy.[58] He worked with phthalocyanines and porphyrins, using chromatographic separation to achieve the purity necessary for therapeutic agents. Acceptable purity was achieved with some porphyrins which were then used to prepare fluorescent disulfonates, bonded to fragments of monoclonal antibodies, for targeting cancer cells. With help from Imperial Innovations he set up a spin-out company, Photobiotics, and has patented some of his work with clinical trials pending. Phillips is a renowned chemical communicator and has given many public lectures with traditional demonstrations of the kind made famous at the RI. Among his lectures is the popular 'A little light relief' on photodynamic therapy.[59] Garry Rumbles, who came to IC with Phillips in 1989, is an expert in steady-state and time-resolved photoluminescence spectroscopy. He worked on molecular photochemistry and the photophysics of conjugated electroluminescent polymers, the frequency up-conversion phenomena, and pioneered optical refrigeration in molecular dye solutions.[60] He left in 2001 to join the United States National Renewable Energy Laboratory, affiliated with the University of Colorado, but he has retained an association with the department as a visiting professor.

Richard Templer came to the department as an RS research fellow in 1989.[61] His fellowship ended in 1991 and he was given a lectureship in physical chemistry. Templer succeeded Phillips as head of department in 2002 and, when the Hofmann Chair was transferred to the head of department, he assumed the title which he continues to hold.[62] John Seddon joined the department in 1991 and, since 1997, has been head of the chemical physics section.[63] Timothy (Tim) Jones, appointed in 1992, is a specialist in electronic materials and nanotechnology. He succeeded O'Brien in the STS/Sumitomo chair in 2000 and headed the electronic materials group until 2007.[64]Andreas Manz came to IC from Ciba Geigy in Basel. He was appointed to the SmithKline Beecham chair in analytical chemistry, created in 1995. It was associated with a new Centre for Analytical Sciences supported by a consortium of pharmaceutical companies, notably SmithKline Beecham and Astra Zeneca.[65] Manz is a pioneer in the chemical applications of 'lab-on-a-chip' technology, but he left in 2004 for a professorship at the Institute of Analytical Sciences in Dortmund.

Anthony Kucernak, a specialist in electrochemical energy storage, was appointed a lecturer in 1995 and joined the interfacial science section in 1997.[66] (After two renamings the section is now known as chemical physics.) For some years Kucernak was also warden of the Selkirk and Linstead halls of residence and was given a publican's license for the Linstead Hall bar. Being a licensed publican is a lifelong privilege, so Kucernak could open a pub should he wish. But so far chemistry appears the stronger draw and he was given a chair in 2008. Also appointed in 1995 were Paul Wilde and Ian Gould;[67] appointed in 1996 were Christopher Braddock, Stuart L. James, and Ramón Vilar.[68]

10.5 Newcomers in the Later 1990s

David Klug came to IC with a RS Research Fellowship (1990–95), held jointly in the chemistry and biochemistry departments. After a further joint position, he received a full appointment in chemistry in 1998 and was made professor of chemical physics in 2002. Together with Templer and Leatherbarrow he founded the Centre (now Institute) of Chemical Biology in 2002. Klug's research interests are varied. When he joined the department they were largely in the area of natural and artificial photosynthesis, and in the development of new spectroscopic tools. Since then he has focussed on the molecular biology of human health, continuing to develop new optical tools, and recently adding miniaturisation, microfluidics, and single molecule techniques to the toolset.[69] Dominic Tildesley was appointed professor of computational chemistry in 1997 but stayed for only one year before moving to head the physical science group at Unilever.[70]

From 1997 new appointments were no longer made in the three old sections, but in the five new ones (see below). Joining the department in that year were lecturers Andrew DeMello, Joachim Steinke and Robert V. Law. In 1998 they were joined by Antonio Garrido Montalban.[71]

Alan Armstrong joined the synthesis section when he returned to the department as reader of organic synthesis in 1999. The recipient of several awards, including the RSC Meldola Medal in 1995 and the Corday–Morgan Prize in 2002, he became head of department in 2015. His research in stereocontrolled synthesis and the synthesis of biologically active compounds includes work on organocatalysis, kinetics, and modelling.[72] New to the department in 1999 was Nicholas (Nick) Quirke. Recruited to head the computational, theoretical and structural chemistry section, he was appointed professor of physical chemistry. Joining as lecturers in 1999 were James Durrant, Ian Mercer, and David J. Otway.[73] In 2000 nine more people joined the staff: Nicholas (Nic) Harrison was appointed professor of computational materials chemistry and Fernando Bresme, George Britovsek, Robert (Rob) Davies, John DeMello, Neil Robertson, and Sophia Yaliraki were appointed lecturers.[74] Clearly, by 2000 the department was buzzing again. The period 1985–2000 saw also some notable Royal Society research fellows, including Julian Gale and Paul J. Dyson who arrived in 1993 and 1995 respectively, and later joined the staff.[75]

10.6 BSc and MSci Courses; New Forms of Information Access; Social Life Among Students

Not only did this period see a major staff turnover, there were changes also to the undergraduate programme. The number of undergraduates had increased since the 1960s and, by 1985, about 90 were admitted each year. By 2000 the number was 96, close to 40 percent of whom were women (today there are between 800 and 900 applicants for about 180 places).[76] A new first year foundation course had already been introduced in 1974. The idea was to present a unified view of the fundamentals of chemistry together with laboratory courses in which students would be introduced to experimental techniques common to the three sections of the department.[77] Lectures were given on states of matter, valence ideas and bonding, physical methods, kinetics, energetics, ionic equilibria, and solution, as well as on inorganic, aliphatic, and aromatic chemistry. Problems classes were held and students were introduced to the mathematical techniques commonly used in chemistry. The foundation course remained largely unchanged into the 1980s. The second and third year lecture courses and laboratories changed slowly, and by 1985 the second year included a course on chemistry and computing. By then examinations in the translation of German and French chemistry were no longer mandatory, but students could take an optional language course (a range of languages was offered), as well as one in cell biology. Further, they no longer had to take both mathematics and physics but could choose one or the other. In the third year there were further optional courses in mathematics, geology, biochemistry, and management economics.[78] By the late 1990s the foundation course had evolved in the light of experience; but it and the other undergraduate courses were (and remain) organised largely along the old lines — inorganic, organic, and physical.

In the early 1990s most students still took the three-year BSc course, but a new four-year MSci was soon to become the norm. It was introduced for several reasons: remedial, since less chemistry was being taught in schools than was the case in the three postwar decades; to keep IC graduates up to the level of graduates from the best European universities and, relatedly, to keep abreast of the expanding field of chemistry. Students could take chemistry alone, but the BSc in chemistry and management, introduced earlier, was joined by two other joint courses: chemistry and biochemistry, and chemistry and biotechnology.[79] Strictly speaking they were not joint courses, but rather chemistry courses with a particular emphasis in the areas named. Further, students could add an extra year, either at a European university or working in industry.[80] At first this meant taking the three year BSc with a fourth year spent elsewhere. However, by 1999 it was possible to take the four year MSci and add a fifth year working in industry or studying abroad. Having four years as the new norm meant that a new third year course had to be designed. The foundation course remained much as described; so, too, the second year course, though with some updating.[81] Examinations were still given at the end of the first and second years. The old third year course, albeit updated, became the basis for the new fourth year course. The new third year included some advanced theoretical chemistry, a laboratory course in advanced methods, and a literature report. The research project which, in the days of the three year BSc, was restricted to the second half of the third year could now begin in the third and continue into the fourth year. As before, in their third and fourth years students could take a number of optional short lecture courses and were introduced to modern equipment in the laboratory.[82] Some time was devoted to helping students with career development skills such as how to write a Curriculum Vitae (CV). Over the four years the number of laboratory hours per week was lower than in the 1970s but the total number of laboratory hours was about the same as before. In the 1990s students spent about 24 hours per week in the lab (some of them in a computer lab) during their second and third years. Their practical experience, as was the case earlier, was greater than that of students at most other universities.[83]

Two other things are worth noting. First, the department ran a few courses in this period for chemists already in the workplace, mostly having to do with the use of microcomputers in a range of analytical instruments. Second, departmental prizes were updated to fit the new courses and to make the financial component of the awards appropriate. A wide range of prizes were, and still are, given. They include the older Harwood and Briscoe prizes as well as many newer ones, two of which are named for Barton and Evans. The Hatton Prize for the top ARCS/BSc chemistry student no longer exists and has been replaced by the Governors' Prize.

As mentioned above, computers were behind much of the change in this period. In the mid-1980s a proto computer network came to the department when a copper cable was installed connecting C1 to the computing centre in the mechanical engineering building. Henry Rzepa relates that, when exploring how to connect C1 electronically to RCS1, he crawled through some underground tunnels, lost his way, and surfaced in the men's toilet, scaring the lone occupant who fled. As it turned out, the buildings were connected, but not underground. Fibre optic cables were strung via a catenary hung between RCS1 and the old lecture block, and then on to C1.[84] The network allowed for some printing at a distance — in those days laser printers cost about £6,000 and the department had only two by the end of the decade. It also gave access to computers in the IC computing centre and, for a few, to the University of London computers in Malet Street. Already in the early 1980s chemists with access to the network could connect to *Chemical Abstracts* via the Science and Technology Network's (STN) international gateway. This allowed the time needed for a brief literature search to shrink to about 10 minutes, saving a trip to the library. The internet as we know it was then in its infancy, but it was soon to change the face of both teaching and research. It is not much of an exaggeration to state that by the early 21st century teaching laboratories were as likely to be filled with computers as with more traditional chemical apparatus. It is also worth noting that ic.ac.uk was one of the very first e-mail addresses in the United Kingdom.

In the 1990s Richard Templer and David Klug set up a laboratory that they interestingly named 'experimental mathematics' rather than, say, 'computational chemistry.' In it students were encouraged to try many types of simulation such as the semi-empirical modelling of molecular collisions, or of chemical equilibria.[85] Templer says that he hopes lectures will one day become redundant, that students will learn more from the internet, that work in computer and conventional laboratories will be combined, and that only tutorial-type instruction will be required in addition. In a related vein, Don Craig notes that the dynamics of laboratory work, both at the undergraduate and research level, has been much affected by the internet. For example, synthetic chemists are today able to work with large molecules, some with several reaction sites. This is because they are helped by growing computer libraries of reaction routes, and by chemical suppliers that sell a wide range of reaction intermediates.

Students still keep lab notebooks, but by the 1990s many were reading and storing information on computers. The 21st century students have their own mobile devices, and spend even less time in libraries than did the students of the 1990s. That journal articles (and much else) can be read anywhere is empowering. Craig said that his was the last generation of students to submit their PhD theses typed on typewriters. And, like students before him, he drew all his diagrams by hand with the aid of chemical stencils. Today's students no longer have, or need, the drawing skills of earlier generations since they construct diagrams from elements downloaded from the internet. Further, they write up their projects or theses using secondary information gathered largely online where they also submit their work. Traditional methods of library research are becoming a thing of the past.

It is difficult to write much about student life since it is ephemeral and not well documented.[86] It seems, however, that late 20th and early 21st century students socialised more across the years than did their predecessors in the 1970s and 80s.[87] Indeed, departmental social life became more active than it had been since the two postwar decades.[88] It also appears that postgraduates have become a more coherent social force and mix more freely with the staff than was once the case. There are a number of possible reasons for the greater sociality among both undergraduates and postgraduates in this period. The IC Chemical Society was reinvigorated by some keen students who organised many events — and that has continued. Further, the four-year undergraduate course and the greater number of women students (close to 40 percent of undergraduates by 2000) have probably made a difference. The staff is also likely to have been a stimulus since the social life of students is always enlivened by interaction with their teachers, and that is more likely to occur when the latter are young. One also has the impression, hard to document, that social life is less beery than it once was. Lord Oxburgh, when Rector, made an effort to curb the kind of drunken behaviour typical among medical students at the start of the academic year — indeed, he tried to discourage excess drinking in the college more generally.[89]

10.7 Departmental Reorganisation, 1992–2000

Serious thought on how to restructure the department began after David Phillips became head in 1992. That something needed to be done was clear, and not simply because of the financial pressures mentioned above. For a start, changes in the science of chemistry prompted a need for new labels to describe what people actually did. The old section names no longer meaningfully described the research being carried out, and they stood in the way of internal cooperation. Further, people from outside the department, potential collaborators, needed to know what was going on. Another problem was that, in 1992, the average age of the academic staff was 57 which was clearly too high; the department was, to a degree, trading on tradition and needed a shake up. As to funding, although the funding bodies knew that chemistry was an expensive discipline, decisions taken during the 1980s made it very difficult for chemistry departments in the United Kingdom to survive. Earlier, under the University grants Committee/ University Funding Council (UGC/UFC), there had been 11 different bands for the funding of students, but this was reduced to four when cutbacks were made during the recessionary period. Chemistry was still in the top HEFCE band, but the differential was not what it had been earlier. Without some major changes at the local level a deficit was close to inevitable. To avoid debt, departments needed to bring in more students, find new sources of income, and new ways to fund research. For some that proved impossible, and several universities closed their chemistry departments in the late 1980s and early 1990s. Closure was unthinkable at IC, so how to reduce costs and bring in more funding? Since staff costs were 85 percent of the budget, the college helped by introducing an attractive early retirement scheme (not just for chemistry).

Phillips said that there was pressure on him to sacrifice some laboratory teaching and to replace it with virtual computer labs, but he refused and decided to look elsewhere. Two areas where cutbacks were already being made were in the stores and in technical support. The stores, though remaining in C1, were run as a franchise by a specialist company, initially Merck.[90] The mechanical and electrical workshops were closed and their work contracted out. Glassblowing was moved to a college facility shared with, and located in, chemical engineering. This move was resented by some chemists who claimed that the newly-named 'college' glassblowers favoured chemical engineering. It was soon realised that the glassblowing service could be undercut by external companies, so much work was then contracted out. The in-house elemental analysis service was closed and its work sent to a service provided by UCL. Charges (though there was still some central support) were introduced for the use of departmental facilities such as the X-ray, NMR, and mass spectrometry machines. The responsibilities of lab technicians were divided, with one group working in the teaching laboratories and another in the research laboratories, each under a chief technician.[91] By the end of the 20th century a degree in chemistry was required for most technician positions. Although newcomers learned much on the job, many took external courses to keep up with modern equipment and with safety rules; most had first-aid certificates. Computer expertise was also necessary since equipment was rapidly becoming computerised.

Phillips had to consider ways of strengthening research activity, and ways to bring in more funds. In this he received much help from Tony Barrett. In 1995 a fund-raising appeal was set up (to mark the 150th anniversary of the founding of the RCC). It brought in a modest £150,000, largely the result of a student telephone campaign. The money was directed to the new Centre for Analytical Sciences. In addition, two staff positions at the Centre were paid for by SmithKline Beecham and AstraZeneca (see above). More ambitious was the building of some strategic alliances with major industries which brought much new funding to the department. Julian Walsh, a fund raiser employed by the college, helped to pave the way toward some of the alliances.[92] Before discussing them it should be noted that perhaps the most notable of Walsh's achievements was his putting in place an agreement with Emory University and the Georgia Institute of Technology.[93] One result was a research programme involving a team led by Barrett, a team from Emory led by Dennis P. Liotta and James P. Snyder, and another IC team led by Charles Coombes, professor of medical oncology. Their research in medicinal chemistry, supported by Cancer Research United Kingdom and the Engineering and Physical Sciences Research Council (EPSRC), led to the patenting of a number of medicines and to their availability for clinical testing.

Most of the funds raised in this period entailed strategic research alliances with industries that saw themselves as making an investment that might pay off in the future. The companies approached included British Petroleum (BP), Air Products, Rhône Poulenc Rorer, Unilever, AstraZeneca, Roche, BASF, and Mitsubishi Chemicals.[94] According to Wakeham, the contracts that were eventually signed allowed for independent, albeit joint, research. As he put it, IC was not being 'bought out' since the research being funded was consistent with the college charter.[95] Further, in forming alliances he saw the chemistry department as providing a model for other departments in the generation of research income; 'the combination of a fund raiser and an objective that has a sharp focus — [and] a clear academic goal — work[s] extremely well.'[96] The new funding meant that by

2000 the annual departmental income had risen to about £3m from the dismal £250,000 of 1992. Some of that income was the result of the staff becoming more vigorous in seeking grants from the research councils and from charitable sources, but most came from industry.

By 1997 not only was new funding coming in, it had also become clearer where funds were likely to come from in the near future. It appeared, however, that to fully address the deficit, some further changes, including some staff cuts (academic and technical) were necessary. The problem was how to make the cuts in a non-arbitrary fashion. As to the academic staff, information was sought on their teaching and research performance, on the nature of research funding being brought in, and whether a fair share of it was being contributed to departmental over-heads.[97] Although the details were kept confidential, every member of staff was made individually aware by letter of where they stood, both with regards to their relative position in bringing in research funds, and to their perceived contributions to the department. A clearer picture of departmen-tal strengths and weaknesses emerged, and it became easier to plan for the future. This was a difficult and, for a few, a painful process. A business ethos had become normalised in universities during the 1980s and 1990s, one in which research staff were expected to pay their way as never before. The old college vote, a system designed by an academic working party to distribute government funds, no longer delivered enough for the department to survive. Those unable, unwilling, or reluctant to face up to this, and to the new university culture, were hurt.

Tony Barrett was especially keen to bring in a new departmental struc-ture, something that occurred at roughly the same time and, to a degree, in coordination with the changes mentioned above. The first suggestion for replacing the old organic, inorganic and physical sections was that there be six new sections: synthesis, advanced materials, biological chem-istry, polymers and catalysis, analytical and instrumental chemistry, and computational chemistry. A seventh section, interfacial science, was added later. However, having seven sections was thought too risky since staff members would be spread thinly and some sections could look weak when it came to the Research assessment Exercise (RAE). After discus-sion, some consolidation was agreed to and five sections were created. Staff members then had to make a decision as to which section they wished to join. In 1997 the sections were: synthesis; computational and structural chemistry; interfacial science; biological and analytical chemistry; and catalysis and advanced materials.[98] Since then some of the groupings and section names have changed. Today there are still five sections: synthesis; chemical biology; chemical physics; materials chemistry; and catalysis, sustainability and applied inorganics. In 2016, however, it is planned to replace the sections with research themes, each with a coordinator rather than a head. Members of staff will be able to associate with more than one of the themes.[99]

10.8 Coda

In the final two decades of the 20th century the percentage of school leavers with A-level chemistry dropped, but the number taking A-level chemistry stayed roughly the same.[100] Competition for places in the undergraduate programme remained high, even with an increase in the number of places. In the same period about 70 percent of the BSc/MSci graduates left to follow careers in chemistry, most of them for jobs in industry, some as teachers, and a few in government or other research laboratories. Earlier, those leaving for industrial positions usually joined large companies; by 2000 the trend was increasingly towards joining small or medium-sized ones. Roughly 15 percent of graduates left for work outside chemistry, and another 15 percent moved on to advanced degrees. Good academic jobs were, and remain, scarce for PhD graduates.[101]

There is little doubt that the RAE has had a major influence not only on IC but on universities more generally. The effect has been mixed. An increase in both competitiveness and accountability may have been beneficial, but the RAE has probably led to short-termism in research, and to the loss of staff who earlier contributed to departmental well-being in ways other than high-level research.[102] More positive, however, is that it has been a factor in the increase in collaborative research.[103] Collaboration and interdisciplinarity are undoubtedly good; but the history of chemistry suggests that there should be room also for the odd individualist, some of whom have made major contributions to the discipline in the past.[104] There should also be room for a few long-term projects with unpredictable outcomes.[105]

Finally, we have a few further thoughts on the internet and its effect on research. Since there is now enormous pressure to publish quickly, most journals have short refereeing times and publish papers online before publishing them in print (if at all). As soon as a paper appears online the social network universe kicks in and people's Twitter feeds let them know of the new arrival. As Don Craig put it, 'modern chemists need to keep up in order to stay out of trouble.'[106] Emphasis on the 'now' is understandable, but it has its downsides. Given the pressure on today's academics there is little time for them to examine the recent, let alone the more distant, chemical literature. As we have seen in earlier chapters, Barton, and especially Wilkinson, were keen students of chemical history. Indeed some of their major inspirations came from looking back to what chemists had done many years before their time. With today's historical ignorance there is bound to be a fair bit of pointless repetition. And, despite all that is now at people's finger tips, much chemical knowledge is effectively lost.[107]

End Notes

1. For example, in a note to Flowers (ICL archives; B\Wilkinson, 6 August 1985), Wilkinson wrote about, 'the disaster that the UGC has inflicted upon the department ... [they keep] throwing spanners in the works'. He was complaining about space cuts to the proposed C2, that the UGC was allowing too few lecture theatres and seminar rooms, and no space for visiting or emeritus professors, and that its ideas on research space were outdated. Flowers' term as Rector ended in September, 1985.

2. ICL archives, B\Wilkinson; Wilkinson to Ash, 3 June 1987; 'the future of the department as a starred department is now in the greatest jeopardy.' Wilkinson loved the department and was genuinely worried about its future. Just before retiring he wrote again to Ash, 'I have to give the college a final and most serious warning; if the present under-funding of this department continues it will inevitably lead to decline and irreparable damage to one of the country's (and the world's) outstanding chemistry departments' (28 September 1988). Sir Eric Ash FRS FREng gained both his BSc and PhD in electrical engineering at IC. He was the Pender professor and head of the department of electrical engineering at UCL before returning to IC as Rector, 1985–1993.

3. The college administration recognised that the department could not easily avoid running a deficit. Earlier it had been seen as more expedient to allow a deficit than to change the vote formula; but since the college managed to balance its books, a change in the formula would have been sensible. What remained of the debt (about £2 million) was forgiven by Sir Richard Sykes when Richard Templer became head of department in 2002. The old vote formula nearly resulted in the closure of the materials department at IC, saved only after Sir John Cadogan wrote a report, at Ash's request, in which he demonstrated the absurdity of the formula, especially when blindly followed by college bureaucrats who took no account of the space needed for labs, and who gave little or no recognition to the different running costs of the departments. Relatedly, Ash could have lost the various grants (no small sum) that BP donated to the college by insisting that the company include a huge amount for overheads. Cadogan, by then negotiating for BP, refused. Ash backed down and a reasonable overhead was agreed on.

4. The department ranked third in the country, behind Oxford and Cambridge. Given that the Oxbridge departments are, relatively, cushioned from economic downturns, and given the IC department's serious financial problems, this ranking was a good result and it greatly boosted morale. (University assessment of the modern type was introduced in the United Kingdom by the Thatcher government). The first assessment exercise was conducted by the UGC in 1986. The first RAE was conducted by the newly formed HEFCE (and its counterparts) in 1992.)

5. Wilkinson continued with his research in retirement and, for that, Johnson Matthey funded a new laboratory which opened on the 8th floor of C1 in 1989. Willie Motherwell told us that on the form outlining his final grant proposal, Wilkinson answered the question about who would benefit from his research with 'those who read my papers.' Wilkinson died suddenly of a heart attack in 1996.

6. Alan Herbert Cowley FRS (1934–), a specialist in organometallic chemistry, was elected FRS in 1988, the year he was at IC. He returned to Texas in 1989 to one of the Robert A. Welch endowed chairs. The Welch endowment is intended to bring outstanding people to Texas universities and it supports them well; but at that time one had to have been resident outside the state for at least one year to be eligible. Some in the department felt resentment toward Cowley and believed, possibly wrongly, that he was waiting to see whether he would be offered the Welch Chair, and that he had never intended staying at IC if he were. But there is an alternative and

equally plausible narrative. Cowley wrote to us that his Texan wife decided she could not live in London. See also (Halton, 2015).

7. Mingos said that Evans invited him to take the chair soon after Cowley left in 1989, but Ash was slow in negotiating a salary and some other details of the contract. As a result he did not take up the position until 1992.

8. For Albery see Chapter Nine.

9. For Ley see note 21 and Chapter Nine. Ley says he left IC only because of the promise of a new and better equipped laboratory, one that allowed him to carry out the work he wanted to do. He also said that he named his new laboratory the 'Whiffen Lab at Cambridge' in homage to the creative organic chemistry carried out in the Whiffen Lab at IC. In doing so he unwittingly linked his new laboratory back to Hofmann and the RCC. William Whiffen, the major donor for whom the IC lab was named in 1920, was the grandson of a Hofmann student with the same name.

10. David Phillips CBE FRS held the Wolfson chair at the RI before coming to IC. He gained both his BSc and PhD at the University of Birmingham and then won a Fulbright Scholarship which allowed him to take up a postdoctoral fellowship at the University of Texas (Austin). While there, he acted as chauffeur to professor Nikolai N. Kondratiev, Deputy director of the Institute of Chemical Physics in Moscow, a delegate to a meeting of the International Union of Pure and Applied Chemistry (IUPAC), Kondratiev invited him to spend a year at the Institute, and Phillips was able to accept under the Royal Society/USSR Academy of Sciences exchange programme. In Moscow his research director was Victor Y. Shliapintokh. For an interesting account of his experiences in the USSR, (Phillips, 2014). As Phillips put it, he learned much about the Russian people and about himself, and returned 'with a taste for good music, Russian literature and language ... and for taking chances in life'. His life and musical interests are interestingly covered in a BBC Desert Island Discs programme of May 2011 (archived on BBC radio iPlayer). Phillips was president of the RSC (2010–2012), was awarded the OBE (1999), CBE (2012), and elected FRS in 2015. He was recently made FIC. For his research and chemical outreach see below.

11. For Lord Porter, Chapter Nine, Note 113; for Sir John Cadogan, Chapter Nine, Note 93. Sir John Meurig Thomas gained his BSc at Swansea and his PhD at QMC. He is an expert in solid state chemistry and heterogeneous catalysis, and a former head of the physical chemistry department at Cambridge. He succeeded Porter as Fullerian professor at the RI in 1986. Kenneth J. Packer FRS, an NMR specialist, was an undergraduate in the

department, 1956–1959, and as noted in Chapter Eight, he witnessed Eddie Abel's explosion. Packer had a career with BP, later becoming a professor at Nottingham. Colin Poole, a graduate of Leeds and Keele universities, is a professor at Wayne State University, and an expert in the separation and detection of small molecules in biological, environmental, and food samples. He came to IC as a Governors' lecturer and visiting professor, 1995–96. (The Governing Body decided to create a number of new lectureships for young scientists and engineers. The idea was to boost research so as to help IC's ranking among the world's universities.) Patrick Camilleri, a senior analyst (physical organic) from SmithKline Beecham came to work with Andreas Manz, 1999–2000. C. R. A. (Richard) Catlow FRS, a specialist in inorganic materials and computational chemistry, was a visiting professor 1993–2002, after which he became head of the chemistry department at UCL where he is currently Dean of Physical Sciences. While at ICL he carried out some work with Nic Harrison (see also, Halton, 2015). Anthony C. (Tony) Jones, a graduate of the University of Manchester, founded Epichem Ltd. which manufactures chemicals for the pharmaceutical and semi-conductor industries. He collaborated with Paul O'Brien from 1996–2000. Alexander (Alec) Smith, a friend of John Albery, worked at Unilever on colloid chemistry and was a visiting professor, 1985–96. Terrance Wright was a visiting professor, 1992–95.

12. Howard Matthew Colquhoun was a graduate of Westfield College and gave courses on industrial chemistry. He is now professor of materials chemistry at the University of Reading.

13. Gibson and his wife cultivated a vineyard in Kent, became distinguished winemakers, and won several awards.

14. The college made early retirement financially attractive; as a result several people took advantage of it — some also beyond 1995. For more on the people in this paragraph see Chapter Nine and below.

15. Emsley wrote most of the CDN articles himself, some under pseudonyms such as 'CDN Mole' and 'Crystal Tips' (an agony aunt column). He published some items by students (with by-lines), and had a sports reporter, and fellow 'mole,' Alan Bailey.

16. A few of the people given the title lecturer or limited-term lecturer in this period were, in fact, postdoctoral research assistants (PDRA), none of whom stayed very long. The true state of affairs is difficult to unravel; nor is it clear exactly what advantage the college or department had in allowing the title of lecturer to be used by those engaged as research assistants to professors.

17. (Rees, 1984, 1995, 1996). When Rees was elected president of the RSC, John Emsley wrote an article in the *CDN* with the headline, 'World Exclusive. Royal Society of Chemistry chooses ex-lab technician as new President'. Rees was proud of having begun as a lab technician (at the Royal Aircraft Establishment at Farnborough). For further biographical details, Chapter Nine, Note 88.

18. For example, (Widdowson, 1988), (Diorazio, Widdowson, and Clough, 1992). See also Chapter Nine.

19. (Motherwell, 1992), for quotation and for his views on 'curiosity-driven' research. Motherwell believes that all great chemists display a personal signature in their work and said that he aspired to do the same. He has also received the RSC Corday–Morgan Prize, was elected FRS in 2004 and FRSE in 2007. One of his PhD students, Michael Shipman, a former undergraduate in the department, was to win the RSC Meldola Medal and later became head of department at the University of Warwick.

20. See Note 5. Robyn Motherwell said that the lab had room for about four people and a small room next door could house a further two. She and Wilkinson published 13 papers together between 1989 and 1997. For R. Motherwell, see also Chapter Nine, Note 80. Wilkinson gave instructions that, on his death, the lab and all his college possessions were to go to Tony Barrett. Barrett told us that he was shocked by this inheritance, but that he found places for the inorganic chemists working in the lab (two went to Malcolm Green in Oxford), and then converted it for his own use.

21. Ley won the RSC Corday Morgan Medal in 1980, the Tilden Medal in 1988, and the Pedler Medal in 1992. He was elected FRS in 1990 and was to win further awards after leaving the department. They included the IC related RSC Perkin Prize (2009) and the Haworth Memorial Lectureship (2012). He was also awarded the RSC Longstaff prize in 2013. Ley is a collector of historical chemistry books, as was former student Franz Sondheimer. Sondheimer gave his book collection, some of which came from the library of William Perkin Jr., to Ley who has given much of his own collection to university and learned society libraries.

22. Money for this AM-500 500 MHz NMR Bruker machine was provided also by Alan Fersht (see Chapter Nine). A part of Ley's windfall was spent on the department's first modelling/visualisation computer system (a combination MicroVax and Evans and Sutherland PS390 system).

23. (Ley, Armstrong, *et al.*, (14 other authors), 1991); this paper won an RSC Prize in 1991, the year marking the sesquicentenary of the CS/RSC. Literature of this period gives the impression that there was heated

international competition, with organic chemists racing to make new types of compounds with large numbers of stereogenic centres. The race is still on, but the work has become more routine (except for the inventive few) — thanks in part to advances in computer assisted design (see Note 29). Ley said that he failed to get a grant for the synthesis of taxol since the granting agency thought that the synthesis was likely to be too simple to warrant the kind of money he was requesting and, further, that it was unlikely to be medically useful (Ley thought it might be a good insect anti-feedant). However, he was given a grant to make the molecule described in the award winning paper. Azadirachtin, deemed to be more interesting by the granting agency, is an excellent antifeedant named for its natural source, the Neem tree, *Azadirachta indica*. The molecule was indeed interesting, but it took Ley and his team 22 years to make. With respect to taxol, the granting agency was wrong on both counts. It, too, took 22 years to make (by a United States team), and has proven effective in the treatment of some cancers.

24. One early success was the preparation of a catalytic oxidant, TPAP, $^{n}Pr_4N[RuO_4]$, collaboratively with WPG. (Ley, Norman, Griffith, and Marsden, 1994).

25. Needless to say the story of Ley ending an evening out in a skip of leaves has gone through several permutations. This version comes from Ley himself.

26. Sir Richard Sykes FRS FAcMedSci has a BSc in chemistry from Queen Elizabeth College, London, and a PhD from the University of Bristol. In 1992, he was still working at Glaxo where he had a major career. He oversaw its merger with BurroughsWellcome, the drug company purchased by Glaxo to form GlaxoWellcome in 1995. A further merger with SmithKline Beecham (formed in a 1989 merger) led to GlaxoSmithKline in 2000. Sykes came to IC as Rector in 2001 after completing this merger. The Wolfson Foundation contributed about £3 million to the new Centre and Glaxo about £1million. Research at the Wolfson Centre is classified as medical and is therefore VAT exempt.

27. In 2006 the Hofmann chair became attached to the head of department. It is not strictly attached; former heads can continue to hold the chair but, when they leave, the chair reverts to the headship. Barrett holds both the Glaxo and Sir Derek Barton chairs.

28. Ernest Ronald Oxburgh FRS honFREng was Rector of IC from 1993–2000. He is a geologist who was educated at Oxford and Princeton, and was later head of the department of earth sciences at Cambridge. Appointed President

of Queen's College, he was also Chief Scientific Advisor to the Ministry of Defence, 1988–1993 (the post now held by Vernon Gibson, see note 48). Oxburgh was knighted in 1992, and made a life peer in 1999. A Chairman of the House of Lords Select Committee on Science and Technology, he was appointed non-executive chairman of Shell in 2004.

29. Barrett's work is focussed on antibiotics, anti-cancer agents and other novel therapeutics. For some natural product work from the 1990s see, for example, (Barrett, Hamprecht, White and Williams, 1996, 1997). In a paper, an interesting artefact of its period, P. L. Fuchs used his own algorithm to claim that the second of these papers had 'the highest IQ (1.83) we have observed thus far' (IQ, intricacy quotient), (Fuchs, 2001). Barrett told us that, since his work of the late 1990s, computer assisted drug design (CADD) has begun to help in deciding which compounds are worth synthesising as possible new drugs. However, given the state of both structural biology and the structural chemistry of receptors, the design quality remains poor. Synthesis is also aided by industrial procedures used in making the kind of chemical building blocks once seen as novel discoveries in academic laboratories. According to Barrett, discovery teams in some pharmaceutical, agrochemical and fine chemical companies are often better than applied teams in academia. However, in his view, although industrial and academic science is now almost a continuum, the best 'blue sky' and fundamental research is still found in universities. Barrett has won many awards, including the RSC Meldola, Harrison, Corday–Morgan, and Tilden awards in 1980, 1981, 1986, and 1994 respectively. He was elected FRS in 1999 and FAc.Med. Sci. in 2003. In 2010 he was the first winner of the RSC Charles Rees Award — cited for his work on multimetallic porphyrazine arrays. (The second winner, in 2012, was Christopher Moody (see Chapter Nine)).

30. In 2010 Argenta Discovery had 140 employees and sold its contract business and the company name for €16.5million to Biofocus Galapagos to form Biofocus Galapagos Argenta; it has become one of the world's largest drug discovery service organisations.

31. For more on Fersht see Chapter Nine, including Note 98. Fersht was elected FRS in 1983 and was the Davy medallist in 1998. At Cambridge he was Herchel Smith professor of organic chemistry, 1988–2010, and director of the Cambridge Centre for Protein Engineering, 1990–2010. For selected papers, (Fersht and Wang, 2010).

32. Robin Leatherbarrow gained his BSc at Liverpool University and DPhil at Oxford. He was Dean of the Faculty of Natural Sciences at IC, 2010–13, leaving ICL to become Pro-Vice-Chancellor at Liverpool John Moores

University. One other person should be mentioned in connection with chemical biology, though, strictly speaking, he does not belong in this history having joined the department only in the 21st century. Anthony (Tony) Cass became professor of chemical biology in 2010, but he has worked at IC since 1983 when he joined the biochemistry department to help set up the Centre for Biotechnology. In 1993, he won (with Allen Hill FRS and Monika Green) the RS Mullard Medal 'in recognition of their contribution to the translation of bioelectrochemical research into the successful launch of molecular sensors for medical use.'

33. Donald (Don) Craig was an undergraduate in the department and gained his PhD with Steve Ley working on insect antifeedant synthesis. He spent a year as a postdoctoral fellow working at Columbia University with Clark Still before returning to the lectureship in 1987.

34. Andrew David Miller gained his BSc from the University of Bristol in 1984 and then moved to Cambridge for his PhD with Alan Battersby. He was a postdoctoral fellow with Jeremy Knowles at Harvard University before coming to IC in 1990. He left in 2010.

35. Since 1989, eight women have won the Meldola (since 2008, the Harrison Meldola) Prize. Two, Charlotte Williams and Marina Kuimova are current members of staff, and one, Rachel O'Reilly, is a PhD graduate.

36. Sue Gibson, personal communication. Susan E. (Sue) Gibson gained her BSc from Cambridge and DPhil from Oxford. From there she won an RS research fellowship which she took to the ETH before moving to a lectureship at the University of Warwick. At IC, her research concerned the reactivity of vinylketene iron carbonyl complexes, and the synthesis of novel cyclic amino acids with medium-sized rings incorporated into gastrin receptor antagonists (Gibson and Middleton, 1995). In 1998 she was appointed to the Daniell chair at KCL, returning to a chair at IC when the KCL department closed in 2003. While at KCL she became the first recipient of the RS Rosalind Franklin Award. It included a monetary component of £30,000 from the Department of Trade and Industry to be used, over three years, to help promote the interests of women scientists. She still holds a chair in the department but wound down her research in 2010 when she took a leave of absence. She returned in 2013 and is now director of the Graduate School. For her 'services to chemistry and science education,' she was made OBE in 2013. See also (Halton, 2015).

37. In 1996 Marsden won the Glaxo–Wellcome Award for innovative organic chemistry and, in 1999, the RSC Meldola Medal. He left for the chair of organic chemistry at Leeds in 2001. See also (Halton, 2015).

38. Christopher J. Parkinson was educated at the University of Sydney where he gained his BSc and PhD. He was appointed a limited term lecturer while carrying out research with Barrett. He left the department in 1998 and, after working in South Africa for a few years on generic pharmaceuticals, he moved back to Australia and is now at Charles Sturt University, NSW. In a letter to us he expressed a perceptive view of the department in the 1990s, 'I felt that there was a sense of history, but that came with a bit of an identity crisis. IC felt a little stuck in time. I think that the school was struggling a lot with how to remain relevant for the next century (and remain financially viable).'

39. In 2001 the College gave both Margaret and David Goodgame honorary ARCS degrees 'for their joint contribution to the welfare of students, and their respective terms as sympathetic and kindly tutors'.

40. One notable explosion occurred in 1986 when one of Woollins' students made $(NSOCl)_3$ from NaN_3 and $SOCl_2$ at low temperature. The bench split from end to end and bits of the aluminium Dewar became embedded in the lab walls. No one was injured. Just as the safety officer was dealing with this event, he was called away to another incident in which an undergraduate making $(Me_3Si)S(SiMe_3)$ used a syringe to remove an aliquot for testing. However, the plunger popped out and the entire reaction went straight up the fume hood, and out into the neighbourhood. It is also said, though no one can quite remember, that some mercaptan escaped at this time. It did not take long for the phones to begin ringing. A major gas leak was wrongly suspected, Exhibition Road was closed, buildings were evacuated, and the college was threatened with a £10,000 fine which, in the end, was not imposed. Woollins now holds a chair, and is Provost and Vice-Chancellor for research, at St. Andrews. For further biographical and research information on the people mentioned in this paragraph see Chapters Eight and Nine.

41. David Michael Patrick (Mike) Mingos FRS gained his BSc at UMIST and his DPhil with Joseph Chatt (see Chapter Eight) at the University of Sussex in 1968. He then held a postdoctoral fellowship at NorthWestern University, returning to Sussex and an ICI fellowship with Ronald Mason (see Chapter Eight) in 1970–1971. From 1971 to 1976 he was a lecturer at QMC and, from 1976 to 1992, a lecturer, then reader, at Oxford University. He was a winner of both the RSC Corday–Morgan and Tilden Prizes, in 1980 and 1988 respectively. Mingos edited the journals *Structure and Bonding* and *Journal of Organometallic Chemistry*; and he wrote three textbooks published while he was at IC, (Mingos, 1995, 1998, 1998b). He was appointed

Principal of St. Edmund Hall, Oxford, in 1999, and became professor of inorganic chemistry at Oxford in 2000. Before leaving IC, Mingos raised money from both the staff and industry to fund the biennial RSC Sir Geoffrey Wilkinson Medal. It was first awarded to Malcolm Green (see Chapter Eight) in 1999. For Mingos, (Strassner, 2015).

42. Sir John Cadogan was instrumental in getting BP to help fund four chairs, two in chemistry (at IC and Cambridge), one at Oxford in robotics/IT, and one at the LSE.

43. Baghurst was another research associate with the title lecturer. He returned to Oxford in 1996 and is now a director of Isis Innovations.

44. Anthony F. Hill gained his MSc from the University of Auckland and his PhD from the University of Bayreuth. He is now head of the chemistry department at the ANU.

45. Paul Lickiss gained his BSc and DPhil from the University of Sussex. He joined the inorganic section after a short period as lecturer at the University of Salford. His interests include organosilicon chemistry, particularly the chemistry of silanols and silyl cations, as well as sonochemistry and, more recently, metal-organic frameworks; see (Lickiss, 1995, 1998). Lickiss is the user coordinator for the new molecular sciences hub at Imperial White City, due to open in 2017.

46. This title is no longer used (it could presumably be revived). Lady Wilkinson helped to set up the chair and donated £10,000 toward a studentship.

47. Working with him on these were two postdoctoral research fellows, Greg Solan and George Britovsek. Solan made the ligand which works the magic for the catalyst, but attached it to Mn which was inactive. Britovsek made the Fe complex which works well, (Gibson, Redshaw, and Solan, 2007). Solan is now at the University of Leicester. Britovsek was appointed a lecturer in the IC department in 2000 and is now a reader; he works on catalysts for alkane oxidation, polymerisation and biomass conversion.

48. Vernon Charles Gibson FRS gained his BSc from the University of Sheffield and his DPhil from the University of Oxford where he studied under Malcolm Green (see Chapter Eight). After holding a NATO postdoctoral fellowship at the California Institute of Technology, he returned to the United Kingdom and to a lectureship, then professorship, at the University of Durham. He was made FRS in 2004 and is the recipient of many awards including the RSC's Corday–Morgan Award (1993), Joseph Chatt Award (2001), and Tilden Medal (2004). Since 2012 he has been Chief Scientific Advisor at the Ministry of Defence.

49. Fifty years earlier entrepreneurial activity was looked upon with some disdain in many universities, though consulting work was seen as acceptable. Even at IC, where entrepreneurial activity has always existed, and has been to a degree encouraged, people were affected by the culture of their time.

50. Paul O'Brien gained his BSc in Liverpool in 1975, and PhD at Cardiff in 1978 working with Bob Gillard (see Chapter Eight). Before coming to IC he was a professor of inorganic chemistry at QMC/Westfield. He was elected FRS in 2013, and was awarded the CBE in the 2016 New Year's honours list for services to science and engineering..

51. (Trindade, O'Brien and Pickett, 2001).

52. There was much competition for these lectureships (see Note 11). Also arriving in 1995 was Phillip Dyer, on a limited term lectureship. He left in 1997 and is today reader in inorganic chemistry at Durham.

53. Nicholas James (Nick) Long gained his PhD at Durham in 1986 and his PhD at the University of Exeter (with Eddie Abel; see Chapter Eight). After a temporary lectureship at Darwin College, Cambridge, he came to IC as a lecturer in 1995. His work concerns the synthesis of transition metal, lanthanide and ferrocene systems, and their applications to homogeneous catalysts. For his book on metallocenes, (Long, 1998).

54. Welton was right about the 'make do' culture at IC, but it was not an artefact of the times. Many people have remarked on it, throughout IC's history. Unlike the ancient universities and many of the civic ones, IC has never had a sizeable endowment to fall back on. The staff have always had to bring in their own research funding and, more generally, have had to 'make do.' This, and the entrepreneurial culture has served the college well.

55. The First Grant scheme was not yet in place and, understandably, Welton asked himself 'how the hell do I get started?' He was grateful for the kinetics lessons. Thomas (Tom) Welton gained his BSc (1985) and DPhil (1990) at the University of Sussex, the latter with Kenneth Seddon. Before coming to IC he spent a year as Eddie Abel's demonstrator at Exeter (for Abel see Chapter Eight). His own research is focussed on solvents that can improve chemical processes, and ionic liquids that can be used to convert biomass into fuels or other chemical products. He is the author of a widely-cited review article, (Welton, 1999). Welton was head of department, 2007–2015.

56. (Spiro and Jaganyi, 1993). Their ideas are now largely accepted. The media interest is recorded in an article in the August 1993 issue of *CDN*. Spiro recounted returning home on the day before publication to non-stop phone

calls. (*Nature* had sent out an advance press release.) He was interviewed for radio and TV, and many tea scum stories appeared in the press.

57. The last of the old guard to retire were Hayward in 2001 and Nicholson in 2002.

58. This work was supported by the EPSRC. See, for example, (Phillips, 1995), (Kwok, Ma, Matousek, Parker, Phillips, and Towrie, 2000). For biographical information see Note 10. While at the RI, Phillips also helped to develop supersonic jet spectroscopy which gives structural information down to $0.5°K$, thus simplifying the fluorescence spectrum.

59. Phillips gave this lecture on several occasions, including at the official opening of the William Perkin Church of England High School, in Greenford, Middlesex, on 15 May, 2014. He has won recognition for his work in chemical outreach, including being awarded the RSC Nyholm Lecture and Medal (1994) and the RS Faraday Medal (1997). He estimates that his live outreach lectures have reached more than a quarter of a million listeners. The citation for the Faraday Medal noted his 'outstanding talents in the communication of scientific principles, methods and applications to young audiences through his many demonstration lectures [delivered] with wit, clarity and enthusiasm'.

60. Garry Rumbles was a PhD student with Phillips at the Davy Faraday Research Laboratory at the RI, returning there in 1987 after three years as a postdoctoral fellow in the United States.

61. Richard Templer gained his BSc in physics from the University of Bristol in 1981, and his DPhil from Oxford in 1986 on physical measurement in archaeology. Having decided to change fields, he spent two years at Princeton University on a Harkness postdoctoral fellowship with Sol Gruner, carrying out biophysical research on lipid membranes. From there he won an RS research fellowship which Gruner recommended he take to Southampton to work with John Seddon. He and Seddon both then moved to IC. Templer was head of department, 2002–2007.

62. Templer decided on a further career change when his term as head of department ended. He had become interested in climate change and, in 2009, was part of a successful bid to the European Institute for Innovation and Technology for funding for a climate knowledge innovation community (KIC). Although still at ICL, he is now director of the United Kingdom arm of Climate-KIC, and director of Education for the whole of KIC. The idea of KIC is to help academics commercialise innovations that could help in limiting climate change or in adjusting to it.

63. John M. Seddon gained his BSc from the University of Stirling in 1975, and his PhD in biophysics from Guy's Hospital Medical School in 1980. After postdoctoral research he held a lectureship at the University of Southampton, joining IC in 1991. He is a specialist in membrane biophysics, in the lyotropic phase behaviour of lipids and surfactants, and in complex membrane geometries, (Seddon, 1990), (Seddon and Templer, 1993).

64. Timothy S. (Tim) Jones gained his BSc and PhD from Liverpool University. While at IC he helped to set up the London Centre for Nanotechnology, run jointly with UCL. Like O'Brien he worked at the well-equipped interdisciplinary research centre in semiconductor materials run by the physicist Bruce Joyce. Jones left in 2007 to join the University of Warwick's Centre for Analytical Science; he is now Pro-Vice Chancellor for Science, Engineering and Medicine at Warwick.

65. Norman Smith was appointed to the Centre as a lecturer, but moved to KCL in 2002; John Graham was a lecturer from 1991–1995. The Centre closed in 2004.

66. Anthony R. J. Kucernak gained his BSc and MSci from the University of Auckland. For his PhD he went to the University of Southampton but carried out some work at the AERE (later AEA Technology), Harwell. At Harwell he was one of 12 authors of a paper that rebutted the work of Fleischmann and Pons on cold fusion (Williams, Kucernak et al., 1989). For Fleischmann see Chapter Eight. Kucernak came to IC after a postdoctoral fellowship at Cambridge with Tim Burstein working on methanol fuel cells. His current research concerns the development of electrochemical energy storage and conversion devices such as batteries, fuel cells, supercapacitors, and electrowetting devices.

67. Paul Wilde, a former undergraduate in the department gained his PhD with Albery. He returned to IC from an associate professorship at the University of Ottawa, another stronghold of electrochemistry. His interests are in the electrochemistry of gold nanoparticles and self-assembling monolayers. Ian Gould gained his BSc and PhD from the University of Manchester, and has an interest in computational chemistry.

68. David Christopher (Chris) Braddock gained his BSc and DPhil (1992) from the University of Oxford. He came to IC in 1997 to work with Tony Barrett and was appointed a lecturer in the new synthesis section where he is now a professor. His work is on stereoselective organic synthesis of natural products using novel methods including asymmetric organocatalysis. Stuart L. James gained his PhD with Mike Mingos and then held a limited term lectureship. He left to work in the 'green technology' industry, and

now holds the chair of inorganic chemistry at Queen's University, Belfast. Ramón Vilar gained his BSc in UNAM, Mexico City and his PhD with Mingos at ICL. A specialist in medical inorganic chemistry, he joined the chemical biology section where he is now a professor. He succeeded Leatherbarrow as head of the section in 2013. Before 2003, when he moved his research to bioinorganic chemistry, he worked on the templating role of anions for the synthesis of complex assemblies in supramolecular and coordination chemistry, (Vilar, 2003).

69. David Klug, who now Chairs the Institute, received his BSc in Physics from UCL in 1984 and his PhD from the RI in 1987. At the RI he worked with George Porter. He cofounded the spin-out company Powerlase with two physical chemistry lecturers, Alan G. Taylor (appointed in 1996) and Ian P. Mercer (appointed in 1999), neither of whom stayed long in the department. Mercer is now a lecturer in physics at University College Dublin.

70. Dominic John Tildesley gained his BSc at the University of Southampton and DPhil at Oxford. He came to IC from the University of Southampton. He is currently President of the RSC (2014–2016).

71. Andrew James DeMello was a BSc student in the department who stayed to work with Garry Rumbles for his PhD (1995) in the field of molecular photophysics. He spent a postdoctoral year at the University of California (Berkeley) working on 'lab-on-a-chip' devices, before returning to the department as AstraZeneca lecturer in Analytical Sciences, joining Manz in the Centre for Analytical Sciences. He won the RSC Corday–Morgan medal in 2009 for work in microfluidics and nanobioanalytical research. In 2011 he moved to the ETH in Zurich, but retained a (0.2 FTE) connection to IC in the MRC Clinical Sciences Centre in the Faculty of Medicine. Joachim H. G. Steinke (1964–2013) gained his first degree from the Heinrich Heine University in Düsseldorf and his PhD from the University of Strathclyde. After postdoctoral years at Cornell and Cambridge he came to IC as a lecturer in the new biological and biophysical chemistry section. Steinke's close friend, Robert V. (Rob) Law was a fellow PhD student at Strathclyde. He held postdoctoral fellowships at the Tokyo Institute of Technology and at Manchester University before joining the department. For Law's memoir of Steinke, see the IC news website, 18 January, 2013. Antonio Garrido Montalban gained a PhD at the University of East Anglia and came to IC as a postdoctoral fellow with Tony Barrett. His was a short stay and he now holds a senior position with Arena Pharmaceuticals in San Diego, CA.

72. Alan Armstrong gained his BSc in the department in 1987, and stayed for his PhD with Ley working on the total synthesis of (+) milbemycin 1 and avermectin B1a (see also Note 23). After a postdoctoral fellowship with Clark Still at Columbia University he took up lectureships at Bath and Nottingham before returning to IC. See (Armstrong, Ahmed, Dominguez-Fernandez, Hayer, and Wailes, 2002).

73. Nicholas (Nick) Quirke was educated at the University of Leicester, spent a postdoctoral year at Cornell, and then had an industrial career becoming head of molecular modelling at BP. After a short period at IC he moved to Dublin as a Faculty Dean, later returning to the department. James Durrant studied for his PhD with George Porter at the RI (also supervised by James Barber, a biochemistry professor at IC). After postdoctoral fellowships in biochemistry, he moved to the chemistry department as a lecturer. He won the RSC Meldola Medal in 1994 and the Tilden Medal in 2012. He is now professor of photochemistry and a member of the nanostructured materials and devices group. David Otway gained his BSc and PhD in the department. As a postdoctoral research assistant he worked with Wilkinson and O'Brien and was given a fixed-term lectureship in the electronics materials group. He left to work with a spin-out pharmaceuticals company, and was later a lecturer at University College, Cork. For Mercer, Note 69.

74. Nicholas (Nic) Harrison gained his BSc in Birmingham and his PhD at Birmingham and the Daresbury Laboratory where he holds a joint appointment as head of the computational materials science group at the Science and Technology Facilities Centre at the Rutherford Appleton and Daresbury Laboratories. At IC he is director of the Institute of Molecular Science and Engineering. John C. DeMello gained his BSc at Oxford and PhD at Cambridge. He is now professor of nanomaterials in the nanostructured materials and devices group. Neil Robertson gained his BSc and PhD at Edinburgh and returned there after two years as a lecturer at IC. George Britovsek gained his BSc at the University of Aachen and was a postdoctoral fellow first at the University of Tasmania and then with Vernon Gibson at ICL. Today he is reader in catalysis (see Note 49). Fernando Bresme gained his PhD on condensed matter research from the Complutense University of Madrid and came to IC as a postdoctoral fellow in 1998 and is now professor of theoretical physics. Sophia Yaliraki gained her BSc from Harvard (1992) and her PhD from MIT (1997). She came to the department on a Governors' lectureship and is now professor of theoretical chemistry. Robert (Rob) Davies gained his BSc at Bristol University (1994) and his PhD from Cambridge (1997). A specialist in inorganic coordination

and organometallic chemistry, he is now a senior lecturer in the synthesis section.

75. Paul Joseph Dyson held a fixed-term lectureship followed by an RS research fellowship, and is now a professor at the École Polytechnique Fédérale in Lausanne. Julian Gale gained his DPhil in chemical crystallography at Oxford. He was appointed reader in theoretical and computational chemistry in 2000, but left in 2003 for Curtin University after being given one of two inaugural 'distinguished' chairs funded by the Government of Western Australia. Three other notable postdoctoral fellows are Marie Louise Smith, John Arnold and Wendy Flavell. Smith gained her BA and DPhil from the University of Oxford where she worked with Jack Baldwin (see Chapter Eight) before taking a postdoctoral fellowship with Tony Barrett. One year later, she was awarded the inaugural RS Dorothy Hodgkin research fellowships. Arnold gained his BSc at the University of Salford and his PhD at the University of California (San Diego). He was a postdoctoral fellow with Wilkinson (1987–1988) before being awarded the RS research fellowship in 1988. He is now professor of theoretical chemistry at the University of California (Berkeley). Flavell is an Oxford-educated chemist. She left the department in 1990 to take up a lectureship at UMIST, and today is professor of surface physics in the School of Physics and Astronomy at the University of Manchester.

76. The number of women PhD students in 2000 was also close to 40 percent, but the number of women postdoctoral fellows was only about 10 percent.

77. A nine-week basic laboratory course was run by Les Pratt; there were also two analytical courses of four weeks each and a six-week synthesis lab.

78. The ancillary options grew in the 21st century to include medicinal biology, medicinal chemistry, various languages, mathematics and physics for chemists, geology, management, and some disciplines in the humanities and social sciences.

79. In the 21st century the joint degrees changed and the following became available: chemistry with a language for science; chemistry with molecular physics; chemistry with medicinal chemistry and, as before, chemistry with management.

80. The year in Europe was basically part of an exchange scheme (the Socrates, then Erasmus, scheme) with students from selected European universities coming to IC.

81. Unilever paid three second year students £1000 each to work for nine weeks in the summer vacation testing new experiments for the second year physical chemistry laboratory.

82. By the 1990s this included high-field multinuclear Fourier transform magnetic resonance spectrometers (the department had machines ranging from 90 to 500 MHz), a laser Raman spectrometer and several infrared spectrometers. Students also had access to high performance liquid chromatography apparatus, ion chromatography, high resolution mass spectrometry, X and Q-band ESR, X-Ray diffractometers, and to a solid-phase peptide synthesis apparatus.

83. Tony Barrett mentioned that he took the long course in gravimetric analysis when he was a student (as did both authors). As noted in earlier chapters, this was an area much emphasised at the college from 1845 until around 1980. He said that the course taught him the importance of precision, something he sees as important and something that, in his view, today's students don't fully appreciate.

84. Because Rzepa arranged this he took the opportunity of extending the fibre cable to his office, and was probably the only person at the college to have a fibre connection to his desktop at that time. Rzepa retired in 2014 as professor of computational chemistry. In 2015 he was awarded the IC Medal in recognition of his outstanding service to the college. We are indebted to him for much information on the history of computing in the department.

85. It is worth noting that the 2013 Nobel Prize in chemistry was shared by three computer simulation modellers: Martin Karplus, Michael Levitt and Arieh Warshel.

86. A chapter on corporate and social life at IC can be found in (Gay, 2007b).

87. Margaret Goodgame remembered much social activity in the 1960s including various outings such as boat trips on the Thames and annual cricket matches between the inorganic and organic chemists. She also remembers an 'Oscar' awards ceremony, possibly in the 1970s, at which she won an 'Oscar' for being the department's 'hardest marker.' It should also be noted that later, in 1986, students produced a lively magazine, *Alchemica Acta*.

88. More generally it can be claimed that there was an increase in sociality during the two postwar periods. In the interwar period, senior staff members saw it as their duty to socialise with young students. For that reason there were formal dinners, clubs with staff and student membership, and so on. After WW2 the pattern continued — Patrick Linstead, for example, was especially interested in promoting the social and cultural life of students. Today attitudes are less paternalistic — not that the earlier paternalism was resented, on the contrary.

89. It is worth considering whether this was because of his disapproval of drunken behaviour, or because he wanted to make student life more comfortable for women — possibly both. Speculation along these lines is complicated by questions of sexism and paternalism which we cannot pursue here. None of this is exclusively a college or departmental matter and depends on wider cultural attitudes. Drinking has declined more generally in the United Kingdom, though binge drinking remains a problem.

90. TUPE (Transfer of Undertaking Protection of Employment) laws protected the workers who became Merck employees in what was essentially a centralised college franchise.

91. Today there are two chief technicians each with seven people working under them: Chris Howard for the teaching labs and Peter Sulsh for the research labs. Howard has worked in the department for over 30 years and Sulsh for over 40.

92. Julian Walsh, a former student in the department, left to become an oil trader for BP. He was later appointed IC's director of strategic alliances by William (Bill) Wakeham, Pro-Rector for Research. Walsh's main role was to raise funds. At first he helped Barrett and the synthesis section; later he was to help the chemical biology section. Sadly Walsh died in 2013. Other departments whose staff collaborated with chemistry, such as the chemical engineering department, joined in building the strategic alliances. As Wakeham, a chemical engineer, put it, 'the discussions which took place between the two departments in the last 18 months exceed the number which took place over several years', (quoted in *IC Reporter*, 11 March–21 April, 1997, 1–2).

93. Among other things, the agreements gave IC access to the Oak Ridge National Laboratory.

94. Major contracts were signed with Rhône Poulenc Rorer and Roche (Barrett), Mitsubishi (Miller), BP (Gibson) and Unilever (some joint projects with chemical engineering). A contract with BASF was negotiated but did not, in the end, come off. AstraZeneca supported the Centre for Analytical Sciences (see above) as did SmithKline Beecham. Glaxo, GlaxoWellcome and, by the late 1990s, GlaxoSmithKline, continued its support of the department in various ways. The connection to Glaxo goes back a long way, as discussed in earlier chapters.

95. This was probably true, but it depends on how one interprets the college charter. The charter states that research 'especially in its application to industry' be carried out at the college. For Wakeham's statements, *op. cit* (Note 92).

96. *op. cit.* (Note 92).

97. This type of evaluation was outside the norm and led to some difficulty with the AUT and the Rector. The MSF Union (forerunner of Amicus) also objected to changes in technician staffing.

98. The heads of section following the 1997 change, though not all of them took office immediately, were David Phillips (Biological and Analytical), Vernon Gibson (Catalysis and advanced materials), Tony Barrett (Synthesis), Nick Quirke (Computational and structural), and John Seddon (Interfacial science).

99. Themes suggested are: advanced catalysis and synthesis; chemical biology and healthcare; environmental and Green chemistry; energy; imaging, sensing and analytical chemistry; and materials and molecular design.

100. Demographic data suggest this is unlikely to stay the same. Applicant numbers could drop in the future.

101. This raises the question of oversupply. Many academics enjoy having large research groups, not only to further the science, but also to further their own ambition.

102. The department can no longer afford to have non-research active people on the staff.

103. Many factors can lead to collaboration. Perhaps the amazing success of the Manhattan Project during WW2, a collaborative scientific effort without historical parallel, became a model of sorts for the later 20th century (IC played a part in the Manhattan Project, see Chapter Seven). Further, new bio-chemical-medical research requires, by its very nature, the cooperation of a wide range of experts.

104. Barton and Wilkinson were both individualists, though not 'odd individualists'. People worked under them in research teams, but both were reluctant to work with other well-established chemists — most of whom they viewed as competitors. Theirs was a successful model in its time, but is not one that fits today's more democratic ethos. As to the term 'odd individualist' we use it to describe a different type. Dennis Evans and Les Pratt (see Chapter Nine) were perhaps examples from the period 1960–1990, fitting the description not because of any general oddness — though they both had eccentricities — but because they stood apart, had few students, and few collaborators. They would have fared less well under today's system. Evans was elected FRS, but would he have been able to survive for long enough to achieve that distinction today? Even though most people adapt to their times, the existence of the RAE (and its successor, the REF) could mean

that some brilliant individualists are/will be excluded from academic careers at major universities.

105. One is reminded of Herbert Brereton Baker, 'Dry Baker' (Chapter Five) who dried chemicals for years because he had some theory that he wished to test on the role of water in chemical reactions. Some of his experimental findings have still not been explained. They, together with his ideas, have been dismissed/forgotten because they are inconsistent with modern theory. But Baker was a careful experimentalist and it remains unclear whether all of his experimental observations should be dismissed.

106. Craig (personal communication). He also said that much new synthesis of interest to the pharmaceutical industry is close to being automated in laboratories in both India and China. So the modern academic synthesist has not only to pay attention to Twitter but has to be ingenious to compete successfully.

107. Symptomatic of the late-century developments was the closure of the departmental library, the removal of its books and journals to the main library, and the use of the freed-up space for computers. The Science Museum Library, which once shared space with the chemistry library, has now closed, and most of its books have been placed in a storage facility at Wroughton. The books are still accessible but not easily. Unless scanned, most old books, unlike most journals, are not at people's finger tips.

Chapter Eleven

Epilogue

11.1 Chemistry's Changing Situation

Before the Second World War Imperial College (IC) was viewed with a certain amount of disdain. Although seen as an excellent technical college, it did not have the kind of recognition it has today. Many in the academic world, if they thought about IC at all, believed that it was not a 'proper' university. A place that gave degrees in mining, and that did not require a classical language for matriculation, could not be taken seriously as a seat of higher learning. This kind of academic snobbery led to fine distinctions, with some outsiders viewing the RCS as being a little above the City and Guild's Central Technical College (C&GCTC) and Royal School of Mines (RSM) — though tainted by association. The war changed people's attitudes, and by the 1960s progressive thinkers from all walks of life saw IC as an institution representative of the modern world. Artists, writers, musicians, historians, theatre directors — and, of course, politicians — were keen to associate with it. Many came to give talks at the college, and some invited students to take part in their activities.[1] Science, technology, and engineering benefited from the changing cultural climate and, by the end of the century, the chemistry department had more than doubled its post-war size.

Although the period after WW2 was pivotal, it is clear that the 20th century as a whole saw the older hierarchy of learning turned on its head. This was related to a changing economy and to the type of industrialisation that was occurring already before the war. The chemical industry grew significantly, a major factor in the department's growth. In the latter part of the century, with many of the problems in the heavy chemical industry solved, the discipline shifted. There has always been latent recognition that the study of matter and its behaviour is fundamental to work in many areas of science. Indeed, as Geoffrey Wilkinson used to say, 'chemistry is the central science.' Such recognition became more overt, and today chemistry is seen as important in many areas: notably in materials science and engineering, nanotechnology, molecular medicine, molecular agriculture, and bioengineering. In recounting the history of the department over 155 years, this book has shown how historical forces bring new areas such as these to the fore, and how, in turn, they influence disciplinary change at the micro level. No doubt the histories of other chemistry departments would tell a similar story. However, although every institutional history can be seen as a case study, in essence each is *sui generis*. We have tried to show something of both the generic, and the distinct in our history of the department.

It has been said both of IC, and the chemistry department, that they are good, but not as good as they think they are. When interpreting such statements, one has to look at who is making them, and why. One person who made this claim in 2003 was Brian Flowers, reflecting on the state of the college when he arrived as Rector 30 years earlier. As he saw it, IC with its relatively small endowment was not adjusting well to the economic and political changes of the 1970s. He believed that the college was very good, but 'not as good as it thought it was,' and that by helping the various departments come to terms with the new realities he had been able, in an indirect way, to raise standards.[2] As to the chemistry department, we have seen that Flowers had something of a struggle with Geoffrey Wilkinson whom he appointed as Head of Department in 1976. Wilkinson was slow in coming to terms with the economic recession, and with the politics that followed. With some justification, however, he saw his department as coming under attack. He rightly saw it as very good, though he probably did not see it as better than it actually was. In his view the department was beginning to decline and he was trying to do what he could to prevent it from declining further. Besides, the claim that a person or institution thinks itself better than it really is spurious, and says more about the judge than the judged. In some circumstances, it can provide a poorly reasoned excuse for not awarding an institution or individual with research grants or other favours. Indeed, Wilkinson saw Flowers as giving poorly reasoned excuses for not supporting the department in the ways that he believed necessary, and for not pushing the UGC to be more generous, and timely in providing for the department's needs. In retrospect we can see that Flowers was better informed than Wilkinson on the changing political and economic climate, and that his advice was prescient and well meant. Although viewed negatively at the time, many of his suggestions were eventually followed. At base, histories are stories about human struggles such as these, about hard work and conflicting views — political, scientific, or other — and about the various outcomes. This history is no exception.

The expansion in higher education in the later 20th century met with some resistance and, in the absence of widespread public support, taxes could no longer be relied on to cover the major cost of university teaching and research in ways they once did.[3] It became clear that taxpayers, students, industry, and other stakeholders would all have to pay something toward the costs, and all would expect something in return. The problem was, and remains, how to distribute the costs, and how the rewards — a new social contract with respect to higher education is still being worked out. As to the chemistry department, by the early 1990s its staff came to understand that to remain among the world's best, they had to become more proactive in seeking industrial support.

By the late 1990s the department had attracted new funding, much of it from the pharmaceutical and energy sectors.[4] Increasingly, smaller 'start-up' companies with a wide range of interests also played a role in supporting research. Relatedly, there has been considerable entrepreneurial activity among members of the staff. Such activity is not new, but cultural change has led to it becoming more valued in the academic world than earlier, especially when it brings in research funding that helps to foster new ventures. As always, the problem is not so much where research funding comes from; nor, provided the public interest is kept broadly in mind, what type of research is prioritised. Rather, it is to make sure that funders cannot buy the results they seek, and that the intellectual independence of universities is safeguarded — no easy problem.

That so much has been accomplished in the department, despite all the difficulties, is in some ways surprising. As Flowers noted, relative to other major universities IC is poorly endowed.[5] The lack of endowment income is due to a lack of foresight earlier in IC's history; in recent years the college has paid more attention to alumni affairs, and to fundraising. In the department the almost permanent shortage of funds has meant that the staff have had to fend for themselves in supporting their projects and their research students. Those with entrepreneurial or competitive sides to their nature, and those with good mentors, have fared better than others. Some people, less aggressive in seeking funds, have found creative ways to help the department other than through their research. However, there have always been a number of clever and less outgoing people for whom seeking major funding has been a difficult undertaking. In the department's competitive environment, this has resulted in some marginalisation.

Before changes introduced by the college allowed for a large professoriate, only a few of the gifted were able to advance their careers by staying on. Herbert Baker used to advise his students, and younger members of staff, that the department was an excellent jumping off point for major careers elsewhere. He was right then, and his claim remains true. As this history has shown, a remarkable number (more than its share) of professors in major British chemistry departments, and in departments all over the world, had their start in the department. The same can be said of people with major industrial careers.

11.2 Some Missed Opportunities

There are many 'what ifs' in history, and it is worth writing a few words on missed opportunities, and on some important areas of 20th century chemistry to which the department did not contribute, at least not in a major way. The point of doing so is not to take away from the excellent work carried out, but to place a few events in a wider context, and to mull briefly on how things could have turned out differently.

As we have seen, early in the 20th century the ionic theory met with opposition from Henry Armstrong, and with little enthusiasm from Herbert Baker. James Philip, however, recognised its importance, as can be seen from his work on the behaviour of solutions. Indeed he accepted not only Arrhenius' new ideas, but those of Ostwald and van't Hoff, and included them in his undergraduate lectures.[6] However, he had too many interests to have championed the founding of a major school of physical chemistry. Had Martin Lowry, another convert to the new ideas, been in a more senior position, the history of the department might have turned out differently.

The department was also slow in coming to terms with new theories in chemical bonding that emerged in the early 20th century, though the ideas of Gilbert N. Lewis, Linus Pauling, and Robert S. Mulliken were gradually taken up. Here, too, there was a junior member of staff, Christopher Ingold, who early engaged with their ideas on bonding, but he left the department in 1924. Pauling introduced what we now call ligand field theory and, in 1948, he suggested the alpha-helix structure of proteins. For this he developed the methods used by Francis Crick, James Watson, and Maurice Wilkins in their structural model of DNA. Molecular biology was perhaps the most important area of 20th century chemistry in which the department did not seriously participate, at least not before the arrival of Alan Fersht in 1978. Here, again, things could have turned out differently had the IC biochemistry department not been closed at the end of WW2, and had the professor, Albert Chibnall, not moved to Cambridge to succeed Frederick Gowland Hopkins in the Sir William Dunn chair of biochemistry (for Hopkins at IC see Chapter Three). It was at Cambridge, a few years later, that much of the exciting work in protein and nucleic acid chemistry was carried out. The Rector, Sir Richard Southwell, was short-sighted in closing biochemistry. An engineer, he saw a technological and nuclear future for the college, and would have also closed down the botany and zoology departments had he been able to get away with it.[7]

Armstrong, as we have seen, was opposed not only to the ionic theory but to electronic theories in general. He was wrongly critical of Robert Robinson for using curly arrows in his diagrams to denote electron movement. Robinson became known for his work in reaction mechanism, having learned much in this regard from both Lapworth and Jocelyn Thorpe when in Manchester (see Chapter Four for Lapworth at IC; for Thorpe, see Chapters Four–Six). Later Robinson won fame for determining the structures of some complex organic molecules, including strychnine. Reaction mechanism and structural organic chemistry were, however, far from being neglected in the IC department; indeed, Thorpe, Ian Heilbron, and others were very active in these areas during the 1930s and 1940s. But without expertise in X-ray crystallography the department was unable to ride the wave (*ca*.1930–1960) that led to the solution of some important natural product molecular structures. Robinson, at Oxford by 1930, had a few good crystallographers at hand, including Dorothy Crowfoot (later Hodgkin). Together, they were among those confirming the structure of penicillin proposed by Ernst Chain. Hodgkin's later work on the structures of vitamin B_{12} and insulin was to bring her fame.[8]

There were some other areas of omission, but none as important as those mentioned above. Physical chemistry could have made more of the electrochemistry introduced by Tom Ellingham and John Bockris, and of the early starts made in polymer chemistry, kinetics, and thermodynamics.[9] Had Fritz Paneth been persuaded to succeed Philip as professor of physical chemistry, radiochemistry could well have developed into a major field, and theoretical chemistry would likely have been added to the section.[10] However, the free radical chemistry that Paneth introduced was taken up by Harry Eméleus and others, and it remained a departmental interest. Although physical chemistry was the weakest of the three old sections, in the larger scheme of things it was reasonably good, and had some notable strengths. Surface chemistry, introduced in the 1950s by Frederick Tompkins and Richard Barrer, was a field for which the department had a worldwide reputation.

11.3 The Importance of Origins

As in other areas of life, chemistry has its prophets. One such was the department's first professor, A. W. (Wilhelm) Hofmann, an early believer in the power of synthetic chemistry to bring radical change to society.[11] He told his students that once the fundamentals of organic chemistry were understood, chemists would be able to synthesise compounds capable of outdoing natural products in many ways, especially, he believed, in the field of medicine. With this in mind he set out on a path that the department's organic chemists have followed to this day. IC has seen many outstanding organic synthesists including, in the 20th century, Jocelyn

Thorpe, Ian Heilbron, Derek Barton, Steve Ley, and Tony Barrett. Of course Hofmann was not a foolproof prophet; he failed to see some of the forks in the road such as the one taken by his student William Perkin — the fork that led to a new colour industry. Hofmann may have thought Perkin foolhardy in embarking on his industrial venture, but both of them believed that industry would play a major role in bringing useful laboratory discoveries to the larger world. As a result, what began as the Royal College of Chemistry (RCC) in 1845, and became the chemistry department at IC in 1907, had no difficulty with the 1907 Charter of Incorporation which stated that IC would provide 'training and research in various branches of science, especially in its application to industry.'

EDward Frankland contributed much both to synthesis and the theory of valency and reaction mechanisms. As a consequence not only synthesis but also reaction mechanism became a focus of research at the RCC already in the 19th century. Both are areas in which organic and inorganic chemists have excelled. Among the outstanding inorganic chemists who have worked in the department are not only Frankland, but notably also Edward Thorpe, Harry Eméleus, J. Stuart Anderson and Geoffrey Wilkinson. Because of the heavy emphasis on the making of interesting compounds, it is perhaps not surprising to see an undergraduate curriculum heavily weighted toward the practical. This focus on the practical has been viewed negatively in some quarters, notably in places where theoretical chemistry is more esteemed than what goes on in the laboratory. We have seen, for example, that Wilkinson was not given tenure at Harvard; this may have been because, at that time, his colleagues thought that without greater mathematical and theoretical skills he would not go far.[12] But Wilkinson's training at IC had prepared him well to think creatively about both synthesis and mechanism — and he did go far.

The knowledge hierarchy, that places theory above experiment has historical roots in a distinction that stretches back to classical times. Until fairly recently those who work with their hands were seen as less cultured than those who simply think and write — or talk. Today it is widely recognised that both theory and practice are essential to progress in the sciences, though in a few pockets of academia theoreticians are still held in higher regard than experimentalists. Of course some theoreticians deserve to be highly regarded, especially if, like Arrhenius, they come up with something as important as ionic theory. This highly suggestive theory had enormous heuristic power, as later did the new ideas on chemical bonding.

Derek Barton, in his 1991 memoir, used the term 'gap jumping' to describe the kind of intuitive skill that he saw himself as possessing, and that he thought essential not only to his own success, but to success in chemistry more generally. However, what he saw as intuitive skill could perhaps be better described as tacit knowledge. Barton undoubtedly possessed much explicit knowledge which, together with an excellent memory, served him well. He will, however, like other chemists, have also acquired much tacit knowledge from his teachers, from reading in the library, from chatting with fellow students, and from many hours spent at the laboratory bench.[13]

The departmental focus on bench work has resulted in a large number of new and important chemical compounds being made first in its laboratories. Even more important, however, are the new procedures that made the various syntheses possible. Indeed, chemists win fame for discovering new laboratory methods and new types of reaction. Both require a modicum of theoretical understanding, though not necessarily the skill needed to create a full-blown mathematical simulation. Two early chemists who exemplify this claim are mentioned in Appendix One. Berzelius was remarkable not only for his theoretical imagination but for the methods he introduced in the laboratory. Young chemists travelled to Stockholm from far and wide to learn about them. And Liebig's *kaliapparat*, which Hofmann brought to the RCC, allowed organic analysis to proceed as never before. These shining examples are hard to match, but arguably several IC chemists have come close. Hofmann himself, Frankland, Barton and Wilkinson, to name four famous examples, drew many young chemists to their laboratories because they, too, pioneered new methods and reactions. It is not theories alone that have heuristic power; methods, tools, reactions, and practices can also be suggestive of new avenues of research. The chemists just mentioned were far from alone. Indeed, the department at IC/ICL has been, and still is, a site of considerable heuristic inspiration.

Since making new compounds can be dangerous, the departmental focus on synthesis and mechanism has had some other consequences.

Young chemists are often drawn to work with people they see as adventurous and not afraid to take a few risks. Charismatic leadership is important and can help to foster active and successful research groups. Among the early professors, Hofmann, Edward Thorpe, William Tilden, and Jocelyn Thorpe all had lively research groups. Even Herbert Baker and Vincent Briscoe, neither of whom gave their students much direction, were able to foster a collaborative laboratory culture. Several of their successors, notably Barton and Wilkinson, were good team leaders. The ways of creating a team spirit, and of getting students to work hard, will depend on norms within the wider culture. However fostered, it helps young chemists to find an identity. The associated camaraderie, spiced by internal (and external) competition — and by the occasional explosion — helps to propel research forward. The boundary between organic and inorganic synthesis became blurred in the later 20th century, but camaraderie and supportive teamwork are still in evidence.

Another reason for the departmental emphasis on practical experience in undergraduate education has to do with the coming together of the RCC and the Government School of Mines (later the RSM) in 1853. As noted in Chapter Two, after a visit to England in 1840, Liebig complained of the dominance of the geologists over the proceedings at that year's BAAS meeting in York. No doubt he was exaggerating, but the geologists were then in the ascendent. When the RCC became a part of the Government School of Mines, the kind of mineralogical analysis carried out by geologists was fused to an analytical tradition derived largely from chemical and apothecarial science. This resulted in undergraduate instruction at the RCC, and later at IC, having a particular slant, further emphasised when Henry Harwood, who worked closely with the IC geologists, took over the teaching of analytical chemistry in 1911. As a result, until the 1970s students at IC spent more hours in the analytical laboratory than did students elsewhere. They carried out many qualitative and quantitative (both gravimetric and volumetric) inorganic analyses, followed by gas analyses and a range of organic analyses, One positive outcome was that they learned the value of precision in their work. However, as we have seen, this type of analytical work became redundant when analysis was taken over by machines with built-in microprocessors, a transition that could have been better exploited in the department. Although some contributions were made to the field of microanalysis, and for a short period under Tom West it was an important research field, it did not survive in the form it then had. Perhaps this was because the department never had a tradition of inventing and developing new physical methods, and the recessionary 1970s and 80s were not the best time to begin.[14] Nonetheless chemists at IC have always been quick to adopt such technologies once proven useful. This was the case with UV, IR and Raman spectroscopy, mass spectrometry, NMR and ESR — also with X-ray crystallography, but more slowly. Much of the research grant money coming to the department in the 20th century was spent on machines to aid research in structure, reaction mechanism, and synthesis.

11.4 Two World Wars

The two world wars were very important in the history of IC, and of the chemistry department. Looking back it is clear that under the leadership of Baker in WW1, and Briscoe and Heilbron in WW2, the work carried out helped to establish the importance of the department in many areas of chemistry. In WW1 the college was determined to show those in power, that scientists and engineers could contribute more to a victorious outcome by doing the kind of work for which they were trained, than by being sent to the front as cannon fodder. As shown in Chapter Five, the work carried out in the chemistry department more than made that point and, as a result, chemists were largely exempted from military service during WW2. IC was the only large college within the University of London to stay in the city during WW2. Despite (or perhaps because of) the associated danger and deprivation, staying put and working hard proved an important morale builder. As we have seen, the government came to rely greatly on college and departmental expertise during both wars, and have relied on it ever since.

11.5 Sociality and the Social Makeup of the Department

Before WW2 the cultural norm was for professors to show paternal concern for their students. Many felt it their duty to teach students how to behave not only in the laboratory, but beyond. Formal dinners were important sites for the socialisation of the young, and inviting students to join in such events was seen as a duty of professors and senior members of staff. Paternalism is no longer much appreciated. Today we live in a more youth-oriented culture, one in which professors no longer stand on dignity, at least not the kind of dignity that was sought after by the young Derek Barton (see Chapter Eight). Today staff are more likely to be on first-name terms with their students, and to want to join in student-led activities. They no longer wish, let alone attempt, to teach students proper decorum, whatever that may now mean. This turn of events would shock Herbert Baker, and other earlier members of staff, were they alive to witness it.

It has often been remarked that interaction among staff in the three old sections would have been enhanced by a departmental tea/coffee room, and that departmental morale would have been higher as a result.[15] Whether such a communal facility would, in fact, have led to greater social and scientific intercourse between people in the three old sections, as well as to heightened morale, is an interesting question.[16] It appears that for many years the separate sections served the department well, keeping people focussed in ways that were then relevant to the chemical discipline. When needed, scientists tend to find ways to communicate with others, and undoubtedly there was contact between people in the different sections, as well as with specialists in other IC departments and beyond. As to morale, we should not forget that labs are social as well as scientific spaces. The departmental labs, together with the IC union, the senior common room, local cafés and pubs, provided the social spaces for friendships to form, for important discussions to take place, and for morale to build, as is still true today.

In Chapter One, reference was made to the cultural geography of South Kensington. The area has many advantages but affordability of accommodation is not among them. Most members of the staff, and many of the students, have been commuters, spending much time travelling back and forth. One might think that this would be a greater problem for the building of morale than the lack of a tea room. However, for the most part departmental morale has been high, though periods of change such as the one in the 1990s, discussed in Chapter Ten, can be stressful. As to morale, it is probably fair to state that the department's location has been important. Perhaps arriving each day at a major cultural hub, with its rather grand and leafy surroundings, often from less stimulating suburban locations, lifts people's spirits. As to collegiality, stopping for the occasional drink, and a scientific chat on the way home has long been common practice. Former students and staff will be glad to know that most of the pubs they remember still exist: the Queen's Arms, the Zetland, the Hoop and Toy, the Gloucester Arms, the Hereford Arms, the Builders Arms, the Anglesea and others. Sadly, a favourite of many, including Wilkinson — the Ennismore Arms — has been replaced by luxury flats. Overall, South Kensington is little changed over the past 50 years, though Exhibition Road is now a fine pedestrian precinct, from which there is a new formal entrance to IC.

Readers may have noted that there were a few quotations from poems and song lyrics in the early chapters. In the late 19th and early 20th centuries, poems and songs were almost *de rigueur* at social gatherings, including formal dinners. Those who spent time composing them gained welcome recognition from their peers. The surviving poems are of varying quality, but they tell us a little about chemical life at the time. We learn, for example, that poets associated with the RCC, the NSS, and the RCS were proud of that fact, that poetic chemists were proud to be chemists, and were proud of the achievements of their contemporaries. Like Hofmann, they believed that chemistry had a glorious future. By the 1950s poetry making and reciting were less fashionable, as were the formal dinners. Other forms of entertainment such as smoking concerts became popular. These usually included performances by a stand-up comic or two, as well as a dramatic skit performed by students and the occasional staff member. In this way, and in a friendly manner, fun could be made of departmental life and of members of the staff. The concerts earned the name 'concert' by including also musical performances — increasingly in the 1960s by pop musicians.[17] Later in the century students had more disposable income and were able to seek entertainment further afield. This had something of a centrifugal effect on departmental social life.

However, this effect was countered by a unifying tendency that resulted from an increase in the number of women students. In the mid-20th century women made up about 10 percent of chemistry undergraduates; by the end of the century they made up about 40 percent and departmental social life became livelier. The feminist movement of the postwar period had an enormous effect on the wider culture, and no doubt contributed to more women seeking higher education later in the century. In this connection, it is worth remembering that already in 1913 Sir Alfred Keogh, IC's second rector, was so impressed by Martha Whiteley that he wrote to Sir Henry Miers, then Vice-Chancellor of the University of London, 'I have ... no intention of allowing her ... to remain in her present position. ... She is fitted to fill far higher posts and ... her upward progress will not be restrained by any consideration of sex.'[18] In 1920 Whiteley was promoted to assistant professor (reader from 1929), the first woman to reach that rank at IC. She was also the founder of ICWA. The 1907 Charter forbade discrimination based on sex, and in the main, though not in all respects, the college has respected it. Early on there were women winners of the Hatton prize for the best graduating student in chemistry, including Mary Boyle in 1901 and Hilda Judd in 1904, setting a pattern. Indeed, later in the 20th century (possibly also earlier, but the records are difficult to access), women at IC received proportionally more first and upper-second class degrees in the sciences than did women at any other British university.[19] One event of the 21st century worth noting is that, in 2013 the chemistry department won the Athena Scientific Women's Academic Network (SWAN) gold award for promoting women in science.[20] At the time it was one of only four science departments in the country to win the gold award, and the first to do so at IC.

As to the more general social mix, it is remarkable how many successful students and members of staff came from poor, some very poor, backgrounds. We have not made a comparative study with other chemistry departments, but it is doubtful that the more established ones will have educated as many poor students as at IC. In earlier chapters we mentioned that fees were lower at IC than at Oxbridge and UCL, and that a classical language was not needed for matriculation. These will have been important factors in admission patterns for the period up to the 1950s. We know from memoirs and letters that, before the founding of the National Health Service, and before the educational reforms of the post-WW2 period, many students had difficulty in clothing and feeding themselves, let alone paying for medical services, or for any kind of entertainment. What helped some poor students to succeed, aside from their own hard work, was a generous scholarship system and, it should be added, the culture of paternalism mentioned above.[21] Mentorship, too, remains important to success. Possibly the department's most outstanding mentor was Vincent Briscoe. We documented his mentorship of two future Nobel laureates, Derek Barton and Geoffrey Wilkinson, but he helped many other students, especially in finding work on graduation.

11.6 Looking to the Future

Aside from the cultural changes already mentioned, perhaps what has brought the most change over the past 40 years has been the availability of cheap computers, and the information technology that accompanies them. It is likely that both will play an increasing role going forward. It is not that the science of chemistry has changed in any fundamental way since the beginning of the computer age, but chemical practice, and what has become possible, have undergone a massive change, something likely to continue. IC was a leader in adopting the new technology, at least in Britain. As mentioned in Chapter Ten, those working in the new computing science area, keen to latch on to the internet, were among the first to register a domain name in the United Kingdom (ic.ac.uk). That did not mean that those in the chemistry department were quick to use the internet, or e-mail once it was up and running; with a few exceptions they were not. In this, perhaps the high age profile of the staff in the 1980s was a factor. However, as we have seen, the department did ensure that its many physical instruments came under computer control, something promoted especially by John Albery. Further, Bryan Levitt and Henry Rzepa pioneered undergraduate courses in computer programming and helped, more generally, with the installation of related technology. The impact on the nature of work for both staff and students has been great and, after a reluctant start, the power of computers, the internet, and wireless technology was soon understood.

The recession and changing economic climate of the late 20th century prompted not only increased collaboration with industry, but also departmental restructuring. The IC department was the first in Britain to replace the long-outdated division of chemical research into inorganic, organic, or physical. New sections were founded, with names that more clearly represent the kind of research carried out. The section names were a further example of heuristic guidance, and led to new forms of collaboration, and to some fine interdisciplinary research.[22] Also positive was the 1990s decision by IC to allow multiprofessorial departments.[23] This has resulted in the retention of gifted people who earlier, frustrated by little hope of promotion, would have left.

Since the early 21st century the three older colleges no longer have a formal role at IC since the distinctions they represented have lost much of their meaning. They have been replaced by a more conventional faculty system. Nonetheless their spirit lives on. Indeed modern institutions do best when they integrate the old with the new; tradition is important in the forming and maintaining of reputation, a reason for the department to keep its interesting and colourful history alive in the minds of new generations of students and, through them, the wider public.[24]

As noted in Appendix One, when Thomas Thomson became Glasgow's first Regius Professor of Chemistry in 1817, he wrote that he wanted his department to 'breed' chemists. Today this seems an awkward way of putting things; but the IC department has undoubtedly been another important chemists' breeding ground. As we have seen, its graduates have found work in Britain and around the world — in universities, industry, and in many other areas. Ever since the department began with just 26 students in Oxford Street, it has been successful. As a result it has grown. In 1873 it moved to larger premises on Exhibition Road and, in 1906, to yet larger premises on what is now Imperial College Road. When the physics department moved to a new building in 1960, chemistry expanded into the vacated space. Further growth led to the demolition of much of the old RCS building, and to the construction of C1 and C2. Over the past quarter century the department has grown yet more, and more space is urgently needed. A major expansion is now underway. Although much undergraduate teaching will continue in the present South Kensington location, in 2017 research will move westward to a building under construction at a new ICL campus named Imperial White City located near the Hammersmith campus.[25] There is much excitement over the move. We wish those working in the department well, that its excellent record in teaching continues, and that its research moves forward as lively and interesting, as 'blue sky' and useful, as it has until now.

End Notes

1. For example, in the early 1960s HG was a student and, together with some others, was invited by George Devine, Artistic Director at the Royal Court Theatre, to give advice on how science and scientists should be portrayed on stage. IC's Rector at the time, Patrick Linstead, encouraged this type of interaction. The Royal Court, then as now, was an experimental theatre, but this particular experiment was probably unprecedented. Interested in the moral dimension of new scientific (especially nuclear) knowledge, Devine brought a number of plays with scientific or technical content to the stage. Also in that period, the Touchstone residential weekend courses, held at Silwood Park, were introduced by Linstead's predecessor Sir Roderic Hill. Led by eminent people, they introduced students to a wide range of cultural topics. Free weekly concerts started earlier in the century; they continue to this day at the main IC campus.

2. Flowers made this claim in conversation with HG in 2003.

3. It is hard to believe that just before WW2, aside from research funding, the Treasury spent only £2,000,000 a year on universities, and that this sum represented about one-third of the total universities' budget. As a consequence, universities played an insignificant role in the consciousness of the nation. By the end of the century things were very different. The state was spending about £10 billion a year, not including research council funding. It is not surprising that when the major expansion in higher education began in the 1960s there was much debate, nor that the debate still continues. In the 1960s Geoffrey Crowther, editor of *The Economist*, was famous for the phrase, 'all to sixteen, half to eighteen, and one-fifth to twenty one'. Although his position had much support, many people were against as many as one-fifth of the population receiving higher education. As the novelist, Kingsley Amis, put it, 'more will mean worse.' His view gained support after 1968, the year in which radical action by students dominated the news worldwide. Margaret Thatcher, Education Secretary in the early 1970s, believed that the universities were 'pushing out poison,' though in this she did not have the sciences principally in mind. Nonetheless university expansion continued, though with less government funding per capita

than earlier. By the early 1990s universities were receiving about half the amount per student (in real terms) they received in 1960. Money had to come from elsewhere, including higher student fees. In the case of IC much came from industry, as noted in Chapter Ten.

4. It helps to have connections. The department built up a rapport with Glaxo already in the 19th century and the connection continues to this day. Sir Richard Sykes, who built his career at Glaxo, later GlaxoWellcome, later GlaxoSmithKline, arranged for much funding during the 1980s and 1990s. He came to IC as Rector in 2001. Similarly, there have been long and continuing ties to British Petroleum (BP), beginning in WW1 when the company was known as the Anglo–Iranian Oil Co. In the late 20th century the connections to BP through Sir John Cadogan and Vernon Gibson undoubtedly helped sustain departmental research.

5. The ancient universities, several of the civic ones, and even a few that were founded by the government in the 1960s have built large endowments which cushion them in difficult times Most of the universities that are close to ICL in the world rankings are far better endowed. Notable in this regard are Oxford, Cambridge (and their colleges), and some of the top universities in the United States. Whatever one thinks of such rankings, it is a testament to the grit and determination of ICL that it does as well as it does, often placing in the top 10. In the late 20th century the entry grades of IC chemistry students were only slightly lower than those at Oxford and Cambridge, but the number of first-class degrees awarded was significantly lower.

6. As mentioned in Chapter Four, Ostwald gave the address at the first ARCS graduation ceremony held in the new RCS building in 1906.

7. That Southwell considered closing down the biological sciences says much about the cultural mood at the end of WW2 when high energy physics and nuclear technology were in the ascendent. The biochemical revolution was not widely anticipated — a lesson for university administrators. The biochemistry department was reopened in 1961 but the head of department, the Nobel Laureate Ernst Chain, was not seriously interested in the new molecular biology.

8. Robinson and Hodgkin were Nobel Laureates in 1947 and 1964 respectively.

9. As we have seen, two famous kineticists, Sir Cyril Hinshelwood and Lord George Porter, came to work in the department in their retirement. Work in the general field of kinetics existed in the department, but it was more routine than that carried out by these two Nobel Laureates in their earlier places of work.

10. When Patrick Linstead became Rector in 1955 he was keen to bring nuclear science to IC, but curiously the department never acquired a research group in radiochemistry. Eric Roberts gave a course in radiochemistry for a few years but it was not a major part of the curriculum. As to theoretical chemistry, William (Bill) Penney, who came to IC as a mathematics student in 1927, would have made an ideal professor in that field (see Chapter Seven). He had studied for a PhD with John H. van Vleck before becoming a lecturer in the mathematics department. As we have seen, he was drawn away by the Manhattan Project during WW2. He returned to IC as Rector in 1967.

11. The Haber–Bosch process, and the synthesis of fertilizers alone more than make his point. The fertilizer industry has been a major contributor to the increase in the world's population from about 1.7b in 1912 to over 7b today. Alwin Mittasch was the engineer at (BASF) who helped to make the process work.

12. In the postwar period, with physics in the ascendant, Linus Pauling may well have been seen as the 'ideal' type when it came to academic chemists. He had an excellent theoretical background, had by then contributed much to the field, and could also perform in the laboratory.

13. The physical chemist, Michael Polanyi FRS (1891–1976), wrote much about tacit knowledge in the practice of science, (Polanyi, 1958, 1966).

14. An exception is David Turner who helped to pioneer photoelectron spectroscopy during the early 1960s.

15. This was the view of Charles Rees, among others. It has been possible to buy tea and coffee in the department since the construction of C1; and there have been attempts to have a congenial communal tea room. But the college caterers have a monopoly on food services, and nothing like a typical academic tea room has ever existed.

16. When Patrick Blackett was head of the physics department and making plans for the new physics building, he insisted there be a tea/coffee room on the top floor, with access to some outdoor space on the roof. He also insisted that everyone, other than undergraduates, have access to it. It became a place where academic, technical and secretarial staff, along with doctoral students and guests, could meet and mingle. By all accounts the facility has been a great success. Creating such a space was seen as a democratic move in 1960; however, whenever Blackett went there for tea or coffee, he always went to the front of the queue.

17. Several members of the department played in the college orchestra which included also some students from the Royal College of Music (RCM). IC has always had good relations, not only with the RCM, but also with the Royal College of Art (RCA). Engineers have worked closely with designers, and there have been a number of joint courses and programmes with both the RCM and RCA.

18. For Miers see Chapter Four and for quotation, Chapter Five. See also Chapter One, Note. 2, on IC's 1907 charter and ICL's 2007 charter.

19. (Gay, 2007b), Chapter 17.

20. SWAN, Scientific Women's Academic Network.

21. The Royal Scholarships, awarded only at IC, were intended to bring gifted young scientists to the RCS. They were not means tested; for several students, including Geoffrey Wilkinson, they were a lifeline. Wilkinson's family was not very poor, but it was working class, and he needed support. J. Stuart Anderson was brought up by a single mother in very poor circumstances. He won a government scholarship to attend IC. Government scholarships, less prestigious than the Royal, were usually means tested and existed before increased support became available in the 1950s. Postwar changes and the introduction of a grant system meant that the generation of students (*ca.* 1950–1975) included many who were the first in their family to attend university. The generous level of support ended when new ideas related to the social contract entered the discussion during the Thatcher and, later, Blair governments. Today students receive more in the way of loans than grants or scholarships. This is because the Blair government took into account the widespread view that those

who profit from higher education should pay a higher proportion of the cost, if not immediately then later in life.

22. As to the sections, further changes are planned. As of January 2016, the current sections will no longer exist since even these are seen as too rigid. Six themes of interest have been chosen to replace them (see Chapter Ten).

23. Already in the early 1960s the department had five professors, and a decade later seven — unusual at that time. However, in the 1990s IC decided to follow the American example and not limit the number of professorships; most well-published and deserving members of staff were given the title.

24. In integrating the old and the new, IC could learn something from the ancient universities. It is good that labs have been named after important figures from the past: Hofmann, Tilden, Harwood, Philip, Briscoe, Evans, etc. It appears that Frankland and Baker have lost out due to the rearrangement of laboratory space. Perhaps labs can be named for them in the new chemistry building at Imperial White City. For clarity it should be noted that the name 'Imperial White City' is named for the district of that name in West London.

25. According to the IC website, 'the building will accommodate all of chemistry's research and postgraduate training, including space for the department to grow to become one of the largest in the world, with research spanning across the whole range of modern Molecular Science.'

Appendix One

Liebig at Giessen; Some Early 19th Century Chemistry

A.1 Justus Liebig's Laboratory in Giessen

A. W. Hofmann was a student at Giessen and brought many of Liebig's research and pedagogical practices to the Royal College of Chemistry (RCC). Liebig had been a student at the University of Bonn before moving to Paris, where he attended lectures by Pierre L. Dulong (1785–1838), Louis J. Thénard (1777–1857) and Joseph L. Gay-Lussac (1778–1850). He was also given entry to Gay-Lussac's laboratory. There he met his exact contemporary Jean-Baptiste André Dumas (1800–1884) with whom he developed a respectful rivalry.[1] After Paris, and with some lucky patronage, Liebig set up his own laboratory at the University of Giessen in 1824. Its original purpose was to train apothecaries, but general chemistry students were soon admitted.[2] Liebig immersed himself in the new organic chemistry and his ambition was to further the science. He also promoted its utility in all sorts of areas, including physiology, food chemistry, agriculture, and sewage treatment. In his sixties he wrote a memoir, recalling that when he started out laboratories for chemical instruction

were more like kitchens filled with all sorts of furnaces and utensils for the carrying out of metallurgical or pharmaceutical processes .... Organic chemistry — or what is now called organic chemistry — had then no existence.'[3]

This was close to the truth and he was right to see himself as a pioneer.

Jack Morrell has given an account of why Liebig's research school in Giessen was so successful, and William Brock's biography tells of Liebig's enormous influence in Britain.[4] Morrell compared Liebig's research school to Thomas Thomson's school in Glasgow, claiming that Liebig was the more successful in attracting students, in producing faithful adherents, in publishing interesting work, and in training a new generation of important chemists. The reasons he gave for that success apply, with some leeway, to Hofmann's later success at the RCC.[5]

By the 1820s many organic compounds were known, but chemists who wanted to determine their formulae faced formidable obstacles. Liebig made an analytical breakthrough with his 'perfection of combustion analysis.' This was prompted by his 1829 discovery of a compound in horse urine that he named 'hippuric acid,' (N-benzoylglycine, $C_6H_5CONHCH_2COOH$).[6] It was an analytical challenge because of its high C to H, O, and N weight ratios. Berzelius, an excellent analyst, had earlier developed a much copied method for determining carbon content. He oxidised compounds with potassium chlorate or copper oxide, and captured the carbon dioxide in a small open bulb of potassium hydroxide floating on mercury in a bell jar. Only small quantities could be analysed at any one time because of the large volumes of carbon dioxide released on combustion. Liebig met the challenge of hippuric acid, and other relatively high molecular weight compounds, achieving greater accuracy, and greater procedural simplicity than had Berzelius. His apparatus, appropriately named the *Kaliapparat*, was constructed by Karl Ettling, a highly skilled glassblower.[7] When it was up and running, chemists in Liebig's laboratory carried out about 400 organic analyses each year.[8] Procedural simplicity allowed the average student to obtain reliable results, and enabled the Giessen research programme to accelerate. The new apparatus became iconic and Giessen students proudly wore pins depicting the potash globes on their jackets. The apparatus came to London with Hofmann. Two former Liebig students, Heinrich Will and Carl Fresenius, described the Giessen methods of analysis in their widely-used textbooks. Fresenius's book, translated and edited by John Bullock, was used in promoting the new college of chemistry in London.[9] Hofmann translated Will's *Outlines of Chemical Analysis* shortly before moving to

London. It, too, was used at the RCC. Liebig purchased a journal and renamed it *Annalen der Chemie und Pharmacie*.[10] He encouraged his students to publish their results, something that helped to build a collective spirit. The journal soon became essential reading for organic chemists working elsewhere. At Giessen, advanced students were expected to teach beginners and to take on other laboratory tasks, a pattern later copied at the RCC.

Liebig's laboratory met certain criteria that, according to Morrell, were important to its success as a research school. One was that there be a 'regular supply of motivated students' and that an *esprit de corps* be fostered among them. Another was in part met by the *kaliapparat* and 'a set of relatively simple, fast, and reliable experimental methods' that allowed 'students ... less than brilliant to carry out and publish competent work.' According to Morrell, deployed on a large scale, the apparatus led to 'a knowledge factory.'[11] Further, the distinction between student and researcher was fluid; young people in Liebig's laboratory were engaged both in learning chemistry and in carrying out research — not unlike the postgraduate students of today. But laboratory conditions were then far less safe. As Liebig told Kekulé, 'if you will be a chemist you must ruin your health. No one who does not ruin his health by study comes to anything today in chemistry.'[12]

Liebig gave entry to young men with technical ability, but who lacked the necessary training in classics to matriculate at the university.[13] Hofmann later welcomed such students to the RCC — as, still later, they were welcome at Imperial College. Students at Giessen went through a fairly rigorous programme in chemical analysis in their first year, a practice copied at the RCC. Those with basic skills were encouraged to move directly into simple research work already in their second year. According to Lyon Playfair there was also a lively social life at Giessen.[14] Sociality is something that could be added to Morrell's criteria for running a successful research school.

A.2 Some Chemical Ideas of the Early to Mid-19th Century

Important to the debates of the early 19th century were Dalton's atomic theory, the electrolytic decomposition of matter by the new voltaic pile,[15] the empirical generalisations known as the laws of constant composition and multiple proportions, Lavoisier's dualism reflected in the binary structure of the names given to common chemicals, and new developments in synthetic and analytical chemistry. Dalton had imagined molecular formulae for some simple compounds, and had then used the formulae to determine relative atomic weights. Assuming that hydrogen was the lightest element, he gave it an atomic weight of one. But deciding on other, relative, atomic weights was no easy matter since his theory allowed for several different formulae to be entertained for any one compound. The simple case of water shows some of the difficulties. Following studies of the volumetric composition of water, Gay-Lussac determined the weight ratio of hydrogen to oxygen. But should water be HO or H_2O_2, etc. (with atomic/equivalent weight O = 8), or H_2O (with O = 16)? Similar debates took place over carbon compounds and whether C = 6 or C = 12 should be used. To complicate things further, not only were other systems of equivalents suggested, the terms 'atomic weight' and 'equivalent weight' were used interchangeably.

There was some standardisation of atomic/equivalent weights and formulae even before the famous Karlsruhe Congress of 1860, but it was far from complete. The congress did not achieve consensus, despite Stanislao Cannizzaro distributing his 1858 paper that stressed the importance of Avogadro's hypothesis of 1811. Early in the century most chemists rejected Avogadro's idea. After 1860 it gained more acceptance. One foundational problem was the question of whether gaseous elements such as H_2, N_2, and O_2 were truly diatomic, something not fully laid to rest until specific heat measurements improved late in the century. That such molecules could exist remained a puzzle until Linus Pauling provided a quantum mechanical explanation in the 1920s.

Among the early believers in Daltonian atomism as a useful, if not totally descriptive, theory was the Swedish chemist, Jöns Jakob Berzelius (1779–1848). Together with Humphry Davy and some others, he was a pioneer in the electrolysis of salts and the isolation of metals.[16] Like many chemists of his generation, Berzelius was introduced to chemistry as a medical student and his early interests were in physiological chemistry. His later reputation as one of the foremost chemists of the 19th century is well deserved. He made advances in all areas of chemistry, introduced new chemical notation (the alpha–numeric system still in use today — though in his day not universally accepted), recognised and named isomerism and catalysis, and was a pioneer in organic chemistry. He was an excellent analyst and produced a table of atomic weights for the known elements. His laboratory techniques were widely copied. However, it was only after 1810 when he moved to the new Karolinska Institute and began accepting a few foreign students, that he became well known outside Sweden. The foreigners were mainly Germans, and they championed his ideas among the nascent chemistry departments at German universities.[17] Berzelius' annual reports, beginning in 1820, and known in German as his *Jahresberichte,* were among the most keenly awaited publications of their day. His *Lehrbuch,* too, in which he introduced the term 'organic chemistry,' was widely read.

Following his early work on electrolysis, Berzelius developed an electrochemical theory of chemical composition. He proposed that all atoms carry an electrical charge. For oxygen, he claimed, a negative charge always prevailed, but for the other elements varying degrees of positivity or negativity were possible. As a result, groups of conjoined atoms were seen as variably charged. Inorganic compounds, according to Berzelius, could be envisaged as consisting of two such groups, one electropositive, the other electronegative. Lavoisier had introduced the term 'radical' and used it to describe stable combinations of atoms that could not be destroyed, except under extreme conditions. Berzelius used the same term, but claimed that radicals were electrically charged and that they had varying degrees of affinity for other radicals or elements.

Berzelius believed that organic compounds, too, were made up of charged radicals containing C and H atoms; possibly also other elements, but not the highly electronegative element, oxygen — though he acknowledged that such radicals combined with oxygen in many organic compounds. Brock has given examples of Berzelius' thinking — using modern formulae as follows:

Sulphuric acid $(SO_3 + H_2O)$ Acetic acid $[(C_4H_6)O_3 + H_2O]$

where the radical C_4H_6 (C=6) plays the same role in acetic acid as sulphur in sulphuric acid.[18] As more organic compounds were prepared during the 1820s and 1830s it became clear that the radical theory did not account for many of them well. Further, some quite complex organic radicals were being made and it was possible to envisage them in different ways. Liebig and Wöhler, for example, isolated what they called the (oxygen containing) benzoyl radical, $C_{14}H_{10}O_2$, from almond oil. Their work on this and the benzoyl series drew much attention, as did Bunsen's claim for the existence of the novel cacodyl radical, $C_4H_{12}As_2$. The fact that many different organic compounds can be made from just a few elements made for a complicated situation, and there was much debate over how to picture both radicals and molecules. The different equivalent weight systems only added to the confusion.

Perhaps, in the longer term, most damaging to Berzelius' composition ideas was his own recognition of isomerism. Already in the early 1820s Liebig and Wöhler had demonstrated that silver fulminate and silver cyanate had the same empirical formula, (Ag(CNO), Ag(OCN)), even though their properties were very different.[19] A few years later Berzelius found that tartaric and racemic acids, too, had the same formula but different properties. He named the phenomenon 'isomerism.' It suggested to others that atoms could be moving around even within stable radicals. Indeed, it suggested that the very idea of stable radicals could be misleading. The idea of a dynamical chemical world, introduced more forcefully to organic chemistry by Alexander Williamson in the 1850s, was to have profound consequences for structural theory.[20]

While Berzelius' laboratory at the Karolinska Institute can be seen as one pole of chemical activity in early 19th century Europe, the other pole was Paris. This is not to imply that no important work was carried out elsewhere. But, in that period, ambitious young chemists were principally attracted either to Paris or to Stockholm (or to both). The French chemists, successors to Lavoisier, influenced by the positivist mood of the post-Napoleonic period, were disinclined to accept the idea of unseen, unverifiable, atoms.[21] Most saw formulae simply as useful conventions. But their instrumentalist philosophy did not hold them back from advancing the discipline. For a while Parisian chemists accepted Berzelian radicals as useful fictions, but it was from Paris that an alternative approach to radicals, namely type theory, emerged.

Dumas had been asked to investigate why acrid fumes were given off by some beeswax candles used to illuminate a ball held at the Tuileries

Palace.[22] He found that chlorine, used in the manufacturing process, had combined with fatty acids in the beeswax, and that the candles gave off hydrogen chloride when burned. Further investigation during the 1830s, notably by Dumas' former student, Auguste Laurent (1807–1853), led to the recognition that chlorine, thought of as typically electronegative, could substitute for the typically electropositive hydrogen, not only in fatty acids but also in other organic compounds. This was a problem for Berzelian radical theory. Further, Laurent suggested to Dumas that they chlorinate acetic acid. The properties of the chlorinated acid were found to be much the same as those of its parent. This supported Laurent's idea that what was important to the properties of organic compounds was the number of carbon atoms present, and the type of molecular skeleton they formed; or, as Dumas later put it,

> *I have tried to show that in organic chemistry there exist types which are capable, without destruction, of undergoing the most singular of transformations according to the nature of their elements [and that contrary to what was claimed by radical theorists] every chemical compound forms a complete whole and cannot therefore consist of two parts. ... Its chemical character is dependent primarily on the arrangement and number of its atoms and in a lesser degree on their chemical nature.*[23]

Others, too, contributed to the development of type theory. Indeed, the first issue of *Revue scientifique et industrielle* (1840) was given over to claimants, each making a case for the superiority of their ideas. Today, Dumas and Laurent are seen as the principal founders of the theory, and Charles Gerhardt (1816–1856) is credited with its mature articulation.[24] Following Laurent, Gerhardt saw substitution as central, noting that it was limited largely to hydrogen atoms. Dumas wrongly thought that any atom could in principle be substituted, provided the overall template was preserved. Gerhardt's formulation of type theory became widely accepted. Substitution remained a major problem for radical theory, but in some other respects the older theory fitted the facts.

The theory of types served organic chemists well for about 35 years. It drew on ideas in crystallography (Laurent published also in that area) — ideas such as isomorphism. Types were envisaged as templates to which compounds of different, but related, composition adhered. The theory avoided deeper questions of chemical structure since the types were seen as instrumental in function. Their purpose was classification, consistency with empirical formulae, and prediction. However a few chemists, Laurent among them, saw the types as capturing something of reality. Liebig followed the French chemists in adopting type ideas and, in the 1850s, Hofmann was to bring type theory to the RCC. Berzelian and type ideas were eventually reconciled within a theory of chemical structure that followed from the valence and structural ideas suggested by, among others, Frankland, Williamson, Kekulé, Couper, and Butlerov.

End Notes

1. The rivalry is discussed in (Hofmann, 1880), pp. 1–80. This rather hagiographical account of Dumas' life and his many contributions to chemistry was published in a special issue of *Nature*. It can also be read as an account of how Hofmann saw the chemical world of his time.
2. At first the laboratory was not officially part of the university. It came under the *aegis* of the university in 1835, when funds became available for its expansion. Hofmann's father, an architect, designed a new laboratory and lecture hall. The influx of chemistry students, rather than just apothecary students, came after 1835.
3. Liebig, as noted in (Brown, 1914), 34, p. 39. Brown translated Liebig's memoir and included it in his book. Liebig acknowledged some earlier work in organic chemistry by Thénard, Berzelius and Chevreul, but claimed that when he started out the field did not exist as a discipline.
4. (Brock, 1997). Liebig's father was a Darmstadt hardware merchant, and a maker of varnishes, paints, and polishes. Liebig received his barony only later in life. For Liebig's research school, (Morrell, 1972), pp. 1–46. The word 'breeders' in the title of Morrell's paper is Thomas Thomson's. Thomson wrote to Robert Jameson, Professor of Natural Philosophy at Edinburgh, stating that he wanted his school to 'breed' chemists. In our view, Morrell's analysis is good. although he was criticised by F. L. Holmes for holding too rosy a view of Liebig and his laboratory, and for being too reliant on Liebig boosters who, blinded by his (and their own) later fame, gilded their memories of the Giessen laboratory. Holmes included Hofmann among the gilders — as for example in (Hofmann, 1876), (Holmes, 1989), pp. 121–164. For another critic of Morrell, see Fruton (Note 13). Fruton's criticism has to do with the originality of Liebig's pedagogy. Although Liebig

was not alone in how he taught students in his laboratory, no one else of his generation had such a formative influence on the RCC. See also (Brock, 1992), pp. 77–88.

5. For the transfer of Liebig's ideas to London, (Jackson, 2006), pp. 1–39. Jackson's focus is heavily methodological, with much emphasis on the contentious literature surrounding research schools. However, one of her conclusions supports one of our own, (Gay, 2000), pp. 135–169. Although Jackson considers both Liebig and Hofmann, and Gay only the latter, both see the importance of a devolved power structure in the RCC's success.

6. Brock (1997), 50. Liebig's interest in horse urine relates, indirectly, to Wöhler's 1828 synthesis of urea.

7. (Liebig, 1831). For Liebig's potash apparatus see also (Sella, 2009), (Jackson, 2015). Central to the apparatus was a series of potash-containing globes for the absorption of CO_2.

8. (Morrell, 1972), p. 27. For nitrogen analysis, both Liebig and Hofmann used Dumas' method. According to Rocke, by about 1860 around 3000 organic chemicals had been described in the chemical literature, (Rocke, 1993), p. 2.

9. (Fresenius, 1846).

10. For the complex history of this journal, (Brock, 1997), pp. 55–57.

11. (Morrell, 1972), pp. 4–5.

12. (Armstrong, 1927), p. 185.

13. For a discussion of the makeup of the student body at Giessen, (Fruton, 1988), pp. 1–66.

14. In his letters to Andrew Ramsay, Playfair mentions several parties and dances. On one occasion Liebig gave a ball for 90 guests. Half way through the evening a 'mystic light appeared,' and 'music was heard at a distance.' Then, in danced 'a band of alchemists and their ladies' all 'magnificently attired' to represent the different planets. Each held a torch that, when shaken, emitted sudden bursts of flame. ICL archives; Andrew Ramsay papers, Playfair to Ramsay, 26 January, 1840.

15. Humphry Davy rightly stated, 'nothing tends so much to the advancement of knowledge as the application of a new instrument.' Quoted in (Paris, 2011). For a synoptic account of the history of chemistry in the 19th century see (Knight, 1998).

16. Davy was sceptical of the existence of atoms. John Herschel, whose son Alexander was later a Hofmann student at the RCC, was critical of Davy's overly positivist stance. Herschel was not fully convinced by the atomic theory but thought that chemists should proceed as though atoms existed and see where that led them. He understood that finding empirical evidence for

the existence of atoms might not be possible, but that did not mean the idea should be dismissed, (Herschel, 1987).

17. The first was Christian G. Gmelin (1792–1860) who went to Stockholm for a few months in 1814. Later a professor in Tübingen, Gmelin was a member of a large chemical dynasty, described in (Walden, 1954). Gmelin and his cousin, Leopold Gmelin (1788–1853), author of the Handbook of Theoretical (later inorganic) Chemistry, travelled to Paris together to study chemistry. Later as a professor at Heidelberg, Leopold Gmelin persuaded both Friedrich Wöhler and Alexander Williamson, to abandon medicine for chemistry. He was therefore an important catalyst for what came later. Wöhler travelled to Stockholm to study with Berzelius and stayed for a few years. He translated much of Berzelius' work into German including the *Lehrbuch*. After Berzelius' death, the *Jahresbericht* continued as a German chemical journal.

18. (Brock, 2000), p. 212. Following Berzelius, Brock used numerical superscripts. We have used today's more conventional subscripts.

19. Liebig took the more dangerous path working with the explosive fulminates. At first their parallel discoveries led to a dispute over analytical procedures. But, when each recognised that the other had given the correct analysis, they became comrades in arms in the fast-developing world of organic chemistry. It was also in the 1820s that Wöhler discovered that the ammonium cyanate he prepared had the same empirical formula as urea extracted from dog urine. Friedrich Wöhler (1800–1882) later succeeded Friedrich Stromeyer as Professor in Göttingen.

20. For example, (Williamson, 1851), pp. 90–94.

21. Interestingly Auguste Comte, (Comte, 1838), supported atomic theory as progressive, even though not proven.

22. (Hofmann, 1880). Dumas was given this task by his father-in-law, Alexandre Brongniart, the chemist, mineralogist, and Director of the Sèvres Porcelain Factory.

23. The full quotation is put together from (Partington, 1954), p. 366 and (Benfey, 1964), p. 44.

24. For a succinct account of type theory and its decline (Leicester, 1971), Chapter Nine; also (Fruton, 2002) Chapter Five. For more detailed treatments, (Brooke, 1975), (Rocke, 1993), and (Rocke, 2010). Laurent and Gerhardt were outsiders in Paris, though gradually accepted into the fold. Sadly, both died young. Laurent had a clear theoretical chemical picture. He early accepted Avogadro's hypothesis, and had a good understanding of molecular weight. He believed in the dimerism of elemental gases such as

hydrogen (though the evidence for it was not yet secure), and that the smallest available reaction unit for such gases was a molecule, not an atom. He detailed his views in (Laurent, 1854), published one year after his death from tuberculosis. Had he lived longer, he could well have led the way through what, in the introduction to his remarkable work, he called 'le labyrinthe de la chimie organique.' But in the early 1850s his views were still speculative and no one knew how to exit the maze. Laurent spent some time in Giessen in 1843 and helped Hofmann with his work at that time.

Appendix Two

Chemistry Teaching at British Universities Before 1850

In the 17th century occasional lectures in chemistry were given at English, Scottish, and other European universities, but few people attended or took the subject seriously. This changed after reforms in medical education made chemistry a compulsory subject at some European medical schools, and when medical bodies began insisting that some chemical education was necessary for those seeking a licence to practise in Britain.[1] Herman Boerhaave (1668–1738) pioneered these developments in Holland.[2] In 1718 he was appointed to the first Chair of Chemistry at Leiden, which he occupied along with chairs in medicine and botany. He had several British students and his treatise, *Elements of Chemistry*, was to influence medical and chemical instruction until the phlogiston — oxygen debates changed the face of chemistry in the late 18th century. According to Thomas Thomson, the *Elements* 'was undoubtedly the most learned and most luminous treatise on chemistry that the world had yet seen.'[3]

The medical school at the University of Edinburgh opened in 1726. All of its founding professors were trained at Leiden and chemistry became a part of the medical curriculum in Edinburgh. Chemical instruction came to Glasgow soon after when William Cullen FRS (1710–1790) was invited to give lectures to medical students there in 1746.[4] Cullen later moved to Edinburgh as Professor of Medicine and Chemistry. He was succeeded in the Glasgow lectureship, and later also in the Edinburgh chair, by the most famous of his Glasgow students, Joseph Black (1728–1799).[5] Chemistry was introduced also at Aberdeen and St. Andrews in the early 19th century.[6] Although practical chemical skills were widely taught outside universities by apothecaries and manufacturing chemists, the Scottish universities were the first to introduce teaching in practical chemistry. However laboratory conditions were poor. Thomas Charles Hope FRS (1766–1844), when a Lecturer in Chemistry at Glasgow, complained of poor equipment and lack of assistance.[7] In 1818 he moved to Edinburgh to succeed Black. He was the first academic chemist in Britain to seriously criticise the phlogiston theory, and the only medical professor to receive praise from the young Charles Darwin. His successors in Edinburgh were the former Liebig students, William Gregory (1803–1858), and Lyon Playfair FRS (1818–1898). Playfair was the first Professor of Chemistry at the university who was not also a qualified physician.[8]

Thomas Thomson FRS (1773–1852) succeeded Hope in Glasgow and was the first occupant of the Regius Chair of Chemistry. He accepted Dalton and Berzelius' ideas, gave them some empirical support, and trained a number of good chemists. He was succeeded, in 1852, by Thomas Anderson (1819–1874), who had been educated in Edinburgh. Anderson had worked also in Stockholm with Berzelius and, for a short time, with Liebig in Giessen. He was an expert in agricultural chemistry, and a champion of Pasteur. Chemistry was taught also at a new college that opened in Glasgow with a 1796 bequest from John Anderson, Professor of Natural Philosophy at the university. He wanted to see more emphasis placed on technical instruction than was normal at the university, and that such instruction be made available also to working tradesmen.[9] He left his large collection of apparatus so that the new college could start on what he considered a proper footing. A medical school was soon founded at Anderson College and a chair in chemistry followed in 1830. The first occupant was Thomas Graham FRS (1805–1869), a former Thomson student who had worked with Hope in Edinburgh. He taught medical students, though others, too, came to his classes.[10] In 1836 Graham moved to London to take up the Chair of Chemistry at University College.

University College (at first named the University of London) opened in 1826.[11] Its first Chemistry Professor, Edward Turner FRS (1798–1837), came from Edinburgh. Earlier he had studied in Göttingen with Friedrich Stromeyer. Turner was interested in Daltonian atomism and much of his research was in atomic weight determination and the testing of Prout's hypothesis. When Graham succeeded Turner in 1836, he brought some physical chemistry to London, notably work on colloids and gaseous diffusion, as well as some work on phosphates. His friend, George Fownes, was appointed to a second Chair when a new laboratory, the Birkbeck, opened in 1846.[12] Fownes, a promising young organic chemist, died prematurely in 1849. He was succeeded by Alexander Williamson FRS (1824–1904) who became Head of Department after Graham's appointment as Master of the Mint in 1855. The arrival of the Royal College of Chemistry (RCC) in 1845, saw the start of a friendly rivalry between the two institutions that has continued to this day.[13]

King's College opened in 1831, five years after University College. John Frederick Daniell FRS (1790–1845), a meteorologist, inventor of the dew point hygrometer, and a specialist in the management of greenhouses, was appointed the first Professor of Chemistry. By chemists he is best remembered for his subsequent invention of the eponymous Daniell cell. King's College opened its medical school in 1840 and Daniell was then responsible for teaching chemistry to the college's own medical students, not simply to those who dropped in. By this period, however, chemistry was taught at most of the London medical schools and fewer students needed to look for instruction elsewhere. Daniell's textbook, *Introduction to the Study of Chemical Philosophy* (1839), illustrates his positivist outlook. He did not accept the existence of the unobserved — and that included atoms. After his death in 1845, he was succeeded by one of his former students, the physician William Allen Miller FRS (1817–1869). Although Miller had worked with Liebig in Giessen, he was more interested in physical chemistry and was later known for his work on stellar spectroscopy carried out with William Huggins. His textbook, *Elements of Chemistry: Theoretical and Practical*, was widely used.[14] The serious teaching of chemistry to science students, not simply to medical students, came only after Charles Loudon Bloxam (1831–1887), one of Hofmann's former students, was appointed Professor in 1870. Bloxam's textbook, *Chemistry, Inorganic, and Organic*, went into 11 editions between 1867 and 1923.[15]

Oxford claims Robert Boyle (1627–91) as its earliest chemist. It was, however, Boyle's assistant Peter Stahl who gave chemistry lectures at the university. Chemistry became part of the medical curriculum with the endowment of the Aldrichian chair in 1798.[16] As in Scotland, the early holders of the chair were physicians. The first, John Kidd FRS (1775–1851), gave lectures on Lavoisier's ideas. Charles Daubeny FRS (1795–1867) attended Kidd's lectures and, after graduating in classics, moved to Edinburgh to study medicine where his chemistry professor was Thomas Hope. Daubeny returned to Oxford, and to the Aldrichian chair in 1822. He lectured on Dalton's atomic theory, and on the ideas of Dulong, Petit, and Gay-Lussac. Although he taught modern chemistry, and was a founder of the Chemical Society in 1841, his own research was not strictly chemical. Something of a vulcanologist, he also spent time in the botanical gardens experimenting on how environmental conditions affect plant growth. Just before his retirement in 1853, he appointed Nevil Story Maskelyne as his assistant. Story Maskelyne gave instruction in practical chemistry in a laboratory at Magdalen College, and in a small laboratory that had been set up in the cellar of a new building at Balliol College. He was later appointed Professor of Mineralogy. Benjamin Collins Brodie FRS (1817–1880) succeeded Daubeny in 1854, becoming the first Waynflete Professor of Chemistry in 1857.[17] Brodie, the son of the physician and surgeon, Sir Benjamin Brodie, President of the Royal Society, spent a few months with Liebig at Giessen where he discovered some solid alcohols in beeswax. He continued his research on alcohols and fatty acids in a private laboratory in London before moving to Oxford.

The situation was less lively at Cambridge, although a chair of chemistry was founded there already in 1702. The professor in the early 19th century was Smithson Tennant (1751–1815), who had worked with William Wollaston on the platinum metals. In 1804 he identified osmium and iridium for which he won the Copley Medal. He also showed that diamond was a form of carbon, but he spent much time away from Cambridge carrying out agricultural experiments at his estate in Somerset. In 1861 George D. Liveing FRS (1827–1924), a former Cambridge wrangler, moved from his position as Professor of Chemistry at Sandhurst to take the chair. Before doing so he spent a few months at the RCC with Hofmann. At Cambridge he gave practical instruction to a few students, both in a small laboratory in the kitchen of a nearby cottage, and in a laboratory at his college, St. John's. Later in the century, he collaborated with James Dewar who held the Jacksonian chair. There were a few other small college laboratories but the first university laboratory for practical instruction and research was built only in 1887.[18]

End Notes

1. Until the late 19th century it was not necessary to attend a university in order to practice medicine. Most future doctors apprenticed with physicians or surgeons and received a licence to practice from the Society of Apothecaries or College of Surgeons. By the early 19th century one had to demonstrate some knowledge of chemistry in order to be certified. The College of Physicians, more exclusive, required a university education for its licence.
2. (Powers, 2012).
3. Boerhaave's *Elements of Chemistry* was published in Latin in 1724 and translated into English in 1741. Quotation, (Thomson, 1830) 1 p. 212. The German physician, Andreas Libavius, is often credited with writing the first chemistry textbook, *Alchemia*, published in 1597. It was he who wrote, 'Beware of deceiving chemistry and take my advice, keep away from it ... . Chemistry is the occupation not of philosophers but of reprobates.'
4. For chemistry at the University of Glasgow, (Fenby, 1989), (Cook, 1953), pp. 561–572. For Cullen, (Bynum, 2004).
5. For Black, (Anderson, 2004). Cullen's student Benjamin Rush, the eminent physician, revolutionary, and Professor of Chemistry at the University of Pennsylvania, may be better known in America, (Yazawa, 2004).
6. For a History of Chemistry at St. Andrews, (Read, 1953).
7. (Fenby, 1989). For Hope, (Trail, 1849), pp. 419–434. For a brief history of chemistry at Edinburgh, (Hirst and Ritchie, 1953), 505–511.
8. Gregory moved from Aberdeen to succeed Thomas Hope in 1844. Playfair succeeded Gregory in 1858, after a short period, 1851–1853, as Professor of Chemistry at the Government School of Mines and five years as Head of Science in the Government's Science and Art Department.
9. After many changes, Anderson college evolved into the University of Strathclyde. For a brief but clear history of Anderson College, (Cranston, 1954).
10. Most famous among the medical students was the explorer and medical missionary, David Livingstone. Other students included Lyon Playfair, the

geologist Andrew Ramsay, and James Young, founder of the British paraffin wax, lamp oil, and lubricant industry. Young worked as a carpenter while taking classes. He moved to London as Graham's assistant before becoming an industrialist, (Butt, 2004).

11. The old University of London (later University College) did not offer science degrees, though chemistry could be used as credit toward the BA degree, and was needed for a medical license. The new University of London was founded in 1836 as an external examining body to serve colleges then in existence, including many beyond London. It soon offered the medical MD, and a range of science and engineering degrees. In its early years the university was run by people worried about giving degrees to those they thought poorly educated. Its BSc curriculum included some exposure to the classics and humanities. The refusal to see a strictly science degree as providing a liberal education was one reason why people at Imperial College later resisted joining the federal teaching university (founded in 1898). They saw no reason for future engineers and scientists to matriculate with Latin, let alone having to study it at university — the university soon dropped the latter requirement. For chemistry at UCL, (Davies and Garratt, 2013).

12. In the early 1840s Fownes, who had a PhD from Giessen, was a Professor at the Pharmaceutical Society where he taught practical chemistry. His *Manual of Elementary Chemistry* (Fownes, 1844) was widely used. For Fownes, (Rowe, 1950) and (James, 2004).

13. In a letter to Liebig, written shortly after his arrival in London, Hofmann notes that he was greeted kindly by Graham, but 'it is clear that the most violent opposition against the College came from him'; quoted in (Bentley, 1969), p. 6.

14. For Daniell, (James, 2004b); for Miller, (Clerke, *revised*. McConnell, 2004). For a brief history of chemistry at King's College, (Hey, 1955).

15. Bloxam succeeded J. E. Bowman as the Junior Professor of Practical Chemistry in 1856, becoming the Senior Professor after the death of W. A. Miller. Later editions of his textbook were edited by others.

16. For chemistry at Oxford, (Williams, Chapman, and Rowlinson, 2009).

17. (Brock, 2004).

18. For a collection of essays covering professors of chemistry at Cambridge from the 18th century to the 21st century, (Archer and Haley, 2005). For Tennant, (Usselman, 2004); for Liveing, (Dampier, *revised*. James, 2004).

Appendix Three

IC Chemistry and the Chemical Society (later RSC)

'....*it is difficult to over-estimate the significance of the Royal College of Chemistry as a factor in the development of the (Chemical) Society.*'[1]

The Chemical Society (CS) and its successor, the Royal Society of Chemistry (RSC) is the oldest chemical society in the world still in existence. There are many parallels between the RCC and the early years of the CS — they were founded within five years of each other and, just like the RCC of 1845, the Society of 1841 was keenly aware of a lack of provision in Britain for practical instruction and original research in chemistry. James Philip, professor of physical chemistry at the Royal College of Science (RCS) from 1894–1909 recognised this in the epigraph above.[1] This brief appendix explores the interactions of these institutions, notes the transformation of the CS to the RSC, and emphasises the pivotal role which RCC, NSS, RCS and ICL chemists have played in our national chemical societies.

A.1 Foundation of the Chemical Society

The Chemical Society of London ('of London' was dropped in 1848), was founded on March 30, 1841 at the Society of Arts in John Street — now John Adam Street. Robert Warington (1807–1867)[2], an analytical chemist later to become Chemistry Director of the Society of Apothecaries and an active promoter of the Royal College of Chemistry (RCC), was instrumental in setting it up. His son, (also Robert Warington), wrote an account of its history for the 1896 jubilee of the Society.[3] There were 77 founding members, including Thomas Graham (Professor of Chemistry at University College and the Society's first President), Lyon Playfair (the second professor of chemistry at the Royal School of Mines (RSM), and John Daniell, professor of chemistry at King's College). Another founder was Warren de la Rue, who joined the RCC four years later in 1845.[4] Two of the founding members became honorary secretaries of the Society — Robert Warington and Edward Frederick Teschemacher (1781–1863). Their sons, named exactly as their fathers, both attended the RCC: E. F. Teschemacher, Jr. (1843–1877), worked with Hofmann in 1859, and Robert Warington, Jr. (1838–1907), with Frankland in 1876.

The aim of the new Society was *'The promotion of Chemistry and those branches of Science immediately connected with it...,'* the creation of a scholarly forum in which people from different fields could discuss chemistry.[3] Its aims, like those of the RCC, were much influenced by Liebig's philosophy.[5] A research journal, library and a museum were to be provided, and a place (originally the Society of Arts) where lectures could be given and discussions held. The journals, albeit renamed far too many times, and library still exist, but the museum was disbanded in 1865. The CS gained a Charter of Incorporation in 1848 after Playfair had pressed for this. The original accommodation at the Society of Arts became too cramped for the successful enterprise, having tried but failed to rent rooms at the newly instituted RCC at Hanover Square, it moved in 1849 to 142 The Strand, and in 1851 rented part of Dr. Pepper's house at 5 Cavendish Square (William Perkin remembered attending lectures there — see Chapter Three, Note 46). Finally in 1857, the Society relocated to Old Burlington House,[1,6] which had been built in 1664 for the Earl of Burlington, a brother of Robert Boyle, Henry Cavendish lived there in his early years. The accommodation was rather uneasily shared with the Royal and Linnaean Societies, and comprised two back rooms of the ground floor. In 1873 the CS moved to better premises in 'New' Burlington House, an extension built (1868) in the Eastern part of the courtyard by Richard Banks and Charles Barry. Here it remains, albeit with substantial room changes.

Of the 556 students who passed through the RCC from 1845 to 1853, 68 were CS members, 23 were Fellows of the Institute of Chemistry, and 22 had joined the Society of Chemistry and Industry (SCI) founded in 1881.[7]

A.2 Related British Chemical Societies

There were many later developments in the CS. In 1972 the process of unification began of the CS, the Royal Institute of Chemistry (RIC, established 1877), the Faraday Society (established 1903) and the Society of Analytical Chemistry (established 1874). The Queen signed a Royal Charter for the new RSC on 15 May, 1980.[1,6]

The Institute of Chemistry (from 1944 the Royal Institute of Chemistry, RIC) was formed as a result of pressure from within the CS to respond to a widespread need for properly qualified chemists, and from dissatisfaction with elective procedures within the CS. In 1876 a resolution was proposed by William Odling and seconded by Edward Frankland that '…it is desirable that an organisation of Professional Chemists is effected.' On 24 February, 1877 an 'Institute of Professional Chemists of Great Britain and Ireland' was set up, with Frankland as President, Frederick Abel and Robert Galloway as Vice Presidents — all these had been at the RCC. Several founding members of the Institute had also been at the RCC: Henry Armstrong, Charles Bloxam, William Crookes, Frederick Field, William Odling, William Perkin, Sr., Hermann Sprengel and Edward Teschemascher, Jr.[7] In 1914 it opened new headquarters at 30 Russell Square, and it became part of the renamed RSC in 1980 after a members' referendum. Presidents of the RIC who were associated with the College are listed in Table 1.[8]

The Society of Chemical Industry (SCI) was founded principally for chemical industrialists and given its present name in 1881. Again several ex-RCC members were involved including Frederick Abel, Henry Armstrong, William Crookes, Edward Frankland, William Odling, William Perkin, Sr., and Hermann Sprengel. The first President was Henry Roscoe, and later Presidents included Abel, Raphael Meldola and W. H Perkin, Sr., After a referendum in 1970, the SCI decided not to become part of the RSC and is still an independent organisation.[6,7]

A.3 Presidents of the CS, RSC, and RIC (Table 1)[8]

Of the 91 Presidents of the CS and RSC since 1841 to the present time, a disproportionately high number of these, in view of the national coverage of the Society, were associated with the RCC and its successor at IC. Some 35 presidents were or are associated with the RCC, RCS or the chemistry department of ICL, either as students, staff or emeriti. Some also held important positions such as secretary or treasurer (some of the secretaries are listed in Table 1). The one founder member later to join the RCC, Warren de la Rue, was twice its President. Lyon Playfair was also a CS founder, and although not a member of the RCC he had a substantial role in its early history. The first professor of the RCC, A. W. Hofmann (1818–1892) was President from 1861–1863 and a Foreign Secretary of the Society (1847–1861); after his return to Germany in 1865, he founded the *Deutsche chemische Gesellshaft* in 1867, very much on the lines of the CS in London. Frederick Abel became a President of the CS (and its Foreign Secretary from 1868–1869); he was also president from 1880–1883 of a then rival body, the Institute of Chemistry, founded in 1877. Sir Ewart (Tim) Jones (1911–2002) was CS president from 1964–1966, of the RIC 1970–1972 and the first President of the newly formed RSC (1980–1982). Most presidents served for two-year terms, but Philip died in his first year of office (1941). Jocelyn Thorpe served for three years (1928–1931) as the Society did not want a change of leadership when in the middle of complicated and ultimately unsuccessful negotiations for different chemical societies to form an umbrella organisation with a 'Scheme of Cooperation.'[1,9] This foundered partly because of the economic depression of 1931. Ultimately the merger of the CS, RIC and other societies to form the RSC achieved much of Thorpe's vision.[9]

A.4 Women in the CS

Women were not allowed to join the CS in the 19th century (a marked difference between the RCC and its successors the RCS and IC, who right from the start in 1845 admitted women). Two prominent CS members also from the RCS, Thomas Edward Thorpe and William Tilden, played an

Table 1: Presidents of the CS, RSC, and RIC from the RCC/RCS/IC

	Life span	President CS/RSC[7]	President RIC[7]	Sec CS/RS[1,6]	Chapter No.
Baron Lyon Playfair FRS	1818–1898	1857–1859	—	—	2
August Wilhelm Hofmann FRS	1818–1892	1861–1863	—	—	2,3
Warren de la Rue FRS	1815–1889	1867–1869 1879–1880	—	—	3
Sir Edward Frankland FRS	1825–1899	1871–1873	1877–1880	—	3
William Odling FRS	1829–1921	1873–1875	—	1856–1869	3
Sir Frederick Abel FRS	1827–1902	1875–1877	1880–1883	—	3
Sir William Perkin, Sr. FRS	1838–1907	1883–1885	—	1869–1883	3
Sir William Crookes FRS	1832–1919	1887–1889	—	—	3
Henry Armstrong FRS*	1848–1937	1893–1895	—	1875–1893	4
Sir Thomas Edward Thorpe FRS CBE	1845–1925	1899–1901	—	—	4
Sir William Augustus Tilden FRS	1842–1926	1903–1905	1891–1894	—	4
Raphael Meldola FRS	1849–1915	1905–1907	1912–1915	—	4
Percy Faraday Frankland FRS	1858–1946	1911–1913	1906–1909	—	3
Sir William Henry Perkin, Jr. FRS	1860–1929	1913–1915	—	—	3
Sir William Jackson Pope FRS*	1870–1939	1917–1919	—	—	4
William Palmer Wynne FRS*	1861–1950	1923–1925	—	1898–1899 1903–1905	4

(Continued)

Table 1: *(Continued)*

	Life span	President CS/RSC7	President RIC.7	Sec CS/RS 1, 6	Chapter No.
Sir Martin Onslow Forster FRS	1872–1945	—	—	1904–1910	4
Herbert Brereton Baker FRS CBE	1862–1935	1926–1928	—	—	6
Sir Jocelyn Field Thorpe FRS	1872–1939	1928–1931	1933–1936	—	6
Sir Gilbert Thomas Morgan FRS	1870–1940	1933–1935	—	1910–1912	4
James Charles Philip FRS	1873–1941	1941–1941	—	1913–1924	6
Harold Johann Thomas Ellingham	1897–1975	—	—	1934–1939	6
Sir Walter Norman Haworth FRS NL	1883–1950	1944–1946	—	—	4
Sir Cyril Hinshelwood FRS NL	1897–1967	1946–1948	—	—	6
Sir Ian Morris Heilbron FRS, DSO	1886–1959	1948–1950	—	—	6–8
Donald Holroyde Hey FRS	1904–1987	—	—	1946–1951	6
Sir Eric Rideal FRS MBE	1890–1974	1950–1952	—	—	8
Joseph Chatt FRS, CBE	1914–1994	—	—	1956–1962	8
Alan Woodworth Johnson FRS	1917–1982	1977–1978	—	1958–1965	7
Sir Christopher Kelk Ingold FRS	1893–1970	1952–1954	—	—	5,6
Harry Julius Emeléus FRS, CBE	1903–1993	1958–1960	1963–1965	—	6,7
Sir Ewart Ray Herbert Jones FRS	1911–2002	1964–1966	1970–1972	—	6,7
—	—	1980–1982	—	—	—

Name				1972–1974	
Thomas West FRS, FRSE, CBE	1927–2010	—	—	1972–1974	9
Lord George Porter FRS, NL, OM	1920–2002	1970–1972	—	—	9
Sir Derek Barton FRS, NL	1918–1998	1973–1974	—	—	7,8
Sir John Cadogan FRS	b. 1930	1982–1984	—	—	9,10
Lord Jack Lewis, FRS	1928–2014	1986–1988	—	—	8
Charles Wayne Rees CBE FRS	1927–2006	1992–1994	—	—	9,10
Edward William Abel CBE	b. 1931	1996–1998	—	—	8
Stephen Victor Ley CBE FRS	b. 1945	2000–2002	—	—	9,10
David Phillips, OBE, FRS	b. 1939	2010–2012	—	—	10
Dominic Tildesley FRS	b. 1952	2014–2016	—	—	10

*At C&GCTC, in 1912 subsumed into IC. See Chapter Four.

active but frustrating role in admitting women to the Society, considered in the main text (Chapter Four).

A.5 Journals of the Society and Their Editors

The Journals of the CS, in their various forms, have been the main vehicles of publication for all the famous chemists of the RCC — Hofmann, Crookes, Frankland, the Perkins, Armstrong and many others. Several RCC and IC– trained chemists became editors for the CS, notably Charles Groves FRS (1841–1920), who worked with Hofmann at the RCC, became deputy editor of the *Journal of the Chemical Society* (JCS) from 1878 and full editor from 1878–1899. William Wynne (1851–1950) was an abstractor for the JCS from 1887–1891 and an editor from 1900–1903, while Gilbert Morgan (1870–1940) was editor from 1904–1906. Clarence Smith (1875–1945), an RCS student from 1894–1897 and then a demonstrator (1897–1899) was editor of the JCS from 1924–1945. Frederick Tompkins FRS (1910–1993) was editor and secretary of the Faraday Division of the Chemical Society and oversaw the production of its journals from 1950–1977. Lionel Charles Cross (1918–1984), an IC student (1936–1940) and briefly on the postwar staff as an organic chemist (1946–1947) became assistant editor in 1948 at the CS, deputy editor in 1958 and, with Robert Cahn, edited the JCS. He became director of publications in 1970, retiring in 1976.[10]

The list of chairmen of the Publications Committee read like an RCS–IC roll–call, and include James Philip (1923–1932), Sir Cyril Hinshelwood (1944–1954), Christopher Ingold (1954–1959), Harry Eméleus (1959–1960), Donald Hey (1960–1964); Tim Jones (1966–1972) and Charles Rees (1981–1985).[1,6]

A.6 Awards of the CS and RSC

Many awards were founded by IC members or commemorate them. There are currently 62 RSC awards, with a third of them founded by, or in honour of, ex-members of the department. In Chapters Three–Ten, we have mentioned some of the IC chemistry staff, past and present, who have received these IC-connected awards, and we apologise to anyone inadvertently omitted. The most prestigious are generally considered to be the Corday–Morgan, Meldola, Pedler, and Tilden awards; the Longstaff prize dates from 1881 and, though not IC-connected, is also celebrated.[11]

End notes

1. Moore and Philip, 1947.
2. Hamlin, 2004; Anon., 1868.
3. Warington *et al.*, 1896.
4. Anon. 1841, Anon.1842.
5. Bud, 1991; Bud and Roberts, 1984.
6. Whiffen & Hey, 1991.
7. Russell, Coley and Roberts, 1977.
8. The RSC website has lists of the Presidents from 1841 to the present.
9. For Abel, De la Rue, and Playfair see Chapter Three; Hofmann Chapters Two and Three; E. R. H. (Tim) Jones Chapter Seven; T. E. Thorpe Chapter Four; J. F. Thorpe Chapter Six and (Kon and Linstead, 1941) p. 447.
10. For Groves see Chapter Three and Tilden, 1920; Clarence Smith see Chapter Four, and Hewitt, 1946; Tompkins see Chapter Eight; Lionel Cross Chapter Eight and (Jones, 1985).
11. The awards are well described on the appropriate RSC websites. In alphabetical order those with IC chemistry connections they are (with dates of the first award in brackets): the *Barrer Award* (1983) for work on porous inorganic materials; the *Bourke Award* (1955) for physical chemists from overseas to lecture in the United Kingdom; *Charles Rees Award* (2008) for excellence in heterocyclic chemistry; *Corday–Morgan prize* (1949) for the most meritorious contributions to chemistry; the *Frankland award* (1982) for research in organometallic or coordination chemistry; the *Harrison–Meldola* Prize (2008); the *Edward Harrison Memorial Prizes* (1921–2008) and the *Meldola Medal and Prize* (1921–2008) for the most meritorious investigations in chemistry; the *Haworth Memorial Lectureship* (1969) for contributions to carbohydrate chemistry; the *Joseph Chatt Award* (1969) for multidisciplinary research in inorganic chemistry and biochemistry; the *Liversidge Award* (1927) for contributions to physical chemistry; the *Lord Lewis Lectureship* (1988) for distinctive chemical or scientific achievements; the *L. S. Theobald Lectureship* (1985) for contributions to analytical chemistry; the *Pedler*

Award (1927) for contributions to organic chemistry from a researcher under the age of 55; the *Perkin Prize for Organic Chemistry* (2008) for research achievement in organic chemistry; the *S. F. Boys–A. Rahman Award* (1980) for innovative research in computational chemistry; the *Sir Derek Barton Gold Medal* (2001) for work in any area of organic chemistry reflecting the interests associated with Sir Derek; the *Sir Edward Frankland Fellowship* (1984) for encouragement of research in organometallic or coordination chemistry of transition metals; the *Sir Eric Rideal Award and Lecture* (1970) for significant and sustained contribution in colloid, interface and surface science; the *Sir Geoffrey Wilkinson Award* (1999) for outstanding contributions to pure or applied research in organometallic chemistry; the *Tilden Prizes* (1939) for advances in chemistry.

For the Corday–Morgan award see also Chapter Four, Note 73; the Meldola awards see Chapter Three, Note 100; the Liversidge Award Chapter Three, Note 133; the Theobald Lectureship, Chapter Six, Note 56; the Pedler Award Chapter Six, Note 59; the Boys–Rahman Award, Chapter Six, Note 45; for the Tilden Prize, Chapter Four, Section 4.2.

Appendix Four

Chemistry Department Staff at IC, 1845–2000

Name	Life span	Appointments at IC
Adams, Michael James	—	TL 1977–1978
Albery, Wyndham John FRS	1936–2013	P 1977 SRF 1989–1992
Alder, John Frederick	—	L 1972–1980
Alexander, Peter	1922–1993	St 1938–1943 S 1951
Allen, Robert D.	—	L 1974–1974
Andersen, Richard Allen	—	TL 1974–1976
Anderson, John Stuart FRS	1908–1990	St 1926–1931 D 1932 AL 1937–1938
Archer, Bernard Lewis	—	St 1945–1946 D 1946 AL 1948–1950
Armstrong, Henry FRS	1848–1937	St 1865–1866 EP 1913–1937 P 1883–1911*
Armstrong, Alan	—	St 1984–1990 R 1999 P 2004–
Ash, Richard	—	L (RA) 1959 L 1978–1995
Atkinson, Bernard	1923–2009	St 1941–1944 L 1944 SL 1962–1990
Avery, John Scales	—	AL 1962 L 1966–1973
Back, Thomas George	—	TL 1974–1976
Baghurst, David Richard	—	L 1992–1994

(*Continued*)

(Continued)

Name	Life span	Appointments at IC
Baker, Herbert Brereton FRS CBE	1862–1935	P 1912–1932
Baker, John William	1898–1967	St 1916–1917 D 1920–1923
Baldwin, Sir Jack FRS	—	St 1957–1964 AL 1963 L 1966–1967
Barnard, John Allan	—	St 1944–1947 S 1951–1953
Barrer, Richard Maling FRS	1910–1996	P 1954 SRF, EP 1978–1996
Barrett, Anthony Gerald Martin FRS	—	St 1970–1975 L 1975 SL 1982–1983 P 1993–
Barrie, James Alexander	—	L 1955 SL 1974–1993
Barrow, Richard Frank	—	St 1934–1937 D 1938–1939
Barton, Sir Derek Richard FRS NL	1918–1998	St 1938–1942 AL 1945 L 1946–1949 P 1957–1978
Bassett, David William	1934–2015	L 1965–1994
Beckwith, Athelstan Laurence FRS	1930–2010	L 1962–1963
Billimoria, Jimmy Daddy	—	D 1947–1950
Binder, John Herman	—	St 1899–1902 S 1902–1903
Bockris, John O'Mara	1923–2013	St 1943–1935 L 1945–1954
Bone, William Arthur FRS	1871–1938	VP 1910–1912 P 1912–1915
Borland, Hugh Alexander Millar	—	St 1892–1895 S 1895–1896
Braddock, David Christopher	—	L 1996 SL 2005 R 2008 P 2015–
Bradley, John Stewart	—	TL 1973–1975
Brady, Oscar Lisle	1890–1968	D 1912–1915; 1919
Brame, John Samuel Strafford	1871–1953	St 1892–1896 D 1896–1897
Bramley, Arthur	1878–1935	St 1906–1909 D 1910–1915
Braude, Ernest Alexander Rudolph	1922–1956	St 1940–1942 RA 1942 L 1947 R 1952 P 1955–1956
Bresme, Fernando	—	RA 1998 L 2000 SL 2005 R 2008 P 2014–
Briscoe, Henry Vincent Aird	1888–1961	St 1906–1909 AL 1912–1916 P 1932–1954
Britovsek, George	—	L 2000 SL 2007 R 2011–
Brown, Leslie Norman	1894–1946	St 1911–1914 S 1920

(Continued)

(*Continued*)

Name	Life span	Appointments at IC
Browning, Kendal Colin	1875–1936	L 1920–1921
Bull, Philip Cecil	1889–1960	St 1908–1911 D 1919 L 1925–1954
Burrows, Henry	1871–1914	St 1894–1897 D 1902–1904
Cadogan, Sir John F. FRS	—	VP 1979–2002
Camilleri, Patrick	—	VP 1999–2002
Capsey, Rev. Harold Vincent	—	St 1897–1900 D 1900–1902
Carlton, Margaret	1895–1969	PA 1920–1942 RA 1943 L 1947–1960
Castleden, Stephen L.	—	TL 1978–1981
Catlow, Charles Richard Arthur FRS	—	VP 1993–2002
Challis, Brian	—	L 1967 SL 1976 R 1981–1986
Chapman Jones, Henry	1854–1932	A 1882 D 1888 L 1908–1915
Christou, George	—	TL 1982–1983
Clark, Cecil Henry Douglas	—	St 1912–1915 S 1920
Clayton, Arthur	1878–1954	St 1903–1905 D 1908–1912
Cobb, Leslie Hamilton	—	St 1935–1939 D 1939–1940
Cole–Hamilton, David FRSE	—	L 1975–1978
Coll, John Charles	—	L 1971–1972
Colquohoun, Howard Matthew	—	VL 1992–1995
Cook, Arthur Herbert FRS	1911–1988	St 1930–1934 AL 1937 L 1946 SL 1947 R 1948
Cornfield, Archibald Harold	1919–1993	St 1937–1940 AL 1946 L 1950–1980
Courtman, Harold Rueben	—	St 1902–1906 S 1908–1911
Couzens, Edward Gordon	—	St 1903–1907 AD 1907–1909
Cowley, Alan Herbert FRS	—	P 1988–1989
Cox, Jeffrey James	—	AL 1963–1964
Craig, Donald	—	St 1980–1986 L 1987 R 1997 P 2000–
Crombie, Leslie FRS	1923–1999	AL 1951 L 1953–1958
Cross, Alexander Dennis	—	L 1957–1960

(*Continued*)

(Continued)

Name	Life span	Appointments at IC
Cross, Lionel Charles	1918–1984	St 1936–1940 D 1946–1947
Cullis, Charles Fowler	—	L 1950–1959
Dagnall, Roy Maurice	—	AL 1963–1965 L 1966–1972
Dalziel, James Andrew Walter	1922–2011	St 1946–1949 L 1953–1961
Dalziel, Mary Estelle (Williams)	—	St 1943–1947 AL 1947 L 1951–1952
David, Ieuan	—	St 1944–1947 AL 1947 L 1952–1956
Davies, Robert Philip	—	L 2000 SL 2007–
de Mayo, Paul José FRS	1924–1994	L 1957–1959
deMello, Andrew James	—	St 1988–1991 L 1997 SL 2000 P 2003–2011
deMello, John	—	L 2000 SL 2004 R 2008 P 2011–
Dobson, Charles Robert	—	St 1906–1909 S 1910–1911
Doyle, William Patrick	—	St 1946–1948 AL 1948–1952
Dowdall, John Patrick de Courmaceul	—	St 1912–1916 S 1919–1920
Drake, Simon Robert	—	L 1990–1993
Ducker, John William	—	AL 1970–1971
Dunn, Frederick Percy	b. 1887	St 1905–1910 PA 1911–1913
Dunne, Anne	—	AL 1956 L 1959–1961
Dunstall, William Arthur Warton	—	St 1914–1919 S 1937–1939
Durrant, James Robert	—	L 1999 SL 1999 R 2002 P 2005–
Dyer, Phillip	—	L 1995–1997
Dyson, Paul Joseph	—	L 1994 RSURF 1995–1998
Egdell, Russell George	—	L 1983–1990
Eiloart, Arnold	—	L 1895
Eldridge, Arthur Alfred	1897–1970	St 1910–1911 D 1911 L 1920 SL 1934–1960
Ellingham, Harold Johann Thomas	1897–1975	St 1914–1916 D 1919 L 1924 AP/R 1939–1944

(Continued)

(Continued)

Name	Life span	Appointments at IC
Elvidge, John Arthur	1922–2011	St 1941–1947 L 1949 SL 1959–1962 R 1962–1965
Eméleus, Harry Julius FRS, CBE	1903–1993	St 1921–1929 AL 1931 L 1936 AP 1940–1945
Evans, Dennis Frederick FRS	1928–1990	L 1956 R 1964 P 1981–1990
Fahy, Michael	—	L 1990–1997
Farmer, Ernest Harold FRS	1890–1952	St, 1941–1947 L 1949 SL 1959–1962 R 1962–1965
Fay, James William John	—	St 1931–1936 D 1934–1936
Fersht, Sir Alan FRS	—	P 1978 VP 1989–1993
Field, Samuel	—	St 1895–1898 D 1898–1900
Finch, George Ingle FRS	1888–1970	L 1912–1915
Findlay, Tristan John Victor	—	L 1957–1960
Fleet, Bernard	—	L 1965–1980
Forster, Sir Martin Onslow FRS	1872–1945	S 1894–1895* D 1895 AP 1902–1919
Frankland, Sir Edward FRS	1825–1899	P 1865–1885
Frankland, Percy Faraday FRS	1858–1946	D 1880–1886
Gale, Julian	—	RF 1993 L 2007 R 2010–1913
Garland, Charles Samuel	1887–1960	St 1905–1909 D 1909–1912
George, Maurice Hilary	1928–2009	L 1965 SL 1980 R 1990–1994
Gibbs, Capt. Ivan R.	1891–1916	D 1913–1916
Gibson, John Frederick	—	L 1965 SL 1979 R 1986–1993
Gibson, Susan Elizabeth OBE	—	L 1990 R 1995–1998 P 2003–
Gibson, Vernon Charles FRS	—	P 1995–2008
Gill, Naida S.	1923–1993	L 1959–1961
Gillard, Robert David	1936–2013	St 1958–1961 L 1961–1964
Godden, William	1884–1954	St 1903–1907 D 1907–1911
Gollins, David	—	L 1992–1996
Goodgame, David M. L.	—	L 1961 SL 1971 R 1973 P 1995 EP 2000–

(Continued)

Name	Life span	Appointments at IC
Goodgame, Margaret	—	L 1962 SL 1986–1998
Goosen, Arthur	—	L 1963
Gordon, Manfred	—	R 1960–1964
Gordon, Peter Graham	—	TL 1968–1970
Gould, Ian	—	L 1995 SL 1999 R 2011–
Graham, John Samuel	—	L 1991–1995
Gray, Harold Heath	—	L 1912–1913
Greenaway, Alfred John	1852–1938	St 1871–1883 D 1873–1881
Griffith, William Pettit	—	St 1954–1960 L 1962 R 1978 P 1994 EP 2003–
Griffiths, Hugh	1891–1954	St 1907–1910 D 1911
Grime, Herbert	d. 1937	St 1888–1891 D 1891–1894
Gundry, P. M.	—	AL 1957–1960
Guthrie, Frederick Bickell	1861–1927	D 1888–1890
Hallman, Peter Stewart	—	AL 1966–1967
Hambly, Frederic John	1868–1960	St 1886–1888 D 1888–1889
Hamer, Miss Frances Mary	1894–1980	L 1951–1956
Hannen, John Troubridge	b. 1900	St 1917–1918 & 1921–1922 L 1943–1960
Harper, Stanley Hugh	—	St 1931–1934 D 1934–1936
Harrison, Nicholas	—	P 2000–
Harwood, Henry Francis	1886–1975	D 1911–1916 L 1917 AP 1934–1940
Hart–Smith, James	1877–1946	St 1895–1898 D 1898–1900
Hatton, Arthur Barker, MBE	1892–1945	St 1914–1916 AD 1916–1919
Haworth, Sir Norman FRS NL	1883–1950	D 1911–1912
Haynes, Richard Kingston	—	TL 1972–1975
Hayward, David	1930–2015	AL 1960 L 1963 SL 1993–2001
Heilbron, Sir Ian Morris FRS DSO	1886–1959	P 1938–1949
Herringshaw, John Francis	—	AL 1944 L 1948–1963

(Continued)

(Continued)

Name	Life span	Appointments at IC
Hewitt, David George	—	AL 1966–1968
Hey, Donald Holroyde FRS	1904–1987	L 1939–1941
Hickman, Kenneth Devereux	1896–1979	St 1913–1916 D 1921–1925
Hill, Anthony	—	L 1992 P 2000–2002
Hills, Sir Graham J. FRSE	1926–2014	L 1949–1962
Himus, Godfrey Wilfred	1894–1964	St 1910–1914; 1923–1924 D 1927–1938
Hinchley, John William	1871–1931	VL 1910–1913 L 1913–1915
Hind, J. W.	—	S 1905–1907
Hinshelwood, Sir Cyril FRS NL OM	1897–1967	SRF 1964–1967
Hird, James Morton	d. 1948	St 1902–1905 D 1905–1907
Hofmann, August Wilhelm FRS	1818–1892	P 1845–1865
Holloway, George Thomas	1863–1917	St 1881–1884 D 1884–1886
Hudson, Robert Francis FRS	1922–2012	St 1940–1945 AL 1945–1947
Hunter, Robert Fergus	1904–1963	St 1922–1926 D 1928
Hutchin, William Henry	—	St 1892–1895 S 1895–1896
Ingold, Sir Christopher Kelk FRS	1893–1970	St 1913–1915 D 1920–1924
Ives, David Jones Gibbs	1906–1983	St 1925–1932 SL 1943
Jackman, Lloyd Miles	—	AL 1953 L 1955 R 1961–1962
Jacobs, Patrick William McCarthy	1923–2013	St 1948–1950 AL 1950 L 1953 SL 1963 R 1965
James, Hugh William	—	St 1895–1899 D 1899–1900
James, Stuart	—	L 1996–1999
Japp, Francis Robert FRS	1848–1925	AP 1881–1890
Jenkinson, Ernest Arthur	—	St 1897–1900 S 1900–1902
Jones, Anthony Capeland	—	VP 1996–2000
Jones, Bernard Mouat FRS DSO	1882–1953	AP 1913–1914
Jones, Chapman Henry	1854–1932	See **Chapman Jones,** Henry
Jones, David William	—	L 1963–1964

(Continued)

(Continued)

Name	Life span	Appointments at IC
Jones, Sir Ewart Ray Herbert FRS	1911–2002	AL 1938 L 1941 R 1945–1947
Jones, Tim	—	L 1991 R 1997 P 1998–2007
Kerr, Ian	—	L/RA 1956–1984
King, Albert Theodore	1885–1939	D 1911 L 1920
King, Alexander CMG	1909–2007	St 1927–1929 D 1931 AL 1938 L 1940–1943
Kington, George Leslie	1922–2013	R 1955–1959
Kipping, Frederick Stanley FRS	1863–1949	D 1890–1897*
Kirby, Gordon William	1934–2011	AL 1960 L 1961–1967
Kirkbright, Gordon Frank	1940–1984	AL 1964 L 65 SL 1975 R 1979–1980
Kirman, Walter	1871–1934	St 1886–1889 A 1889–1892
Kitchener, Joseph Alfred	1916–2009	AL 1938–1943 L 1948 SL 1954–1961
Klug, David	—	L 1995 R 1999 P 2001–
Kon, George Armand Robert FRS	1890–1951	St 1913–1916; 1919 RA 1923 L1925 AP 1934–1942
Kucernak, Anthony	—	L 1995 SL 2001 R 2004 P 2008–
Law, Robert Vernon	—	L 1997 SL 2004 R 2009–
Leach, Frederick Peacock	d. 1948	St 1900–1905 D 1906–1907
Leatherbarrow, Robin	—	L 1984 R 1999 P 2002–2013
Letcher, Roy Melville	—	L 1968–1969
Levitt, Bryan Phillip	—	L 1962 SL 1981–1986
Lewis, Lord Jack of Nuneham, FRS	1928–2014	L 1956–1957
Ley, Steven Victor CBE, FRS	—	PD 1975 L 1976 P 1983–1992
Lickiss, Paul	—	L 1993 SL 1999 R 2001 P 2015–
Linstead, Sir Reginald Patrick FRS	1902–1966	St 1920 D 1928 AL 1931 L 1933–1938 P 1949–1955
Little, Henry Frank Victor	b. 1887	St 1905–1908 D 1908–1915
Lock, Colin James Lyne	1933–1996	AL 1960–1963

(*Continued*)

Name	Life span	Appointments at IC
Locket, George Hazelwood	—	D 1927–1931
Long, Nicholas	—	L 1995 SL 1998 R 2002 P 2006–
Lown, James William	—	AL 1959–1962
Lowry, Thomas Martin FRS	1874–1936	St 1898–1901 L 1901–1911* L 1913
Maddock, Alfred Gavin	1917–2009	St 1936–1940 RA 1940–1941
Magnus, Phillip FRS	—	St 1962–1968 AL 1966 L 1969–1975
Manning, Alexander Bernard	—	St 1912–1913 PA 1913–1921
Manz, Andreas	—	P 1995–2004
Marle, Major Ernest Robert	—	St 1899–1901 S 1903–1904
Marsden, Arthur Whitcombe	b. 1911	St 1929–1936 AL 1936–1946
Marsden, Stephen P.	—	St 1987 L 1994 SL 2000–2001
Marshall, G. N.	—	S 1901–1903
Mason, Frederick Alfred	1888–1947	D 1914–1916
Mason, Sir Ronald FRS	—	L 1960–1963
Masters, Anthony Frederick	—	TL 1975–1977
Meek, Geoffrey Arthur	—	AL 1949–1952
Meldola, Raphael FRS	1849–1915	St 1868 D 1872–1877
Mercer, Ian	—	PDRA 1992–1994, 1995–1997 L 1999–2001
Micklethwait, Frances Mary Gore, MBE	1868–1950	St 1898–1901 RA 1901–1918
Miers, Sir Henry Alexander FRS	1858–1942	L 1886–1895*
Miller, Andrew	—	L 1992 P 2002–2008
Millidge, Alfred Frank	—	St 1934–1936 D 1936–1937
Mingos, David Michael Patrick FRS	—	P 1992 VP 1999–2002
Montalban, Antonio Garrido	—	St 1995–1997 L 1998–2002
Moody, Christopher John	—	L 1979 R 1989–1990
Moody, Gerald Tattersall	1864–1943	D, L 1884–1907*

(*Continued*)

Name	Life span	Appointments at IC
Moore, Walter Roman	—	St 1906–1910 AD 1910–1911
Morgan, Sir Gilbert Thomas FRS	1870–1940	St 1894–1897 AD 1897 D 1902 AP 1908–1912
Morrison, George Anderson	—	AL 1959–1961
Moss, Gerard P.	—	St 1956–1959 PD 1963 AL 1964–1966
Motherwell, William FRS	—	St 1975–1977 L 1983 R 1990–1993 EP 2013–
Murgatroyd, John Blackburn	b. 1903	D 1925–1929
Murray, Humphrey Desmond	1899–1960	D 1922–1929
Newell, William Copeman	—	St 1932–1934 S 1934–1936
Newitt, Edward James	—	St 1949–1953 AL 1953 L 1955–1957
Newth, George Samuel	1851–1936	A 1882 D 1909–1910
Nicholson, David	—	AL 1962 L 1966 R 1992–2002
Norris, Richard K Kenneth	—	AL 1971–1972
O'Brien, Paul FRS CBE	—	P 1994–1999
Oldham, Keith B.	—	AL 1955–1957
O'Shaughnessy, Bernard	1876–1960	St 1900–1903 D 1903–1904
Otway, David Jonathan	—	St 1988–1994 PDRA 1996 L 1999–2001
Owen, Leonard Newton	1914–1999	L 1943–1949 SL 1950–1951 R 1952 P 1961 EP 1978
Packer, Kenneth FRS	—	St 1956–1959 VP 1992–1995
Paneth, Friedrich Adolf FRS	1887–1958	L 1933 R 1938
Parkinson, Christopher	—	L 1993–1995
Parsonage, Neville	—	L 1960 R 1989–1995
Parsons, Leslie George Brett	1897–1947	St 1926–1929 S 1930–1934
Parsons, Roger FRS	—	AL 1950–1951
Payne, Douglas Sutherland	—	St 1941–1945 AL 1947–1949
Peacock, Raymond Dixon	1927–2012	L 1953–1958

(*Continued*)

(*Continued*)

Name	Life span	Appointments at IC
Pearson, Thomas Gibson	1908–1962	D 1933–1937 AL 1938–1939
Penn, Francis Richard	—	St 1893–1896 S 1896–1898
Philip, James Charles OBE FRS	1873–1941	D 1897–1899* A 1900 L 1902–1908 P 1914–1941
Phillips, David OBE, FRS	—	P 1989 SRF, EP 2006–
Phillips, Lawrence	—	L 1965–1979
Pickard, Joseph Allen	—	St 1904–1907 S 1907–1909
Poë, Anthony John	1929–2015	AL 1955 L 1958 SL 1967–1970
Pollard, Alfred George	1893–1973	St 1913–1915 D 1920 L 1927 SL 1947–1961
Pollard, George Potticary	—	St 1927–1928, 1936–1937 D 1937–1940
Poole, Colin	—	L 1996 P 1997
Pope, Sir William Jackson FRS	1870–1939	D 1890* L 1895–1901*
Porter, Lord George OM FRS NL	1920–2002	VP 1979–2002
Pratt, Leslie	1929–1991	AL 1959 L 1960 SL 1966–1988
Price, David Christopher	—	St 1949–1951 AL 1955–1957
Prosser, Alan Philip	—	AL 1953–1957 L 1960–1969
Purcell, Ronald Herbert	1905–1969	St 1922–1927 D 1929 AL 1932 L 1938–1946
Quirke, Nicholas	—	P 1998–2006, 2011–
Read, Roger Wayne	—	L 1977–1978
Rees, Charles Wayne FRS, CBE	1927–2006	P 1978 EP 1993–2006
Rees, Lovat Victor Charles FRSE	1927–2006	L 1958 SL 1970 R 1979 P 1986–1993
Rideal, Sir Eric Keightley FRS MBE	1890–1974	SRF 1955–1967
Ridley, Damon Donald	—	TL 1971–1972
Riley, Henry Lister	1899–1986	St 1919–1923 D 1923 L 1931–1933
Roberts, Eric Richard	1915–1975	St 1934–1938 AL 1940 L 1945 SL 1953–1975

(*Continued*)

(*Continued*)

Name	Life span	Appointments at IC
Robertson, Neil	—	L 2000–01
Robertson, Philip Wilfred	1884–1969	D 1910 L 1911–1919
Rodger, James Wyllie	1867–1897	St 1884–1888 A 1889 D 1894–1897
Rogers, Donald	1921–1999	R 1961 P 1965–1980
Ross, John David McBeath	b. 1889	St 1915–1919 D 1918–1919
Rumbles, Gary	—	L 1989 SL 1996 R 2000 VP 2001–
Russell, Richard	—	TL 1972–1974
Rydon, Henry Norman	1912–1991	St 1929–1933 D 1933–1937 L 1947 R 1950–1952
Rzepa, Henry	—	St 1968–1974 L 1980 R 1993 P 2003 EP 2014–
Sammes, Peter	—	St 1957–1963 AL 1964 L 1967 R 1971–1975
Schaffner, Karl	—	TL 1966–1968
Scott, Alastair Ian FRS	1928–2007	L 1957–1958
Scott, William Dallas	—	St 1925–1929 D 1929
Seddon, John	—	L 1991 R 1993 P 1999–
Shahak, Israel	—	TL 1971–1972
Sharadsky, Edward T.	—	L 1973–1974
Sharp, Barry Leonard	—	TL 1972–1975
Sharp, David William Arthur FRSE	1931–2013	AL 1957–1959 L 1960–1961
Shepherd, Alfred	—	St 1901–1904 S 1904–1906
Simmons, Thomas Arthur	—	St 1909–1910 D 1910
Skapski, Andrzej Czeslaw	—	St 1957–1963 AL 1965 L 1966–1998
Sklarz, Benjamin	—	L 1961–1965
Sladden, Cyril Edgar	—	AD 1912–1915; 1918–1919
Smith, Alexander L.	—	VP 1985–1996
Smith, Clarence	1875–1945	St 1894–1897 A 1897–1899 D 1901–1903
Smith, Edward	—	St 1965–1968 L 1978 SL 1981–2009 SRF 2009–

(*Continued*)

(*Continued*)

Name	Life span	Appointments at IC
Smith, Marie–Louise	—	RSURF 1996–1998
Smith, Norman	—	L 1994–2002
Smith, Peter William George	—	TL 1954–1957
Snook, Richard David	—	RF 1977–1985
Spencer, Douglas Arthur	1901–1979	St 1918–1920 D 1920 AL 1931–1933
Spiro, Michael	—	L 1960 R 1965 P 1992 EP 1994–
Steinke, Joachim	1964–2013	L 1997 SL 2003 R 2008–2013
Stewart, Kenneth	d. 2003	St 1932–1936 D 1937–1940
Stick, Robert Vyent	—	L 1973–1975
Stocker, Charles Frederick	1899–1927	St 1916–1917, 1919 D 1922–1924
Stoessl, Albert	—	AL 1957–1960
Sugden, James Netherwood	1894–1944	St 1913–1915 D 1919 L 1922 SL 1943–1944
Sutcliffe, Martin Berry	—	L 1966–1987
Sutherland, James Kenneth	1932–2001	R 1958–1970
Tapp, James Stewart	—	St 1933–1935 S 1935–1936
Taylor, Alan Geoffrey	—	L 1974–1975
Taylor, Deryck Arnold	—	TL 1974–1975
Templer, Richard	—	RF 1989 L 1994 R 1997 P 2001–
Theobald, Leslie Stuart	1896–1979	St 1919–1922 D 1925 AL 1932 L 1937 R 1954–1965
Thomas, Sir John Meurig FRS	—	VP 1987–1991
Thomas, Peter James	—	AL 1953–1955
Thomas, Susan Elizabeth OBE	—	See **Gibson,** Susan Elizabeth OBE
Thompson, Kenneth Clive	—	AL 1968–1969
Thorpe, Sir Jocelyn Field FRS CBE	1872–1939	St 1892–1893 P 1914–1938 EP 1939
Thorpe, Sir Thomas Edward FRS	1845–1925	P 1885–1894; 1909–1912
Tilden, Sir William Augustus FRS	1842–1926	P 1894–1909
Tildesley, Dominic John	—	P 1995–1997

(*Continued*)

(Continued)

Name	Life span	Appointments at IC
Timmons, Christopher John	—	AL 1950–1953
Tompkins, Frederick Clifford FRS	1910–1995	R 1947 P 1959–1977
Turner, David Warren FRS	—	St 1951–1955 AL 1955 L 1958 R 1963–1967
Turtle, Edgar Ernest	—	St 1934–1937 RA 1937–1940
Tutton, Alfred Edwin Howard FRS	1864–1938	St 1883–1886 A 1887 D 1889–1895
Vilar, Ramón	—	TL 1996 L 1999 SL 2003 R 2007 P 2011–
Waight, Eric Stanmore	1927–2003	St 1945–1950 AL 1953 L 1957 SL 1967 R 1972–1992
Walkley, John	—	AL 1960–1961 L 1962–1966
Warren, Frank Louis	1905–1980	St 1925–1928 D 1928–1931
Watson, Walter Henry	—	St 1881–1884 S 1894–1895
Weedon, Basil Charles Leicester FRS	1923–2003	St 1940–1946 L 1947 R 1957–1960
Welch, Archibald John Edmund	1915–1988	St 1934–1938 AL 1941 L 1945 SL 1951–1982
Welton, Tom	—	L 1995 SL 2000 R 2002 P 2004–
West, Ralph Winton	1895–1968	St 1914–1916 D 1919–1927
West, Thomas Summers FRS, FRSE, CBE	1927–2010	L 1955 R 1963 P 1965–1975 VP 1975–1978
Weston, R. J.	—	TL 1977–1979
Whalley, Margaret (Elvidge)	1923–1984	St 1949–1952 AL 1952–1956
Whitby, George Stafford	1887–1972	St 1903–1906 D 1906–1910
Whitehead, James	d. 1936	St 1896–1899 S 1899–1900
Whiteley, Martha Annie OBE	1866–1956	St 1892–1902 D 1902 L 1915 AP 1920–1934
Widdowson, David Arthur	—	L 1965 R 1982–2005
Wiechers, Adaam	—	AL 1961 L 1963–1966
Wilde, Paul	—	St 1978–1984 L 1995 SL 2004–

(Continued)

Name	Life span	Appointments at IC
Wilkinson, Sir Geoffrey FRS NL	1921–1996	St 1939–1941 PD 1941–1943 P 1955 EP 1988–1996
Williams, David	—	T 1960–1964 RA 1968 L 1982 R 1991 P 1996–2003
Winter, Ernest Roy Sealey	—	St 1936–1940 L 1945–1949
Winter, Ramsay Middleton	1897–1963	D 1919–1921
Withers, John Charles	—	D 1911–1913
Wood, Geoffrey F.	—	AL 1956–1957
Wood, John Lukes	—	L 1960–1966 SL 1967 R 1976–1977
Woollins, Derek FRSE	—	L 1983 R 1988–1994
Wootton, William Ord	1884–1912	St 1902–1905 D 1908–1910
Wright, John Jessen	—	AL 1968 L 1971
Wright, Terrance	—	VP 1991–1994
Wynne, William Palmer FRS	1861–1950	St 1881–1884 AP 1891–1902 L 1885–1890*
Yaliraki, Sophia	—	L 2000 SL 2004 P 2012–
Young, George Brent	—	L 1977–1980; 1981–1993 SL 1993–2001
Young, Leslie	1911–1992	St 1930–1932 AL 1953–1955

A = Assistant; AD = Assistant Demonstrator; AL = Assistant Lecturer; D = demonstrator; EP = Emeritus professor; L = lecturer; NL = Nobel Laureate; P = Professor; PA = Professor's assistant; PD = postdoctoral (at IC); PDRA = Postdoctoral Research Assistant; R = Reader; RA = Research Assistant; RF = Research Fellow; RSURF = RS University Research Fellow; S = staff (unspecified); SL = Senior lecturer; SRF = Senior Research Fellow; St = Student; T = Technician; TL = Temporary Lecturer; VL = Visiting Lecturer; VP = Visiting Professor.

* C&GCTC member during this period

Bibliography

Archival references, internet sources, and name/date for published references are given in the endnotes. Full citations for the name/date references are given below. Following convention, initials only are given for the first names of authors of chemistry papers. With a few exceptions, all other author names are given as in the original publications. Classified as Anon. are unsigned articles and those signed only with initials. Chemical journal titles are abbreviated as in Chemical Abstracts (CASSI); when this does not contain titles for older (CS) journals we use the CS/RSC Royal Society of Chemistry abbreviations.

ODNB OUP is the acronym for *Oxford Dictionary of National Biography*, Oxford University Press, and CUP that for Cambridge University Press. We have used the electronic edition of the *ODNB;* some entries are more recent, or have been updated, since the original publication date of 2004. *DSB* is the acronym for the *Dictionary of Scientific Biography* (ed. C. C. Gillispie, 1970–1980) and *New DSB* for post-2007 editions (ed. N. Koertge), Scribner, N. Y.

Abel, E. W. 1996. Sir Geoffrey Wilkinson 1921–1996 IN MEMORIAM. *Inorg. Chem.* **35**:7463–7464. http://doi.org/c6468g

Abel, E. W., M. A. Bennett, R. Burton and G. Wilkinson. 1958. Transition metal complexes of seven-membered ring systems. Part I. The cycloheptatriene-metal complexes and related compounds. *J. Chem. Soc.* 4559–5563. http://doi.org/fqpbfq

Abel, F. A. 1845. On some of the products of oxidation of cumol by nitric acid. *Mem. Proc. Chem. Soc.* **3**:441–447. http://doi.org/cbzdf4

Abel, F. A. 1896. The history of the Royal College of Chemistry and reminiscences of Hofmann's professorship. *J. Chem. Soc., Trans.* **69**:580–596. http://doi.org/c8dt8p

Abel, F. A and T. H. Rowney. 1849. Analysis of the water of the Artesian Wells, Trafalgar Square. *Quart. J. Chem. Soc.* **1**:97–103. http://doi.org/cgttbq

Abel, F. A and Nicholson, E. C. 1850. Researches on Strychnine. Part 1. On the composition of strychnine and of its salts. *Quart. J. Chem. Soc.* **2**:241–263. http://doi.org/d7ffsz

Abney, W. De W and T. E. Thorpe. 1896. On the determination of the photometric intensity of the coronal light during the solar eclipse of the 16th April 1893. *Proc. R. Soc.* **60**:15–17. http://doi.org/dkkww2

Adley, T. J and L. N. Owen. 1966. Thio-Sugars Part I. The thiopyranose ring. *J. Chem. Soc. C.* 1287–1290. http://doi.org/czdwqm

Adloff, Jean-Pierre and George B. Kauffman. 2010. Alfred G. Maddock (1917–2009), an inspired radiochemist. *Chem. Educator* **15**:237–242.

Agnew, R. A. L. 2004. Clark, Sir James, first baronet (1788–1879). *ODNB*. OUP. http://doi.org/dcktvz

Albery, W. J. 1980. The application of the Marcus Relation to reactions in solution. *Ann. Rev. Phys. Chem.* **31**:227–263.

Allen, G., K. Dusek, J. W. Kennedy and R. Koningsveld. 1977. Professor Manfred Gordon — a general appreciation. *Br. Polym. J.* **9**:85–88.

Allen, R. D., D. H. R. Barton, M. Girijavallabhan, P. G. Sammes and M. V. Taylor. 1973. On the trapping of sulphenic acids from penicillins with thiols. *J. Chem. Soc. Perkin Trans.* **1**:1182–1187. http://doi.org/fqpp3n

Allmand, A. J and H. J. T. Ellingham. 1924. *Principles of applied electrochemistry.* London: Longmans, Green

Amabilino, D. B., D. J. Williams, J. F. Stoddart and 7 others. 1998. Oligocatenanes Made to Order. *J. Am. Chem. Soc.* **120**:4295–4307. http://doi.org/cv538b

Anderson, J. S. 1932. Carbon-oxygen linkage in metal carbonyls. *Nature* **130**:1002.

Anderson, J. S and L. O. Brockway. 1937. The molecular structures of iron nitrosocarbonyl Fe $(NO)_2(CO)_2$ and cobalt nitrosocarbonyl $Co(NO)(CO)_3$. *Trans. Faraday Soc.* **33**:1233–1239. http://doi.org/dwhshp

Anderson, J. S., E. F. Bradbrook, A. H. Cook and R. P. Linstead. 1938. Phthalocyanines and associated compounds. Part XIII. Absorption spectra. *J. Chem. Soc.* 1151–1156. http://doi.org/dnwbf9

Anderson, R. G. W. 1989. Yeast and the Victorian brewers: Incidents and personalities in the search for the true ferment. *J. Inst. Brewing* **95**:337–345. http://doi.org/rm7

Anderson, R. G. W. 2004. Black, Joseph (1728–1799). *ODNB*. OUP. http://doi.org/cfmsjx

Andrew, C. 2009. *Defend the Realm: The authorized history of MI5*. London: Allen Lane

Ankianiec, B. C., V. Christou, D. T. Hardy, S. K. Thomson and G. B. Young. 1994 Mechanisms of Thermolytic Rearrangement of cis-bis(silylmethyl) platinum(II) Complexes. beta-Carbon-Transfer Predominates over Hydrogen-Transfer. *J. Am. Chem. Soc.* **116**:9963–9980. http://doi.org/dwdtqd

Anon. 1841 (pub. 1843). A List of the Officers and Members of the Chemical Society of London. *Mem. Proc. Chem. Soc. Lond.* 1841, 1, B001–B008. http://doi.org/cksgnz

Anon. 1842. (untitled). *Proc. Chem. Soc. Lond.*, 1, A001. http://doi.org/cwmqv5

Anon. 1868. obit. Robert Warington. *J. Chem. Soc., Trans.* **21**:31–34. http://doi.org/bdb3sq

Anon. 1871. obit. James Sheridan Muspratt. *J. Chem. Soc.,Trans.* **21**:620–621. http://doi.org/bvsmph

Anon. 1871. obit. Augustus Matthiessen. *J. Chem. Soc., Trans.* **24**:615–617. http://doi.org/bvsmph

Anon. 1873. obit. Henry Minchin Noad. *J. Chem. Soc., Trans.* **33**:233–234. http://doi.org/fszjvj

Anon. 1874. obit. Baldwin Francis Duppa. *J. Chem. Soc., Trans.* **27**:1199–1200. http://doi.org/cm24q9

Anon. 1875. obit. Henry Medlock. *J. Chem. Soc., Trans.* **28**:1317–1318. http://doi.org/dz7ztq

Anon. 1878. obit Thomas Hall. *J. Chem. Soc., Trans* **33**:230–232. http://doi.org/fszjvj

Anon. 1878. obit. Henry Minchin Noad. *J. Chem. Soc., Trans.* **33**:233–234. http://doi.org/fszjvj

Anon. 1880. obit. William George Valentin. *J. Chem. Soc., Trans.* **37**:260. http://doi.org/cqzqq8

Anon. 1881. obit. John Stenhouse. *J. Chem. Soc., Trans.* **39**:185–188. http://doi.org/cxw8c4

Anon. 1883. obit. Frank Hatton. *J. Chem. Soc., Trans.* **43**:257–258. http://doi.org/fbngbd

Anon. 1884. obit. James Young. *J. Chem. Soc., Trans.* **45**:630–632. http://doi.org/dczbzx

Anon. 1886. obit. Frederick Field. *J. Chem. Soc., Trans.* **49**:347–353. http://doi.org/ffn6c5

Anon. 1888. obit. Thomas Samuel Humpidge. *J. Chem. Soc., Trans.* **53**:513–517. http://doi.org/bp4p4v

Anon. 1889. obit. James Smith Brazier. *J. Chem. Soc., Trans.* **55**:289–299. http://doi.org/bc4hhz

Anon. 1890. obit. Warren de la Rue. *J. Chem. Soc., Trans.* **57**:441–445. http://doi.org/fsvm5n

Anon. 1891. obit. Edward Chambers Nicholson. *J. Chem. Soc., Trans.* **59**: 464–465. http://doi.org/cgj335

Anon. 1892. The Science Museum and the Tate Gallery. *Nature* **45**:385–386. http://doi.org/cgg22g

Anon. 1896. obit. Alfred Tribe. *J. Chem. Soc., Trans.* **49**:352–353. http://doi.org/ffn6c5

Anon. 1897. obit. James Wyllie Rodger. *Nature* **56**:129. http://doi.org/d29cwr

Anon. 1907. obit. George E. Davis. *J. Proc. Inst. Chem. GB Irel.* **31**:16. http://doi.org/b9kjgz

Anon. 1915. obit. Joseph William Thomas. *J. Chem. Soc., Trans.* **107**:588–589. http://doi.org/b8v6k5

Anon. 1918. obit. Henry George Plimmer. *J. Roy. Microscopical Soc.* **38**:349–358.

Anon. 1922. obit. Cornelius O'Sullivan. *J. Chem. Soc., Trans.***121**:2900–2901. http://doi.org/fg853b

Anon. 1922. obit. William Gowland. *J. Chem. Soc., Trans.* **121**:2907–2909, http://doi.org/fg853b

Anon. 1922. obit. John Spiller. *J. Chem. Soc., Trans.* **122**:748–749. http://doi.org/cs6zq5

Anon. 1925. obit. Horace Tabberer Brown, 1848–1925. *Proc. R. Soc. A* **109**:2. http://doi.org/d2t4jg

Anon. 1926. obit. Francis Robert Japp. *J. Chem. Soc.* 1008–1920. http://doi.org/dmk2m5

Anon. 1928. obit. Henry Richardson Procter. *J. Chem. Soc.* 3300–3307. http://doi.org/bdwzkg

Anon. 1935. obit. William Richard Eaton Hodgkinson. *J. Proc. Inst. Chem. GB Irel.* **59**:274–275. http://doi.org/fj4qpp

Anon. 1936. obit. George Samuel Newth. *J. Proc. Inst. Chem. GB Irel.* **60**:258. http://doi.org/c392c6

Anon. 1939. obit. Alfred Edward Howard Tutton. *Obit. Not. Fells. Roy. Soc.* **2**:621–626.

Anon. 1945. obit. Arthur Barker Hatton. *J. Proc. R. Inst. Chem. GB Irel.*, **5**:198. http://doi.org/fswfx4

Anon. 1946. obit. John T. Hewitt. *J. Chem. Soc.* 68–70. http://doi.org/bqfkcz

Anon. 1955. obit. Arthur Clayton. *J. Proc. R. Inst. Chem.* **79**:451. http://doi.org/cq2xr5

Anon. 1960. obit. Philip Cecil Bull. *J. Proc. R. Inst. Chem.* **34**:305. http://doi.org/bp5t8x

Anon. 1960. obit. Frederick John Hambly. *J. Proc. R. Inst. Chem.* **84**: 231–2. http://doi.org/fc94bf

Anon. 1963. H. J. T. Ellingham and the R. I. C., 1945–1962. *J. Roy. Inst. Chem.* **87**:31–34. http://doi.org/d7j682

Anon. 1969. obit. Ronald Herbert Purcell. *J. Royal Naval Scientific Service* **24**:271.

Anon. 1971. Professor A. S. C. Lawrence. *Symp. Faraday Soc.* **5**:8. http://doi.org/b72wtt

Anon. 1976. Thomas Ellingham, 1897–1975. *Chem. Br.* **12**:322–323.

Anon. 1980. obits. Douglas Arthur Spencer (1901–79) and Kenneth Charles Devereux Hickman (1896–1979). *The Photographic Journal.* **120** (February): 70–71.

Anon. 2014. Jack Lewis (1928–2014). *Chem. World*, **11**:4.

Ansell, G. F. 1870. *The Royal Mint: Its working, conduct and operations, fully and practically explained.* London: E. Wilson

Archer, Mary. 1997. An interview with Professor Harry Julius Eméléus (1903–1993). 7 March 1989. RSC Historical Group. *Occasional Papers* **1**.

Archer, Mary. 2004. Porter, George, Baron Porter of Luddenham (1920–2002). *ODNB.* OUP. http://doi.org/c3hxdq

Archer, Mary and Christopher Haley (eds.). 2005. *The 1702 chair of chemistry at Cambridge: Transformation and change.* CUP

Armstrong, A., G. Ahmed, B. Dominguez-Fernandez, B. R. Hayter, and J. S. Wailes. 2002. Enantioselective epoxidation of alkenes catalyzed by 2-fluoro-N-carbethoxytropinone and related tropinone derivatives. *J. Org. Chem.* **67**:8610–8670. http://doi.org/cn8jn5

Armstrong, E. Frankland. 1910. *The simple carbohydrates and the glucosides* London: Longman, Green

Armstrong, E. Frankland. 1940. Jocelyn Field Thorpe. *Nature* **145**:1001. http://doi.org/bdkdzj

Armstrong, E. Frankland. 1944. Gerald Tattersall Moody, 1864–1943. *J. Chem. Soc.* 358–359. http://doi.org/fg6vxh

Armstrong, E. Frankland. 1945. The Royal College of Chemistry. *Nature* **156**:524–527. http://doi.org/fq8zm3

Armstrong, E. Frankland and J. L. Simonsen. 1945. M. O. Forster. *Obit. Notes Fells. Roy. Soc.* **5**:243–261. http://doi.org/b72xt9

Armstrong, E. Frankland. 1946. Obit. of M. O. Forster. *J. Chem. Soc.* 550–557. http://doi.org/bqwf9z

Armstrong, Henry E. 1874. *Introduction to the Study of Organic Chemistry*. London: Longmans

Armstrong, Henry E. 1887. An explanation of the laws which govern substitution in the case of benzenoid compounds. *J. Chem. Soc., Trans.* **51**:258–268. http://doi.org/b7848g

Armstrong, Henry E. 1888. The origin of colour and the constitution of colouring matters. *Proc. Chem. Soc.* **4**:27–33. http://doi.org/bbmqzn

Armstrong, Henry E. 1895. The nature of chemical change and the conditions which determine it. *J. Chem. Soc., Trans.* **67**:1122–1172. http://doi.org/c96wkh

Armstrong, Henry E. 1896. Notes on Hofmann's scientific work. *J. Chem. Soc., Trans.* **69**:637–732. http://doi.org/fvzzj3

Armstrong, Henry E. 1909. A dream of fair hydrone and The thirst of salted water or the ions overboard. *Science Progress*, **3** (2):484–499 and (12):638–654.

Armstrong, Henry E. 1922. Adrian Brown. *J. Chem. Soc., Trans.* **121**:2889–2907. http://doi.org/fg853b

Armstrong, Henry E. 1927. A message from old Leipzig through London (to Germany). *Chem. & Ind.* 185–188.

Armstrong, Henry E. 1927b. Poor common salt! *Nature* **120**:478. http://doi.org/d9kjwp

Armstrong, Henry E. 1928. Horace T. Brown. *J. Chem Soc.* 1061–1066. http://doi.org/dm8h9r

Armstrong, Henry E. 1937. Horace Brown Memorial Lecture. *J. Inst. Brewing* **43**:375–386. http://doi.org/rqd

Armstrong, Henry E and W. J. Pope. 1891. Sobrerol, product of the oxidation of terebenthene (oil of turpentine) in sunlight. *J. Chem. Soc., Trans.* **59**:315–320. http://doi.org/fdmq4w

Armstrong, Henry E and T. M. Lowry. 1902. The sulphonation of camphor. 1. camphorsulphonic acid (reychler): the formation of anhydramides. *J. Chem. Soc., Trans.* **81**:1441–1462. http://doi.org/d47h42

Ash, R., R. W. Baker and R. M. Barrer. 1967. Sorption and surface flow in graphitized carbon membranes. I. The steady state. *Proc. R. Soc. A* **299**:434–454. http://doi.org/dn5zxs

Ashwell, Margaret. 2002. Elsie May Widdowson C.H., 1906–2000. *Biog. Mems. Fells. Roy. Soc.* **48**:483–506. http://doi.org/fkjm9h

Attard, G. S., R. H. Templer, W. S. Smith, A. H. Hunt and S. Jackowski. 2000. Modulation of CTP:phosphocholine cytidylyltransferase by membrane curvature elastic stress. *Proc. Natl. Acad. Sci. USA* **97**:9032–9036. http://doi.org/d9qqvn

Averley, G. 1983. The social chemists: English chemical societies in the eighteenth and early nineteenth centuries. *Ambix* **33**:99–128.

Avery, John S. 1972. *The quantum theory of atoms, molecules and photons.* London: McGraw Hill

Ayrton, H. M. 1919–20. On a new method of driving off poisonous gases. *Proc. R. Soc. A* **96**:249–256. http://doi.org/b7nsvt

Baker, H. B. 1885. Combustion in dried gases. *J. Chem. Soc., Trans.* **47**:349–352. http://doi.org/dmn7z5

Baker, H. B. 1894. Influence of moisture on chemical change. *J. Chem. Soc., Trans.* **65**:611–624. http://doi.org/fr7692

Baker, H. B. 1898. The drying of ammonia and hydrogen chloride. *J. Chem. Soc., Trans.* **73**:422–426. http://doi.org/bgjcwt

Baker, H. B. 1907. The atomic weight of tellurium. *J. Chem. Soc., Trans.* **91**:1849–1861. http://doi.org/cjcc8z

Baker, H. B. 1922 and 1923. H. B. Baker, The change in properties of substances on drying. Part One. *J. Chem. Soc., Trans.* **121**:568–574. http://doi.org/bhz6vn. Part Two. *ibid.* 1223–1224. http://doi.org/ff8fx9

Baker, H. B. 1924. Frank Clowes. *J. Chem. Soc., Trans.* **125**:985–987. http://doi.org/bkh5gn

Baker, H. B. 1927. Experiments on molecular association. *J. Chem. Soc., Trans.* 949–958. http://doi.org/bj5vjj

Baker, H. B. 1928. The constitution of liquids: Some new experiments. *J. Chem. Soc., Trans.* 1051–1055. http://doi.org/bcjdmg

Baker, J. W. 1958. *Electronic Theories of Organic Chemistry.* OUP

Baldwin, J. E., D. H. R. Barton and J. K. Sutherland. 1965. The nonadrides. Part IV. The constitution and stereochemistry of byssochlamic acid. *J. Chem. Soc.* 1787–1798. http://doi.org/b2vc3q

Baldwin, J. E., D. J. Blythin and E. S. Waight. 1969. Structure of hydrocyansalide and related 2,3-diaminobenzofurans. *J. Chem. Soc. C,* 735–738. http://doi.org/dbbr2v

Ball, P. 2014. 'How the Pelican got its hue'. *Chem. World.* **11**(7): 34–35.

Barber, M. S., J. B. Davis, L. M. Jackman and B. C. L. Weedon. 1961. Nuclear magnetic resonance (NMR) I. The groups of carotenoids and related compounds. *J. Chem. Soc.,* 2870–2881. http://doi.org/crx6ph

Barlow, W and W. J. Pope. 1906. A development of the atomic theory leading to a demonstration of the nature of valency. *J. Chem. Soc., Trans.* **89**:1675–1744. http://doi.org/cctcpq

Barrer, R. M. 1938. The sorption of polar and non-polar gases by zeolites. *Proc. R. Soc. A.* **167**:392–420. http://doi.org/ctk7mv

Barrer, R. M. 1978. *Zeolites and clay minerals as sorbents and molecular sieves.* London: Academic Press

Barrer, R. M. 1978b. Sir Eric Keighley Rideal 1890–1974. *Chem. Br.* **11**:231.

Barrer, R. M and J. W. Baynham. 1956. Synthetic potassium aluminosilicates. *J. Chem. Soc.* 2882–2891. http://doi.org/bbw4cf

Barrer, R. M and D. L. Peterson. 1964. Intracrystalline sorption by synthetic mordenites. *Proc. R. Soc. A* **280**:466–485. http://doi.org/dt5t9j

Barrett, Anne. 2004. Whiteley, Martha Annie (1866–1956). *ODNB.* OUP. http://doi.org/ft8j9k

Barrett, A. G. M., D. H. R. Barton and G. Johnson. 1978. The chemistry of tricarbonyl iron complexes of precalciferol2 and tachysterol. *J. Chem. Soc., Perkin Trans.* **1**: 1014–1017. http://doi.org/btdss8

Barrett, A. G. M., D. Hamprecht, A. J. P White and D. J. Williams. 1996. Total Synthesis and Stereochemical Assignment of the Quinquecyclopropane-Containing Cholesteryl Ester Transfer Protein Inhibitor U-106305. *J. Am. Chem. Soc.* **118**:7863–7864. http://doi.org/dzgrv2

Barrett, A. G. M. 1997. Iterative Cyclopropanation: A Concise Strategy for the Total Synthesis of the Hexacyclopropane Cholesteryl Ester Transfer Protein Inhibitor U-106305. *J. Am. Chem. Soc.* **119**:8608–8615. http://doi.org/c72s67

Barrett, A. G. M and D. H. R. Barton. 2004. Linstead, Sir (Reginald) Patrick (1902–1966). *ODNB.* OUP. http://doi.org/cztp7p

Barrett, P. A., C. E. Dent and R. P. Linstead. 1936. Phthalocyanines part VII. Phthalocyanine as a coordinating group. A general investigation of the metallic derivatives. *J. Chem. Soc.* 1719–1736. http://doi.org/c3qgm6

Barrow, K. D., D. H. R. Barton, Ernst Chain, C. Conlay, T. C. Smale, R. Thomas and E. S. Waight. 1971. Fusicoccin. Part I. The nature of the substituent groups. *J. Chem. Soc. C.* 1259–1264. http://doi.org/c2zstz

Barton, D. H. R. 1944. The application of the method of molecular rotation differences to steroids; Part I. *J. Chem. Soc.* 659–665. http://doi.org/bscqss

Barton, D. H. R. 1946. Part II. Unsaturated sterols and their derivatives. *J. Chem. Soc.* 512–522. http://doi.org/bxmwx4

Barton, D. H. R. 1946b. Part III. Steroidal hormones and bile acids. *J. Chem. Soc.* 1116–1123. http://doi.org/d9v8j9

Barton, D. H. R. 1950. The conformation of the steroid nucleus. *Experientia* **6**:316–320.

Barton, D. H. R. 1953. The stereochemistry of cyclohexane derivatives. *J. Chem. Soc.* 1027–1040. http://doi.org/fp2csf

Barton, D. H. R. 1991. *Some recollections of gap jumping.* Washington: ACS

Barton, D. H. R. 1996. Ingold, Robinson, Winstein, Woodward, and I. *Bull. Hist. Chem.* **19**:43–47.

Barton, D. H. R. ed. 1996. *Reason and Imagination: Reflections on Research in Organic Chemistry.* Selected papers of D. H. R. Barton. London: World Scientific

Barton, D. H. R and P. Alexander. 1943. The excretion of ethylquinone by the flour beetle. *Biochem. J.* **37**:463–466.

Barton, D. H. R and R. D. Cookson. 1956. The principles of conformational analysis. *Quart. Rev. Chem. Soc.***10**:44–82. http://doi.org/bz5trg

Barton, D. H. R and F. McCapra, P. J. de Mayo and F. J. Thudium. 1960. Long-range effects in alicyclic systems. Part III. *J. Chem. Soc.* 1297–1311. http://doi.org/db8g4h

Barton, D. H. R and G. Quinkert. 1960. Photochemical transformations. Part VI. Photochemical cleavage of cyclohexadienones. *J. Chem. Soc.* 1–9. http://doi.org/dd5845

Barton, D. H. R., J. M. Beaton, L. E. Geller and M. M. Pechet. 1960. A new photochemical reaction. *J. Am. Chem. Soc.* **82**:2640–2641. http://doi.org/bcsrk4

Barton, D. H. R., G. W. Kirby, J. B. Taylor and G. M. Thomas. 1963. The biogenesis of Amaryllidacea alkaloids. *J. Chem. Soc.* 4545–4558. http://doi.org/bh873q

Barton, D. H. R., A. L. J. Beckwith and A. Goosen. 1965. Photochemical transformations. Part XVI. A novel synthesis of lactones, *J. Chem. Soc.* 181–190. http://doi.org/dbrhwx

Barton, D. H. R., G. W. Kirby, W. Steglich, G. M. Thomas, A. R. Battersby, T. A. Dobson and H. Ramuz. 1965. Investigations on the biosynthesis of morphine alkaloids. *J. Chem. Soc.* 2423–2438. http://doi.org/fjf639

Barton, D. H. R., H. N. Rydon and J. A. Elvidge. 1968. Reginald Patrick Linstead, 1902–1966. *Biog. Mems. Fells. Roy. Soc.* **14**:309–323. http://doi.org/b7gb4n

Barton, D. H. R and P. D. Magnus. 1971. Experiments on the synthesis of tetracycline. Part I. Introduction to the series. *J. Chem. Soc., C.* 2164–2166. http://doi.org/cm96f7

Barton, D. H. R., A. A. J. Gunatilaka, T. R. Jarman, D. A. Widdowson, M. Bard and R. A. Woods. 1975. Biosynthesis of terpenes and steroids. Part X. The sterols of some yeast mutants doubly defective in ergosterol biosynthesis. *J. Chem. Soc., Perkin Trans.* **1**: 88–92. http://doi.org/bgddm7

Barton, D. H. R and S. W. McCombie. 1975. A new method for the deoxygenation of secondary alcohols. *J. Chem. Soc., Perkin Trans.* **1**: 1574–1585. http://doi.org/frpvx8

Barton, Ruth. 1998. Huxley, Lubbock and half a dozen others: Professionals and gentlemen in the formation of the X-Club, 1851–1864. *Isis*, **89**:410–444.

Bastianson, O and O. Hassel. 1946. Structure of the so-called *cis* Decalin. *Nature* **157**:765. http://doi.org/c9rc6w

Bate, D. M., R. S. Lehrie, E. J. Place, S. L. Willis, D. S. Campbell and C. D. Hull. 1997. The first sample of synthetic rubber made by William Tilden in 1892: Modern work reveals a mystery. *Polymer* **38**:5261–5266.

Beardwood, P and J. F. Gibson. 1992. Iron-sulfur dimers with benzimidazolate-thiolate terminal chelating ligands. Models for Rieske-type proteins, *J. Chem. Soc., Dalton Trans.* 2457–2466. http://doi.org/cbzkb4

Bedson, P. P. 1926. Sir Edward Thorpe. *J. Chem. Soc., Trans.* 1031–1050. http://doi.org/dmk2m5

Beesley, R. M., C. K. Ingold and J. F. Thorpe. 1915. The formation and stability of *spiro*-compounds. Part 1. *Spiro*-compounds from cyclohexane. *J. Chem. Soc., Trans.* **107**:1080–1106. http://doi.org/dgqwk6

Beesley, R. M and J. F. Thorpe. 1920. A system of nomenclature, and some derivatives of methane-II-cyclopropane and of methane-III-cyclopropane. *J. Chem. Soc., Trans.***117**:591b–620. http://doi.org/d9s9fg

Benfey, O. T. 1964. *From vital force to structural formulas.* Boston: Houghton Mifflin

Bennett, M. A., A. D. Danopoulos, W. P. Griffith and M. L. H. Green. 1997. The contributions to original research by Professor Sir Geoffrey Wilkinson. *J. Chem. Soc., Dalton Trans.* 3049–3079. http://doi.org/dtzxgz

Bentley, Jonathan. 1969. The Work in England of A. W. von Hofmann, Professor of Chemistry at the Royal College of Chemistry, 1845–1865. MSc thesis. University of Leicester

Bentley. 1970. The chemical department of the Royal School of Mines: its origins and development under A. W. Hofmann, *Ambix* **17**:153–181.

Besant, Walter and G. E. Mitton. 1903. Mayfair, Belgravia and Bayswater in *The Fascination of London.* London: Adam and Charles Black

Bircumshaw, L. L. *rev* Sally M. Horrocks. 2004. Haworth, Sir Walter Norman (1883–1950). *ODNB.* OUP. http://doi.org/b4vfjt

Blackman, M. 1972. George Ingle Finch 1888–1970. *Biog. Mems. Fells. Roy. Soc.* **18**:223–239. http://doi.org/cvnthq

Blakeley, Phyllis R. 1968. Henry How. *Dictionary of Canadian Biography.* University of Toronto Press

Bloxam, C. L and F. A. Abel. 1851. *Handbook of Chemistry: Theoretical, Practical and Technical.* London: John Churchill

Blyth, J and A. W. Hofmann. 1845. On styrole and some of the products of its decomposition. *Mem. Proc. Chem. Soc.* **3**:334–358. http://doi.org/cwf42v

Boase, G. C. *rev.* Iwan Rhys Morus. 2004. Noad, Sir Henry Minchin (1815–1877). *ODNB.* OUP. http://doi.org/fwmzqf

Bockris, J. O'M. 2007. Memories of Brian Evans Conway. *Modern Aspects of Electrochemistry.* 4:7–13.

Bockris, J. O'M. 2013. On Martin Fleischmann: An obituary and more. *J. Condensed Matter Nucl. Sci.* **11**:1–7.

Bockris, J. O'M., J. F. Herringshaw, B. E. Conway, H. M. Fleischmann, R. Parsons, and 7 others. 1947. *Disc. Faraday Soc.* **1**:328–334. http://doi.org/d66wht

Bolton, R. E., C. J. Moody, M. Pass, C. W. Rees and G. Tojo. 1988. Formal synthesis of the antitumour antibiotic CC-1065. *J. Chem. Soc., Perkin Trans.* 1. 2491–299. http://doi.org/d5m59x

Bone, W. A. *rev.* Ian St. John. 2004. Snelus, George James (1837–1906). *ODNB.* OUP. http://doi.org/c4r59n

Boswell, P. H., A. A. Eldridge and H. F. Harwood. 1916. *A Memoir on British Resources of Sands Suitable for Glass Making.* London: Longmans

Bousfield, W. R and T. M. Lowry. 1905. The electrical conductivity and other properties of NaOH in aqueous solution as elucidating the mechanism of conduction. *Phil. Trans. Roy Soc. A* **204**:253–322. http://doi.org/fxbhrc

Bowden, K., I. M. Heilbron, E. R. H. Jones and B. C. L. Weedon. 1946. The preparation of acetylenic ketones by oxidation of acetylenic carbinols. *J. Chem. Soc.* 39–45. http://doi.org/fmdkpv

Bowen, Edward J. 1967. Cyril Norman Hinshelwood. *Chem. Br.* **3**:534–536.

Braude, E. A. R., J. Hannah and R. P. Linstead. 1960. Hydrogen transfer. Part XVI. Dihydride of nitrogenous heterocycles as hydrogen donors. *J. Chem. Soc.* 3249–3257. http://doi.org/cqvhw7

Brereton Evans, Clare de. 1897. Enantiomorphous forms of ethypropylpiperidonium. *J. Chem. Soc., Trans.* **71**:522–526. http://doi.org/cm9skm

Brereton Evans. 1898. The teaching of chemistry in D. Beale, L. H. M. Soulsby and J. F. Dove (eds.). *Work and Play in Girls Schools by Three Headmistresses.* London: Longmans

Briscoe, H. V. A. 1915. The atomic weight of tin. *J. Chem. Soc., Trans.* **107**: 63–86. http://doi.org/dcb2z5

Briscoe, H. V. A., P. L. Robinson and H. C. Smith. 1927. The density of boron trichloride and the suspected variation in the atomic weight of boron. *J. Chem. Soc.* 282–290. http://doi.org/dq79qs

Briscoe, H. V. A., P. F. Holt, J. W. Matthews and P. M. Sanderson. 1937. Some new characteristic properties of certain industrial dusts. *Nature* **139**:753–754. http://doi.org/djj225

Brock, William H. 1972. Hofmann, August Wilhelm von, *DSB*. **6**: 461–464 (N.Y: Scribner)

Brock, William H. 1972b. Frankland, Edward, *DSB*. **5**:124–127 (N.Y: Scribner)

Brock, William H., ed. 1973. *H. E. Armstrong and The Teaching of Science, 1880–1930*. CUP

Brock, William H. 1976. The Spectrum of Science Patronage, in Turner (1976)

Brock, William H., (ed). 1984. *Justus von Liebig und August Wilhelm Hofmann in ihren Briefen*, (1841–1873). Weinheim: Verlag Chemie

Brock, William H. 1992. Liebig and Hofmann's impact on British scientific culture, in C. Meinel and H. Scholz (1992)

Brock, William H., ed. 1996. Science for All: Studies in the history of Victorian Science and Education. Aldershot: Ashgate

Brock, William H. 1997. *Justus von Liebig: The Chemical Gatekeeper*. CUP

Brock, William H. 2000. *The Chemical Tree: A History of Chemistry*. N.Y: Norton

Brock, William H. 2004. Brodie, Sir Benjamin Collins, second baronet (1817–1880). *ODNB*. OUP. http://doi.org/bj2gth

Brock, William H. 2004b. Crookes, Sir William (1832–1919). *ODNB*. OUP. http://doi.org/frw3m6

Brock, William H. 2004c. Mansfield, Charles Blachford (1819–1855). *ODNB*. OUP. http://doi.org/dn5qq7

Brock, William H. 2004d. Gordon van Praagh (1909–2003). *ODNB*. OUP. http://doi.org/dbf3x2

Brock, William H. 2008. *William Crookes (1832–1919) and the Commercialization of Science*. Aldershot: Ashgate

Brock, William H. 2011. *The case of the poisonous socks: Tales from chemistry*. London: RSC Historical Group Newsletter

Brock, William H. 2012. Note on Tutton. *Roy. Soc. Chem. Newsletter*. **62**:6–7.

Brock, William H and R. M. Macleod. 1976. The Scientists' Declaration: reflexions on science and belief in the wake of *Essays and Reviews*, 1864–1865. *Brit. J. Hist. Sci.* **9**:39–66.

Brooke, J. H. 1975. Laurent, Gerhardt and the philosophy of chemistry. *Hist. Studs. Phys. Sci.* **6**:405–429.

Brown, James Campbell. 1914. *Essays and addresses*. London: J and A Churchill

Brunton, Thomas Lauder. 1885. *A textbook on pharmacology, therapeutics and materia medica*. London: Macmillan

Buckton, G. B. 1861. On the stibethyls and stibmethyls. *Quart. J. Chem. Soc.* **13**:115–121. http://doi.org/dm8nfq

Buckton, G. B and A. W. Hofmann. 1856. Researches on the action of sulphuric acid on the amides and nitriles, together with some remarks upon conjugated sulpho-acids. *Philos. Trans. R. Soc.***9**:453–459. http://doi.org/d7zx4d

Bud, R. 1991. The Chemical Society — a glimpse at the foundation. *Chem. Br.* **27**: 230–232.

Bud, Robert and Gerrylynn K. Roberts. 1984. *Science versus Practice: Chemistry in Victorian Britain.* Manchester University Press

Burrit, J. 1939. obit. Albert Theodore King. *J. Chem. Soc.* 1228–1229. http://doi.org/fj7xkq

Burstall, F. H. 1952. Frances Mary Gore Micklethwait (1868–1950). *J. Chem Soc., Trans.* 2946–2947. http://doi.org/dgg894

Butt, John. 2004. Young, James (1811–1883). *ODNB.* OUP. http://doi.org/bp3nrn

Bynum, W. F. 2004. Cullen, William (1710–1790). *ODNB.* OUP. http://doi.org/cxz7h8

Cadogan, J. I. G. 2003. Sir Ewart Jones, (1911–2002). *Chem. Br.* 38 (8), 45.

Cadogan, J. I. G. *rev.* 2004. Donald Holroyde Hey (1904–1987). *ODNB.* OUP. http://doi.org/bh2g7p

Cadogan, J. I. G and D. I. Davies. 1988. Donald Holroyde Hey (1904–1987). *Biog. Mems. Fells. Roy. Soc.* **34**:295–320. http://doi.org/djbxw5

Callendar, H. L. 1920. William Watson, (1868–1919). *Proc. Roy. Soc.* A **97**:1–3. http://doi.org/dcrgvv

Camilleri, P. D., S. Eggleston, H. S. Rzepa and M. L. Webb. 1994. Aromatic C-H...O hydrogen bonding in 3-chloro-α-(2-(dibutylamino)ethyl)-6-trifluomethyl-9-phenanthrene methanol hydrochloride. *J. Chem. Soc., Chem. Commun.* 1135–1170. http://doi.org/fpb5zd

Carrière, Justus (ed.). 1893. *Berzelius und Liebig, ihre briefe von 1831–1845.* Munich: J. H. Lehmann

Cathcart, B. 2004. Penney, William George, Baron Penney (1909–1991). *ODNB.* OUP. http://doi.org/fq657k

Challenger, Frederick. 1950–1951. Frederick Stanley Kipping, 1863–1949. *Obit. Not. Fells. Roy. Soc.* **7**:183–219. http://doi.org/fkm9s5

Challenger, Frederick. 1951. Frederick Stanley Kipping. *J. Chem. Soc.* 849–862. http://doi.org/dvr4d8

Challenger, Frederick. *rev.* John Shorter. 2004. Kipping, Frederick Stanley (1863–1949). *ODNB.* OUP. http://doi.org/bhxsr4

Chambers, J. D and G. E. Mingay. 1966. *The Agricultural Revolution, 1750–1880.* N. Y: Schocken

Chambers, Theodore G. 1896. 1920. *Register of the Associates and Old Students of the Royal College of Chemistry, Royal College of Science and Royal School of Mines.* London. RSM

Chapman, D. L. 1916. Ivan Richard Gibbs. *J. Chem. Soc., Trans.* **109**:370. http://doi.org/dtndq9

Chapman Jones, Henry. 1881. *Text-Book of Practical Organic Chemistry for Elementary Students.* London: Joseph Hughes

Chapman Jones, Henry. 1895. *Science and the Practice of Photography.* London: Iliffe

Chapman Jones, Henry. 1898. *Quantitative Inorganic Analysis.* London: Macmillan

Church, A. H and W. H. Perkin. 1857. On some new colouring matters, derivatives of dinitrobenzene. *Quart. J. Chem. Soc.* **9**:1–8. http://doi.org/bg5564

Church, A. H and Edward Kinch. 1906. *Church's Laboratory Guide: A manual of practical chemistry for colleges and schools, specially arranged for agricultural students.* 8th edition. London: Gurney and Jackson

Clarke, Hans T., John R. Johnson, and Sir Robert Robinson (eds.). 1949. The chemistry of penicillin. Princeton University Press

Clayton, G. C. 1924. *J. Chem. Soc., Trans.* **125**:2693–2698. http://doi.org/fs67bf

Clerke, A. M. *rev* A. McConnell. 2004. Miller, William Allen (1817–1870). *ODNB.* OUP. http://doi.org/bpdh2q

Clowes, F. 1900. William Thorp. *J. Chem. Soc., Trans.* **77**:599–600. http://doi.org/fbktnt

Coffey, S. 1971. Ernest Harry Rodd 1888–1970. *Chem. Br.* **7**:251–252.

Coffey, S. *rev*, 2004. Lapworth, Arthur (1872–1941). *ODNB.* OUP. http://doi.org/brsjdc

Coffey, S. 2004b. Barton, Sir Derek Harold Richard (1918–98). *ODNB.* OUP. http://doi.org/ch7mx2

Coley, N. G. *rev*, 2004. Lapworth, Arthur (1872–1941). *ODNB.* OUP. http://doi.org/brsjdc

Coley, N. G. 2004b. Barton, Sir Derek Harold Richard (1918–1998). *ODNB.* OUP. http://doi.org/ch7mx2

Colquhoun, M. H., J. F. Stoddart and D. J. Williams. 1986. Second-sphere coordination: A novel role for molecular receptors. *Angew. Chem. Int. Ed.* **25**:487–507. http://doi.org/cdbp4s

Colton, R., R. Levitus and G. Wilkinson. 1960. Some complex compounds of rhenium. *J. Chem. Soc.* 4121–4126. http://doi.org/ffmj5z

Comte, Auguste. 1838. *Cours de philosophie positive.* vol. 3. Paris: Bachelier

Cook, Alan H. 1960. Ian Morris Heilbron, 1886–1959. *Biog. Mems. Fell. Roy. Soc.* **6**:65–85. http://doi.org/d5bkk5

Cook, Alan H. *rev* K. D. Watson. 2004. Heilbron, Sir Ian Morris (*formerly* Isidor Morris) (1886–1959). *ODNB*. OUP. http://doi.org/c2bpv8

Cook, Alan H and R. P. Linstead. 1934. Fused carbon rings. Part II. The synthesis of cis-α-0:3:3-bicyclooctanone and related compounds. *J. Chem. Soc.* 946–956. http://doi.org/dpmn73

Cook, J. W. 1953. The University of Glasgow. *J. Roy. Inst. Chem.* **77**:561–572. http://doi.org/djwmhb

Cooper, Ann. 2004. Cole, Sir Henry (1808–1882), civil servant. *ODNB*. OUP. http://doi.org/czdxnn

Costa, A. B. 1976. Thorpe, Jocelyn Field. *DSB*. **13**:388–389. (N.Y: Scribner)

Cotton, F. A. 1997. Geoffrey Wilkinson. *L'Actualité Chimique*. **9** (2):30.

Cotton, F. A. 2014. *My life in the golden age of chemistry: More fun than fun*. London: Elsevier

Coulson, C. A. 1973. Francis Boys, 1911–1972. *Biog. Mems. Fells. Roy. Soc.* **19**:94–115. http://doi.org/c59svd

Courtney, W. P. *rev*. Robert Brown. 2004. Ansell, George Frederick (1826–1880). *ODNB*. OUP. http://doi.org/czdt84

Cranston, J. A. 1954. The Royal Technical College, Glasgow. *J. Roy. Inst. Chem.***78**:16–124. http://doi.org/bcqfxp

Creese, Mary R. S. 1997. Martha Annie Whiteley (1866–1956): Chemist and editor. *Bull. Hist. Chem.* **20**:42–45.

Creese, Mary R. S. *rev*. 2004. Maclean, Ida Smedley (1877–1944). *ODNB*. OUP. http://doi.org/d6qdxz

Crombie, L. 2000. Ralph Alexander Raphael, 1921–1998. *Biog. Mems. Fells. Roy. Soc.* **46**:465–481. http://doi.org/fsbks6

Crookes, W. 1852. On selenocyanides. *Quart. J. Chem. Soc*. **4**:12–19. http://doi.org/dpqchs

Curthoys, M. C. 2004. Gowland, William (1882–1922). *ODNB*. OUP. http://doi.org/fv44wz

Cuthbertson, D. P. 1956. William Godden (1884–1954). *J. Chem. Soc.* 224. http://doi.org/bwcdnk

Dale, H. H. 1948. Frederick Gowland Hopkins, 1861–1947. *Obit. Notes Fells. Roy. Soc.* **6**:115–145. http://doi.org/crwn83

Dale, H. H. *rev*. 2004. Hopkins, Sir Frederick Gowland. *ODNB*. OUP. http://doi.org/c75b9x

Dampier, W. C. D. *rev*. Frank A. J. L. James. 2004. Liveing, George Downing (1827–1924). *ODNB*. OUP. http://doi.org/fg8rpk

Danielli, J. F., M. Danielli, J. B. Fraser, P. D. Mitchell and L. N. Owen. 1947. BALINTRAV: a new non-toxic thiol for intravenous injection in arsenical poisoning: 1. Biological observations. 2. Chemical observations. *Biochem. J.* **41**:325–333.

Daus, E. R. 1971. De La Rue, Warren, *DSB*, **4**:18–19 (N.Y: Scribner)

Davies, A and P. Garratt. 2013. *UCL Chemistry Department 1828–1974*. St Albans: Science Reviews (2000) Ltd

Davies, D. H., J. Hall and E. H. Smith. 1991. Non-oxidative conversion of ketone carbonyls into carboxy carbonyls. *J. Chem. Soc., Perkin Trans.* **1**:2691–2698. http://doi.org/cm8rvs

Davies, F. 2004. Bernard Henbest (1924–2004). *Chem. World.* **1**(5): 11.

Davis, William J. 2004. Divers, Edward (1837–1912). *ODNB.* OUP. http://doi.org/dpxg9p

Davison, A., J. A. McCleverty and G. Wilkinson. 1963. Spectroscopic studies on alkyl and hydrido transition metal carbonyls and π-cyclopentadienyl carbonyls. *J. Chem. Soc.* 1133–1138. http://doi.org/cxt3qz

Day, P. *rev.* 2004. Anderson, John Stuart (1908–1990). *ODNB.* OUP. http://doi.org/dv5bpn

De la Rue, W. 1845. On Cochineal (*Coccus cacti*). *Mem. Proc. Chem. Soc.***1**: 454–480. http://doi.org/c8mqk7

Diorazio, L. J., D. A. Widdowson and J. M. Clough. 1992. A new synthesis of aryl fluorides: The reaction of caesium fluoroxysulfate with arylboronic acids and derivatives. *Tetrahedron.* **48**:8073–8088.

Donald, M. B. 1954. Hugh Griffiths. *J. Chem. Soc.* 4710–411. http://doi.org/crhm7c

Down, J. L., J. Lewis, B. Moore and G. Wilkinson. 1959. The solubility of alkali metals in ethers. *J. Chem. Soc.* 3767–3773. http://doi.org/btb6m6

Doyle, F. P. 1993. John Nayler, 1927–1993. *Chem. Br.* **29**(6):531.

Duchovic, R. J and J. A. Vilensky. 2007. Mustard Gas: Its pre-World War I history. *J. Chem. Ed.* **84**:944–948. http://doi.org/cvwkwp

Dungavell, I. 2004. Webb, Sir Aston (1849–1930), architect. *ODNB.* OUP. http://doi.org/b3wjqs

Dunstan, A. E. 1954. John Samuel Strafford Brame (1871–1953). *J. Chem. Soc.* 2664. http://doi.org/fwwffh

Eaborn, C and G. J. Leigh. 1996. Joseph Chatt, 1914–1994. *Biog. Mems Fells. Roy. Soc.* **42**:96–110. http://doi.org/brbwtt

Edgar, J. L and F. A. Paneth. 1941. The separation of ozone from other gases. *J. Chem. Soc.* 511–519. http://doi.org/dpzkpx

Egerton, A. C. 1942. James Charles Philip (1873–1941). *Biog. Mems. Fells. Roy. Soc.* **4**:51–62. http://doi.org/drhq2n

Egerton, A. C. *rev* K. D. Watson. 2004. Bone, William Arthur (1871–1938). *ODNB*. OUP. http://doi.org/bj8jsb

Eiloart, Arnold. 1892. *A Guide to Stereochemistry*. N. Y: Wilson *et. al.*

Eisenstein, S. 1974. Perkin, William Henry. *DSB*. **10**:515–517 (N.Y: Scribner)

Eisner, U and R. P. Linstead. 1955. Chlorophyll and related substances. Part II. The synthesis of chlorin. *J. Chem. Soc.* 3742–3749. http://doi.org/czdwqm

Eldridge, A. A. 1957. Martha Annie Whiteley, 1866–1956. *Proc. Chem. Soc.* **1**:182–183. http://doi.org/brkdq7

Eldridge, A. A. 1961. H. V. A. Briscoe. *Chem. & Ind.* 1837–1838.

Eldridge, A. A and H. V. A. Briscoe. 1915. First Aid in the laboratory and workshop. London: E. Arnold

Eley, D. D. 1976. Eric Keightley Rideal, 1890–1974. *Biog. Mems. Fells Roy. Soc.* **22**:381–413. http://doi.org/bc3vqw

Eldridge, A. A. *rev*. 2004. Rideal, Sir Eric Keightley (1890–1974). *ODNB*. OUP. http://doi.org/b2kw8q

Ellingham, H. J. T. 1944. Reducibility of oxides and sulphides in metallurgical processes. *J. Soc. Chem. Ind.* **36**:125–133.

Eldridge, A. A. 1945. James Netherwood Sugden. *J. Chem. Soc.* 76–77. http://doi.org/cms2rh

Elvidge, J. A. 1991. Arthur Herbert Cook, 1911–1988. *Biog. Mems. Fells. Roy. Soc.* **37**:86–102. http://doi.org/d2vkc2

Eldridge, A. A. 1999. The Linstead days in the chemistry department at Imperial College, especially 1949 through 1954. *J. Porphyrins Phthalocyanines* **3**:392–396.

Eméleus, H. J. 1926. The inhibition of the glow of phosphorus. *J. Chem. Soc.* **129**:1336–1344. http://doi.org/c3tvvg

Eméleus, H. J. 1960. Friedrich Adolf Paneth, 1887–1958. *Biog. Mems. Fells. Roy. Soc.* **6**:227–246. http://doi.org/cxt94q

Eméleus, H. J. 1962. Henry Vincent Aird Briscoe, 1888–1961. *Proc. Chem. Soc.* 191–193. http://doi.org/fsnqpp

Eméleus, H. J. 1964. Thomas Gibson Pearson (1908–1962). *Proc. Chem. Soc.* 126–127. http://doi.org/ffx9xs

Eméleus, H. J and H. V. A. Briscoe. 1937. Preparation and properties of methyl-dideuteroamine. *Trans. Faraday Soc.* 127–30. http://doi.org/ff8438

Eméleus, H. J and J. S. Anderson. 1938. *Modern Aspects of Inorganic Chemistry*. London: George Routledge and Sons

Emeléus, H. J and A. J. E. Welch. 1939. The thermal and photochemical oxidation of the chlorinated silanes. *Trans. Faraday Soc.* 1928–1937. http://doi.org/fmqjpb

Emsley, John. 2000. *The Shocking History of Phosphorus.* London: Macmillan

Evans, D., J. A. Osborn and G. Wilkinson. 1968. Hydroformylation of alkenes by use of rhodium complex catalysts. *J. Chem. Soc. A.* 3133–3142. http://doi.org/dh97q7

Evans, D. F. 1959. The determination of the paramagnetic susceptibility of substances in solution by nuclear magnetic resonance. *J. Chem. Soc.* 2003–2005. http://doi.org/bsnpdg

Evans, D. F. 1960, 1961. Magnetic properties of singlet–triplet transition. Part 1V. Unsaturated compounds. *J. Chem. Soc.* http://doi.org/bm26rk. Part IV. Unsaturated compounds. *J. Chem. Soc.* 1735–1745. http://doi.org/bm26rk. Part V. Mechanism. *ibid.* 1987–1993. http://doi.org/dgv6qh

Evans, D. F. 1974. A new type of magnetic balance *J. Phys. E: Scientific Instruments.* **7**:247–249.

Evans, D. F and J. P. Maher. 1962. Proton magnetic resonance spectra of Grignard reagents and related metal alkyls. *J. Chem. Soc.* 5125–5128. http://doi.org/bxg3cq

Evans, D. F and G. V. Fazakerley. 1971. Studies on Grignard reagents. Part III. Proton resonance spectra on alkyl and aryl Grignard reagents. *J. Chem Soc.* A: 184–189. http://doi.org/frxnj6

Evans, D. F., G. V. Fazakerley and R. F. Phillips. 1971. Organometallic compounds of bivalent europium, ytterbium and samarium. *J. Chem. Soc.* A: 1931–1934. http://doi.org/b7954k

Evans, D. F., and C. Y. Wong. 1992. Nuclear magnetic resonance studies of beryllium complexes in aqueous solution. *J. Chem. Soc., Dalton Trans.* **13**: 2009–2012. http://doi.org/d2zd8m

Everett, D. H. 1984. Eugen Glueckauf, 1906–1981. *Biog. Mems. Fells. Roy. Soc.* **30**:193–224. http://doi.org/fpt3xh

Eyre, J. Vargas. 1958. *Henry Edward Armstrong 1848–1937: The doyen of British chemists and pioneer of technical education.* London: Butterworths

Eyre, J. Vargas and E. H. Rodd. 1947. Raphael Meldola, 1849–1915 in (Findlay and Mills, 1947)

Farmer, E. H. 1922. Muconic and hydromuconic acids. Part I. The addition of ethyl sodiocyanoacetate and ethyl sodiomalonate to ethyl muconate. *J. Chem. Soc., Trans.* **121**:2015–2022. http://doi.org/c2bv5v

Farmer, E. H and J. Ross. 1926. The formation and stability of assorted alicyclic systems. Part III. The change from "meta"- to "para"- bridged rings. *J. Chem. Soc., Trans.* 3233–3240. http://doi.org/bn3z92

Farmer, E. H., B. Das Laroia, T. M. Switz and J. F. Thorpe. 1927. The bearing of hexatriene chemistry on the reactive form of conjugated hydrocarbons. *J. Chem. Soc., Trans.* 2937–2958. http://doi.org/fxgf3

Farrar, Wilfred Vernon. 1973. Lapworth, Arthur. *DSB.* **8**:31–32. (N.Y: Scribner)

Farrar, Wilfred Vernon. 1997. *Chemistry and the chemical industry in the 19th century: The Henrys of Manchester and other studies* (*variorum*) eds. Richard L. Hills and W. H. Brock. Aldershot: Ashgate

Fenby, David V. 1989. The lectureship in chemistry and the chemical laboratory, University of Glasgow, 1747–1818. (in James, 1989)

Fersht, Alan R and Qinghua Wang (eds.). 2010. *The selected papers of Sir Alan R. Fersht.* London: ICP

Finch, G. I. 1924. *The making of a mountaineer.* London: Arrowsmith

Finch, G. I and A. C. Egerton. 1938. William Arthur Bone. *Obit. Not. Fells. Roy. Soc.* **2**:587–611. http://doi.org/d6w9zv

Findlay, Alexander and William Hobson Mills (eds.). 1947. *British Chemists.* London: Chemical Society

Fleck, Lord Alexander. 1964. Ramsay Middleton Winter. *Proc. Chem. Soc.* 71. http://doi.org/cdwhw7

Fontani, M and M. Costa, and M. V. Orna. 2015. *The lost elements — The Periodic Table's shadow side.* OUP

Forgan, Sophie and Graeme Gooday. 1994. A fungoid assemblage of buildings". Diversity and adversity in the development of college architecture and scientific education in nineteenth century South Kensington. *History of Universities.* xiii: 153–192.

Forgan, Sophie. 1996. Constructing South Kensington: the buildings and politics of T. H. Huxley's working environments. *Brit. J. Hist. Sci.* **29** (4):435–468.

Forster, M. O. 1896. Studies of the terpenes and allied compounds. New derivatives from α-dibromocamphor. *J. Chem. Soc., Trans.* **69**:36–60. http://doi.org/c5583f

Forster, M. O. 1927. Sir William Augustus Tilden. *J. Chem. Soc., Trans.* 3190–3202. http://doi.org/dmxpgn

Forster, M. O and F. M. G. Micklethwait. 1902. Stereoisomeric halogen derivatives of α-benzoylcamphor. *J. Chem. Soc., Trans.* **81**:160–167. http://doi.org/ccx4mg

Forster, M. O and H. E. Fierz. 1905. Camphorylcarbamides and isomeric camphorylcarbamides. *J. Chem. Soc., Trans.* **87**:110–121. http://doi.org/bh26zf

Foulkes, Major-General C. H. 2001. reprint of 1934 edition. *Gas!: The Story of the Special Brigade.* London: Naval and Military Press

Fownes, George. 1844. *Manual of Elementary Chemistry.* London: J. Churchill

Frankland, E. 1850. On the isolation of the organic radicals. *Quart. J. Chem. Soc.* **2**:263–296. http://doi.org/cx4gcm

Frankland, E. 1852. On a new series of organic bodies containing metals. *Philos. Trans. R. Soc.* **142**:417–444. http://doi.org/cwb3t8

Frankland, E. 1859. Researches on organo-metallic bodies. *Philos. Trans. R. Soc.***149**:401–415. http://doi.org/bjtgvk

Frankland, E. 1866. *Lecture Notes for Chemical Students, Embracing Mineral and Organic Chemistry*. London: J. van Voorst

Frankland, E. 1866b. Contributions to the notation of organic and inorganic compounds. *J. Chem. Soc., Trans.* 372–395. http://doi.org/cnqncz

Frankland, E. 1866c. The water supply of the metropolis during the year 1865–1866. *J. Chem. Soc., Trans.* **19**:239–248. http://doi.org/d5q642

Frankland, E. 1877. *Experimental Researches in pure, applied, and physical chemistry*. London: J. van Voorst

Frankland, E. 1901. *Sketches from the life of Sir Edward Frankland*. London: G. R. Spottiswoode

Frankland, E. 1902. ed. by his daughters M. N. W and S. J. C. *Sketches from the life of Sir Edward Frankland*. London: G. R. Spottiswoode

Frankland, E and Francis R. Japp. 1884. *Inorganic Chemistry*. London: J and A. Churchill

Freemantle, Michael. 2014. *The Chemists' War, 1914–1918*. London: RSC

Fresenius, C. Remigius. 1846. *Instructions in Chemical Analysis*; transl and ed. J. L. Bullock. London: J. Churchill

Friend, J. N. (ed.). 1914–1919. *A Textbook of Inorganic Chemistry*, 9 vols. London: Charles Griffin and Co

Fruton, Joseph S. 1988. The Liebig research group — a reappraisal. *Proc. Am. Phil. Soc.* **132**:1–66.

Fruton, Joseph S. 2002. *Methods and Styles in the Development of Chemistry*. Philadelphia: APS

Fuchs, P. L. 2001. Increase in intricacy — a tool for evaluating organic syntheses. (Tetrahedron Report 577). *Tetrahedron* **57** (2001), 6855–6875.

Galyer, A. Lee and G. Wilkinson. 1976. New synthesis of hexamethyltungsten (VI). The octamethyltungstate-(VI)ion. *J. Chem. Soc., Dalton Trans.* 2235–2238. http://doi.org/c77xrq

Gardner, John. 1846. An Address delivered in the Royal College of Chemistry (June 3rd, 1846). *The Chemist* **7**:296.

Garner, W. E. 1948. Percy Faraday Frankland, 1858–1946. *Obit. Not. Fells. Roy. Soc.* **5** (16):697–715. http://doi.org/bsz65p

Garner, W. E. 1948b. Percy Faraday Frankland (1858–1946). *J. Chem. Soc.* 1996–2005. http://doi.org/fpwbz9

Garner, W. E. *rev*. Colin A. Russell. 2004. Frankland, Percy Faraday (1858–1946). *ODNB*. OUP. http://doi.org/fw3pbk

Gaubert, P, R. P. Linstead and H. N. Rydon. 1937. Investigation of the olefinic acids. Part XVI. The synthesis of Δ^{10}-*n*-undecenoic acid. *J. Chem. Soc.* 1971–1974. http://doi.org/bwph9v

Gauld, Alan. 2004. Barrett, Sir William Fletcher (1844–1925). *ODNB*. OUP. http://doi.org/dtcz64

Gay, Hannah, 2000. Pillars of the College": Assistants at the Royal College of Chemistry, 1846–1871. *Ambix* **47**:135–69.

Gay, Hannah. 2000b. Association and Practice: The City and Guilds of London Institute for the Advancement of Technical Education. *Annals of Science* **57**:369–398.

Gay, Hannah. 2003. Science and opportunity in London, 1871–1885: the diary of Herbert McLeod. *History of Science*, **41**:427–458.

Gay, Hannah. 2007. The Declaration of Students of the Natural and Physical Sciences revisited: Youth, science and religion in mid-Victorian Britain, in (Sweet and Feist, 2007), Ch.1.

Gay, Hannah. 2007b. *The History of Imperial College London, 1907–2007: Higher education in research in science, technology and medicine*. London: ICP

Gay, Hannah. 2008. Technical assistance in the world of London science, 1850–1900, *Notes and Recs. Roy. Soc.* **62**:51–75. http://doi.org/dnmbc2

Gay, Hannah. 2010. Chemist, entomologist, Darwinian and man of affairs: Raphael Meldola and the making of a scientific career'. *Annals Sci.* **67** (1):79–119.

Gay, Hannah. 2012. Before and after *Silent Spring*: From chemical pesticides to biological control and integrated pest management — Britain, 1945–1980. *Ambix*. **59**:88–108.

Gay, Hannah and John W. Gay. 1997. Brothers in Science: Science and fraternal culture in nineteenth-century Britain. *Hist. Sci.* **35**:425–453.

Gay, Hannah and Anne Barrett. 2002. Should the cobbler stick to his last? Silvanus Phillips Thompson and the making of a scientific career. *Brit. J. Hist. Sci.* **35**:151–186.

Gay, I. D and F. C. Tompkins. 1966. Decomposition of nitrous oxide on nickel oxide catalyst at low temperatures and pressures. *Proc. R. Soc.* A **293**:19–35. http://doi.org/cfzcpj

Gee, G. 1952. Ernest Harold Farmer, 1890–1952. *Obit. Notes Fells. Roy. Soc.* **8**:159–65. http://doi.org/bz7d5g

Gibbs, Philip. 1935. *England Speaks*. N. Y: The Literary Guild

Gibson, C. S. 1939. Alfred John Greenaway 1852–1938. *J. Chem. Soc.* 207–209. http://doi.org/crg447

Gibson, C. S. 1941. William Jackson Pope, 1870–1939). *Biog. Mems. Fells. Roy. Soc.* **3** (9):291–324. http://doi.org/bhv8wn

Gibson, C. S. *rev.* K. D. Watson. 2004. Pope, Sir William Jackson, 1870–1939. *ODNB.* OUP. http://doi.org/d5cd3q

Gibson, C. S and T. P. Hilditch. 1948. E. F. Armstrong. *Biog. Mems. Fells. Roy. Soc.***5**:607–715. http://doi.org/bjdvjq

Gibson, J. F., D. O. Hall, J. H. M. Thornley and F. R. Whatley. 1966. The iron complex in spinach ferredoxin. *Proc. Nat. Acad. Sci.* (USA). **56**:987–990.

Gibson, S. E and R. J. Middleton. 1995. Synthesis of 7-, 8- and 9-membered rings via endo Heck cyclisations of amino acid derived substrates. *J. Chem. Soc., Chem. Commun.* 1743–1744. http://doi.org/cs6mdw

Gibson, V. C., C. Redshaw and G. A. Solan. 2007. Bis(imino)pyridines: Surprisingly reactive ligands and a gateway to new families of catalysts. *Chem. Rev.* **107**:1745–1776. http://doi.org/d4347t

Gillard, R. D and G. W. Wilkinson. 1963. Triethylenetetramine complexes of cobalt (III) and rhodium (III). *J. Chem. Soc.* 3193–3200. http://doi.org/c6brzh

Glueckauf, E. 1959. Professor F. A, Paneth, 1887–1958. *Proc. Chem. Soc.*103–105. http://doi.org/fdb2nb

Goddard, Nicholas. 2004. Warington, Robert (1838–1907). *ODNB.* OUP. http://doi.org/d56sh4

Goodall, Francis. 2004. Nicholson, Edward Chambers (1827–1890). *ODNB.* OUP. http://doi.org/dmv98s

Gooday, Graeme J. N. 2004. Playfair Lyon, first Baron Playfair (1818–1898). *ODNB.* OUP. http://doi.org/dsg9j3

Gooday. 2004b. Guthrie, Frederick, (1833–1886). *ODNB.* OUP. http://doi.org/ffc9fp

Goodgame, D. M. L., I. Jeeves, F. L. Phillips, and A. C. Skapski. 1975. X-ray evidence for cis-binding by platinum of two inosine-5'-monophosphate molecules via the N(7) positions. *Biochim. Biophys. Acta.* **378**:153–57.

Goodgame, D. M. L., D. A. Grachvogel and D. J. Williams. 1999. A new type of metal-organic large-pore zeotype, *Angew. Chem. Int. Ed.* **38**:153–56. http://doi.org/dcdmzb

Goodgame, M and B. Piggott. 1971. Metal complexes of the virus inhibitor 2-α-hydroxybenzylbenzimidazole. *J. Chem. Soc.* (A), 826–829. http://doi.org/dvszf6

Goodgame, M and K. W. Johns. 1980. Metal complexes of cytosine. *Inorg. Chim. Acta.* **46**:23–27.

Goosen, A. 1981. Frank Louis Warren, 1905–1980. *Chem. Br.* **17**:579.

Graham, T., A. W. Hofmann and Henry Allsopp. 1853. Report on the alleged adulteration of pale ales by strychnine. A report on the Report can be found in *Quart. J. Chem. Soc.* **5**:173–177. http://doi.org/fsdfhw

Green, M. L. H and W. P. Griffith. 1998. Geoffrey Wilkinson and Platinum Metals Chemistry. *Platinum Met. Rev.* **42** (4): 168–173.

Green, M. L. H. 2000. Sir Geoffrey Wilkinson, 1921–1996. *Biog. Mems. Fells. Roy. Soc.* **46**:593–606. http://doi.org/crdb7d

Green, M. L. H., L. Pratt and G. Wilkinson. 1958. Bis*cyclo*pentadienylrhenium hydride. *J. Chem. Soc.* 3916–3922. http://doi.org/fs5ds7

Green, M. L. H. 2000b. Dennis Frederick Evans, 1928–1990, *Biog. Mems. Fells. Roy. Soc.* **46**:166–175. http://doi.org/cfz92b

Greenaway, Frank. 2004. William Charles Henry (1804–1892), physician and chemist. *ODNB*. OUP. http://doi.org/cgjprm

Greenaway, Frank. 2004b. Church, Sir Arthur Herbert (1834–1915). *ODNB*. OUP. http://doi.org/dpnt6z

Greenwood, Norman N. 1993. Harry Julius Eméleus CBE (1903–1993). *Biog. Mems. Fells. Roy. Soc.* **42**:123–50. http://doi.org/ftx5jz

Greenwood, Norman N. 2004. Eméleus, Harry Julius (1903–1993). *ODNB*. OUP. http://doi.org/dj64fq

Gregg, S. J. 1961. Prof. H. T. S. Britton. *Chem. & Ind.,* 172–173.

Gregory, R. A. 1949. Mr. W. M. Heller. *Nature* **164**:14–15. http://doi.org/bc4rt8

Grieg, James. 1979. *Silvanus P. Thompson, Teacher.* London: Science Museum

Griffith, W. P. 1967. *Chemistry of the rare platinum metals (Os, Ru, Ir and Rh).* London: Wiley Interscience

Griffith, W. P. 1997. Geoffrey Wilkinson, 1921–1996. *Chem. Br.* **33** (1):52–53.

Griffith, W. P. 2004. Sir Geoffrey Wilkinson (1921–1996). *ODNB*. OUP. http://doi.org/fw5j59

Griffith, W. P. 2008. Wilkinson, Geoffrey. *New DSB.* **7**:306–314. (N.Y: Scribner)

Griffith, W. P. 2013. Johnson, Matthey and the Chemical Society by *Platinum Met. Rev.* **57**(2):110–116. http://doi.org/rn2

Griffith, W. P., J. Lewis and G. Wilkinson. 1958. Some nitric oxide complexes of iron and copper. *J. Chem. Soc.* 3993–3998. http://doi.org/fc8n35

Grummit, W. E., L. Yaffé, J. Guéron, and G.Wilkinson. 1946. 'The fission yields of Ba^{139} and Ba^{140} in neutron fission of U^{235} and U^{238}.' *Can. J. Res.* 25B:364–370.

Gundry, P. M and F. C. Tompkins, 1956. Chemisorption of metals on nickel films. Part I. Kinetic studies. *Trans. Faraday Soc.* **52**:1609–1617. http://doi.org/d33knj

Haber, L. F. 1986. *The Poisonous Cloud: Chemical warfare in the First World War.* OUP

Haile, N. 2004. Buckland, William (1784–1856), geologist and dean of Westminster. *ODNB.* OUP. http://doi.org/d9ft3r

Hall, N. 1985. Jack Baldwin — jousting to protect the enchanted land. *Chem. Br.* **21**:981–982.

Halton, B. 2015. A Legacy of Lancashire — Its Chemists, Biochemists and Industrialists. Victoria University of Wellington

Hamer, F. M. (ed.). 1964. Heterocyclic compounds: Cyanine dyes and related compounds. N.Y: John Wiley

Hamlin, Christopher. 1990. *A Science of Purity: water analyses in nineteenth-century Britain.* University of California Press

Hamlin, Christopher. 2004. Warington, Robert (1807–1867). *ODNB.* OUP. http://doi.org/fgvdvd

Hammond, P. W. 2004. Thorpe, Sir Thomas Edward (1845–1925). *ODNB.* OUP. http://doi.org/fvch74

Harper, S. H., G. A. R. Kon and F. C. J. Ruzicka. 1934. Synthesis of polycyclic compounds related to the sterols. Part II. Diels hydrocarbon $C_{18}H_{16}$'. *J. Chem. Soc.* 124–128. http://doi.org/bmr3j3

Harrison, Mark. 2004. Keogh, Sir Alfred (1857–1936). *ODNB.* OUP. http://doi.org/dgrcj9

Hartley, Harold. 1971. Henry Armstrong (1848–1937). *Studies in the History of Chemistry.* Oxford: Clarendon Press. 195–222.

Hartley, Harold. *rev* K. D. Watson. Jones, Bernard Mouat (1882–1953). *ODNB.* OUP. http://doi.org/d4szqf

Hartog, P. J. rev. Anita McConnell. 2004. Augustus Matthiessen (1831–1870). *ODNB.* OUP. http://doi.org/d94z3w

Hartley, Harold. *rev.* A. J. Meadows. 2004. Rue, Warren de la, (1815–1889). *ODNB.* OUP. http://doi.org/c7xs46

Hartley, Harold. *rev.* Trevor I. Williams. 2004. Muspratt, James Sheridan (1821–1871). *ODNB.* OUP. http://doi.org/fpk8sg

Harvey, B. G., H. G. Heal, A. G. Maddock and E. L. Rowley. 1947. The chemistry of plutonium. *J. Chem. Soc.* 1010–1021. http://doi.org/fnmw3h

Haworth, W. N and A. T. King. 1912. The structure of camphenic acid. *J. Chem. Soc., Trans.* **101**:1975–1981. http://doi.org/bhp7zz

Hayward, David O. 2002. *Quantum mechanics for chemists.* London: RSC

Hayward, David O and B. M. W. Trabnell. 1964. *Chemisorption.* London: Butterworth

Heilbron, I. M. 1947. *The life and work of George Gerald Henderson.* London: RIC

Heilbron, I. M. 1949. Concerning amino-acids, peptides and purines. *J. Chem. Soc.* 2099–2107. http://doi.org/drkckm

Heilbron, I. M and H. M. Bunberry (eds.). 1934–1937. *Dictionary of Organic Compounds.* 3 vols. OUP

Heilbron, I. M., P. W. Carter and B. Lythgoe. 1939. The lipochromes and sterols of the algal classes. *Proc. R. Soc.* B **128**:82–109. http://doi.org/b5hqzc

Heilbron, I. M and E. R. H. Jones. 1940. The chemistry of the sterols. *Ann. Rev. Biochem.* **9**:135–172.

Heilbron, I. M., J. R. Catch and A. H. Cook. 1942. Purification and chemistry of penicillin. *Nature* **150**:633–634. http://doi.org/drts5v

Heilbron, I. M, E. R. H. Jones, J. T. McCombie and B. C. L. Weedon. 1945. Formation of ethers and esters from propenylvinylcarbinol and related compounds, and their simultaneous rearrangements. *Nature* 88–90. http://doi.org/fj4h8b

Hekke, G. R. van. 1976. Tilden, Sir William Augustus. *DSB.* **13**:410–411. (N.Y: Scribner)

Herringshaw, J. F. 1980. Leslie Stuart Theobald (1896–1979). *Chem. Br.* **16**:379.

Herschel, J. F. W. 1987 (first published, 1830). *A preliminary discourse on the study of natural philosophy.* University of Chicago Press

Hevesey, George *rev.* Joseph Gross. 2004. Paneth, Friedrich Adolf (1887–1958). *ODNB.* OUP. http://doi.org/b2v2vc

Hewitt, J. T. 1946. Clarence Smith, 1875–1945, *J. Chem. Soc.* 68–70. http://doi.org/bqfkcz

Hey, D. H. 1955. King's College, London. *J. Roy. Inst. Chem.* **79**:305–315. http://doi.org/d5f7pf

Hickman, K. C. D and R. P. Linstead. 1922. A modified methyl-orange indicator. *J. Chem. Soc., Trans.* **121**:2502–2506. http://doi.org/cjp64m

Himmel, S .E and G. B. Young. 1988. Mechanisms of thermal rearrangement of diarylbis(pyridine)platinum(II) complexes: reductive carbon-carbon elimination versus hydrogen-transfer. *Organometallics* **7**:2440–2450. http://doi.org/cj3ng6

Hirst, E. L and M. Ritchie. 1953, The University of Edinburgh. *J. Roy. Inst. Chem.* **77**:505–511. http://doi.org/fv29vf

Hoblyn, E. H. T. *rev* 2004. Hinchley, John William (1871–1931). *ODNB,* OUP. http://doi.org/b4r293

Hofmann, A. W. 1849. Researches on the volatile bases. I. On the action of cyanogen on aniline, toluidine and cumidine, *Quart. J. Chem. Soc.* **1**:159–173. http://doi.org/c723tk; III. On the action of chloride, bromide and iodide on cyanogen of quinine. *ibid.* 285–317. http://doi.org/fmhrwr

Hofmann, A. W. 1850. V. On the action of acids and bases upon cyaniline. *Quart. J. Chem. Soc.* **2**:300–335. http://doi.org/dqr3kd

Hofmann, A. W. 1850b . Researches regarding the molecular constitution of the volatile organic bases. *Philos. Trans. R. Soc.,* **140**:93–131. http://doi.org/fg43j7

Hofmann, A. W. 1851. Researches into the molecular constitution of the organic bases. *Philos. Trans. R. Soc..* **141**:357–398. http://doi.org/fk7559

Hofmann, A. W. 1865. *Introduction to Modern Chemistry, Experimental and Theoretical; embodying twelve lectures delivered in the Royal College of Chemistry.* London: Walton and Maberley

Hofmann, A. W. 1865b. On the combining power of atoms. *Proc. Roy. Inst.* **4**:401–430.

Hofmann, A. W. 1871. A page of scientific history: Reminiscences of the early days of the Royal College of Chemistry'. *Quart. J. Sci.* April:145–153.

Hofmann, A. W. 1876. *The life work of Liebig.* London: Macmillan

Hofmann, A. W. 1880. Jean Baptiste André Dumas. *Nature* **21**:6, 1–40.

Hofmann, A. W and A. Cahours. 1857. Researches on the phosphorus bases. *Phil. Trans. R. Soc.* **147**:575–599. http://doi.org/dgphb5

Holland, T. H and L. J. Spencer. 1943. Henry Alexander Miers, 1858–1942. *Obit. Notes Fells. Roy. Soc.* **4**:368–380. http://doi.org/d7ksbd

Hollis, H. P. *rev.* A. J. Meadows. 2004. Herschel, Alexander Stewart (1836–1907). *ODNB.* OUP. http://doi.org/fczh6h

Holman, M. J. de K. 1978. The Purleigh Colony: Tolstoyan togetherness in the late 1890s' in Malcolm Jones (ed.), *New Essays on Tolstoy*, ch. 9. CUP

Holmes, F. L. 1989. The complementary of teaching and research in Liebig's laboratory. (Olesko, 1989)

Horrocks, Sally. 2011. Martha Annie Whiteley (1866–1956), in Jan Apotheker and Livia Simon Sarkadi, *European Women in Chemistry.* Weinheim: Wiley–VCH, 31–34.

Howell, O. Rhys. 1955. Bernard Mouat Jones. *J. Chem. Soc.* 1638–1639. http://doi.org/fkj4t4

Hudson, R. F and K. Wade. 1990. Graham Robert Martin, 1920–1989. *Chem. Br.* **26**:449.

Hunt, L. B. 1984. The First Organometallic Compounds: William Christopher Zeise and his platinum complexes. *Platinum Met. Rev.* **28**(2):76–83.

Hyde, B. G and P. Day. 1992. John Stuart Anderson, 1908–1990. *Biog. Mems. Fells. Roy. Soc.* **38**:1–26. http://doi.org/d3nbjp. Published also in *Hist. Recs. Austral. Sci.* **9**:127–49.

Ingold, C. K. 1921. Formation of unsaturated and of cyclic compounds from halogenated open-chain derivatives. I. Products derived from α-halogenated glutaric acids. *J. Chem. Soc., Trans.* **119**:305–329. http://doi.org/b9xczm

Ingold, C. K. 1922. The structure of the benzene nucleus. Part I. Intra-nuclear tautomerism. *J. Chem. Soc., Trans.* **121**:1133–1143. http://doi.org/frxr8s

Ingold, C. K. 1941. Jocelyn Field Thorpe, 1872–1939. *Biog. Mems. Fells. Roy. Soc.* **3**:530–544. http://doi.org/b9vrdr

Ingold, C. K. 1953. *Introduction to the principles of organic chemistry.* Cornell University Press

Ingold, C. K. 1968. Oscar Lisle Brady, 1890–1968. *Chem. Br.* **4**:554.

Ingold, C. K and J. F. Thorpe. 1921. The simultaneous occurrence of 1:2- and of 1:3- additions to "nascent" glutaconic ester. *J. Chem. Soc., Trans.* **119**: 492–501. http://doi.org/dqgfqj

Ingold, C. K and J. W. Baker. 1923. *Spiro*-compounds derived from cyclobutane. *J. Chem. Soc., Trans.* **123**:122–133. http://doi.org/brbrrx

Ingold, C. K., C. W. Shoppee and J. F. Thorpe. 1926. The mechanism of tautomeric interchange and the effect of structure on mobility and equilibrium. Part I. The three-carbon system. *J. Chem. Soc., Trans.* **129**:1477–1488. http://doi.org/bk6qr9

Ingold, C. K and J. F. Thorpe. 1928. The hypothesis of valency-deflexion. *J. Chem. Soc., Trans.* 1318–1321. http://doi.org/djn7w6

Irvine, J. C. 1917. Thomas Purdie, 1843–1916. *J. Chem. Soc., Trans.* **111**: 359–369. http://doi.org/dtwf4v

Irvine, J. C. 1941. Gilbert Thomas Morgan, 1872–1940. *Obit. Not. Fells. Roy. Soc.* **3**:355–362. http://doi.org/fq4xtv

Irvine, J. C. *rev.* K. D. Watson. 2004. Morgan, Sir Gilbert Thomas (1870–1940). *ODNB.* OUP. http://doi.org/dnzfg7

Irvine, J. C. *rev.* K. D. Watson. 2004b. Henderson, George Gerald (1862–1942). *ODNB.* OUP. http://doi.org/dgscch

Irvine, J. C. 2007. NMR in organic chemistry: the fabulous fifties. *Encyclopedia of Magnetic Resonance.* N.Y: John Wiley, 2007

Jackman, Lloyd M. 1964. *Applications of nuclear magnetic resonance in organic chemistry.* N.Y: Pergamon

Jackson, Catherine. 2006. Re-examining the research school: August Wilhelm Hofmann and the re-creation of a Liebigian research school in London. *Hist. Sci.* xliv:1–39.

Jackson, Catherine. 2015. The "wonderful properties of glass": Liebig's *Kaliapparat* and the practice of chemistry in glass. *Isis* **106**:43–69.

Jacobs, P. 1996. Frederick Clifford Tompkins 1910–1995. *Chem. Br.* **32** (5):78.

James, F. W and J. S. Anderson. 1937. Interchange of hydrogen isotopes in complex cobaltamines. *Nature* 139:109. http://doi.org/c7bjmq

James, Frank A. J. L. 1981. The letters of William Crookes to Charles Hanson Greville Williams, 1861–1862: The detection and isolation of thallium. *Ambix* **28**:131–157.

James, Frank A. J. L. (ed.). 1989. *The development of the laboratory: Essays on the place of experiment in industrial civilization.* London: Macmillan

James, Frank A. J. L. 2004. Fownes, George (1815–1849). *ODNB.* OUP. http://doi.org/b7tspn

James, Frank A. J. L. 2004b. Daniell, John Frederic (1790–1845). *ODNB.* OUP. http://doi.org/fh39dk

James, Frank A. J. L. 2004c. McLeod, Herbert (1841–1923). *ODNB.* OUP. http://doi.org/ch2kxc

James T. E. *rev* Robert Sharp. 2004. O'Sullivan, Cornelius (1841–1907). *ODNB* OUP. http://doi.org/fh33m8

Japp, F. R. 1900. Sir Edward Frankland, KCB, DCL, LLD, FRS. *Mins. Proc. Inst. Civ. Eng.* **139**:343–349.

Jardine, F. H. 1981. Chlorotris(triphenylphosphine) rhodium(I): its chemistry and catalytic reactions. *Prog. Inorg. Chem.* **28**:63–184.

Jardine, F. H. 1981. Carbonylhydridotris-(triphenylphosphine)rhodium(I). *Polyhedron* **1**:569–605.

Jayne-Williams, D. J. 1963. Stanley Edward Jacobs DSc, ARCS, (1905–1963). *J. Appl. Bacteriology* **26**:1–2.

Jeffreys, R. A. 1980. Douglas Spencer, 1901–1979. *Chem. Br.* **16**:556.

Jeffreys, R. A and M. D. Gauntlett. 1981. Frances Mary Hamer, 1894–1980. *Chem. Br.* **17**:31.

Jennings, J. N and Alexander King. 1939. The Imperial College expedition to Jan Mayen Island. *The Geographical Journal* **94**(2):115–131. http://doi.org/d7j7b6

Johnson, A. W. 1946 and 1950. *The chemistry of the acetylenic compounds.* I. *The acetylenic alcohols.* II. *The acetylenic acids.* London: E. Arnold

Johnson, A. W. 1982. Alfred Spinks 1917–1982. *Chem. Br.* **18**:362.

Johnson, A. W., F. L. Rose and C. W. Suckling. 1984. Alfred Spinks, 1917–1982. *Biog. Mems. Fells. Roy. Soc.* **30**:566–594. http://doi.org/cktnrw

Johnson, A. W., E. R. H. Jones and R. A. Raphael. 1943. Studies in the polyene series. Part X. Condensation of 3-methylpent-2-en-4-yne (1:2-dimethylvinyl-acetylene) with butaldehyde, crotonaldehyde, and citrol. *Nature* 265–68. http://doi.org/b7bbqq

Johnson, B. F. G., W. P. Griffith, R. J. H. Clark, J. Evans, B. H. Robinson and P. R. Raithby. 2015. In memory of Lord Jack Lewis, *Dalton Trans.* **44**: 3896–3903. http://doi.org/2c3

Jones, B. M. *rev.* 2004. Baker, Herbert Brereton (1862–1935). *ODNB.* OUP. http://doi.org/c46rb8

Jones, E. R. H. 1962. Ian Morris Heilbron, 1886–1958. *Proc. Chem. Soc.* 242–245. http://doi.org/d7k2vr

Jones, E. R. H. 1983. Alan W. Johnson, 1917–1982. *Chem. Br.* **19**:930–932.

Jones, E. R. H. *rev* 2004. Johnson, Alan Woodworth (1917–1982). *ODNB.* OUP. http://doi.org/fpjd4v

Jones, E. R. H. 1985. Lionel Charles Cross, 1918–1984. *Chem. Br.* **21**:164.

Jones, E. R. H., T. Y. Shen and M. C. Whiting. 1951. Acetylenic compounds. Part XXIX. The reaction between nickel carbonyl and disubstituted acetylenes. *J. Chem. Soc.* 48–52. http://doi.org/cnd4rs

Jones, E. R. H and Peter Garratt, 1982. Franz Sondheimer 1926–1981. *Biog. Mems. Fells. Roy. Soc.* **28**:503–536. http://doi.org/fhrfvr

Jones, E. R. H and R. Bonnet. 1984. Alan Woodworth Johnson 1917–1982. *Biog. Mems. Fells. Roy. Soc.* **30**:317–348. http://doi.org/fpjd4v

Jones, J. H. 2003. Sir Ewart Ray Herbert Jones (1911–2002). *Biog. Mems. Fells. Roy. Soc.* **49**:263–282. http://doi.org/fqqcz7

Jones, Simon. 2007. *World War 1: gas warfare, tactics and equipment.* Oxford: Osprey

Jordan, L. A and J. F. Thorpe. 1915. The formation of coumarin derivatives and the preparation of stable coumarinic acids. *J. Chem. Soc., Trans.* **107**: 387–406. http://doi.org/dsvnmz

Joule, J. 2001. James Sutherland 1932–2001. *Chem. Br.* **37** (9):73.

Kauffman, George B. 1983. Julius Bredt and the structure of camphor: On the threshold of modern stereochemistry. *J. Chem. Ed.* **60**:341–342. http://doi.org/fh848h

Kay-Shuttleworth, Ughtred James. 1868. *First Principles of Modern Chemistry.* London: John Churchill and Son

Kealy, T. J and P. L. Pauson. 1951. A new type of organo-iron compound. *Nature* **168**:1039. http://doi.org/d8sd7g

Keas, Michael N. 1992. The nature of organic bases and the ammonia type, in (Meinel and Scholz, 1992)

Keeble, F. W. 1941. Henry Edward Armstrong, 1848–1937. *Obit. Notes Fells. Roy. Soc.* **3**(9):229–245. http://doi.org/brw2m5

Kekulé, F. A. 1857. *Lehrbuch der organische chemie.* Vol. 1. Erlangen: Encke

Kelly, P. F., A. M. Z. Slawin, D. J. Williams and J. D. Woollins. 1992. Caged explosives: Metal stabilized chalcogen nitrides. *Chem. Soc. Rev.* 245–252. http://doi.org/b5w6n9

Khan, N., T. H. Morris, E. H. Smith and R. Walsh. 1991. Alkenyl sulphides and ketene S,S-dithioacetals as olefin components in the Paterno-Buechi Reaction. *J. Chem. Soc., Perkin Trans.* 1:865–870. http://doi.org/dqbtc8

King, Alexander. 2006. *Let the cat turn round: One man's traverse through the twentieth century.* London: Commonwealth Partnership for Technical Management

King, Alexander and J. S. Anderson. 1933. *Chemical Calculations: Their theory and practice.* London: Thomas Murby

King, Alexander and H. Fromherz. 1951. *English–German chemical terminology: An introduction to chemistry in English and German*, 2nd. ed. London: Thomas Murby

King, David and John Enderby. 2004. Frederick Clifford Tompkins, 1910–1995. *Biog. Mems. Fells. Roy. Soc.* 309–313. http://doi.org/btxhkw

Kipping, F. S. 1888. Synthetical formation of closed-carbon chains in the aromatic series *J. Chem. Soc., Trans.* **53**:21–47. http://doi.org/cgtj56

Kipping, F. S and W. J. Pope. 1898. Stereoisomeric derivatives of camphor. *J. Chem. Soc., Trans.* **73**:569–588. http://doi.org/ckhtws

Kitchener, Joseph. 1961. *Ion exchange resins.* London: Methuen

Knight, David (ed.). 1998. *The development of chemistry, 1789–1914*: Selected *essays.* London: Routledge

Knight, David and Helge Kragh (eds.). 1998. *The making of the chemist: the social history of chemistry in Europe, 1789–1914.* CUP

Kolbe, H and E. Frankland. 1849. On the products of the action of potassium on cyanide of ethyl. *Quart. J. Chem. Soc.* **1**:60–74, http://doi.org/cqckdm

Kon, G. A. R and J. F. Thorpe. 1919. The chemistry of the cyanoacetamide and Guareschi condensations. *J. Chem. Soc., Trans.* **115**:686–704. http://doi.org/c4fgqj

Kon, G. A. R., A. Stevenson and J. F. Thorpe. 1922. The occurrence and effect of keto-enol tautomerism between a ring compound and its open-chain isomeride. *J. Chem. Soc., Trans.* **121**:650–655. http://doi.org/c4r8x2

Kon, G. A. R and R. P. Linstead. 1925. The chemistry of the three-carbon system. Part III. The αβ — βγ change in unsaturated acids. *J. Chem. Soc., Trans.* **127**:616–624. http://doi.org/bvxn8c

Kon, G. A. R and R. P. Linstead. 1941. Sir Jocelyn Field Thorpe. *J. Chem. Soc.* 444–464. http://doi.org/bbd8dr

Kopperl, S. J. 1972. Haworth, Walter Norman. *DSB.* **6**:184–186. N.Y: Scribner

Kopperl, S. J. 1973. Kipping, Frederick Stanley, *DSB.* **7**:372–373. N.Y: Scribner

Kopperl, S. J. 1976. Thorpe, Thomas Edward. *DSB.* **13**:389–390. N.Y: Scribner

Krige, John and Dominique Pestre. 2014. *Science in the twentieth century.* N. Y: Routledge

Kwok, W. M., C. Ma, P. Matousek, A. W. Parker, D. Phillips and M. Towrie. 2000. Picosecond time-resolved study of dimethylamino benzonitrile in polar and non-polar solvents. *J. Phys. Chem.* A. **104**:4188–4197. http://doi.org/fn4vx7

Laidler, K. J. 2004. Hinshelwood, Sir Cyril Norman (1897–1967). *ODNB.* OUP. http://doi.org/cpw5wk

Latimer. 1938. *Oxidation states of the elements and their potentials in aqueous solution.* N.Y: Prentice Hall

Laurent, Auguste. 1854. *Méthode de Chimie.* Paris: Mallot-Bachelier

Laurie, A. P. 1916. Sir Arthur Herbert Church. *J. Chem. Soc., Trans.* **109**:374–379. http://doi.org/dtndq9

Leffek, Kenneth T. 1996. *Sir Christopher Ingold: A major prophet of organic chemistry.* Victoria, BC: Nova Lion Press

Leffek, Kenneth T. 2004. Ingold, Sir Christopher Kelk (1893–1970). *ODNB.* OUP. http://doi.org/cnm3kw

Leicester, Henry M. 1971 (reprint of 1956 edition). *The Historical background to chemistry.* N.Y: Dover

Ley, Steven V., Alan Armstrong, *et. al.* (14 other authors). 1991. Total synthesis of the anthelmintic macrolide avermectin B1a. *J. Chem. Soc., Perkin Trans.* I: 667–692. http://doi.org/b9r6xh

Ley, Steven V., J. Norman, W. P. Griffith, S. P. Marsden. 1994. Tetrapropylammonium Perruthenate, $Pr_4N^+RuO_4^-$, TPAP: A catalytic oxidant for organic synthesis. *Synthesis* 639–666. http://doi.org/fg3r2h

Ley, Steven V and Rebecca M. Myers. 2002. Sir Derek Harold Richard Barton (1918–1998). *Biog. Mems. Fells. Roy. Soc.* **48**:1–23. http://doi.org/dkvghq

Lickiss, P. D. 1995. The Synthesis and Structures of Organosilanols. *Adv. Inorg. Chem.*, **42**:147–262.

Lickiss, P. D. 1998. Silicenium Ions — Experimental Aspects in *The Chemistry of Organic Silicon Compounds*, eds. Z. Rappoport and Y. Apeloig **2**(11): 557–594.

Liebig, J. 1831. Über einen neuen Apparat zur Analyse organischen Körper: und über die Zusammensetzung einiger organischen Substanzen. *Pogg. Ann. Physik.* **21**:1–43.

Liebig, J. 1840. *Organic chemistry in its application to agriculture and physiology.* transl. Lyon Playfair. London: Taylor and Walton

Liebig, J. 1964. *Animal chemistry, or Organic chemistry and its application to physiology and pathology.* transl. W. Gregory. N.Y: Johnson reprint

Linstead, R. P. 1927. The effect of conditions on isomeric change in unsaturated acids. *J. Chem. Soc.* 2579–2585. http://doi.org/cr73s5

Linstead, R. P. 1934. Phthalocyanines. Part I. A new type of synthetic colouring matter. *J. Chem. Soc.* 1016–1017. http://doi.org/dk3wb3

Linstead, R. P. 1952. George Armand Robert Kon, 1890–1952. *Obit. Notes Fells. Roy. Soc.* **8**:170–192. http://doi.org/ft2kqd; and *J. Chem. Soc.* 4550–4560. http://doi.org/b8g4tg

Linstead, R. P. 1957. Ernest Alexander Rudolph Braude. *Proc. Chem. Soc.* 297–298. http://doi.org/bt2tc7

Linstead, R. P., J. A. Elvidge, P. Sims and B. A. Orkin. 1950. The third isomeric (*cis-trans-*) muconic acid. *J. Chem. Soc.* 2235–2241. http://doi.org/dwz8kd

Linstead, R. P., J. C. Lunt and B. C. L. Weedon. 1951. Anodic syntheses IV: Synthesis of (+) and (−) — tuberculostearic acids. *J. Chem. Soc.* 1130–1132. http://doi.org/dqn58m

Linstead, R. P., J. A. Elvidge, and M. A. Whalley. 1955. *A Course in modern techniques of organic chemistry.* London: Butterworths

Linstead, R. P., J. A. Elvidge and P. G. Sammes. 1966. *A Course in modern techniques of organic chemistry.* London: Butterworths

Linstead, R. P and B. C. L. Weedon. 1956. *A Guide to Qualitative Organic Analysis.* London: Butterworth

Locket, George Hazlewood, with A. H. B. Bishop. 1939. *Introduction to Chemistry.* Oxford: Clarendon Press

Long, N. J. 1998. *Metallocenes.* Oxford: Blackwell

Macintosh, F. C and T. L. Sourkes. 1990. Judah Hirsch Quastel, 1899–1987. *Biog. Mems. Fells. Roy. Soc.* **36**:380–418. http://doi.org/drx4zt

MacKenzie, A. R., C. J. Moody and C. W. Rees. 1986. Synthesis of the bacterial coenzyme methoxatin'. *Tetrahedron* **42**:3259–3268.

Mackenzie, W. J. M. 2000. *The secret history of the SOE: The Special Operations Executive, 1940–1945.* London: St. Ermin's Press

Maclean, Ida Smedley. 1943. *The metabolism of fat.* London: Methuen

MacLeod, Roy. 1993. The chemists go to war: The mobilization of civilian chemists and the British war effort. *Annals Sci.* **50**:455–481.

MacLeod, Roy. 2004. Pedler, Sir Alexander (1845–1918). *ODNB.* OUP. http://doi.org/b7vvjt

MacLeod, Roy. 2004b. Liversidge, Archibald (1846–1927). *ODNB.* OUP. http://doi.org/dvgj6r

MacLeod, Roy. 2004c. Holland, Sir Thomas Henry (1868–1947). *ODNB.* OUP. http://doi.org/fqx567

MacLeod, Roy. 2009. *Archibald Liversidge FRS: Imperial Science under the Southern Cross.* Sydney University Press

Macy, Marianne. 2013. John Bockris on modern electrochemistry and the start of cold fusion. *Infinite Energy* **111**:31–34.

Maher, J. P and D. F. Evans. 1965. Thallium–proton spin–spin coupling constants. *J. Chem. Soc.* 637–644. http://doi.org/dzn3t2

Mander, Lewis. 2003. Charles William Shoppee, 1904–1994. *Biog. Mems. Fells. Roy. Soc.* **49**:495–508. http://doi.org/b6psw2

Mann, F. G. 1975. Pope, William Jackson, *DSB.* **9**:84–89. N.Y: Scribner

Mare, P. B. D. de la. 1969. Philip Wilfred Robertson 1884–1969. *Chem. Br.* **6**:525–526.

May, Alex. 2004. King, Alexander (Alex) (1909–2007). *ODNB.* OUP. http://doi.org/c9xnzn

McCance, Robert A and Elsie M. Widdowson. 1940. *The chemical composition of foods.* London: HM Stationery Office

McLeod, Herbert. 1874. Apparatus for measurement of low pressures of gas. *Proc. Phys. Soc. Lond.* **1**:30–34; also in *Phil. Mag.* **48**(1874), 110–113.

McLeod, Herbert.1905. Sir Edward Frankland. *J. Chem. Soc., Trans.* **87**:574–590. http://doi.org/bcxr3z

McWilliam, R. C. 2004. Barry, Sir John Wolfe- (1836–1918). *ODNB.* OUP. http://doi.org/bx5n9f

Meadows, A. J. 1972. *Science and Controversy: A Biography of Sir Norman Lockyer.* London: Macmillan

Meadows, A. J. 2004. Lockyer, Sir Joseph Norman (1836–1920). *ODNB.* OUP. http://doi.org/czx2qp

Meinel, Christoph. 2005. Molecules and croquet balls, in Soraya de Chadarevian and Nicholas Hopwood (eds), *Models: The third dimension of science.* Stanford University Press, Ch. 9.

Meinel, Christoph and Hartmut Scholz (eds.). 1992. *Die allianz von wissenschaft und industrie: August Wilhelm Hofmann (1818–1892).* Weinheim: VCH

Meldola, Raphael. 1873. *Elementary Inorganic Chemistry: the non-metallic elements.* London: Thomas Murby

Meldola, Raphael. 1908. William Henry Perkin, 1838–1907. *Proc. R. Soc.* A **80**:38–59. http://doi.org/dmb952

Meldola, Raphael. 1908b. William Henry Perkin, 1838–1907. *J. Chem. Soc., Trans.* **93**:2214–2257. http://doi.org/cmkwxg

Meliconi, Ilaria. 2004. Browning, John (1830/31–1925). *ODNB.* OUP. http://doi.org/fb84q8

Mellanby, Kenneth. 1967. *Pesticides and pollution.* London: Methuen

Mendeleev, Dimitri, trnsl. George Kamensky. 1891. *The Principles of Chemistry*. 2 vol. 5th ed. London: Longman Green and Co

Merck, George and Robert Galloway. 1845. Analysis of the water of the thermal spring at Bath (King's Bath). *Mem. Proc. Chem. Soc.* **3**:262–273. http://doi.org/djstk4

Messel, R. 1907. Hermann Johann Philipp Sprengel. *J. Chem. Soc., Trans.* **91**:661–663. http://doi.org/cm8w3f

Miller, William Allen. 1855–1857. *Elements of Chemistry: Theoretical and Practical*. 3 Parts. London: John W. Parker and Son

Miller, William Allen. 1880. eds. Henry E. Armstrong and Charles E. Groves. *Elements of Chemistry: Theoretical and Practical*. Part 3, Organic Chemistry. Longmans, Green and Co

Mingos, D. M. P. 1995 and 1998. *Essential Inorganic Chemistry*, Vols 1 and 2. OUP

Mingos, D. M. P. 1998b. *Essential Trends in Inorganic Chemistry*. OUP

Moody, C. J. 2015. Charles Wayne Rees CBE. *Biog. Fells. Mems. Roy. Soc.***61**:351–338. http://doi.org/93s

Moody, G. T and W. H. Mills. 1941. Sir William Pope (1870–1939). *J. Chem. Soc.* 697–715. http://doi.org/d6wwhk

Moore, T. S and J. C. Philip. 1947. *The Chemical Society 1841–1941: A historical review*. London: Chemical Society

Morgan, G. T. 1939. Personal reminiscences of Chemical Research. *Chem and Ind.* 665–672

Morgan, G. T and F. M. G. Micklethwait. 1905. The diazo-derivatives of the benzenesulphonylphenylenediamines. *J. Chem. Soc., Trans.* **87**:73–87. http://doi.org/cj5d27

Morgan, G. T and D. D. Pratt. 1938. *The British Chemical Industry: Its rise and development*. London: Edward Arnold

Morley, H. F. 1924. 'Herbert McLeod. *J. Chem. Soc., Trans.* **125**:990–992. http://doi.org/bkh5gn

Morrell, Jack B. 1972. The chemist breeders: The research schools of Liebig and Thomas Thomson. *Ambix* **19**:1–46.

Morrell, Jack B. 2004. Perkin, William Henry Jr. (1860–1929). *ODNB*. OUP. http://doi.org/cg2j9z

Morrell, Jack B. 2004b. Perkin, Arthur George (1861–1937). *ODNB*. OUP. http://doi.org/bftwqf

Morris, Peter J. T. 2004. Abney, Sir William de Wiveleslie (1843–1920). *ODNB*. OUP. http://doi.org/bh65r2

Morris, Peter J. T. *rev.* 2004. Tilden, Sir William Augustus, 1842–1926. *ODNB* OUP. http://doi.org/cvckjj

Morris, Peter J. T. 2015. *The Matter Factory: A history of chemistry laboratories.* Reaktion Books

Morris, Peter J. T and Anthony S. Travis. The role of physical instrumentation in structural organic chemistry in (Krige and Pestre, 2014)

Motherwell, W. B. 1992. A curiosity-driven search for new chemical reactions, *Aldrichimica Acta* **25**(3):71–80.

Muspratt, Edmund Knowles. 1917. *My life and work.* London: John Lane Bodley Head

Muspratt, J. S and A. W. Hofmann. 1848. On nitraniline, a new product of decomposition of nitrobenzol. *Mem. Proc. Chem. Soc.* **3**:110–125. http://doi.org/dnw722

Newitt, D. M. 1940. *High pressure plant and the properties of fluids at high pressures.* Oxford: Clarendon Press

Newitt, D. M., R. P. Linstead, E. T. Boorman, W. A. Bone, R. H. Sapiro and J. F. Thorpe. 1937. Hydrolyses of esters and the Knoevenagel reaction. *J. Chem. Soc.* 876–883. http://doi.org/dqvd4w

Newlands, J. A. R. 1882. On the Discovery of the Periodic Law. *Chem. News.* **46**:278–279.

Newlands, J. A. R. 1884. *On the Discovery of the Periodic Law.* London: E and F. N. Spon

Newth, George S. 1895. *A textbook of inorganic chemistry.* London: Longman, Green

Nicholson, D and N. G. Parsonage. 1982. *Computer simulation and the statistical mechanics of adsorption.* London: Academic Press

Nicholson, E. C. 1845. On the composition of caffeine and some of its compounds. *Mem. Proc. Chem. Soc.* **3**:321–329. http://doi.org/fj79bj

Nicholson, R. M and Nicholson, J. W. 2012. Martha Whiteley of Imperial College, London: A Pioneering Woman Chemist. *J. Chem. Educ.* **89**:598–601. http://doi.org/7fz

Nye, Mary Jo. 1993. *From Chemical Philosophy to Theoretical Chemistry: Dynamics of matter and dynamics of disciplines, 1800–1950.* University of California Press

Nye, Mary Jo. Atomic and molecular science, 1900–1960 in (Krige and Pestre, 2014)

Nyholm, R. S. 1957. The renaissance of inorganic chemistry. *J. Chem. Educ.* **34**:166–149. http://doi.org/ccgvm8

Olesko, Kathryn M. (ed.). 1989. Science in Germany: The intersection of institutional and intellectual issues. *Osiris* Vol. 5.

Osborn, J. A., F. H. Jardine, J. F. Young and G. Wilkinson. 1966. The preparation and properties of tris(triphenylphosphine)halogenorhodium(I) and some reactions thereof including catalytic homogeneous hydrogenation of olefins and acetylenes and their derivatives. *J. Chem. Soc.* A. 1711–1732. http://doi.org/cz5n68

Osborne, Peter. 2004. Finch, George Ingle (1886–1970). *ODNB*. OUP. http://doi.org/dkj9c5

Paneth, F. A. 1942. *The Origin of Meteorites.* OUP

Paneth, F. A and G. P. Thompson. 1935. Helium content of the strtoasphere. *Nature* **136**:717–718. http://doi.org/cttd2s

Paneth, F. A and Glückhauf. 1938. Identification and measurement of helium formed in beryllium by γ-rays. *Proc. R. Soc.* A **165**:229–238. http://doi.org/b4pc8h

Paris, John Ayrton. 2011. Reprint of 1831 edition. *The Life of Sir Humphry Davy.* vol 2. CUP

Parsonage, N. G. 2001. Some notes on David Nicholson's contribution to modelling adsorption. *Molecular Simulation* **27**:283–286. http://doi.org/cgghfp

Parsons, Roger. 2009. John Bockris at Imperial College. *J. Solid State Electrochem.* **13**:977–980. http://doi.org/ccqvtj

Parsons, Roger and J. O'M. Bockris. 1949. The kinetics of the hydrogen evolution reaction at mercury cathodes. *Trans. Faraday Soc.* **45**:916–928. http://doi.org/ckm5n4

Partington, J. R. 1954. An advanced treatise on physical chemistry. Vol. 5. London: Longmans

Partington, J. R. 1961–1970. A History of Chemistry. 4 vols. London: Macmillan

Pattenden, Gerald. 2001. Leslie Crombie (1923–1999). *Biog. Mems. Fells. Roy. Soc.* **47**:125–140. http://doi.org/br3sxf

Partington, J. R. 2005. Basil Charles Leicester Weedon, 1923–2003. *Biog. Mems. Fells. Roy. Soc.* **51**:424–436. http://doi.org/fqnmdv

Payne, F. *rev.* N. G. Coley. 2004. Jones, Henry Bence (1813–1873). *ODNB*. OUP. http://doi.org/bv4zcp

Peacock, R. D and D. W. A. Sharp. 1959. The infrared spectra of alkali salts of complex fluoro-acids. *J. Chem. Soc.*, 2762–2767. http://doi.org/bmtcxk

Pedige, J., C. Chandrasena, C. K. Ingold and J. F. Thorpe. 1922. The chemistry of polycyclic structures Part III. Intra-annular tautomerism of α-campholytic acid. *J. Chem. Soc., Trans.* **121**:1542–1551. http://doi.org/dx6qdx

Penney, W. G. 1935. *The Quantum Theory of Valency*. London: Methuen

Penney, W. G and J. S. Anderson. 1937. Note on co-ordination numbers eight. *Trans. Faraday Soc.* **33**:1363–1368. http://doi.org/btjwj9

Perkin, William. H. 1857. Action of chloride of cyanogen on naphthalamine. *Quart. J. Chem. Soc.*, **9**:8–15. http://doi.org/brqq7g

Perkin, William. H. 1869. On the newest colouring matters. *Proc. Roy. Inst.* **5**:566–574.

Perkin, William. H. 1896. The origin of the coal-tar colour industry, and the contributions of Hofmann and his pupils. *J. Chem. Soc., Trans.* **69**:596–637. http://doi.org/fgk4xn

Perkinb, William H. Jr and F. Stanley Kipping. 1894. *Organic Chemistry,* 2 vols. Edinburgh: W and R. Chambers

Perkinb, William H. Jr and J. F. Thorpe. 1897. Synthesis of *t*-camphoronic acid. *J. Chem. Soc., Trans.* **71**:1169–194. http://doi.org/d6rkc2

Philip, J. C. 1910. *The Romance of Chemistry*. London: Seeley

Philip, J. C. 1910b. *Physical Chemistry: Its bearing on biology and medicine.* London: E. Arnold

Philip, J. C. 1925. Prof. F. R. Japp FRS. *Nature* **116**:510. http://doi.org/c8dn5r

Philip, J. C. 1928. Sir William Augustus Tilden. *Proc. R. Soc.* A **117**:1–5. http://doi.org/dx9k2f

Philip, J. C. 1933. Henry Chapman Jones. *J. Chem. Soc.* 468–469. http://doi.org/ddh6hc

Philip, J. C. 1935. Arthur Bramley, 1878–1935. *J. Chem. Soc.*, 1896–1897. http://doi.org/bmgq8c

Phillips, David. 1995. The photochemistry of sensitisers for photodynamic therapy. *Pure Appl. Chem.* **67**:117–126. http://doi.org/crvhc2

Phillips, David. 2014. Remembrances of a UK scientist in Russia, 1966–1967. *Science Progress.* **97**(3):261–274.

Piller, G. J. 2004. Tizard, Sir Henry Thomas, *ODNB*. OUP. http://doi.org/c447nq

Pippard, Brian. 2002. Schoolmaster-Fellows and the campaign for science education. *Notes. and Rec. Roy. Soc.* **56**:63–81.

Plater, M. J., Harrison, W. T. A., Rzepa, H. S. 2015. 'Syntheses and structures of pseudo-mauveine: the first crystal structures of a mauveine chromophore and a synthetic derivative', *J. Chem. Res.* **19**:677–738. http://doi.org/bcj5

Playfair, Lord Lyon. 1896. Personal reminiscences of Hofmann and the conditions which led to the establishment of the Royal College of Chemistry and his appointment as professor. *J. Chem. Soc., Trans.* **69**:575–579. http://doi.org/btvn66

Polanyi, Michael. 1958. *Personal Knowledge: Towards a post-critical philosophy*. University of Chicago Press

Polanyi, Michael. 1966. *The tacit dimension.* N. Y: Doubleday

Pollard, A. G and A. C. Chibnall. 1934. The proteins of grasses: The cystine content of certain grasses and other pasture plant proteins. *Biochemical J.* **28**:326–336.

Pollard, A. G and C. P. Stewart. 1934. Biochemistry. *Ann. Rev. Prog. Chem.* **31**:322–367.

Pope, W. J. 1892. The crystalline forms of the sodium salts of substituted aniline acids. *J. Chem. Soc., Trans.* **61**:581–588. http://doi.org/dx7kp6

Pope, W. J. 1896. Substances exhibiting circular polarisation in the amorphous and crystalline states. *J. Chem. Soc., Trans.* **69**:971–980. http://doi.org/fwjzht

Pope, W. J. 1917. The national importance of chemistry in A. C. Seward. ed. *Science and the Nation*. CUP. 2–3, 14.

Pope, W. J. 1934. William Barlow (1845–1934). *Biog. Mems. Fells. Roy. Soc.* **1**(4):367–370. http://doi.org/fvwwtz

Pope, W. J. 1938. Thomas Martin Lowry, (1874–1936). *Biog. Mems. Fells. Roy. Soc.* **2**(6):287–293. http://doi.org/czpc4n

Pope, W. J and S. J. Peachey. 1900. Asymmetric optically active sulphur compounds. *d*-methylethylthetine platinichloride, *J. Chem. Soc., Trans.* **77**: 1072–1075. http://doi.org/cdrjd3

Poulton, E. B. 1917. Raphael Meldola. *J. Chem. Soc., Trans.* **111**:349–359. http://doi.org/dtwf4v

Power, D'A. *rev.* N. G. Coley. 2004. Pavy, Frederick William (1829–1911). *ODNB*. OUP. http://doi.org/fgs7r4

Powers, John C. 2012. *Inventing chemistry: Herman Boerhaave and the reform of the chemical arts*. University of Chicago Press

Prout, E. R and F. C. Tompkins. 1946. The thermal decomposition of silver permanganate. *Trans. Faraday Soc.* **42**: 468–472. http://doi.org/c78hhm. http://doi.org/c78hhm

Pugh, R. J. 2009. Joseph Alfred Kitchener (1916–2009). *J. Coll. Interfac. Sci.* **338**:326–337.

Raphael, R. A. 1982. Franz Sondheimer 1926–1981. *Chem. Br.* **18**:274.

Rayner-Canham, M. F and G. W. Rayner-Canham. 1999. A tale of two spouses. *Chem. Br.* **35**(10):45–46.

Rayner-Canham, M. F. 2008. *Chemistry was their life: Pioneer British Women Chemists, 1880–1949*. Imperial College Press

Read, John. 1953. The United College of St. Salvator and St. Leonard, in the University of St. Andrews. *J. Roy. Inst. Chem.* 8–18. http://doi.org/bqgrsj

Read, John. 1958. The life and work of Perkin. *Perkin Centenary London: 100 Years of synthetic dyestuffs*. Supplement No. I *Tetrahedron*

Reeks. Margaret. 1920. History of the Royal School of Mines in (Chambers, 1920)

Reeks. Margaret. 1920b. *Register of the Associates and Old Students of the Royal School of Mines and History of the Royal School of Mines*. London: RSM

Rees, C. W. R. 1984 and 1996. *Comprehensive heterocyclic chemistry*. vols. 1 and 2. London: Elsevier

Rees, C. W. R. 1995. *Comprehensive organic functional group transformations*. London: Elsevier

Rees, C. W. R. 1998. Sir Derek Barton, 1918–1998. *Chem. Br.* **34**(6):75–76.

Rees, Lovat V. C. 1997. Richard Maling Barrer 1910–1996. *Chem. Br.* **33**(3):73–74.

Rees, Lovat V. C. 1998. Richard Maling Barrer, 1910–1996. *Biog. Mems. Fells. Roy. Soc.* **44**:37–49. http://doi.org/bn2ckr

Reid, Wemyss. 1899. *Memoirs and correspondence of Lyon Playfair*. London: Cassell and Co

Reynolds, Capt. J. W. 1851. On "propylene", a new hydrocarbon of the series C_nH_n. *Quart. J. Chem. Soc.* **3**:111–120. http://doi.org/d7h42t

Ridd, J. H. 1971. Sir Christopher Ingold, 1893–1970. *Chem. Br.* **7**:163.

Rideal. Eric Keightley. 1930. *An introduction to surface chemistry*. CUP

Rideal. Eric Keightley. 1968. *Concepts in catalysis*. London: Academic Press

Ridge, B. 1992. Henry Norman Rydon, 1912–1991. *Chem. Br.* **28**:732.

Roberts, Gerrylynn K. 1973. The Royal College of Chemistry (1845–1853): A social history of chemistry in early Victorian England. PhD dissertation. The Johns Hopkins University

Roberts, Gerrylynn K. 1976. The Establishment of the Royal College of Chemistry: An Investigation of the social context of early-Victorian Chemistry. *Hist. Studs. Phys. Sci.* **7**:437–485. http://doi.org/bhjh

Roberts, Gerrylynn K. 1992. Bridging the gap between science and practice: The English years of August Wilhelm Hofmann, 1845–1865 in (Meinel and Scholz, 1992)

Roberts, Gerrylynn K. 1996. C. K. Ingold at University College London: educator and department head. *Bull. Hist. Chem.* **29**:65–82.

Robinson, Robert. 1956. The Perkin family of organic chemists. *Endeavour* **15**:92.

Robinson, Robert. 1936–1938. Perkin, Arthur George. *Obit. Nots. Fells. Roy. Soc.* **2**:444–450. http://doi.org/bj94tq

Robinson, Robert. 1938. A. G. Perkin. *J. Chem. Soc.* 1738–1754. http://doi.org/d5j6bg

Robinson, Robert. 1947. Arthur Lapworth, 1872–1941. *Obit. Not. Fells. Roy. Soc.* **5**:554–572. http://doi.org/dnc9cw

Robinson, Robert. 1976. *Memoirs of a minor prophet: 70 years of organic chemistry*. N.Y: Elsevier

Rochow, E. G and E. Krahé. 2001. *The Holland sisters: Their influence on the success of Perkin, Kipping and Lapworth*. Berlin: Springer

Rocke, Alan J. 1993. *The quiet revolution: Hermann Kolbe and the science of organic chemistry*. Berkeley: University of California Press

Rocke, Alan J. 2004. Hofmann, August Wilhelm, 1818–1892. ODNB. OUP. http://doi.org/ddmrq3

Rocke, Alan J. 2010. *Image and reality: Kekulé, Kopp and the scientific imagination*. University of Chicago Press

Rodd, E. H. 1940. Henry Edward Armstrong, 1848–1937 *J. Chem. Soc.* 1418–1439. http://doi.org/dwdptj

Rodd, E. H. 1951. William Palmer Wynne 1861–1950. *Obit. Notes Fells. Roy. Soc.* **7**:519–526. http://doi.org/bj293g

Rodd, E. H. 1951b. William Palmer Wynne. *J. Chem. Soc.* 1936–1941. http://doi.org/fww93k

Rodd, E. H., ed. S. Coffey *et. al.* 1964. *Rodd's Chemistry of Carbon Compounds*. London: Elsevier

Rodd, E. H. *rev.* Brock. 2004. Armstrong, Henry Edward (1848–1937). *ODNB*. OUP. http://doi.org/brdjtq

Rose, K. *rev.* 2004. Rothschild, (Nathaniel Mayer) Victor, third Baron Rothschild (1910–1990). *ODNB*. OUP. http://doi.org/bs6x83

Rowe, J. S. 1950. The life and work of George Fownes FRS (1815–1849). *Annals Sci.* **6**:422–435.

Rowney, T. H and H. How. 1845. Analyses of the ashes of the orange tree. *Mem. Proc. Chem. Soc.* **3**:370–77. http://doi.org/ds5m9q

Russell, Colin. A. 1982. Edward Frankland, founder of organometallic chemistry. *Chem. Br.* **18**(10):737–738.

Russell, Colin. A. 1986. *Lancastrian Chemist: The early life of Sir Edward Frankland*. Open University Press

Russell, Colin. A. 1992. August Wilhelm Hofmann — Cosmopolitan Chemist in (Meinel and Scholz, 1992)

Russell, Colin. A. 1996. *Edward Frankland: Chemistry, controversy and conspiracy in Victorian England*. CUP

Russell, Colin. A. 1999. The Frankland Enigma. *Chem. Br.* **35**(9):43–45.

Russell, Colin. A. 2004. Frankland, Sir Edward (1825–1899). *ODNB* OUP. http://doi.org/c22jhm

Russell, Colin. A. 2004b. Odling, William (1829–1921). *ODNB*. OUP. http://doi.org/d22n74

Russell, Colin. A. 2004c. Armstrong, Edward Frankland (1878–1945). *ODNB*. OUP. http://doi.org/dm4zjj

Russell, Colin. A. 2004d. Lowry, Thomas Martin (1874–1936). *ODNB*. OUP. http://doi.org/b35f4t

Russell, Colin. A. 2004e. Charles Wayne Rees, 1927–2006. *ODNB*. OUP. http://doi.org/dzf6mj

Russell, Colin. A. 2008. Frankland, Edward. *New DSB* **3**:62–65. (N.Y: Scribner)

Russell, Colin. A., N. G. Coley and G. K. Roberts. 1977. *Chemists by profession: The origin and rise of the Royal Institute of Chemistry*. Open University Press

Rydon, H. N. 1937. The resolution of *cis*- and *trans*-norcaryophyllenic acid. *J. Chem. Soc.* 1340–1342. http://doi.org/b52scp

Rydon, H. N. 1962. *Peptide Synthesis*. London: RIC

Rydon, H. N. 1967. Reginald Patrick Linstead, 1902–1966. *Chem. Br.* **3**:126–127.

Rzepa, H. S., J. Whitaker and M. J. Winter. 1994. Chemical applications of the World-Wide-Web system. *J. Chem. Soc., Chem. Commun.* 1907–1910. http://doi.org/ccpw8q

Sakurai, J. 1913. Edward Divers. *J. Chem. Soc., Trans.* **103**:746–55. http://doi.org/c3f5gc

Sanders, J. 2004. Raphael, Ralph Alexander (1921–1998). *ODNB*. OUP. http://doi.org/dw3rxf

Schaffer, Simon. 2004. Sprengel, Hermann Johann Philipp. *ODNB*. OUP. http://doi.org/b7pw8h

Schlapp, R and W. G. Penney. 1932. Influence of crystalline fields on the susceptibilities of salts of paramagnetic ions. II. The iron group; especially Ni, Cr and Co. *Phys. Rev.* **42**:666–686. http://doi.org/d6g56b

Schorlemmer, C. 1864. Ueber die Identität des Aethylwasserstoffs und des Methyls. *Annalen der Chemie* **132**:234–238.

Schrock, R. R. 2001. In memory of John Anthony Osborn. *Adv. Synth. Catal.* **343**:3–4.

Scott, A. 1905. Lyon Playfair. *J. Chem. Soc., Trans.* **87**:600–605. http://doi.org/bcxr3z

Scott, A. 1916. Presidential address. *J. Chem. Soc., Trans.* **109**:338–368. http://doi.org/fj9snb

Seddon, J. M. 1990. Structure of the inverted hexagonal (H_{II}) phase and non-lamellar phase transitions of lipids. *Biochim. Biophys. Acta.* **1031**:1–69.

Seddon, J. M and R. H. Templer. 1993. Cubic phases of self-assembled amphiphilic systems. *Phil. Trans. R. Soc.* A **344**:377–401. http://doi.org/dtpwkz

Sella, A. 2008. Classic Kit; The Sprengel Pump. *Chem. World* **5**(2):67.

Sella, A. 2009. Classic Kit: Liebig's *Kalliapparat*. *Chem. World* **6**(9):69.

Sella, A. 2011. Classic Kit: The McLeod Gauge. *Chem. World* **8**(9):74.

Seyferth, D. 2001. Zinc alkyls: Edward Frankland and the beginnings of Main Group Organometallic Chemistry.' *Organometallics* **20**:2940–2454. http://doi.org/btg4mb

Shakeshaft, John. 2009. Alfred Gavin Maddock, *St. Catharine's Magazine*. Cambridge

Sharp, D. W. A. 1994. Harry Emeléus, 1903–93. *Chem. Br.* **30**:505.

Sharp, D. W. A. 2003. *The Penguin Dictionary of Chemistry* 3rd. ed

Shaw, B. L. 1994. Joseph Chatt (1914–1994). *Chem. Br.* **30**:1011.

Sherfield, Lord. 1994. William George Penney OM, KBE, 1909–1991. *Biog. Mems. Fells. Roy. Soc.* **39**:282–302. http://doi.org/dz39mv

Shoppee, C. W. 1972. Christopher Kelk Ingold, 1893–1970. *Biog. Mems. Fells. Roy. Soc.* **18**:349–411. http://doi.org/fv6d6f

Shortland, A and G. Wilkinson. 1972. Hexamethyltungsten. *J. Chem. Soc., Chem. Commun.* **318a**. http://doi.org/dmms26

Sidgwick, N. V. 1950. *The Chemical elements and their compounds*. 2 vols. OUP

Simonsen, J. L. *rev*. K. D. Watson. 2004. Forster, Sir Martin Onslow, (1872–1945). *ODNB*. OUP. http://doi.org/dw6xq4

Smith, J. H. 2004. Flowers, Brian Hilton, Baron Flowers (1924–2010). *ODNB*. OUP. http://doi.org/xz4

Smith, R. Angus. 1865. *Chem. News* **11**:297–299.

Smithels, Arthur *rev*. Graeme J. H. Gooday. 2004. Thompson, Silvanus Phillips (1851–1916). *ODNB*. OUP. http://doi.org/b2zhgt

Spencer, D. A and H. D. Murray. 1939. *Colour in theory and practice*. London: Chapman and Hall

Spencer, D. A and W. Randerson. 1934. *North Sea Monster: A novel*. London: Houghton and Scott-Snell. Rev. *Nature* 1934. **134**:85. http://doi.org/d82w2q

Spencer, L. J. 2004. Alfred Edwin Howard Tutton (1864–1938). ODNB, OUP. http://doi.org/dwvh6f

Spiller, J. 1905. Frederick A. Abel. *J. Chem. Soc., Trans.* **87**:565–570. http://doi.org/bcxr3z

Spiller, J. 1907. George Bowdler Buckton. *J. Chem. Soc., Trans.* **91**:663–665. http://doi.org/cm8w3f

Spiro, M and D. P. Sidebottom. 1973. The electrophoretic term of the Fuoss–Onsager conductance equation. *J. Chem. Soc., Faraday Trans.* 1. **69**:1282–1286. http://doi.org/fpgcpv

Spiro, M and D. Jaganyi. 1993. What causes scum on tea? *Nature* **364**:581. http://doi.org/dtpfbx

Spitler, E. G. 1974. Paneth, Friedrich Adolf. *DSB*. **10**:288–289. (N.Y: Scribner)

Sprengel, H. 1865. Researches on the vacuum. *J. Chem. Soc., Trans.* **18**:9–21. http://doi.org/cwbd95

Spring, Robin J. 2004. Bloxam, Charles Loudon (1831–1887). *ODNB*. OUP. http://doi.org/dfxvw5

Steele, R. *rev.* K. D. Watson. 2004. Abel, Sir Frederick Augustus, (1827–1902). *ODNB*. OUP. http://doi.org/cqdz4x

Steele, R. *rev.* Yolande Foote. 2004. Buckton, George Bowdler (1818–1905). *ODNB*. OUP. http://doi.org/d4vbmb

Strassner, T. 2015. Professor D. M. P. Mingos FRS. *J. Organomet. Chem.* **792**. 293:1–4. http://doi.org/7f2

Stronach, G. *rev.* K. D. Watson. 2004. Stenhouse, John (1809–1880). *ODNB*. OUP. http://doi.org/d7dm59

Sturdy, S. 2004. Haldane, John Scott (1860–1936). *ODNB*. OUP. http://doi.org/dp2jvm

Sutton, Michael A. 2004. Newlands, John Alexander Reina (1837–1898). *ODNB*. OUP. http://doi.org/ffc5vk

Sutton, Michael A. 2011. A nutritional revolution. *Chem. World*. **8**(11):56–59.

Sutton, L. E. 1951. Samuel Sugden (1892–1950). *Obit. Not. Fells. Roy. Soc.* **7**:492–503. http://doi.org/dmvqhv

Sweet, William and Richard Feist (eds.). 2007. *Religion and the Challenges of Science*. Aldershot: Ashgate

Taylor, Hugh Stott and Eric K. Rideal. 1919. *Catalysis in Theory and Practice*. London: Macmillan

Thompson, Harold. 1973. Cyril Norman Hinshelwood, 1897–1967. *Biog. Mems. Fells. Roy. Soc.* **19**:374–431. http://doi.org/brcz6q

Thompson, Michael. 1987. Appreciation of Theobald. *Anal. Proc.* **24**:135. http://doi.org/b8m8mp

Thomson, John M. 1917. David Howard. *J. Chem. Soc., Trans.* **111**:342–347. http://doi.org/dtwf4v

Thomson, Thomas. 1830. *The History of Chemistry*. London: Henry Colburn and Richard Bentley

Thorpe, J. F. 1928. Francis Robert Japp, 1848–1925. *Proc. R. Soc.* A. **118**:iii–vi. http://doi.org/dj6dqh

Thorpe, J. F. 1929. Presidential address: Cooperation in Science and Industry. *J. Chem. Soc., Trans.* 834–852. http://doi.org/dpwm5v

Thorpe, J. F. 1931. Presidential address: Part 1. A retrospect. Part II. The outcome of some recent research work. *J. Chem. Soc.* 1002–1023. http://doi.org/dxr8rz

Thorpe, J. F. 1935. Herbert Brereton Baker, 1862–1935. *Obit. Notes Fells. Roy. Soc.* **4**:522–526. http://doi.org/dq8xr6

Thorpe, J. F., M. A. Whiteley, H. ter Meulen and J. Heslinga. 1926. *A Student's Manual of Organic Chemical Analysis: Qualitative and Quantitative.* London: Longmans, Green

Thorpe, J. F., R. Robinson and A. J. Greenaway. 1932. *The Life and Work of Professor William Henry Perkin.* Chem. Soc. London

Thorpe, T. E. 1874. *A Manual of Inorganic Chemistry* 2 vols. London: W. Collins and Co

Thorpe, T. E. 1875. Researches upon the specific volumes of liquids. *Proc. R. Soc.* **24**:283–298. http://doi.org/b8jtzd

Thorpe, T. E. 1876. On phosphorus pentafluoride. *Proc. R. Soc.* **25**:122–123. http://doi.org/dtz7d5

Thorpe, T. E., (ed.). 1878. Coal, its history and uses. London: Macmillan

Thorpe, T. E. 1894. On the relation between the viscosity (internal friction) of liquids and their chemical nature. *Proc. R. Soc.* **55**:148–159. http://doi.org/d5dsgh

Thorpe, T. E. 1896. *Humphry Davy: Poet and Philosopher.* London: Cassell and Co

Thorpe, T. E. 1902. *Essays in Historical Chemistry.* London: Macmillan

Thorpe, T. E. 1905. *A yachtsman's guide to the Dutch waterways.* London: Edward Stanford

Thorpe, T. E. 1906. *Joseph Priestley.* London: Dent

Thorpe, T. E. 1909. *History of Chemistry.* London: Watts

Thorpe, T. E. 1909b. Note on the detection of white or ordinary phosphorus in the igniting composition of lucifer matches. *J. Chem. Soc. Trans.* **95**:440–441. http://doi.org/dxdjwb

Thorpe, T. E. 1924. Herbert McLeod, 1841–1923. *Proc. R. Soc.* **105**:10–11. http://doi.org/dpjd7h

Thorpe, T. E. et. al. 1941–1956. *Thorpe's Dictionary of Applied Chemistry,* 12 vols. London: Longmans Green and Co

Thorpe, T. E and A. P. Laurie. 1887. On the atomic weight of gold. *J. Chem. Soc., Trans.* **51**:565–576. http://doi.org/cs87qn

Thorpe, T. E and J. W. Rodger. 1889. On thiophosphoryl fluoride. *J. Chem. Soc., Trans.* **55**:306–323. http://doi.org/d74ntb

Thorpe, T. E. 1894. On the relation between the viscosity (internal friction) of liquids and their chemical nature, Bakerian Lecture. *Proc. R. Soc.* **55**: 148–159. http://doi.org/d5dsgh

Thorpe, T. E and F. J. Hambly. 1889. The vapour density of hydrogen fluoride. *J. Chem. Soc., Trans.* **55**:163–184. http://doi.org/fgvk23

Thorpe, T. E and A. E. Tutton. 1890. Phosphorous Oxide, Part 1. *J. Chem. Soc., Trans.* **57**:545–573. http://doi.org/d8f3wb

Tilden, W. A. 1874. On aqua regia and the nitrosyl chlorides. *J. Chem. Soc., Trans.* **27**:630–636. http://doi.org/cxvs56

Tilden, W. A. 1875. On the action of nitrosyl chloride on organic bodies; part II, On turpentine oil. *J. Chem. Soc., Trans.* **28**:514–518. http://doi.org/csn5pn

Tilden, W. A. 1876. *Introduction to chemical philosophy: The principles of theoretical and systematic chemistry.* London: Longman, Green

Tilden, W. A. 1880. *Practical Chemistry: The principles of chemical analysis.* London: Longmans

Tilden, W. A. 1884. On the decomposition of terpenes by heat. *J. Chem. Soc., Trans.* **45**:410–420. http://doi.org/dk9ptb

Tilden, W. A. 1888. The constitution of the terpenes and of benzene. *J. Chem. Soc., Trans.* **53**:879–888. http://doi.org/bq2m75

Tilden, W. A., ed. 1889. *Watts' Manual of chemistry, theoretical and practical, based on Fownes Manual* 2, vols. 2nd ed. London: J. Churchill

Tilden, W. A. 1892. Note on the spontaneous conversion of isoprene into caoutchouc. *Proc. Birmingham Phil. Soc.* 183.

Tilden, W. A. 1904. Presidential Address. *J. Chem. Soc.* **85**:493–505, http://doi.org/ftc5hv

Tilden, W. A. 1909. The Mendeléef Memorial Lecture. *J. Chem. Soc., Trans.* **95**:2077–2105. http://doi.org/dzj3x9

Tilden, W. A. 1910. *The elements: Speculation as to their nature and origin.* 4th edition. London: Harper and Bros

Tilden, W. A. 1918. Sir William Ramsay KCB, FRS: *Memorials of his life and work.* London: Macmillan

Tilden, W. A. 1919. Sir Alexander Pedler FRS. *J. Chem. Soc., Trans.* **115**:436–438. http://doi.org/fnmwts

Tilden, W. A. 1920. Charles Edward Groves. *J. Chem. Soc., Trans.* **117**:464–466. http://doi.org/dd832t

Tilden, W. A. *rev.* S. Glasstone. 1936. *Chemical discovery and invention in the twentieth century.* London: Routledge

Tilden, W. A. 1921. *Famous Chemists: The men and their works.* London. George Routledge and Sons

Tilden, W. A and W. A. Shenstone. 1877. Isomeric nitrosoterpenes. *J. Chem. Soc., Trans.* **31**:554–561. http://doi.org/c4xjxz

Tilden, W. A and M. O. Forster. 1895. Action of nitrosyl chlorides on amides. *J. Chem. Soc., Trans.* **67**:489–493. http://doi.org/c7qrnn

Tilden, W. A and J. Perry. 1900. The specific heats of metals and the relation of specific heat to atomic weight. Bakerian Lecture. *Philos. Trans. R. Soc., A* **194**:233–255. http://doi.org/fwv3ks

Tilden, W. A and H. Burrows. 1902. The constitution of limettin. *J. Chem. Soc., Trans.* **81**:508–512. http://doi.org/fj8gzr

Tilley, R. D and J. M. Thomas. 1992. John Stuart Anderson, 1908–1990. *Chem. Br.* **28**:812.

Tizard, H. T. *rev.* 2004. Miers, Sir Henry Alexander, 1858–1942. *ODNB.* OUP. http://doi.org/cjhsdd

Todd, Lord and J. W. Cornforth. 1976. Robert Robinson 1886–1975. *Biog. Mems. Fells. Roy. Soc.* **22**: 414–527. http://doi.org/bq7rqj

Trail, Thomas Stewart. 1849. Memoir of Dr. Thomas Charles Hope, late professor of chemistry in the University of Edinburgh. *Trans. Roy. Soc. Edinburgh.* **16**:419–434.

Travis, Anthony S. 2004. Perkin, Sir William Henry (1838–1907). *ODNB.* OUP. http://doi.org/fdj5x3

Travis, Anthony S. 2008. Mansfield, Charles Blachford. *New DSB.* **5**:18–20. (N.Y: Scribner)

Trindade, T, P. O'Brien and N. L. Pickett. 2001. Nanocrystalline semiconductors: synthesis, properties and perspectives. *Chem. Materials* **13**:3843–358. http://doi.org/br5jx7

Turner, G. L'E (ed.). 1976. *The patronage of science in the nineteenth century.* Leiden:Kluwer

Tutton, A. E. H. 1911. *Crystallography and practical crystal measurement.* London: Macmillan

Ubbelohde, A. R. 1981. Dudley Maurice Newitt, *Biog. Mems. Fell. Roy. Soc.* **27**:365–378. http://doi.org/bn9p99

Ubbelohde, A. R. *rev.* 2004. Newitt, Dudley Maurice (1894–1980). *ODNB.* OUP. http://doi.org/c6r7c5

Usselman, Melvyn C. 2004. Tennant, Smithson (1761–1815). *ODNB.* OUP. http://doi.org/fjpqjx

Usselman, Melvyn C. 2004. Field, Frederick (1826–1885). *ODNB.* OUP. http://doi.org/ch2r5q

Valentin, W. G. 1872. *Introduction to Inorganic Chemistry.* London: Churchill

Valentin, W. G. 1879. *Twenty Lessons in Inorganic Chemistry.* London: Collins

Vilar, R. 2003. Anion-templated synthesis. *Angew. Chem. Int. Ed.* **42**:1460–1477. http://doi.org/bn76rf

Volhard, Jacob and Emil Fischer. 1902. *August Wilhelm von Hofmann: Ein lebensbild.* Berlin: Deutschen chemischen gesellschaft

Walden, Paul. 1954. The Gmelin chemical dynasty. *J. Chem. Educ.* **31**:534–541. http://doi.org/fj3pvn

Ward, E. R. 1975. Eminent Victorian: Charles Mansfield. *Chem. Br.* **115**:297–304.

Ward, E. R. 1984. The death of Charles Blachford Mansfield. *Ambix*, **31**:68–69.

Wardlaw, W. 1941. Sir Gilbert Morgan, 1870–1940. *J. Chem. Soc.*, 689–697. http://doi.org/d6wwhk

Warren, F. L. 1954. Ernest Harold Farmer, 1890–1952. *J. Chem. Soc.* 1654–1659. http://doi.org/bhjkcr

Warington, R. 1896. 'The Foundation of the Chemical Society'. *Jubilee Chem. Soc. Lond.* 115–122.

Watts, Henry. 1890. *A Dictionary of Chemistry and allied branches of other sciences.* London: Longmans, Green

Watson, K. D. 2004. Jones, Sir Ewart Ray Herbert [Tim] (1911–2002). *ODNB.* OUP. http://doi.org/fscbd7

Waymark, J. 2004. Tilden, Philip Armstrong (1887–1956). *ODNB.* OUP. http://doi.org/b6t8m9

Webb, K. R. 1965. Sprengel and the Vacuum Pump. *Chem. Br.* **1**:569–571.

Webb, K. R. *rev.* Anthony S. Travis. 2004. Meldola, Raphael (1849–1915). *ODNB.* OUP. http://doi.org/bvgmg4

Welton, T. 1999. Room-temperature ionic liquids. Solvents for synthesis and catalysis. *Chem. Rev.* **99**(8):2071–2084. http://doi.org/bbwzr9

West, Thomas Summers. 1973. *Analytical Chemistry.* London:Butterworth

West, Thomas Summers. 1985. Gordon Frank Kirkbright, 1938–1984. *Chem. Br.* **21**:274–275.

Wetzel, Walter. 1992. Origins of and education and career opportunities for the profession of 'chemist' in the second half of the nineteenth century in Germany. in (Knight and Kragh, 1998)

Whiffen, D. H and D. H. Hey. 1991. *The Royal Society of Chemistry: The first 150 years.* London: RSC

Whitby, George Stafford. 1960. Looking back over fifty years of rubber science. *Proc. Inst. Rubber Industry.* **7**(5):155–175.

Whitehead, Roger. 2004. Widdowson, Elsie May (1906–2000). *ODNB.* OUP. http://doi.org/bjdkgf

Whiteley, M. A. 1900. The oxime of mesoxamide and some allied compounds. *J. Chem. Soc., Trans.* **77**:1040–1046. http://doi.org/c9xpr2

Whiteley, M. A and H. Mountain. 1909. 1:3-diphenyl-2-thiobarbituric acid and some coloured derivatives. *Proc. Chem. Soc.* **25**:121–123. http://doi.org/c2fs88

Whiteley, M. A and E. H. Usherwood. 1923. Oxime of mesoxamide (isonitrosomalonamide) and some allied compounds. Part III. Ring formation in the tetrasubstituted series. *J. Chem. Soc., Trans.* **123**:1069–1089. http://doi.org/cp5hkx

Whiteley, M. A and G. A. R. Kon. 1940. Sir Jocelyn Thorpe. *The Analyst* **65**:483–484.

Whiting, D. A. 2000. Leslie Crombie. *J. Chem. Soc. Perkin Trans.* 1. 2303–2304. http://doi.org/cdvkk3

Widdowson, D. A. 1988. Arenetricarbonylchromium(0) complexes in organic synthesis. *Philos. Trans. R. Soc.* A **326**:595–610. http://doi.org/cb64km

Wilkinson, G. 1961. Professor H. V. A. Briscoe. *Nature* **192**:604. http://doi.org/d7fsvc

Wilkinson, G. 1974. The long search for stable transition metal alkyls. Nobel Prize lecture. *Science* **185**:109–112. http://doi.org/fg757n

Wilkinson, G. 1975. The iron sandwich, a recollection of the first four months. *J. Organomet. Chem.* **100**:273–278.

Wilkinson, G., M. Rosenblum, M. C. Whiting and R. B. Woodward. 1952. The structure of iron bis-cyclopentadienyl. *J. Am. Chem. Soc.* **74**:2125–2126. http://doi.org/dm8dzq

Williams, C. G. 1860. On isoprene and caoutchine. *Philos. Trans. R. Soc.,* **150**:241–255. http://doi.org/djmgh5

Williams, D. E., A. R. J. Kucernak *et. al.* 1989. Upper bounds on "cold fusion" in electrolytic cells. *Nature* **342**:375–384. http://doi.org/d5mv4g

Williams, Robert J. P., Allan Chapman, and John S. Rowlinson (eds.). 2009. *Chemistry at Oxford: A history from 1600 to 2005.* London: RSC

Williams, S. J. 2009. 'Robert Yvent Stick — a Colourful Character,' (article and interview). *Aust. J. Chem.* **62**:503–509. http://doi.org/bqqb85

Williams, Trevor I. 2004. Muspratt, James (1793–1886). *ODNB.* OUP. http://doi.org/dgksm3

Williams, Trevor I. 2004b. Muspratt, Edmund Knowles (1833–1923). *ODNB.* OUP. http://doi.org/b6whhv

Williams, Trevor I. 2004c. Howard, David (1839–1916). *ODNB.* OUP. http://doi.org/d75vcd

Williams, Trevor I. 2004d. Griess (Johann) Peter (1829–1888). *ODNB*. OUP. http://doi.org/cwbn4v

Williamson, Alexander. 1851. Suggestions for the dynamics of chemistry derived from the theory of etherification. *Proceedings of the Royal Institution* **1**:90–94.

Winter, E. R. S., M. Carlton and H. V. A. Briscoe. 1940. The interchange of heavy oxygen between water and inorganic oxy-anions. *J. Chem. Soc.* 131–38. http://doi.org/bchx39

Wislicenus. J. 1900. Sir Edward Frankland. *Berichte Deutsches Chem. Gesell.* **33**:3847–3874.

Wolfrom, Melville L. 1958. Harold Hibbert (1877–1945). *Biog. Mems. Nat. Acad. Sci.*, 143–180.

Woollins, J. D. 2012. How not to discover a new reagent. The evolution and chemistry of Woollins Reagent. *Synlett.* **23**: 1154–69. http://doi.org/r2s

Wynne, W. P. 1937. H. E. Armstrong FRS. *Nature* **140**:140–142. http://doi.org/djxzkv

Yazawa, M. 2004. Rush, Benjamin (1746–1813). *ODNB*. OUP. http://doi.org/d6tths

Zeise, W. C. 1831. Von der Wirkung zwischen Platinchlorid und Alkohol, und von den dabei entstehenden neuen Substanzen, *Ann. Phys. Chem (Poggendorff).* **21**:497–541. http://doi.org/djptqv

Zimmerman, David. 1996. *Top secret exchange: The Tizard mission and the scientific war*. Montreal: McGill-Queen's Press.

Abbreviations/Acronyms

A	Assistant
ACS	American Chemical Society
AL	Assistant Lecturer
ANU	Australian National University (Canberra)
AP	Assistant Professor
ARC	Agricultural Research Council (later AFRC, Agricultural and Food Research Council)
ARCS	Associate of the Royal College of Science
ARSM	Associate of the Royal School of Mines
AUT	Association of University Teachers
BAAS	British Association for the Advancement of Science
C1	Departmental chemistry building, constructed 1968
C2	Departmental extension to C1
CGLI	City and Guilds of London Institute for the Advancement of Technical Education
C&G	City and Guilds College
C&GCTC	City and Guilds Central Technical College
CASSI	CAS (Chemical Abstracts) Source Index
CDN	Chemistry Department News
CHoSTM	Centre for the History of Science, Technology and Medicine
CGLI	City & Guilds London Institute for the Advancement of Technical Education

CNRS	Centre National de la Recherche Scientifique
COSHH	Control of Substances Hazardous to Health
CS	Chemical Society (preceded the RSC)
CTC	Central Technical College
CUP	Cambridge University Press
D	Demonstrator
DIC	Diploma of Imperial College
DNB	Dictionary of National Bigraphy
DSB	Dictionary of Scientific Biography
DSc	Doctor of Science
DSIR	Department of Scientific and Industrial Research (replaced by the SRC in 1965)
DUS	Director of Undergraduate Studies
EP	Emeritus Professor
EPSRC	Engineering and Physical Sciences Research Council
ESR	Electron Spin Resonance (sometimes called EPR, electron paramagnetic resonance)
ETH	Eidgenössische Technische Hochschule (Zürich)
HSC	Higher School Certificate
FAc. Med. Sci.	Fellow of the Academy of Medical Sciences
FIC	Fellow of Imperial College
FRS	Fellow of the Royal Society
FRSE	Fellow of the Royal Society of Edinburgh
FTE	Full Time Equivalent
GCE	General Certificate of Education
HEFCE	Higher Education Funding Council for England
HMSO	Her Majesty's Stationery Office
HSC	Higher School Certificate
HSE	Health and Safety Executive
IC	Imperial College
ICL	Imperial College London
ICP	Imperial College Press
ICST	Imperial College of Science and Technology (used until 1988)
ICSTM	Imperial College of Science and Technology and Medicine (used 1988–2007)

ICWA	Imperial College Womens' Association
JCS	Journal of the Chemical Society
KCL	King's College London
KIC	Knowledge and Innovation Community
LCC	London County Council (now called Greater London Authority, GLA)
Lt.	Lieutenant
MIT	Massachusetts Institute of Technology, Cambridge, Massachusetts
MRC	Medical Research Council
MSci	Master of Science
MSF	Manufacturing Science and Finance Union
NHS	National Health Service
NL	Nobel Laureate
NMR	Nuclear Magnetic Resonance
NPL	National Physical Laboratory, Teddington
NSS	Normal School of Science
ODNB	New Oxford Dictionary of National Biography
OTC	Officers Training Corps
OU	The Open University
OUP	Oxford University Press
P	Professor
PDRA	Postdoctoral Research Assistant
QMC	Queen Mary College (now QMUL)
QMUL	Queen Mary University of London
R	Reader
RA	Research Assistant
RAE	Research Assessment Exercise (later REF)
RAMCM	Royal Army Medical College at Millbank
RCA	Royal College of Art
RCC	Royal College of Chemistry
RCM	Royal College of Music
RCS	Royal College of Science
RCSA	Royal College of Science Association
REF	Research Excellence Framework (replaced the RAE in 2007)

RF	Research Fellow
RI	Royal Institution
RIC	Royal Institute of Chemistry
RIMAC	Research Institute for Medicine and Chemistry
RS	Royal Society
RSC	Royal Society of Chemistry
RSM	Royal School of Mines
RSURF	Royal Society University Research Fellow
SCI	Society of Chemical Industry
SERC	Science and Engineering Research Council
SML	Science Museum Library
SOE	Special Operations Executive
SRC	Science Research Council (later,1981, SERC and then, 1994, EPSRC)
SRF	Senior Research Fellow
St	Student
SWAN	Scientific Women's Academic Network
THES	Times Higher Educational Supplement
UCL	University College London
UCLH	University College Hospital
UFC	Universities Funding Council (replaced the UGC; wound up 1992)
UGC	University Grants Committee
UKAEA	UK Atomic Energy Authority
ULIRS	University of London Intercollegiate Research Service
UMIST	University of Manchester Institute of Science and Technology
V&A	Victoria and Albert Museum, South Kensington
VL	Visiting Lecturer
VP	Visiting Professor
WW1	First World War
WW2	Second World War

Illustration Credits

We would like to thank all those who gave permission for use of the illustrations listed below, particularly to Anne Barrett and her staff at IC archives. While every attempt has been made to obtain copyright permission for the others, there are a very few photographs for which permission could not be traced.

Illus. 1–7.   IC archives
Illus. 8.   Elizabeth Rogers
Illus. 9.   IC archives
Illus. 10.   *Proc. Roy. Inst.*
Illus. 11.   IC archives
Illus. 12.   IC archives; from *Science and Art* articles on the RCS, 1893–1894
Illus. 13.   IC archives
Illus. 14.   *RCS Magazine*, 1894
Illus. 15.   *The Chemical World*, 1912
Illus. 16–19.   Edward Cahen album, RCS, IC archives
Illus. 20.   IC archives
Illus. 21–23.   IC archives
Illus. 24.   'Grey Moon' (Douglas Spencer), *Phoenix*, 1923
Illus. 25.   IC archives
Illus. 26.   (Leffek, 1996)
Illus. 27.   'Grey Moon' (Douglas Spencer), *Phoenix*, 1925
Illus. 28.   Still from ICI film, 1932; copy in chemistry department (Henry Rzepa)
Illus. 29.   P. C. Bull, IC archives

Illus. 30–32.	IC archives
Illus. 33.	IC archives, Geoffrey Wilkinson papers
Illus. 34–37.	IC archives
Illus. 38.	Malcolm Green
Illus. 39.	IC archives
Illus. 40.	IC website
Illus. 41–44.	IC archives
Illus. 45.	Royal Society of Chemistry and Royal Mail
Illus. 46.	Richard Willson cartoon owned by chemistry department
Illus. 47.	IC archives
Illus. 48.	IC archives
Illus. 49.	Andy Bell, 1990
Illus. 50.	Royal Society of Chemistry
Illus. 51.	Andy Bell, 1985
Illus. 52.	IC archives
Illus. 53.	Royal Society of Chemistry, Steve Ramsey
Illus. 54.	IC archives
Illus. 55.	Bill Griffith, 2015
Illus. 56–58.	IC website
Illus. 59.	Hannah Gay, 2015
Illus. 60.	IC archives
Illus. 61.	IC archives

Illustrations

Top left: Illus. 1. A. Wilhelm Hofmann, founding professor at the RCC, 1845–1865.
Top right: Illus. 2. Sir Edward Frankland, professor at the RCC, and at the Normal School, 1865–1885.
Bottom: Illus. 3. Lord Lyon Playfair, chemist to the Geological Survey, 1845–1851; professor of practical chemistry at the Government (later Royal) School of Mines, 1851–1853.

Left: Illus. 4. The Royal College of Chemistry at 299 Oxford Street, 1857.
Right: Illus. 5. The Museum of Practical Geology, Jermyn Street, 1896. Earlier the building also housed the Royal School of Mines. The two buildings no longer exist.

Left: Illus. 6. William Crookes in 1850, aged 18 when he was Hofmann's student and assistant.
Right: Illus. 7. William Perkin; a 'selfie' taken in 1852 when he was 16 years old and Hofmann's student. Crookes and Perkin were both later elected FRS and received knighthoods. Crookes was elected President of the Royal Society, 1913–1915.

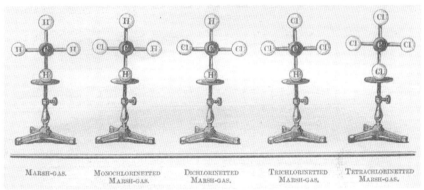

| MARSH-GAS. | MONOCHLORINETTED MARSH-GAS. | DICHLORINETTED MARSH-GAS. | TRICHLORINETTED MARSH-GAS. | TETRACHLORINETTED MARSH-GAS. |

Top left: Illus. 8. Herbert McLeod FRS, student at the RCC, teaching assistant to Hofmann, 1860–1865, and to Frankland, 1865–1870. Photo taken in 1881, when McLeod was professor of chemistry at the Royal Indian Engineering College at Cooper's Hill, near Egham.

Top right: Illus. 9. Sir Frederick Augustus Abel FRS, one of Hofmann's first students in 1845. After a major career in ordnance at the Royal Arsenal, Woolwich, he was appointed the first director of the Imperial Institute in South Kensington in 1893.

Bottom: Illus. 10. McLeod helped Hofmann to design these molecular models (based on drawings by Alexander Crum Brown). McLeod built the models together with the trades- man, James Blakeman (who also made the retort-type stands). The atoms were represented by coloured croquet balls (see Chapter Three), and the models were first shown by Hofmann at a Friday Evening Discourse at the Royal Institution in 1865 (illustration from *Proc. Roy. Inst.* 4 (1865)). Stereochemical ideas were still in the future.

Top: Illus. 11. The Royal College of Science building which housed the chemistry department on its lower two floors from 1873–1906. This photo was taken in 1896, from the Royal Horticultural Society Gardens, before the Science and Geology Museums were built. The building was renamed the Huxley Building in 1906 and, in 1978, was taken over by the Victoria and Albert Museum and named the Henry Cole Wing. Until 1975 chemistry students took mathematics classes in this building.
Bottom: Illus. 12. Sir Edward Thorpe FRS, in his office. This photograph was taken during Thorpe's first period as head of department, 1885–1894.

Top left: Illus. 13. Sir Edward Thorpe FRS, professor of chemistry. This photograph was taken during his second term as head of department, 1909–1912.

Top right: Illus. 14. Sir William Tilden FRS, professor of chemistry and head of department, 1894–1909.

Bottom: Illus. 15. A section of the main analytical laboratory on the ground floor of the 1906 RCS building. Photo taken in 1912.

Top: Illus. 16. Sir Gilbert Morgan FRS, in 1906.
Bottom: Illus. 17. Sir Martin Forster FRS, in 1906. Both were assistant professors in the first decade of the 20th century.

Top left: Illus. 18. Martha Whiteley in 1907, when she was a demonstrator in organic chemistry.

Top right: Illus. 19. Frances Micklethwait in 1907, when she was an assistant to Gilbert Morgan.

Bottom: Illus. 20. Henry Armstrong FRS in 1909, close to retirement from his department at the City and Guilds Technical College. The photo was taken when he was on a holiday in Canada. Armstrong became an Emeritus professor in the RCS department in 1913.

 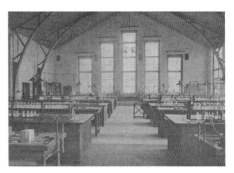

Top left: Illus. 21. Herbert Brereton Baker FRS, professor of chemistry and head of department, 1912–1932; photograph taken in 1914.

Top right: Illus. 22. The undergraduate organic chemistry laboratory, 1912.

Bottom: Illus. 23. Sir Jocelyn Thorpe FRS, professor of organic chemistry, 1914–1938; seen here with his favourite piece of apparatus, the test tube. Smoking in laboratories was commonplace until new safety regulations were brought in during the 1970s.

Should all the Phase Rule be forgot
And never brought to mind
Then the ballads o' this Scot
Will bring back Auld lang Syne.

Top left: Illus. 24. Cartoon of James Philip, professor of physical chemistry, 1909–1941, by 'Grey Moon' (Douglas Spencer), Phoenix, 1923. Philip was known for his songs and ballads, and for entertaining at many departmental and college social functions.

Top right: Illus. 25. The physical chemistry laboratory, 1912 (now part of the NMR Suite).

Bottom: Illus. 26. From left, Douglas Spencer, Hilda Usherwood Ingold, and Christopher Ingold, ca. 1923.

Illus. 27. Cartoon by 'Grey Moon' (Douglas Spencer), Phoenix, 1925. John Murgatroyd, Harry Riley, Douglas Spencer, James Sugden, Herbert Brereton Baker, and Jocelyn Thorpe.

Top: Illus. 28. Sir Patrick Linstead FRS, when a young lecturer in the department. The picture is a frame taken from an early colour film made in 1932 by ICI about its Monastral Pigments (see Chapter Six for Linstead's role in making these pigments).

Bottom: Illus. 29. Sir Ian Heilbron FRS, professor of organic chemistry, 1938–1949. This photo is said to have been taken by P. C. Bull in the 1940s. Bull, a lecturer in the department, was a serious photographer.

Illus. 30–31. Some staff members in 1933.
Top from left: H. J. Emeléus, M. Carlton, P. C. Bull. R. P. Linstead, G. A. R. Kon, H. V. A. Briscoe, J. C. Philip and H. T. Tizard.
Bottom from left: J. F. Thorpe, M. A. Whiteley, E. H. Farmer and A. King.

Illus. 32. IC Home Guard on sentry duty outside Buckingham Palace during WW2. On the right is Charles Benjamin Alcock, a chemistry undergraduate, 1942–44, and later a professor in the IC metallurgy department. In 1964 he became head of the metallurgy and materials department at the University of Toronto.

Top: Illus. 33. Geoffrey Wilkinson is seen here between Leo Yaffe on the left, and Alan Nunn May on the right. Wilkinson was a postgraduate student when he was seconded to the Tube Alloys project in 1943. Yaffe was later professor of chemistry at McGill University. Nunn May, a former Cambridge student and a physics lecturer at King's College, London, was convicted of espionage in 1946. This photo was taken on Mount Royal, Montreal, in the Autumn of 1943.

Bottom left: Illus. 34. Vincent Briscoe, professor of inorganic chemistry, 1932–1954.

Bottom right: Illus. 35. Some members of the Bockris electrochemistry group in 1947. From left, Roger Parsons, John O'Mara Bockris, John Herringshaw, and Brian Conway. Parsons and Conway were both later FRS.

Top: Illus. 36. The RCS building in 1957. The view is from the chemistry side, the physics department is barely visible on the right.
Bottom: Illus. 37. Students working in what was then named the Hofmann laboratory (now Harwood) in 1962.

Top left: Illus. 38. Dennis Evans FRS, professor of chemistry, 1981–1990, seen here in Vigeland Park, Oslo, in 1962. (Photo by Malcolm Green.)

Top right: Illus. 39. Margaret Goodgame, working at an infrared spectrometer in the early 1960s.

Bottom: Illus. 40. RCS1, photo taken in 2006.

Illus. 41 and 42. Segments from collegevleaving picture, 1965–1966.
Top: from left, J. F. Gibson, G. Wilkinson, D. M. L. Goodgame, M. Goodgame,
M. H. George, B. Atkinson, M. Spiro, F. C. Tompkins, and R. M. Barrer.
Bottom: from left, D. H. R. Barton, C. N. Hinshelwood, T. S. West, E. Rideal,
D. O. Hayward, J. L. Wood, J. Walkley, E. R. Roberts, and B. Fleet.

Illus. 43. On the left Frederick Tompkins, professor of physical chemistry, receiving a
farewell gift from Geoffrey Wilkinson on his retirement in 1977. Tompkins was a member
of staff for 30 years, having been appointed as a Reader in 1947.

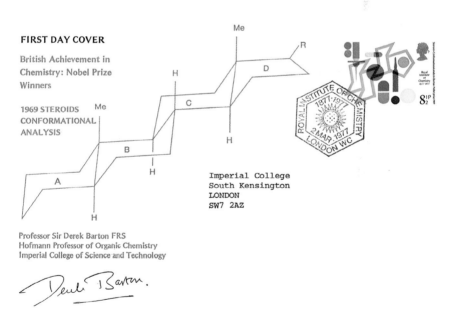

Top: Illus. 44. Sir Derek Barton FRS and Nobel Laureate, professor of organic chemistry, 1957–1978. Photograph taken in the Whiffen Laboratory ca. 1970.
Bottom: Illus. 45. First day cover (2 March, 1977) of a postage stamp in a series acknowledging 'British Achievement in Chemistry.' This stamp recognised Barton's contribution to conformational analysis and his Nobel Prize.

Left: Illus. 46. Cartoon of Geoffrey Wilkinson, by Richard Willson.
Right: Illus. 47. Sir Geoffrey Wilkinson FRS and Nobel Laureate, professor of inorganic chemistry, 1956–1988; head of department, 1976–1988. Photo taken in the early 1990s, when he was an Emeritus professor.

Bottom left: Illus. 48. Richard Barrer FRS, professor of physical chemistry, 1954–1977, and head of department, 1955–1976.
Bottom right: Illus. 49. John Albery FRS, professor of physical chemistry, 1978–1989, head of department, 1988–1989. Photograph taken in Oxford in 1990, on the occasion of a cricket match between the IC chemistry postgraduates XI, and a team from University College, Oxford.

Top: Illus. 50. Charles Rees FRS, Hofmann professor of organic chemistry, 1978–1993, wearing a bow tie and shirt dyed in Perkin's mauve.

Bottom: Illus. 51. Steven Ley FRS, professor of organic chemistry, 1983–1992, and head of department, 1989–1992. He is seen here celebrating his 40th birthday in 1985. Visible faces from left: Willie Motherwell, Don Craig, Stephen de Lazlo, Andy Dengel, Steve Ley, Jerry Edmunds, Howie Broughton, and in front, Andy Merritt.

Top: Illus. 52. Tony Barrett FRS, Glaxo professor of organic chemistry, 1993 to the present; since 1999 also the Sir Derek Barton chair of synthesis. He is seen sitting in his office, in front of a desk that once belonged to Sir Jocelyn Thorpe.

Bottom: Illus. 53. David Phillips, FRS, CBE professor of physical chemistry, 1989–2006, and head of department, 1992–2002. He is seen here with his 'glass baby,' used to illustrate his popular public lectures on photodynamic therapy.

Top: Illus. 54. The Advanced Analytical Laboratory, before refurbishment.
Bottom: Illus. 55. The Barton Laboratory, which now occupies the old AAL space.

Top: Illus 56. Richard Templer, professor of biophysical chemistry, 2002-, head of department, 2002–07, and Hofmann professor, 2006–. He is seen here loading a sample into an X-ray chamber.

Middle: Illus 57. Tom Welton, professor of Sustainable Chemistry 2004–, head of department, 2000–2014; seen here with a student in a publicity photograph.

Bottom: Illus 58. Alan Armstrong, former student in the department, professor of organic chemistry, 2004–, and head of department, 2014–; with students in another publicity photograph.

Top: Illus. 59. The chemistry department, C1 and C2, November 2015.
Bottom: Illus. 60. Architect's impression of the molecular sciences hub, at Imperial's White City campus. Departmental research is expected to move into the building in 2017.

Illus. 61. Chemistry department leaving photograph taken in 2000.

Front row from left: A. Garrido Montalban, J. M. Seddon, J. R. Durrant, D. M. L. Goodgame, D. A. Widdowson, A. D. Miller, V. C. Gibson, D. Phillips, A. G. M. Barrett, A. Kucernak, D. Craig, S. P. Marsden, H. Braunschweig, E. H.Smith, and D. J. Otway.

Second row from left: N. Quirke, V. Viney, D. Pappoe, J. Gale, C. Oriel, D. Klug, D. Nicholson, R. Templer, J. H. G. Steinke, P. D. Likiss, N. Long, C. W. Rees, W. P. Griffith, A. Armstrong, F. Bresme, G. Britovsek, D. C. Braddock, H. S. Rzepa, R. J. Leatherbarrow, and G. B. Young.

Third row: P. Sulsh, sixth from left; R. V. Law, seventh from left.

Second row from top: T. Welton, third from left, C. Sausman, seventh from left, and behind him, E. Poggioli.

Name Index

References are to book page numbers; endnotes are indicated by an 'n' between the page number and the endnote number. A bold typeface normally indicates a major entry, often biographical.

A

Abel, Edward William (Eddie), 258, **288n82**–83
  and IC explosion, 258, 289n84, 380n11
Abel, Frederick Augustus, 37, 439–441
  biog. notes, 28, 30–31, **61n6,** 67n55, 72n106, 73n111
  cordite, 61n6
  memoir, 16, 20n11
  research, 48–49, 61n6, 66n41, 72n106
Abel, John Sangster, 30, 63n19
Abney, William de Wiveleslie, 109n20, 109n22
Acland, Arthur H. D., 202n133
Adams, Michael James, 447
Adlington, Robert M., 284n65
Albert, Adrien, 350n88

Albert (Prince Albert), 13, 19n3, 21n26–27, 37n56
Albery, W. John, 447
  as head of dept., 358–359
  biog. notes & research, 309, 314, 327–328, **354n111**, 412
Alder, John Frederick (Fred), 320, 346n67, 447
Aldrich, Dennis, 321
Alexander, Peter, 226, **239n84**, 277n15
Allchin, Alfred, 83
Allmand, Arthur, 173, 198n91
Allen, Robert D., 447
Andersen, Richard Allen, 343, 447
Anderson, James C. (Jim), 362
Anderson, John, 236n57
Anderson, John (of Anderson College), 432
Anderson, John Stuart, 447

543

biog. notes, 167–169, **196n71, 80**, 341n36, 405, 417n21
research, 169–170, 196n76, 78
textbook with Emeléus, 168–169, **195n68**, 314
Andrews, Thomas, 19n8
Ansell, George Frederick, 30, 63n21
Appleton, Edward, 236n57,60
Archer, Bernard Lewis, 281n39, 447
Archer, Mary, 236n58, 353n110
Armstrong, Alan, 361, 369, **392n72**, 447
Armstrong, E. Frankland (Frank), 22n28, 82, **110n24**, 230n11
Armstrong, Henry Edward, 439, 441, 447
  and the Chemical Society, 97, 102, 118n76,
  biog. notes, 92–95, 113n43, **119n81**, 82, 119n87–90, 126n141
  closure of C&GCTC dept., 87, 99, 102
  his department at C&GCTC, 92–98, 120n94
  memorial lecture, 60n2
  on teaching and examinations, 98, 105, 120n92–93, 124n120, 200n122
  personality & interests, 92, 97, 119n83, 402–403
  research, 93–95, 105, 30n41, 121n97, 122n105, 123n110, 114–115, 146n6
Arnold, John, 393n75
Arrhenius, Svante, 87, 97, 195n64, 403, 405
Arrol, William, 239n78
Ash, Eric Albert, 310, 338n21, 357, 362, **378n2**, 380n7

Ash, Richard, 265, 295n113–114, 359, 447
Ashby, Eric, 203n152
Asquith, Herbert H., 134
Aston, Francis William, 160
Atkinson, Bernard, 447
  assistant director, 306, 332, 336n12
  biog. notes, 232n18, 191n35, 266, 268, 274, **336n12**
  dept. of chemistry history 1960–1989, 189n21
  planning, 274, 301n149
  research, 326
Attfield, John, 83
Austen, W. C. Roberts, 128n155
Avery, John, 447
  biog. notes, 287n78, 291n92, 301n145, 318, **345n57**
  research, 318, 345n58
Ayrton, Hertha, 152n53
Ayrton William, 152n53

B

Back, Thomas George, 447
Baeyer, Adolf von, 43, 73n114, 121n97
Baghurst, David, 365, 387n43, 447
Bailey, Alan, 381n15
Bailey, Neil, 294n102
Baker, Herbert Brereton, 448
  biog. notes, 131–132, **145n1**, 155, 197n84, 203n149, 241
  research, 131, 164, 166–167, 145n2–3, 146n4, 190n31, 190n43, 194n61, 397n105
  WW1-related work, 133–136, 147n11, 13, 149n23, 27, 151n44, 152n51, 53, 218, 408

head of dept. & inorganic section, 106, 160–171, 186n1, 188n20, 189n26, 190n27–28

Baker, John William, 141, 180, 202n132, 448

Baker, Muriel, 132, 136, 146n5, 149n27

Baldwin, Jack E., 254, **284n65**, 448

Balfour, Arthur, 157, 188n12

Baly, Edward Charles Cyril, 230n9

Barclay, Alexander, 137, 150n30

Baring, William Bingham (Lord Ashburton), 11–12

Barlow, Alan, 300n143

Barlow, William, 94, 96, **121n99**

Barnard, John Allan, 448

Barnett, Robert E., 111n29

Barrer, Richard Maling
  as head of dept, 243, 264, 266, 47n142, 306–307, 310, 336n13, 337n18, 20
  barrerite mineral, 265
  biog. notes, 243, 263–264, **295n105**
  expansion of physical chemistry, 269, 359
  research, 263–267, 295n107, 295n115–116, 404

Barrett, Anthony G. M. (Tony), 448
  and departmental structure, 375–376, 396n98
  biog. notes, 323–325, 328, 359, 362, 383n27, **384n29**, 394n83
  early research, 324, 328, 348n78, 350n86–87
  industry-related research, 362–363, 384n29, 395n94
  research, 7, 17, 362, 382n20, **384n29,** 392n94, 405

Barrett, William Fletcher, 66n36

Barrie, James Alexander (Jim), 265, 295n108, 353n104, 359, 448

Barron, Andrew Ross, 317, 343n48

Barrow, Richard Frank, 448

Barry, John Wolfe, 88, 115n54

Barton, Derek Harold Richard, 448
  at CNRS, Gif-sur-Yvette 310, 325, 339n27–28
  at Glasgow and Harvard, 243, 245–247, 276n8
  Barton departmental prize and chair, 322
  biog. notes, 243, 245, 252, 276n8, **276n12**, 278n23, 279n19, 283n53, 286n72, 310, 320–324, 339n28, 396n104
  Briscoe as mentor, 243–246, 276n13, 278n26–27
  during WW2, 216, 234n35
  lectureship in physical and inorganic chemistry, 245, 278n22
  memoir on gap jumping, 7, 346n69
  Nobel Prize, 312–313, 340n33, 341n36
  relations with Heilbron 244, 276n14, 277n17
  research, 244, 252–255, 277n15, 17, 21, 285n67–68, 71, 320–326, 347n71, 348n78, 349n81, 405
  structure and conformational analysis, 253–254, 284n62, 312–313, 340n33, 35, 356n117
  student years, 244, 247–248
  work at RIMAC, 255, 321–322

Bassett, David, 326–327, **352n102**, 359, 448

Battersby, Alan R., 285n68

Beale, William Phipson, 94, 121n99

Beardwood, Peter, 345n60
Beckwith, Athelstan L. J., 254, 448
Beesley, R. M., 178, 201n128
Beilby, George, 135, 150n35
Bell, Ronald Percy, 353n109,
354n111
Benedetti-Pichler, A. A., 239n79
Bennett, Martin A., 261, 288n82,
292n97
Bennett, Michael, 294n102
Berger, Capel, 77n155
Berzelius, Jöns Jacob, 9, 50, 406,
422–425, 426n3, 428n18, 432
Bevan, W. H. (Major), 212
Billimoria, Jimmy Daddy, 448
Binder, John Herman, 448
Bjerrum, Jannik, 287n78
Black, Joseph, 432, 435n5
Blackett, Patrick M. S., 417n16
Blackman, V. H., 185
Bleibtreu, Herman, 17, 28, 48
Blow, David, 326, 352n97
Bloxam, Charles Loudon,
  biog. notes, 28, 30, 61n6, **63n20**,
  433, 436n15, 439
  diary and papers at KCL, 16, 33,
  66n36, 67n58
Blunt, Anthony, 34n39
Blyth, John, 28
Boar, Robin, 321
Bochmann, Manfred, 317
Bockris, Bernhardt Patrick (John)
  O'Mara, 448
  biog. notes, 226, 239n83, 85,
  268–269, **299n128**–130,
  299n134
  research, 227, 268, 299n132, 404
Boer, Jan Hendrik de, 215, 233n30
Boerhaave, Herman, 431, 435n3

Bone, William, 104, 127n150,
  128n151, 142, 184, 185n81, 448
Bopp, August, 24n56
Borland, Hugh Alexander Millar, 448
Boston, Bill & Ivy, 210
Boswell, Percy, 143, 191n37
Bottinger, Henry, 65n30
Bousfield, William Robert, 123n111
Bowler-Reed, John, 226, 239n83
Bowman, J. E., 436n15
Boyle, Mary, 89, 411
Boyle, Robert, 434, 438
Boys, Samuel Francis (Frank), 164,
  192n45
  S.F.Boys–Rahman RSC award
  (RSC), 446
Braddock, David Christopher (Chris),
  368, 390n68, 448
Bradley, John Stuart, 316, 342n45,
  448
Brady, Oscar Lisle, 126n143, 149n25,
  160, 448
Bragg, W. Lawrence, 123n112,
  354n113
Brame, John Samuel Strafford,
  111n29, 448
Bramley, Arthur, 102, 126n142, 172,
  448
Brande, William Thomas, 12
Braude, Ernest, A. R., 242–243,
  250–252, **275n6**, 276n7, 281n41,
  448
Brazier, James Smith, 30, 63n19
Bresme, Fernando, 369, 392n74,
  448
Briscoe, Henry (Vincent) Aird
  biog. notes, 103, 116n62,
  159, 207–208, **229n1**–2, 242,
  448

Briscoe departmental prize & lab., 250, 371, 418n24

departmental reorganisation, 270–271

head of dept., 207–210, 241

mentorship of Barton and Wilkinson, 243–249, 276n13, 412

research 135, 164, 167–168, 194n59, 197n84, 229n3, 255

WW1-related work, 143–144, 152n52

WW2-related work, 211–214, 215–223, 233n30, 234n35, 408

Britovsek, George, 369, 387n47, 392n74

Britton, Hubert, 173, 198n91

Brock, William H., 420, 423, 426n4, 428n18

Brockway, Lawrence O., 170, 196n76

Brodie, Benjamin Collins, 29, 434

Brønsted, Johannes Nicolaus, 96, 354n111

Brough, John Cargill, 35, 66n44

Brown, Adrian, 32, **64n29,** 120n95

Brown, Frederick Douglas, 33

Brown, Horace Tabberer, 33, 65n31

Brown, James Campbell, 36, 66n45

Brown, Leslie Norman, 448

Browning, John, 29, 62n12, 449

Bruce, David, 138

Brunton, Thomas Lauder, 80, 108n14

Bubb, William Arthur (Bill), 347n73

Buckland, William, 12, 19n6,8, **20n18**

Buckton, George, 29, 41, **62n13,** 73n107

Buff, H. L., 24n56

Buff, H. R., 24n56

Buff, J. Heinrich, 17

Bull, Philip Cecil, 449
  biog. notes, 159, 166, 182–183, **189n22,** 193n50, 203n149, 210

Bullock, John Lloyd, 11, 22n40, 60n4
  and founding of RCC, 11–12, 21n23, 420

Bunberry, Hugh Mills, 208, 230n8

Bunsen, Robert W. E., 10, 20n9, 52, 79, 175

Burgess, Guy, 234n39

Burroughs, William S., 291n94

Burrows, Harry, 115n58, 449

Burton, Ray, 288n82

Burton, William, 111n29

Buston, Harold W., 204n163

Butler, Beatrice, 151n49

Butler, J. A. V., 298n130

C

Cadogan, John Ivan George, 359, 379n3, 387n42, 443, 449
  biog. notes, 282n52, 325, **351n93**

Cahn, Robert, 444

Cahours, Auguste, 29

Callaghan, James, 334n2, 335n7

Camilleri, Patrick, 359n11, 449

Cannizzaro, Stanislao, 73n108, 84, 422

Capsey, Rev. Harold Vincent, 449

Carlton, Margaret, 164, **192n43,** 198n96, 210, 226, 449

Carr, Francis Howard, 120n95

Castleden, Stephen L., 449

Cass, Anthony (Tony), 384n32

Catlow, Richard, 359, 380n11, 449

Cawley, Charles Mills, 205n165

Cecil, Lord Sackville, 45

Chadwick, Edwin, 11

Chadwick, James, 221

Chain, Ernst, 237n64, 273–274, 301n146–147, 404, 415n7

Challis, Brian, 349n84, 359, 449

Chapman, Ernest Theophron, 65n31, 449

Chapman Jones, Henry, 81, 103, **28n109,** 449

Chatt, Joseph, 255, 286n75

Chaudret, Bruno, 316–317

Cheesman, Geoffrey H., 169

Chibnall, Albert, 163, **192n38,** 204n161, 403

Christie, Malcolm G., 151n47

Christou, George, 317, 449

Church, Arthur Herbert, 41, 48, 55, 69n70

Churchill, Winston, 145

Clarendon, Earl of, 14, 22n36

Clark, Cecil Henry Douglas, 449

Clark, James, 13, 21n22, 22n40, 27

Clayton, Arthur, 117n71, 449

Clode, Ben, 191n34

Clowes, Frank, 29, 59, 77n155, 101

Cobb, Judith, 277n19

Cobb, Leslie Hamilton, 210, 231n16, 449

Cobley, Bert, 300n137

Cockcroft, John, 238n75, 276n9

Cognet, Christine, 277n19

Cole, Henry, 4, 7n4

Cole-Hamilton, David, 316–317, 343n47, 449

Coll, John Charles, 449

Collcut, Thomas Edward, 114n44

Colman, H. G., 104

Colquhoun, Howard Matthew, 309, 389n12, 449

Colton, Ray, 261, 290n86, 291n92, 292n97, 293n99

Comte, Auguste, 428n21

Conant, James, 218

Condy, Henry B., 30

Consterdine, Frederick G., 213, 231n13

Conway, Brian, 269, 298n130

Cook, Arthur Herbert, 449
  biog. notes, 184, 210, **237n65,** 240n87, 242, 250,
  penicillin work during WW2, 222, 237n67

Cook, James W., 283n53

Cooper, Bransby, 29, 62n12

Coppen, Ernest Alfred, 82, 110n25

Coppins, Richard, 23n50, 44, 70n80, 73n112

Cornfield, Archibald, 256, 337n17, 449

Coryell, Charles, 280n37

Cotton, F. Albert, 168, 256, **280n37,** 288n79, 338n76, 341n38

Courcy, Flora de, 190n32

Courtman, Harold Reuben, 449

Couzens, Edward Gordon, 449

Cowley, Alan Herbert, 358, 379n6, 449

Cox, Anthony, 301n148

Cox, Jeffrey James, 449

Craig, Donald (Don), 449
  biog. notes, 361, 363–364,
  385n33
  research, 363–364, 397n106

Croker, F. W. L. (Les)
  and WW2, 137, 150n33, 213, 216

biog. notes, 159, **189n21**, 306
memoir, 189n21, 226, **232n18,**
234n36
Crombie, Leslie, 202n140, 252,
282n52, 449
Crookes, William, 439, 441
and Chemical News, 66n44
at the RCC, 20n14, 38–40
biog. notes, 38–40, **68n62**
research, 39–40, 68n61, 76n147,
77n156
Crosby, P. M., 340n29
Cross, Alexander, 255, 286n76, 449
Cross, Lionel Charles, 444, 450
Crossley, Arthur William (Lieut. Col),
139
Cullen, William, 431, 435n4
Cullis, Charles Fowler, 268, 298n127,
450

D

Dagnall, Roy, 319, 346n64, 450
Dalton, John, 11n3, 421–422
Dalziel, J. A. W. (Jimmy), 265,
284n76, 286n74, 450
Dalziel, Mary Estelle, 284n74, 76,
450
Daniell, John Frederick, 433, 436n14,
438
Danielli, J. F., 235n56
Darwin, Charles, 47, 72n98, 432
Daubeny, Charles G. B., 3, 11n6
Dave, Laxmi, 261
David, Ieuan, 286n74, 450
Davies, Robert (Rob), 369, 392n74,
450
Davis, George E., 75n136

Davison, Alan, 261, 262n97
Davy, Humphry, 422, 427n15–16
Day, James, 59
Day, James N. E., 139
Debus, Heinrich, 34
DeMello, Andrew James, 369,
391n71, 450
DeMello, John, 369, 392n74, 450
Dent, Charles E., 204n163
Devonshire, Duke of, 37
Dewar, James, 29, 61n6; 19n90, 435
Dey, B. B., 127n149
Dickens, Frank, 204n163
Diels, Otto, 202n139
Disraeli, Benjamin, 20n20
Divers, Edward, 29, 63n21
Dixon, Harold Baily, 123n115,
128n151, 131
Djerassi, Carl, 278n30
Dobson, Charles Robert, 450
Doherty, Annette, 361
Donald, Maxwell B., 205n165
Donaldson, Ronald, 185
Donnan, Frederick G., 105, 159,
198n100
Dowdall, John P. M. de C., 137,
150n31, 450
Down, James (Jimmy), 261–262,
278n98
Downey, William Eric, 195n62
Doyle, William Patrick, 450
Drake, Simon Robert, 450
Ducie, (Earl of Ducie), 12
Ducker, John William, 450
Dumas, Jean-Baptiste A., 35, 419,
424–425, 426n1, 428n22
Dunn, Frederick Percy, 450
Dunne, Anne, 262, 272, 450

Dunstall, William Arthur Watson, 450

Duppa, Frank Baldwin, 52, 54, **71n120**

Durrant, James, 369, 392n73, 450

Dyer, Peter Swinnerton, 338n24

Dyer, Phillip, 388n52, 450

Dyson, Paul J., 369, 393n75, 450

E

Ebdon, Les, 350, 355n116

Edwards, Freddy, 189n21

Egan, Harold, 298n130

Egdell, Russell George, 327, 353n103, 360, 450

Egerton, Alfred, 171, 197n85, 223

Eiloart, Arnold, 108n12, 450

Eisner, Ulli, 282n49

Eldridge, Arthur, 450
  and MSc in the chemistry of food and drugs, 158
  biog. notes, 89–90, 103, 136–137, 152n52, 162, 166, 171, 190n32, 191n37, 255
  correspondence with Barton, 245–246, 278n26
  Diamond Jubilee lecture, 110n25, 125n127, 149n26, 188n12

Elizabeth (Queen, wife of George VI), 229

Ellingham, Harold Johann Thomas (Tom), 450
  and WW2, 210, 212–213, 218
  biog. notes, 143, 172–173, 193n51, **197n88**–89
  Ellingham diagrams; research, 173, **198n92**, 404
  Ellingham papers, 234n45

Elvidge, John Arthur (Jack), 451
  biog. notes & research, 227, 240n87, 251, 271–272, **281n45**, 300n140

Emeléus, Harry Julius, 442, 444, 451
  biog. notes, 167–169, **194n60**, 195n65, 69, 210
  research, 166–168, 194n61, 195n62–63, 195n67
  textbook with Anderson, 168, 195n68
  work during WW2, 213, 219–221, 236n58

Emsley, John, 360, 381n15, 382n17

Erdmann, Otto L., 61n9

Evans, Clare de Brereton, 95, 122n103

Evans, Dennis Frederick, 451
  biog. notes, 259–261, 283n54, 290n87, 291n94 344n54, 358–359
  Evans departmental medal and lab., 344n54, 371, 418n24
  personality, 261, 396n104
  research, 259–260, 291n88, 91–93, 318, 344n52–53

Eyre, John Vargas, 119n81

F

Fahy, Michael, 451

Falmouth, Viscount (E. H. J. Boscawen), 236n60

Faraday, Michael, 9, 12, 37, 39, 69n72

Farmer, Ernest Harold, 451
  biog. notes, research, 181–182, **202n143**, 203n144–147

Farmer, John Bretland, 89

Fay, James William John, 451

Fender, Brian, 265

Fersht, Alan Roy, 451
    biog. notes, 314, **358n98**, 359, 363,
        384n31
    research, 326, 363, 382n22, 403

Field, Frederick, 20n11, 28–29,
    37–38, 48, **67n55**, 439

Field, Samuel, 451

Fieser, Louis, 246, 284n62

Finch, George Ingle, 105, 128n152,
    142, 195n62, 451

Findlay, Tristan, 269, 451

Fischer, Ernst Otto, 196n73, 279n35,
    313

Fischer, Hans, 251

Flavell, Wendy, 393n75

Fleet, Bernard, 315–320, 451

Fleischmann, Martin, 269, 299n134

Fleming, Alexander, 237n64

Florey, Howard, 237n64

Flowers, Brian Hilton, 275n5,
    305–311, 334n6, **336n8,**
    337n18–22, 338n24, 339n26,
    341n39, 379n1, 400–401

Forster, Martin, 451
    biog. notes, 89–90, **116n63**–64
        117n67–69, 32n70, 129n157
    research, 91, 125n125–126

Foster, George Carey, 24n57

Fowler, Alfred, 64n26

Fownes, George, 433, 436n12

Frankland, Edward, 439, 441, 451
    applied & extramural work, 57–59,
        67n54
    as Playfair's assistant, 11
    biog. notes, 51–52, 56–57, 60n3,
        73n115

Frankland RSC award and lab. 314,
    418n24, 445
    lectures and his *Lecture Notes*, 33,
        61n8, 65n34
    memoir, 51, 73n115, **76n144**
    notation, 35
    research, 51–54, 74n121–131, 174,
        405
    safety of drinking water, 58–59
    Sir Edward Frankland chair, 310,
        340n29
    textbook, with Japp, *Inorganic
        Chemistry,* 55, 75n138

Frankland, Frederick William, 76n144

Frankland, Percy Faraday, 56,
    76n139, 138, 451

Friend, J. Newton, 89

Fresenius, Carl R., 13, 49, 420

Frisch, Otto, 218, 234n43

Fromherz, Hans, 173, 198n96

Fuchs, Klaus, 225

Fuchs, P. L., 384n29

G

Gagnon, Paul E., 204n163

Gale, Julian, 369, 393n75, 451

Galloway, Robert, 60n4, 282, 439

Gardner, John, 22n35, 37
    and founding of RCC, 11–12,
        61n6

Garland, Charles Samuel, 111n29,
    451

Garner, William, 296n120

Garton, R. S. (Reg), 252

Gay, Hannah
    biog. notes, 289n84, **291n92,** 94,
        294n102, 353n105, 414n1

Gay, Ian D., 297n122, 124

Gay-Lussac, Joseph Louis, 419, 422

George (King George V), 137–138

George (King George VI), 229

George, Maurice Hilary, 253n104, 327, 359, 451

Gerhardt, Charles, F., 49, 62n12, 64n24, 83, 425

Gerloch, Malcolm, 294n102

Geyger, Adolf, 24n56

Gibbs, Ivan R., 152n54, 451

Gibbs, Philip, 166

Gibson, John Frederick, 451
   biog. notes & research, 81n13, 263, 319, **345n60**, 359

Gibson, Susan (Sue), 364, 385n36, 451

Gibson, Vernon Charles, 451
   biog. notes, 360, 365, **387n48**, 395n94, 396n98,
   research, 365, 415n4
   Sir Geoffrey Wilkinson chair, 387

Gilchrist, Percy, 33, 65n33

Gill, Naida, 262, 451

Gillard, Robert David (Bob), 261, 292n97, 451

Gillett, Ian, 355n116

Gilman, Alexander William (Alec), 58, 76n148

Gilpin, William C., 216, 234n38

Gladstone, William, 12, 21n20

Glueckauf, Eugen, 174, 199n103

Gmelin, Christian G. & Leopold, 428n17

Godden, William, 111n29, 451

Gollins, David, 384, 451

Goodgame, David, 451
   biog. notes, 262, 364, 386n39
   research, 263, 318, **344n55**

Goodgame, Margaret, 452
   biog. notes, 262, 364, 386n39, 394n87

research, 263, 318, **344n56**

Goosen, Arthur, 202n143, 285n70, 452

Gordon, Manfred, 265, 269, 300n135, 333, 452

Gordon, Peter Graham, 452

Gould, Ian, 368, 390n67, 452

Gow, Alexander, 142

Gowland, William, 30, 64n22

Grace, N. S., 115n59

Graham, John Samuel, 390n65, 452

Graham, Thomas, 9, 19n4, 8, 58, 77n151, 176, 199n109, 433, 436n13, 438

Gray, Charles H., 204n163

Gray, Harold Heath, 452

Green, Arthur, 43

Green, Malcolm L. H., 258, 261, 289n84, 290n87, 291n94, 292n97, 341n41, 344n54, 382n20

Green, Mino, 280n37, 337n15

Greenaway, Alfred John, 43, 70n75, 452

Gregory, William, 10, 32, 435n8

Griess, Peter, 24n56, 33, 36, **65n30**

Griffith, William Pettit (Bill), 452
   biog. notes, 261, 263, 286n76, 290n87, 292n97, 294n100, 341n39, 341n41, 344n54, 364
   Chemistry of the Rarer Platinum Metals, 345n59
   research, 319, 383n24

Griffiths, Hugh, 126n143, 452

Grime, Herbert, 452

Grossjean, John Joseph, 30

Grove, William, 119n88

Groves, Charles, 45, 71n84, 119n89, 124n122, 444

Groves, Leslie R. (General), 221
Grummitt, William E., 225, 239n80, 35
Guéron, Jules, 225, 238n75, 239n80, 279n31
Gundry, P. M., 297n121, 452
Guthrie, Frederick, 35, 47, 71n97
Guthrie, Frederick Bickell, 81, 109n23, 452
Gutowsky, H. S., 283n55
Guzmán, Ernesto Carmona, 317

H

Hadrell, J. T., 23n45
Hagerty, Elizabeth G., 111n29
Hahn, Otto, 198n101
Halban, Hans von, 238n75, 239n78
Haldane, John Burdon Sanderson, 140
Haldane, John Scott, **16n13**, 133–136, 140,
Haldane, Richard Burdon, 147n13
Hall, Thomas, 29, 62n16
Hallman, Peter Stewart, 452
Hambly, Frederick, 80, **107n10**, 109n17, 452
Hamer, Frances Mary, 252, 282n51, 452
Hanley, J. A., 114n149
Hannen, John Tronbridge, 220, 452
Hanson, James R. (Jim), 321, 347n71
Hantzsch, Arthur R., 44, 208
Harper, Stanley, 252, 282n52, 452
Harrington, Bernard James, 94, 121n99
Harrison, Nicholas (Nic), 369, 392n74, 452
Hartley, Brian, 326, 352n98

Hartley, Harold, 148n20, 160
Harvey, A. W., 122n102
Harwood, Henry F., 452
    biog. notes, 103, 162–163, 165, 167, **191n37**, 210–211
    Harwood departmental prize and lab., 163, 371, 418n24
Hassel, Odd, 254, 284n62, 312
Hart-Smith, James, 452
Hatton, Arthur Barker, 149n22, 452
Hatton, Frank,
    departmental Hatton prize, 108 n11, 371
Haworth, Norman, 442, 445, 452
    biog. notes & research at IC, 104, **127n148**
    Nobel Prize, 127n148, 209, 230n10, 312
Hay, Mrs., 191n35, 219, 235n50
Haynes, Leonard John, 227
Haynes, Richard Kingston, 347n73, 452
Hayward, David O., 326, 352n101, 389n57, 452
Heal, Henry G., 224, 238n74, 239n79
Heilbron, Isidor (Ian) Morris, 452
    as Barton's doctoral supervisor, 244, 276n14, 277n15,17
    biog. notes, 207–210, **230n7**, 9, 231n13, 242–243, 274n3
    circumstances of leaving IC, 242–243
    organic labs. reconstruction, 209–210, 230n11, 231n12, 272
    research, 209–210, 221, 230n9, 263, 404–405
    work in WW2, including vitamin A, 221–223, 237n63,67, 408

Heller, William Mayhowe, 98, 124
n12048
Henbest, Harold (Bernard), 223,
227–228
Henderson, George G., 208, 230n7
Henry, William Charles, 19n3
Herschel, Alexander Stewart, 45,
71n86,87, 427n16
Herschel, John, 427n16
Herringshaw, John Francis, 268–269,
299n131, 452
Hewitt, David George, 453
Hewitt, John T., 111n29
Hey, Donald H., 442, 444, 453
biog. notes & research, 210,
231n14, 232n24, 276n14,
282n52
Hibbert, Harold, 89, 116n61
Hickman, Kenneth, 453
biog. notes, 161, 164–166, **190n27**,
32, 193n51
memoir, 161, 190n27
research, 165, 193n48, 203n154
WW1-related work, 139, 145,
149n24
Hieber, Walter, 169, 196n73
Hill, Anthony F., 365, 387n44, 453
Hill, Roderic, 242, 277, 414n1
Hillier, Ian, 295n110
Hills, Graham John, 268–269,
297n125, 453
Himus, Geoffrey Wilfred, 89, 105,
128n152, 453
Hinchley, John William, 105,
128n153, 143
Hind, J. W., 453
Hinshelwood, Cyril, 442, 444, 453
biog. notes, 267, 296n119, 416n9
Hird, James Morton, 453

Hodd, G. W., 117n70
Hofmann, August (Wilhelm),
440–441, 453
accommodation in London, 13–14,
21n22, 22n32
appointment as first professor at
RCC, 13, 15
biog. notes, 13, **21n25**, 14n41,
24n56, 25n58,59; 66n45,
419–421, 436n13
early teaching at the RCC, 13–14,
17, 20n15, 31–33, 64n27,
426n4
extra-mural work, 18, 57–59
Hofmann departmental lab. & chair
310, 418n24
Introduction to Modern Chemistry,
34, 66n39
molecular models, 34, 66n38
personality & philosophical views,
2, 14, 27–28, 59n1, 403–404
students and assistants, 17, 22n33,
28–31, 48–49
research at the RCC, 23n44,
48–51, 60n2, 66n43, 69n71,
72n101, 102,105, 73n107,
108, 407
Hofmann, Hanna, 18, 25n59
Hofmann, P. W., 24n56
Holland, Kathleen, 43, 70n77
Holland, Lilian, 43, 70n77
Holland, Mina, 43, 70n77
Holland, Thomas Henry, 161,
183,188n20
Holloway, George Thomas, 111n29,
453
Holmes, Arthur, 191n37
Holmes, John, 111n29
Holt, Charles, 189n26, 194n59

Holzmann, Maurice, 24n56, 38, 67n56
Hope, Thomas Charles, 432, 435n7
Hopkin, W. K., 30
Hopkins, Frederick Gowland, 56, 66n40, 20n163, 403
Hornsby (Miss), 159, 188n20
Horrocks, William H., 143, 152n51
How, Henry, 28, 48, 60n4
Howard, Albert, 111n29
Howard, Chris, 395n91
Howard, David, 45, 71n85
Howard, Luke, 45
Hudson, Robert Francis (Bob), 226, 239n82, **281n3**, 453
Hughes, Edward D., 180
Humboldt, Alexander von, 27
Humphrey, H. A., 128n153
Humpidge, Thomas, 55, 75n136
Hunter, Robert Fergus, 117n70, 187n10, 192n165, 453
Hutchin, William Henry, 453
Huxley, Thomas Henry, 4, 30, 37, 52, 73n119, 75n137

I

Idris, T, H, W. (Howell), 87, 114n52
Ingold, Christopher, 442, 444, 453
  biog, notes, 38n117–119, 121, 200, 202n130
  WW1-related work, 137, 145, 150n35, 153n56, 177, 200n119
  research with Jocelyn Thorpe, 177–180, 200n123, 201n124–126,128, 403
Ingold, Hilda Usherwood, 179, 199n114, 200n122

Ives, David Jones Gibbs, 453

J

Jackman, Lloyd M., 250–253, 283n54, 453
Jacobs, Patrick William McCarthy, 267–268, 297n123–124, 453
Jacobs, Stanley, 163, 192n41
James, F. W., 196n78
James, Hugh William, 453
James, Stuart L., 368, 390n68, 453
Japp, Francis R., 60n3, 99, 118n78, 453
  biog. notes, 55, **75n137**
  textbook with Frankland, *Inorganic Chemistry* 55, 75n138
Jardine, Fred, 342n43, 44
Jenkinson, Ernest Arthur, 453
Johnson, Alan Woodworth, 228–229, 232n25, **240n89**
Johnson, Nigel P., 261
Joliot, Frédéric, 238n75
Jones, Anthony Copeland, 359, 380n11, 453
Jones, Bernard Mouat, 453
  biog. notes, 106, **147n16**,
  WW1-related work, 134–135, 145, 148n19–20
Jones, C. G., 120n95
Jones, Chapman Henry, (see Chapman Jones, Henry)
Jones, David E. H., 257–258, 288n81
Jones, David G., 227
Jones, David William, 453
Jones, Ewart R. H. (Tim), 440, 442, 445, 453

biog. notes, 210, 213, 223, **236n62**, 240, 250, 276n8

research, 221, 223, 237n63–64, 286n72

work in WW2, 213, 221–223, 276n14

Jones, Francis, 131

Jones, Henry Bence, 13, 21n27, 25n61, 41, 66n36

Jones, Richard, 316

Jones, Timothy S. (Tim), 367–368, **390n64**, 454

Jordan, Louis A,. 200n123

Joynson, Edmund, 16, 23n47

Judd, Hilda, 89, 411

Judd, John W., 87, 89

Julia, Marc, 227

K

Karrer, Paul, 209, 230n10

Kealy, Tom, 279n35, 314

Keeler, Christine, 291n94

Kekulé, August, 8, 18, 27, 74n127–128, 79, 112n40, 201n125, 421, 426

Keogh, Alfred, 132–134, 137, 146n6, 147n13, 152n52, 55, 411

Kerr, Ian S., 265, 295n113, 454

Kidd, John, 434

Kinch, Edward, 55, 75n135

King, Albert Theodore, 90, 104, **127n148–149**, 454

King, Alexander, 454

biog. notes 161, 172–174, 189n21, **318n94**, 96–98, 217, 234n44

work in WW2, 216–217, 234n39–41

King, David A., 227, 267, 289n84, 297n122

Kington, George L., 265, 293n98, 295n109, 327, 454

Kipping, Frederick Stanley, 454

biog. notes, 43, 70n77, **125n128**, 134n137

Modern Organic Chemistry, with Perkin, 100, 125n129

research at the C&GCTC, 95,100, 122n101, 125n129

Kirby, Gordon William, 254, 284n64, 454

Kirchoff, Gustav, 24n57, 39

Kirkbright, Gordon F., 319–320, 338n21, **346n65**, 454

Kirman, Walter, 109n17, 454

Kitchener, H. Herbert (Lord Kitchener), 132–133, 135, 138, 146n6, 147n13

Kitchener, Joseph A., 167,172, 174, 210, 219, 268, 454

memoir of dept. 192n39, 298n126

Klug, David, 368, 372, 391n69, 454

Knapp, Friedrich L, 15, 22n38

Knowles, Jeremy R., 234n38, 340n29

Koch, Heinz Peter, 214, 233n30

Kolbe, A. W. Hermann, 51–52, 65n30,31, 73n118, 74n127, 281n42

Kon, George, 454

biog. notes, 141, 180–181, 202n134, 210, 221, 227

research, 180–181, 202n138–139

Kowarski, 238n75

Kroto, Harold Walter (Harry), 288n81

Kucernak, Anthony, 368, **390n66**, 454

Kuhlman, C. F., 24n56

Kuimova, Marina, 385n35

L

Lamy, Claude-Auguste, 68n61
Lapworth, Arthur,
  biog. notes, 73, 70n77, 100–101,
    125n133, 126n136
  research, 100, 123n112, 125n135,
    126n139, 179
Laurent, Auguste, 41, 49, 425–426,
  428n24
Lavoisier, Antoine-Laurent, 422–424
Law, Robert Vernon, 369, 391n71,
  454
Lawrence, A. Stuart C., 210, 219,
  232n46
Leach, Frederick Peacock, 454
Leatherbarrow, Robin, 363, 368,
  384n32, 391n68, 454
Leibius, Adolph, 24n56
Lennard-Jones, John, 195n70, 296n120
Letcher, Roy Melville, 454
Levitt, Bryan, 454
  and departmental computing, 328,
    412
  biog. notes & research, 326–327,
    332, **353n108**, 360
  director of UG studies, 336n12,
    353n108
Lewis, Gilbert N., 179, 403
Lewis, Jack, 259, **290n85**, 290n86, 454
Lewy, Bergnart C., 79, 107n3
Ley, Steven Victor (Steve), 454
  as head of dept., 359
  biog. notes, 323–324, 329n28,
    349n85, 358–359, 361–362,
    380n9, **382n21**, 383n25, 443
  research, 319, 324, 350n87, 352n99,
    361–362, 382n22–23, 383n24,
    383n24, 383n33, 392n72, 405

Lickiss, Paul, 454
  biog. notes & research, 365,
    387n45
Liebig, Justus,
  advice on foundation of RCC,
    22–23
  biog. notes, 9, 24n56, **426n4**,
    427n5–8,13
  following in Britain, 9–10, 19n6,
    419–421
  laboratory in Giessen, 48, 63n21,
    419–421, 426n3–4, 427n13–14
  philosophy, 9–10, 19n5, 22n37,
    407
  research, 18n1,19n3, 41–43, 407,
    428n19
Lindemann, Frederick, 230n11
Linstead, Reginald (Patrick), 454
  and Barton, 276n8, 286n72
  as professor of organic chemistry,
    250–255
  as undergraduate, research student,
    and lecturer, 181, 183–185,
    202n138, 203n155–157, 204n158
  biog. notes, 181, 183–185,
    203n150, 241–243, 275n4, 405
  expansion after Robbins
    Committee report, 306–307, 327,
    332n2, 333n3, 336n14
  introduction of course in English,
    272, 332
  introduction of tutorial system, 272
Linstead Hall 368
'Linstead Memorandum' (dept.
  constitution), 242–243, **275n5**,
  306, 314, 336n14
Modern Techniques in Organic
  Chemistry, 272, 300n140

opening of biochemistry dept., 273,
    301n147–148
  research, 184–185, 202n138,
    203n150–157, 204n158, 250–252,
    263, 281n41–42, 282n46, 49
Little, Victor, 89, 103, 116n62, 144,
  454
Liveing, George D., 96, 434, 436n18
Liversidge, Archibald, 55, 75n133,
  109n23
Liversidge RSC award, 55, 445
Lloyd George, David, 140
Lock, Colin, 261, 292n97, 454
Locket, George Hazlewood, 187n10,
  454
Lockyer, James, (RCC architect) 13
Lockyer, J. Norman, 33, 46–47, 54,
  64n26, 74n131, 81, 109n20,
  110n25, 113n43
Lodge, Oliver, 41
Long, Nicholas James (Nick), 366,
  388n53, 454
  Sir Edward Frankland BP chair, 366
Lonsdale, Kathleen, 294n102
Lown, James William, 283n54, 454
Lowry, Geoffrey, 189n25, 218
Lowry, Thomas Martin, 454
  and Brønsted–Lowry theory. 96
  biog. notes, 95, **123n109**, 138, 179,
    192n45, 403
  research 96–97, 100, 123n110–112
Lubatti, Octavius Francis, 188n15
Lubinkowski, Jacek (Jack), 311
Lygo, Barry, 361

M

Machin, Peter, 355n116
Macintosh, Charles, 11n3
Maclean, Ida (see Smedley, Ida)

Macmillan, Alexander, 64n26
MacPherson, Cluny, 136, 150n28
Maddock, Alfred G., 224–225,
    238n74, **238n75**, 290n85, 454
Madell, Arthur, 300n137
Magnus, Philip, 323, 340n33,
    348n77, 454
Maher, John, 291n93
Manning, Alexander Bernard, 185,
    454
Mansfield, Charles, 29, 42, 69n73
Manz, Andreas, 368, 381n11,
    391n71, 455
Marle, Ernest Robert, 454
Marsden, Arthur Whitcombe, 192n41,
    256, 455
  and WW2, 210, 214, 231n16
Marsden, Steven (Steve), 361, 364,
    383n24, 385n37, 454
Marshall, Edward (Ed), 365
Marshall, G. N., 454
Martin, Graham, 216, 224, 231n15,
    232n21, 235n50
Martin, Hubert, 205n165
Martin, Nicholas, H., 204n163
Martius, Carl, 24n56
Maskelyne, Nevil Story, 121n98, 434
Mason, Ronald, 262, 291n92,
    294n10, 318, 455
Masters, Anthony Frederick, 455
Mather, Thomas, 55
Matlin, Stephen, 349n82
Matthews, Francis E., 46
Matthews, Janet, 167, 194n59
Matthey, Edward, 31, 64n24
Matthiessen, Augustus, 17, **24n57**,
    97, 119n87
Maule, George, 42, 60n4, 67n55
May, Alan Nunn, 225, 239n78

Mayo, Paul Jose de, 252, 283n53, 450

McCance, Robert, 185

McCombie, John, 348n75

McCombie, Stuart, 322, 348n75

McCleverty, Jon A, 261, 292n97

McFarlane, William, 261, 292n97

McLeod, Herbert, 15–16, 29, 70n80–83, 73n119, 107n8, 126n136
   account of RCC labs, 16, 18, 44–45
   and Hofmann's molecular models, 33–34, 66n38
   biog. notes, 44–46, 58, **66n37**, 70n79,83
   diary 15, **23n43**, 36, 60n2–3, 66n43, 67n47–51
   extra-mural work, 58–59, 77n156
   McLeod gauge, 46, 71n90

Meakins, Reginald, J., 227

Meek, Geoffrey Archer, 455

Medlock, Henry, 30, 63n20

Meldola, Raphael, 46, 90, 439, 441, 455
   biog. notes, 46–47, **71n91**,93
   Meldola and Harrison-Meldola awards, 47, 72n100, 445
   Meldola Blue, 47

Mendeleev, Dimitri, 40, 92

Mercer, Ian P., 369, 391n69, 455

Merck, Georg, 24n56, 29, 62n12

Merck, Wilhelm, 62n12

Mertis, Konstantinos (Kostas), 316, 342n45

Meyer, J. Lothar, 40, 82

Meyer, Stefan, 174

Meyer, Victor, 175

Miall, Stephen, 124n116

Micklethwait, Frances E., 91, **117n71**, 455
   WW1-related work, 137–138, 141,145

Miers, Henry, 455
   biog. notes & research, 94, **121n98**, 122n100,101

Miller, Andrew David, 364, 385n34, 394n94, 455

Miller, William Allen, 433, 436n14

Millidge, Alfred Frank, 455

Mills, Edmund, J., 45

Mingos, Michael, 455
   biog. notes, 359, 364, 380n7, **386n41**
   research, 364, 390n68

Moissan, Henri, 82, 112n30

Moldenhauer, Helen, 24n56

Mole, H. B., 120n95

Mond, Ludwig, 54

Montalban, Antonio Garrido, 369, 391n71, 455

Moody, Christopher, 455
   biog. notes & research, 325, **350n92**, 359–360, 384n299

Moody, Gerald T., 98, 122n100, 124n117, 455

Moore, Albert, 300n137

Moore, Brian, 261–262, 293n98

Moore, Walter Roman, 117n71, 456

Morgan, Frank, 239n78

Morgan, Gilbert, 442, 444, 456
   biog. notes, 82, 88–89, 103, **117n70**, 118n73
   Corday–Morgan prize, 91, 118n73, 445
   research, 91, 117n71–72

Morgan, Sydney, 116n60

Morley, Henry Foster, 128n155

Morley, Reginald, 30, 63n21
Morris, William, 69n71
Morrison, George Anderson, 456
Moss, Gerald (Gerry), 323, 456
Motherwell, Robyn, 339n28, **349n80**,
    361, 382n20
Motherwell, William B. (Willie), 456
    biog. notes, 323, 339n28, 348n79,
        349n80, 359–362, **382n19**
    research, 361, 382n19
Mountain, Harold, 118n75
Mugdan, M., 277n15
Müller, Hugo, 60n5
Müller, P. H., 237n68
Mulliken, Robert S., 290n87, 403
Munro, James, 222–223
Murchison, Roderick, 36
Murgatroyd, John Blackburn, 456
Murray, Humphrey Desmond, 166,
    193n50, 456
Murray, Keith, 286n72, 456
Muspratt, Edmund, 19n3
Muspratt, James, 1, 19n3
Muspratt, James Sheridan, 29, 48,
    61n9, 72n104

N

Naik, Kurversti G., 205n165
Napper, S. S., 120n95
Naylor, John H. C., 301n147
Nernst, W. H., 101, 118n78, 230n11
Newell, William Copeman, 456
Newitt, Dudley, 184, 196n81
Newitt, Edward James, 456
Newlands, Benjamin E. R., 40
Newlands, John Alexander Reina,
    biog. notes, 40, **68n63**, 64
    his early Periodic table, 40
Newman, Arthur C. C., 204n163

Newth, George Samuel, 456
    biog. notes, 55–56, 103, **75n134**,
        112n31
    memoir, 76n143
Nicholls, Lewis, 205n165
Nicholson, David, 326–327,
    353n106, 389n57, 456
Nicholson, Edward,
    biog. notes, 28, 38, 43, **60n4**,
        73n111
    research, 48–50, 61n6, 63n20,
        67n55, 72n106
Noad, Henry, 29, 48, **62n12**
Nobel, Alfred, 61n6
Norris, Richard K. Kenneth, 456
North, Barker, 108n13
Northcote, Augustus Beauchamp, 30,
    63n21
Norton, James, 186n4
Nye, Mary-Jo, 178, 201n125,129
Nyholm, Ronald Sydney (Ron),
    292n95, 348n76

O

O'Brien, Paul, 456
    biog. notes & research, 366, 368,
        381n11, **388n50**
Odling, William, 29, **62n14**, 68n64,
    441, 459
Oldham, Keith B., 456
Oppenheimer, J. Robert, 221
Orléans, Phillipe d' (Comte de Paris),
    64n23
Osborn, John Anthony,
    biog. notes, 261, **262n97**, 342n43,
        44
O'Shaughnessy, Bernard, 456
Ostwald, Wilhelm, 87, 97, 403,
    415n6

O'Sullivan, Cornelius, 33, 65n32, 128n155

Otway, David J., 369, 392n73, 456

Owen, Lancelot, 115n59

Owen, Leonard Newton (Len), 456
biog. notes & research, 220, 235**n55**–56, 251, 274, 283n58

Owens, Mary E., 55

Oxburgh, Ernest Ronald (Ron), 310, 357, 362, 373, **383n28**

P

Packer, Kenneth J., 288, 359, 380**n11**, 456

Page, Albert B. P., 188n15, 214

Palmieri, Luigi, 74n131

Paneth, Friedrich (Fritz) Adolf, 456
and Tube Alloys, 210, 224, 238n75, 239n77–78
biog. notes, research, 172, 174–175, 18–19, 195n69, **198n100**–102, 199n102, 404

Parkinson, Christopher, 364, **386n38**, 456

Parsonage, Neville, 270, 326–327, 353n105,107, 359, 456

Parsons, Leslie George Brett, 456

Parsons, Roger, 268–269, 298n130, 299n132, 456

Partington. J. R., 126n139

Pauling, Linus, 179, 290n87, 403, 416n12

Pauson, Peter, 279n35, 314

Pavy, Frederick William, 25, 62n15, 111n29

Payne, Douglas Sutherland, 226, 239n83, 276n10, **286n74**, 456

Payne, Grace, 226, 239n83

Peachey, Stanley John, 122n102

Peacock, Raymond, (Ray), 255, 286n76, 456

Pearson, Thomas Gibson, 166, 174, 193n52, 457

Peccei, Aurelio, 234n44

Pechet, Maurice, 255, 285n71, 321

Peel, Robert, 10, 12, 19n6, 8, 21n19, 51

Pedler, Alexander, 3, 55, 75n132

Peierls, Rudolf, 218, 234n43

Penn, Francis Richard, 457

Penney, William George,
and Manhattan Project, 221, 236n60
as Rector, 303, 334n4
biog. notes, 196n78, 221, **236n59**–61, 416n10

Penson, Lilian, 242

Pepper, John Henry, 36, 67n46, 438

Percy, Eustace, 300n143

Perkin, Arthur George, 43, 70n78

Perkin, Frederick Mollwo, 43–44

Perkin, William H. Sr., 438–439, 441
account of the RCC labs, 16, 18, 23n48, 25n61
biog. notes, 29, 38, 40–42, **68n65**
Perkin departmental lab., 418n24
Perkin's mauveine & other work, 40–42, 50, 68n69, 69n70–71, 72n99, 405
Perkin RSC prize, 446
recollections of Hofmann, 28, 68n68

Perkin, William Henry Jr., 441, 446
biog. notes, 43, 101, 123n107, 137, 150n33, 171–172, 175
Modern Organic Chemistry, with Kipping, 100, 134n129

Perry, John, 88, 115n56

Philip, James Charles, 1, 4, 440, 442, 444, 457
  biog. notes, 89–90, 101, **118n78**, 171–172, 186, **197n85**, 209, 215, 233n32
  Philip departmental lab., 418n24
  research, 171–172, 402
  work in WW1, 139, 141, 145, 146n6
Philip (Prince Philip), 250–251
Phillips, David, 457
  and departmental reorganisation, 357–358, 373–377, 396n98
  as chemical communicator, 367, 389n59
  as head of dept., 357–359
  biog. notes 314, 357, 367, **380n10**
  research, 367, 389n58
Phillips, Laurie, 323–324, 351n95, 457
Phillips, Trevor, 355n116
Pickard, Joseph Allen, 457
Pirie, Norman W., 247
Playfair, Lyon, 421, 427n14, 432, 435n8, 438, 440–441
  as chemist to the Geological Survey, 10, 20n8
  biog. notes, 9–11, 19n4,6, **19n8**
  lab. on Duke Street, 51
  Playfair's papers at IC, 19n6
  and the RCC, 15, 19n8
Plimmer, Henry George, 91, 117n72
Poë, Anthony John (Tony), 262, 294n101, 457
Pollard, Alfred George, 457
  biog. notes, 143, 163–164, 188n14–15, 192n38, 210, 214, 256

  MSc course on agricultural chemistry, 158, 163, 188n14–15, 214
Pollard, George Potticary, 457
Pons, Stanley, 299n134, 390n66
Pontecorvo, Bruno, 225
Poole, Colin, 359, 390n11, 457
Pope, T. H., 120n95
Pope, William Jackson, 441, 457
  biog. notes, 94–96, **122n100,** 102, 147n9
  research, 95–96, 123n107, 306
  WW1 work, 100, 123n108, 133, 137,147n9
Porter, George, 328, **354n113**, 359, 416n9, 457
Porter, Helen Kemp, 185
Potter, Charles, 188n15
Potter, Edmund C., 298n130
Potter, F. M., 127n149
Praagh, Gordon van, 219, 235n47
Pratt, Leslie (Les), 457
  biog. notes & research, 259, 283n54, **290n87**, 293n99, 318, 344n51, 359
Price, David, 29, 61n9
Price, David Christopher, 457
Procter, Henry R., 64n28
Prosser, Alan Philip, 457
Prout, E. R., 296n120
Purcell, Ronald Herbert, 457
  biog. notes & research 164, 166, 169, **192n44,**195n62,69, 210, 213, 218
  work for Admiralty in WW2, 210, 213, 218
Purdie, Thomas, 55, 75n136

Q

Quastel, Juda Hirsch, 185–186, 204n163
Quinkert, Gerhardt, 254, 285n69
Quirke, Nicholas (Nick), 369, **393n73**, 396n98, 457

R

Raistrick, Harold, 284n65
Ramsay, Andrew, 427n14, 436n10
Ramsay, William, 105, 122n103, 138, 230n9
Randerson, William, 193n51
Ransome, Thomas, 51, 73n117
Raphael, Ralph,
 biog. notes & research, 228–229, 233n28, 237n63, **240n92**, 276n14
Read, Roger Wayne, 457
Reeks, Margaret, 114n47
Rees, Charles Wayne, 444, 457
 biog. notes, 282n52, 310, 314, 324, **350n88**, 359, 361, 416n15
 Charles Rees RSC award 325, 350n92, 384n29, 445
 Hofmann chair, 310, 350n90
 president of RSC, 325, 25n17, 443
 research, 324–325, 350n89, 360–361,
Rees, Lovat Victor Charles, 457
 biog. notes & research, 265–266, 295n108, 112, 326, **352n100**, 359
Reeves, George, 200n118
Reid, Cyril, 235n54
Renwick, F. F., 120n95
Reynolds, Henry C., 70n81
Reynolds, John W. 29, 62n17
Rich, E. M., 122n102

Richards, Rex Edward, 259
Richards, Theodore W., 166, 207, 229n2
Rideal, Eric Keightley, 442, 457
 biog. notes, 143 **152n50**, 264, 267, 296n118
 Sir Eric Rideal award, 296n118, 446
Ridley, Damon Donald, 457
Riley, Henry (Harry) Lister, 159, 164, 166, 193n55, 457
Robbins, Lionel Charles, 303–304, 334n3, 338n21
Roberts, Eric, 457
 biog. notes & research, 162, 211, 255–256, 272, **287n77**, 317, 416n10
 History of the Chemistry Department, 173, 189n24,191n37, 287n77
Roberts, Gerrylynn, 11, 20n12
Roberts, John D. (Jack), 253
Roberts, Meirion Wyn, 297n122
Robertson, J. M., 250
Robertson, Neil, 369, 392n74, 458
Robertson, Philip W., 103–104, 127n145
Robinson, Robert, 22–23, 28, 97, 101, 123n115, 126n139, 223, 276n8, 278n30
Rodd, Ernest, 119n81, 125n124
Rodger, James, 458
 biog. notes, research, 80–82, 91, **107n10**
Rogers, Donald (Don), 267, 328–329, 333, 337n17, **355n114,** 458
Roscoe, Henry, 62n12, 79, 107n2, 131, 145n2, 440
Rose, Thomas Kirk, 11n29

Rosenblum, Myron, 279n35
Ross, John David McBeath, 137,
150n31, 182, 458
Ross, Walter C. J., 227
Rossiter, Edmund C., 120n95
Rothschild, N. M. Victor, 236,
234n39
Rowney, Thomas, 29, 61n7, 108
Rücker, Arthur, 81, 109n20
Rue, Warren de la, 28, 36, **60n5**, 438,
440–441,
Rumbles, Garry, 367, **389n60**, 458
Runge, Friedlieb F., 48
Rush, Benjamin, 435n5
Ruskin, John, 69n71
Russell, Colin, 13, 22n28, 74n126
Russell, H. C., 205 n165
Russell, Richard, 347n73, 458
Rydon, Henry (Harry), 458
biog. notes, research, 185,
204n160, 271, 300n138, 330
Rzepa, Henry, 458
and departmental computing,
332–323, 356n119–120, 371,
394n84, 412
biog. notes, 125n124, 325, 351n94,
351n95, 394n84
research, 325, 332, 351n95

S

Sammes, Michael, 258, 281n44,
289n84
Sammes, Peter, 324, 340n33, 341n81,
82, 458
Sanders, Jeremy, 331–332, 356n11
Sayers, Bruce, 338n24
Schaffner, Karl, 458
Schorlemmer, Carl, 53, 74n122
Schryver, Samuel, 185, 204n161

Scott, Alastair (Ian), 252, 283n53,
339n28, 458
Scott, George, 46
Scott, William Dallas, 205n165, 458
Seaborg, Glen, 224, 248, 279n32
Sebba, Felix, 227, 239n86
Seddon, John, 458
biog. notes, research, 367, 389n61,
390n63, 396n98
Sell, Eugen, 24n56
Shahak, Israel, 458
Sharadsky, Edward T., 458
Sharp, Barry Leonard, 320, 346n66,
458
Sharp, David William Arthur, 255,
286n76, 458
Shen, T. Y., 238n71
Shenstone, William A., 84
Shepherd, Alfred, 458
Sheppard, Richard N. (Dick), 265,
295n111
Sherwood, Constance, 188n20
Shields, John, 91
Shipman, Michael, 382n19
Shoppee, Charles William, 179–180,
186n4, **202n123**
Sidgwick, Nevil, V., 91, 179,
201n129
Simmons, Thomas Arthur, 458
Simonsen, John Lionel, 235n55
Simpson, George, 60n4
Sinkinson, (sister of Eric Sinkinson),
151n49
Sinkinson, Eric, 151n49
Skapski, Andrzej, 329, 364, 458
Sklarz, Benjamin, 254, 284n64, 458
Sladden, Cyril Edgar, 104, 458
Sloggett, Arthur, 134
Smedley, Ida, 98 118n76, **124n121**

Smith, Alexander (Alec), 359,
    380n11, 458
Smith, Anthony S., 354n112
Smith, Clarence, 82, 110n27, 444,
    458
Smith, Edward (Ed), 325–326,
    352n96, 458
Smith, Harold, 208, 230n5
Smith, John, 311, 337n17
Smith, Marie Louise, 395n75, 459
Smith, Norman, 390n65, 459
Smith, Peter William George, 459
Smits, Andreas, 164
Snelus, George James, 33, 65n33
Snook, Richard D. (Dick), 320,
    346n67, 459
Sobrero, Ascanio, 122n105
Solan, Gregory (Greg) 387n47
Sollas, William J., 55
Solomon (stores man), 158
Sondheimer, Franz, 215, 229,
    233n30, 248, 276n14, **278n30**
Southwell, Richard, 220, 236n57,
    240n93, 242, 300n143, 403,
    415n7
Spencer, Douglas, 9–12, 193n48, 50,
    193n51, 459
Spiller, John, 30, 38, 64n22
Spiller, William, 29, 43
Spinks, Alfred, 228, 240n90
Spiro, Michael, 459
    biog. notes, 269, 327–328,
        353n109, 353n110, 359, 388n56
    MSc course in research, 330, 333
    research, 328
Sprengel, Hermann, 29, 61n10, 439
Spring, Frank S., 227
Steinke, Joachim H. G., 369, 391n71,
    459

Stenhouse, John, 25n59, 45–46, 48,
    61n6, 63n21, **71n84**, 83
Stern, Leo, 44
Stewart, Kenneth, 220, 235n54, 459
Stick, Rober Yvent, 322, 347n73, 459
Stock, Alfred, 168, 195n63
Stocker, Charles Frederick, 459
Stoddardt, James Fraser, 355n115
Stoessl, Albert, 255, 286n76, 459
Stokes, George G., 74n126
Stone, F. Gordon A., 288n83
Sugden, James Netherwood,
    162–163, **191n33**–34, 459
    WW1-related work, 138, 143,
        152n51
    killed by a flying bomb in WW2,
        162, 191n35
Sugden, Samuel, 106, 129n158
Sulsh, Peter (Pete), 395n91
Sutcliffe, Martin Berry, 326–327, 459
Sutherland, J. K. (Hamish), 254,
    284n64, 459
Swanson, Alan, 32n24
Sykes, Richard, 362, 366, 379n3,
    383n26, 415n4

T

Tapp, James Stewart, 459
Tate, William, 116n63
Taylor, Alan G., 391n69, 459
Taylor, Deryck Arnold, 459
Taylor, Geoffrey, 221, 236n60
Taylor, Hugh Stott, 195, 195n64
Templer, Richard, 459
    as head of dept. from 2002, 379n3,
        389n62
    biog. notes & research, 367–368,
        389n61, 62

Tennant, Smithson, 434, 436n18

Teschemacher, Edward Frederick Sr., 438

Teschemacher, Edward Frederick Jr., 438, 439

Thatcher, Margaret, 333n2, 335n7, 338n22, 414n3

Theobald, Leslie, 459
  biog. notes, 165–167, **194n56**, 58, 210, 255–256
  Theobald Lecture award, 34n56, 286n76, 445

Thimann, Kenneth V., 204n163

Thirsk, Reginald, 299n134

Thomas, John Meurig, 326, 359, 380n11, 459

Thomas, Joseph W., 59, 77n157

Thomas, Peter James, 459

Thomas, Sidney Gilchrist, 33

Thomas, Susan (see Gibson, Susan)

Thompson, George Paget, 102n102

Thompson, Kenneth Clive, 459

Thompson, Silvanus Phillips, 47, 71n97

Thomson, Thomas, 9, 413, 420, 426n4, 431–432

Thorp, William, 29, 59, 77n155

Thorpe, Jocelyn Field, 459
  as head of the organic section, 156, 175–186
  as president of the CS, 175–176, 440, 442,
  biog. notes, 82, 106, 138, 157, 110n28, 129n157, 133, 171, 175–180, **199n104**–105, 209, 291n89, 349n90
  SK lachrymator ,137, 148n19, 150n36
  WW1-related work, 133, 138–141, 149n22, 27, 150n35–36, 15n41,44

research, 156, 176–180, 200n123, 201n124, 128, 202n136, 263, 312, 404–405

Thorpe, Lady (J. F. Thorpe's wife), 141–142, 149n22, 151n43
  memoir, 149n22

Thorpe, Thomas (Edward), 441, 459
  admission of women to the CS, 91, 118n76, 440
  biog. notes, 79–80, 82, 106, **107n1**–2, 8, 110n28, 124n116, 146n6
  departmental reorganisation, 82–83
  Dictionary of Applied Chemistry, 81, 106, 128n155–156
  head of dept., 80, 102–103
  research, 80–81, 106, 107n9, 108n14–16, 112n32, 127n145, 404, 407

Thurston, Eric, 158, 188n17

Tilden, Philip Armstrong, 114n44

Tilden, William Augustus, 440, 441, 459
  admission of women to CS, 91, 118n76, 440–441
  as head of dept. & RCS Dean, 85–87
  biog. notes, 24n57, 30, 60n3, 66n43, 83–85, **112n33**, 116n65
  books by Tilden, 92, 114n44, 115n56, **119n79**
  founder of the RCS Chem. Soc., 106
  memoir, 112n34, 113n43
  planning of RCS-1, 87–88, 114n44
  research, 84, 88, 112n35, 39. 113n42, 115n55–56, 58
  RSC Tilden award, 92, 445–446

Tildesley, Dominic John, 368, 391n70, 459

Timmons, Christopher John, 460

Tizard, Henry Thomas, 172, 174
    and WW2, 209–218, **231n11**
Todd, Alexander, 128n156, 257,
    356n117
Tomlinson, John, 298n130
Tompkins, Frederick C., 444,
    460
    biog. notes and research, 266–267,
        296n120¸ 297n121–122, 326,
        404
Tribe, Alfred, 23n45
Turner, David Warren, 460
    biog. notes & research, 251–252,
        282n50, 324, 416n14
Turner, Edward, 432–433
Turtle, Edgar Ernest, 460
Tutton, Alfred E. H., 460
    biog. notes, 80–81, **108n12**,
        109n18
    research, 80, 108n13–14
Tyndall, John, 32, 52, 66n36

U

Urey, Harold, 195n67
Usherwood, Hilda, (see Ingold,
    Hilda Usherwood)

V

Valentin, William, 29, 33, 36,
    65n35
Van't Hoff, J. H., 87, 97, 403
Victoria (Queen Victoria), 19n3,
    21n26–27, 46, 58, 69n71, 88,
    115n57
Vilar, Ramón, 368, 390n68,
    460
Vleck, John H. van, 236n59, 403
Volhard, Jacob, 15, 23n45

W

Waight, Eric Stanmore, 253,
    283n58, 359, 460
Wakeham, William (Bill), 357–358,
    18, 395n92, 95
Wakley, Thomas, 11
Walkley, John, 269, 460
Wallace, Alfred Russel Wallace, 47
Wallach, Otto, 202n137
Walsh, Julian, 375, 395n92
Walshe, Nigel, 350n87
Walter, L. Edna, 98
Ward, William J. V., 205n165
Warington, Robert Sr., 437–438
Warington, Robert Jr., 59, 77n155,
    128n155, 438
Warren, Frank Louis, 182, 197n86,
    202n143, 460
Waterhouse, Alfred, 120n91
Watson, Walter Henry, 111n29,
    460
Watson, William, 134, 138, 148n17,
    150n28
Way, John T., 59
Weaver, Warren, 218
Webb, Aston, 84, 114n44, 46,
    127n150
Weedon, Basil C. L. (Jimmy), 460
    biog. notes & research, 228,
        237n67, 240n91, 251, 253, 272,
        251n43
Weizmann, Chaim, 144
Welch, Archibald (John) Edmund,
    460
    biog. notes & research, 190n32,
        211, **231n17**, 255–256, 266–261,
        288n80, 317–318
Wellcome, H. S., 87

Wells, H. G., 146n6, 203n148

Welton, Thomas (Tom), 460
  biog. notes & research, 366,
    368n54, 55

West, Ralph Winton, 185, 460

West, Thomas Summers (Tom), 460
  biog. notes & research, 319–320,
    333, 337n18, **346n63**, 68, 404

Weston, R. J., 460

Whalley, Margaret, 250, 272,
  300n140, 460

Whiffen, William Jr, , 157–158,
  380n9

Whiffen, William Sr, 30, 157–158

Whitby, George Stafford, 460
  biog. notes, 88–89, **115n59**,
    116n60
  memoir of RCS, 115n59,64

Whitehead, James, 460

Whiteley, Martha Annie, 460
  admission of women to CS, 91,
    118n76, 122n103
  and T. E. Thorpe's *Dictionary* ,106,
    128n155–156
  biog. notes, 89, 91, **118n74**, 165,
    176–177
  WW1-related work, 138–139,
    141–142, 145, 151n39, 43,
    152n55, 411

Whiting, Mark, 223, 238n71, 279n35

Widdowson, David Arthur (Dave),
  460
  biog. notes & research, 324,
    340n33, **347n74**, 361, 382n18
  director of undergraduate studies,
    324

Widdowson, Elsie, 185, 204n162

Wiechers, Adriaan, 285n70, 460

Wilde, Paul, 368, 390n67, 460

Wilkinson, Geoffrey, 461
  and structure of ferrocene, 249,
    279n35, 289n84, 313–314
  and Brian Flowers 334n6, 336n10,
    377n18–20, 338n24, 378n1
  as emeritus professor, 349n80,
    379n5, 382n20
  as student during WW2, 212,
    228, 232n25, 238n28–29,
    238n76, 243, 247–248,
    276n11, 279n31
  at Berkeley, Harvard and MIT, 225,
    229n2, 248–249, 279n35,
    280n36,37, 348n76
  biog. notes, 219, 224, 232n25,
    236n59, 243, 255, 276n9,11,
    278n29, 279n32, 287n78,
    288n79, 292n95, 335n7,
    344n49,50, 348n76, 357–358,
    400, 417n21
  Briscoe as supervisor & mentor,
    219, 225, 248–249
  Frankland professorship, 310,
    340n29
  head of dept., 306–311, 314,
    334n6, 335n7, 337n18–20,
    338n21, 338n24, 357–358,
    378n1–2
  memoir, 212, 276n11
  Nobel Prize, 196n73, 281n38,
    311–314, **341n36**, 343n47
  research, 219, 239n79–80,
    249, 261–263, 279n31, 35,
    289n84, 290n85, 292n97,
    293n98–99, 294n100, 315–316,
    342n43–45, 349n80, 379n5,
    382n20, 405
  Sir G.Wilkinson RSC award,
    386n41, 446

Sir Geoffrey Wilkinson dept. chair, 365

textbook *Advanced Inorganic Chemistry*, 168–169, 256–257, 317

Wilkinson's catalyst, 315–316, **342n44**

with Tube Alloys in Canada, 224–225, 232n21, 238n74–76, 239n77–79, 248, 279n31

Wilkinson, John,
biog. notes, 225–227, **231n15**
memoir of his brother Geoffrey, 276n11

Wilkinson, Lisa, 287n78, 335n7, 386n46

Wilkinson, P. A., 237n69

Will, Heinrich, 13, 420

Williams, Charles H. Greville, 40, 68n61, 113n42

Williams, Charlotte, 385n35

Williams, David J., 329, 355n115, 461

Williams, John, 30

Williams, Mary E. (see Dalziel, Mary Estelle)

Williamson, Alexander W., 34, 50, 73n109, 424, 426, 428n17, 433

Wilson, Harold, 334n2, 335n7

Wilson-Smith, Marjorie, 187

Winpenny, Richard, 344n55

Winter, Ernest Roy Sealey, **229n4**, 39n74, 461

Winter, Ramsay Middleton, 190n29, 461

Wislicenus, Johannes, 43, 70n76

Withers, John Charles, 461

Witt, Otto, 72n99

Wöhler, Friedrich, 51, 424, 427n6, 427n17,19

Wood, Geoffrey F., 461

Wood, John Lukes, 269, 461

Woodbridge, W. R., 120n95

Woodward, Robert Burns, 137, 150n33, 201n127, 245–246, 249, 278n25,30, 279n35, 282n49, 314, 346n69, 348n76

Woollins, John (Derek), 461
biog. notes, **345n62**, 359
research, 319, 329, 345n62, 386n40

Wootton, William Ord, 117n71, 461

Worley, Frederick P., 123n115

Wright, Christine, 306

Wright, Herbert, 116

Wright, John Jessen, 461

Wright, Terrance, 359, 380n11, 461

Wynne, William Palmer, 441, 444, 461
biog. notes, 89–90, 99, **124n122**,128n155, 151n44
research, 99

Y

Yaffé, Leo, 279n31

Yaliraki, Sophia, 369, 392n74, 461

Young, George (Brent), 461
biog. notes & research, 319, 345n61, 364

Young, J. Francis, 342n43

Young, James, 25n62, 80, 435n10

Young, Leslie, 204n163, 461

Young, Sidney,
biog. notes, 76n142, 103, 110n25, 112n30, 115n56
memoir, 32n190

Z

Zeidler, Othmar, 237n68

Zeise, William C., 74n125, 170